A Complete Guide to

BUILDING and PLANT MAINTENANCE

by / **THOMAS F. SACK**

Building and Plant Engineer

Prentice-Hall, Inc.

Englewood Cliffs, N. J.

Ninth Printing..... June, 1969

PRINTED IN THE UNITED STATES OF AMERICA
16009—B&P

INTRODUCTION

This book was developed to provide for the tremendous and apparent need of a comprehensive source of information on building and plant maintenance. The sanitation and maintenance field is coming into its own, as capital expenditure for facilities, equipment and materials is increasing, requiring additional maintenance to fully utilize their potential. With the increase of mechanical facilities such as automatic boilers, air conditioning equipment and air handling units, good maintenance is essential. Because these conveniences are becoming more widely utilized, building superintendents and plant engineers require guidance in their care.

They are expected to be experts in practically every phase of building maintenance, from pest control to electrical maintenance. With the constant progress of new equipment in recent years, they must have continuing knowledge of the methods of making the physical changes required to adapt this equipment to the building, and to modify existing methods of maintenance. An outstanding example of this is the installation of data processing equipment in all types of business.

With regard to the physical maintenance phase of building care, many new products are being used with relation to the installation of various types of ceiling materials, resilient floor coverings, carpeting, lighting, and so on. Vinyl waxes and plastic paints are only two of these fairly new products.

The increase in memberships in professional and technical societies and the appearance of new technical periodicals, shows that a very strong demand exists for this type of information. From personal experience at several conferences, and through extensive discussions with other building superintendents and plant engineers, the book which encompasses a concentration of this information, as this one does, will do much to satisfy this demand.

How Profits Have Been Increased
Through Use of These Techniques

Many modern techniques of maintenance are described throughout this book. First, let us consider lighting maintenance and some of the savings that can be realized through group replacement of fluorescent lamps over spot replacement. Group relamping can be accomplished at convenient times—during vacation shutdowns, after working hours, or on Saturdays. This prevents work interruptions and wasted time, as regular employees are not distracted by the maintenance men. Another saving is the elimination of damage and burning out of starters and ballasts caused by blinking and slow start in aged lamps. Ballast life can be reduced as much as 45 per cent as a result of these conditions. Labor savings up to 75 per cent can be achieved, and up to 30 per cent savings can be achieved by purchasing in large quantities.

Boiler maintenance is of prime importance in any plant operation. Boilers must be cared for to protect the initial capital investment in them, and to prevent accidents through faulty operation and lack of maintenance, which can cost many dollars. Above all, proper boiler maintenance can prevent downtime, which can prove to be a very costly item in the operation of any plant or building.

Another area of building and plant maintenance that can be a costly one if not cared for, and probably one of the most overlooked, is roof maintenance. This book covers treatment of roof damage, inspection methods, and repair hints. All of these lead to dollar savings.

More savings can be realized through the many descriptions of products such as paints and floor coverings. Information is given on their composition, correct use, application, and care required after installation or application. *Proper maintenance effects longer usage, which means dollar savings.* The fewer times a floor has to be replaced, the more dollar savings are realized. The same is true of painting in a building or plant. The use of an improper product applied in maintaining a floor or wall can cause much damage, resulting in additional labor and material expenditure, and sometimes additional capital outlay.

Complete job descriptions for floor care, high cleaning, window washing, care of outside areas, lavatory servicing and cleaning, and others, are outlined. The job description covers areas assigned, and allotted usages of materials necessary for specific periods. Such information results in the employee's having knowledge of his area of responsibility, which simplifies rescheduling or training a replacement in the event of vacations or illness. It also effects proper inventory control by supplying a close estimation of supplies and materials needed.

Proper training results in dollar savings. Teaching an employee to utilize his time correctly and use various products properly will do much in eliminating wasted time and material.

Direct and indirect costs of accidents are listed, which emphasize the fact that safety precautions, as outlined, should be followed without reservation. The article on safety goes on to prove the corollary that, "If accidents cut profits, safety makes cents."

Downtime resulting from breakdown of machines and equipment must be avoided. The employer is entitled to receive the utmost in efficiency of operation, therefore it is no longer sufficient for a building superintendent or plant engineer to know a little bit about a lot of things. As buildings and the machinery and equipment in them become more modernized, specialized knowledge is the requirement of the men employed to manage them. Complete information at one source is practically impossible to find. This book will provide this source of concentrated information for use by building superintendents and plant engineers everywhere.

THOMAS F. SACK

CONTENTS

1 / CLEANING PROCEDURES AND PRACTICES

(*Source: Buildings* magazine, November 1958, March 1960)

Cleaning costs now represent approximately 33 per cent of the total tab for operating the average building. This fact is leading management men to invest in more administrative study, planning and development time to upgrade their cleaning and maintenance programs and make more efficient use of their cleaning manpower.

With payroll costs representing 90 to 95 per cent of an average building's cleaning costs, man-hour productivity becomes the vital key to stepped-up efficiency and cleaning cost reduction. The *time* it takes to perform the cleaning job is the element which makes or breaks a cleaning program.

How to Determine Cleaning Costs

Comparison of payroll cleaning costs with other buildings can be misleading, as labor rates vary from city to city, and cleaning costs per square foot depend upon quality standards, method of calculating square foot areas, the type of occupancy, the proportion of problem areas, open areas, air conditioning, and so on.

To determine your total annual cleaning cost in dollars, include the following factors:

1. Wages, including overtime.
2. Fringe costs, including payroll taxes, uniforms, vacation pay, pensions, sick leaves, insurance and holiday pay.

The sum of the above items will give your total annual payroll cleaning costs. Next, determine the number of square feet in your building that require cleaning services on any kind, and divide the total annual cleaning cost by the number of square feet.

Now, determine your hours per square foot per year by calculating your average hourly wage. Consider all payroll fringe costs, as well as base rates. Divide your annual payroll cleaning cost per square foot by this average hourly wage. The result—your hours-per-square-foot-per year. This final unit of measurement reflects your true payroll costs. It is the unit by which the results of time and method studies of cleaning operations can be most accurately measured.

This unit of measurement could be called your performance rating figure. Figure 1-1 gives the various classifications of performance ratings. Time study experts suggest that a production rate of .30 man-hours per square foot of rentable area is the acceptable standard for a clean building. If your rating falls below this figure, review the cleaning program—study the job being done, decide how it should be done, and set up the cleaning operation on a regular, controlled basis.

Area vs. Group

There are two common methods of organizing the cleaning personnel:

1. The assignment of specific working areas to individual cleaners.
2. Group, squad or platoon cleaning.

Under the first method, one employee performs all routine cleaning operations within a designated area and is held responsible for the manner in which the area is maintained. Under a group cleaning organization, a gang is assigned certain areas, in which they work together. Each member of the gang is assigned certain operations and the entire group is under the direction of a working supervisor. In some instances, both methods are used simultaneously in the same building. Regular office spaces may be assigned to individuals on an area basis; while the washing of corridors, floors, windows, etc. is done on a group basis.

Figure 1-1

PERFORMANCE RATING FOR OFFICE BUILDINGS

If your figure is:	Your program is:
20-25 per cent	Excellent
25-30 per cent	Very good
30-35 per cent	Good
35-40 per cent	Average
40-45 per cent	Poor
Over 45 per cent	Very poor

The advantages of assigning cleaning work to individuals on an area basis have been enumerated as follows:

1. Reduces monotony, said to be the greatest foe of accomplishment. The variety of duties incident to complete responsibility for a designated area tends to make the work more interesting, removes tiring repetition and increases the amount of work per employee.

2. Work can be arranged to meet conditions of traffic.

3. Diversification of responsibility builds employee interest and provides a "prestige incentive".

4. The diversified work plan improves morale by alternating light and heavy work.

5. Responsibility for poor work, broken articles, possibly petty thievery can best be handled and pinpointed when work is on an assigned area basis.

6. There is less chance to forget important operations. One man, familiar with all operations on "his" floor is less likely to miss something than are a number of men with jobs that parallel and cross each other.

7. Labor turnover is decreased. Training new men is costly, and the diversity of work with its lessened monotony increases tenure. It is the satisfied and encouraged man, not the mechanized man, who does the most work, and the best work and stays longer.

Two methods have been developed for planning individual work assignments; the man-hour method and the Gilbert Formula. Both methods involve the preparation of charts which are used in setting up equitable work loads and are described.

The Man-hour Method

The man-hour method has been widely adapted in the setting up of work schedules and job specifications. A study is made of areas to be cleaned, and work schedules are developed which include each item or operation, the specifications for cleaning and the man-hours required. This guide serves as a logical starting place for a study of cleaning operations and will be helpful in controlling costs. With this method the relative cost of each job is determined. When reductions are necessary, the costs are weighed against the results attained by performance. It also indicates highest cost jobs where studies should be made for labor reduction, and has proved valuable in estimating the staffing and allocation of man-hours for a prospective building operation.

The man-hour production rate for all categories of operation can be determined by filling in actual man-hours for cleaning and maintenance operations (Figure 1-2) and using the formula illustrated in Figure 1-3.

Gilbert Formula

The distinguishing feature of the Gilbert Formula (Figure 1-4) is the adoption of "work units" instead of a designated square foot area as a basis for assigning quotas to cleaning personnel. The immediate objective is a more equitable division of work, with benefits in improved results and increased efficiency. Many buildings have used this formula as a base to develop their own system.

The formula's basic steps are:

1. A complete inventory of each regularly cleaned suite in the building must be made. It must list each piece of furniture and equipment and figure the amount of carpet and other floor coverings.

2. The work load for each room is then calculated by multiplying each item by the allotted number of work units. After these calculations have been made, addition gives the total number of work units for each room.

3. Then find the work load being carried by each cleaner. For instance, if the employee cleans three rooms which, by step two, have been found to contain 300, 430 and 320 work units respectively, then that employee is carrying a work load of 1,050 work units.

4. By comparing "work units," carried by each employee, it is possible to discover any unbalanced distribution of the work load. Actual working experience shows that a cleaner can handle from 240 to 250 work units per hour of work.

5. A reassignment of schedules can be made to equitably distribute the work load on a 250-work unit per hour basis, or 300-work units per hour in air conditioned buildings.

Figure 1-2

Man-hour Study Chart

	Hours Per Year
Cleaning	
Offices and Public Areas (including Supervision)	....
General Maintenance which includes:	
Carpenters	....
Electricians	....
Plumbers	....
Steam Fitters	....
Elevator Mechanics	....
Marble Men	....
Plasterers	....
Tile Setter	....
Painters	....
Wall Washers	....
Utility Men	....
Boiler Operators	....
Air Conditioning Men	....
Freight Elevator Operators	....
Elevators	
Passenger—Operators and Starters	....
If Operatorless—Starters Only	....
Watchmen	....
Window Washers	....
Total (Hours Per Year)	....
Building Production Rate (Man-hours per Sq. Ft.)	

$$\frac{\text{Man-hours}}{\text{Rentable Area}} = \quad \text{................}$$

$$\frac{\text{Man-hours}}{\text{Gross Area}} = \text{............}$$

Figure 1-3

Man-hour Distribution in Building Operation

Number of Employees	Operation	Man-hours per day With Operators	% of Total Hours	Man-hours per day Without Operators	% of Total Hours
59	Cleaning	472	62.1	472	72
6	Watchmen	48	6.3	48	7.3
15	Elevators	120	15.8	16	2.4
11	Maintenance	88	11.6	88	13.4
3	Painters	24	3.1	24	3.7
1	Window cleaners	8	1.1	8	1.2
95		760	100.0	656	100.0

Total Operation with Operators .... .62 man-hours per sq. ft. Rentable Area

Total Operation without Operators .... .54 man-hours per sq. ft. Rentable Area

Cleaning Operation .... .387 man-hours per sq. ft. Rentable Area

Based on Rentable Area of 317,000 square feet.

FOR DETERMINING THE CLEANING ASSIGNMENT IN ANY GIVEN BUILDING

The application of this formula will reflect by means of work units an equitable distribution of area to be cleaned

STEP NO. 1—You will list on Columnar Form (see sample) room no. of each suite—together with square feet of net Rentable Area. Next secure the no. of sq. ft. of Carpet—Rugs—Linoleum—Concrete or other floor covering in each office and list these amounts in proper column. Next count the no. of Desks—Chairs—Tables—Files—Lamps—Couches—Book Cases—Clothes Trees—Wash Basins—Safes—Cabinets—Shelves in each office and list amounts in proper columns.

| RENTAL AREA | | SQ. FT. FLOOR COVERING | | | | FURNITURE AND OTHER EQUIPMENT | | | | | | | | | | | | | TOTAL FURN. UNITS | FURN. WORK UNITS | FLOOR WORK UNITS | SPACE ADJUST UNITS | TOTAL WORK UNITS |
ROOM NO.	NET SQ.FT.	CARPET	RUGS	LINOL.*	CONCR.	DESK	CHAIR	TABLE	FILE	LAMP	COUCH	BOOK CASE	CLOTHES TREE	WASH BASIN	SAFE	CABINET	SHELF	MISC					
1424-50	1370	1200	--	--	170	7	34	11	7	1	--	2	1	1	--	1	--	1	73	80	197		277
1436	507	--	364	--	143	4	13	5	5	2	--	1	1	1	--	--	6	--	37	41	69		-110

STEP NO. 2—Divide total No. of Sq. Ft. of net rentable area in building by your established base No. of Sq. Ft. per Hour allotted to each cleaner. This gives you the No. of Hours work necessary per night—divide that figure by the No. of hours each cleaner works per night. This will give you the No. of cleaners necessary under the Sq. Ft. Allotment System.

STEP NO. 3—Total each column of above form for entire building. Then divide each result by the No. of cleaners shown in Step No. 2. This gives you the Avg. No. of Sq. Ft. of floor covering and the Avg. No. of furniture and equipment units each cleaner should have under the Sq. Ft. Allotment System.

STEP NO. 4—Allot 1½ work units for each ten (10) sq. ft. of Carpet & Rugs shown—Allot one (1) work unit for each ten (10) sq. ft. of Linoleum or other Floor Covering, including Concrete. Allot two (2) work units for each desk—Allot one (1) work unit for each piece of Furniture and Equipment shown. (Note) One work unit to be allotted for each bay of sectional Book Cases and one work unit for each bay of shelving. This will give you the total No. of work units in each of the above columns and also a basis for completing the totals in the last five columns of the form. Now transfer detailed information for each office to individual cleaners schedule card (sample below) and the totals will show the No. of work units each cleaner has under your Sq. Ft. Allotment System. This will show you the inequality in your present system.

STEP NO. 5—Results as shown by Steps 1 to 4 will give you the total no. of work units in the bldg. for each column. You can now determine from these results the base no. of work units each cleaner should be allotted and then rearrange the schedules using WORK UNITS as a base instead of sq. ft.

INDIVIDUAL CLEANERS SCHEDULE

CLEANER - MARY HUSOCK

Room No.	AREA	CARPET	RUGS	L-C	DESK	CHAIR	TABLE	FILE	LAMP	COUCH	BOOK CASE	CLOTH TREE	WASH BASIN	SAFE	CAB	SHELF	MISC	ADJ. UNITS	TOTAL FURN. UNITS	TOTAL WORK UNITS	
																		SCHEDULE NO. 3			
SOUTH 7th FL.	7000		718	7000	73	206	27	11	--	--	1	20	--	--	--	--	--	--	338	1219	
TOT. WORK UNITS		108	700	146	206	27	11	15	--	1	20	20	--	--	--	--		--	--	1219	
AVE WORK UNITS	210	190	392	104	130	38	55	15	2	12	13	6	3	4	24		--	--	1200	

NOTE—Experience has shown that a woman cleaner should do approximately 200 work units per hour or 1200 work units per six (6) hour night. However, each building can adjust the hourly base up or down where unusual conditions seem to warrant such a change. The hourly allotment given is based on a cleaner doing no scrubbing—no wall washing—no cleaning of venetian blinds—wood and glass partitions—electric light fixtures and no polishing of doors—jam or trim. If cleaners have toilet rooms or other special space to clean proper work units should be assigned in column marked MISC. If space is of very unusual character and exceptionally hard to clean—additional work units may be allotted in space adjustment column.

Figure 1-4 / **Gilbert Formula.**

Group or Squad Cleaning

The group or squad system follows the trend toward specialization. Rather than have one person clean several rooms in a given area and perform all the tasks involved, squads are formed and broken into teams that specialize in one phase of cleaning. Several squads may be employed in one building and each squad is usually comprised of two man teams. In a typical office building the work of each squad fits into one of five general classifications: (1) vacuum carpets, (2) damp mop floors, (3) empty wastebaskets, (4) dust furniture, and (5) special duties.

A daily work ticket is made up for each team telling exactly what is to be done, where it is to be done, and the time allowed. Each squad, composed of ten to twenty-five men, has a senior cleaner in charge. It is his responsibility to inspect all work.

Users of the squad system report the following advantages:

1. Morale is higher.

2. Closer supervision is possible.

3. More work is done with fewer men and the general quality of the work improves.

4. Less equipment is necessary.

5. There is an equitable distribution of work to each worker.

6. Appraisals of employee proficiency have greater validity.

Supervision and Inspection

From a study of any of the cleaning methods, it is readily seen that the final measure of success is based on the amount and type of supervision and inspection. A good system of inspection or follow up is the only way management can properly control the cleaning operations and insure full value for money spent. The progressive cleaning program incorporates the best tools, training, incentives and organization for the purpose of achieving and maintaining high individual productivity and quality levels. Therefore, the worker must not only be properly educated in efficient basic cleaning techniques, but he must be given proper incentive. Call it morale, job interest, or teamwork—it's the human side of the cleaning program and should be underlined as one of the basic and more important elements.

Rating forms and check lists are frequently used as a basis for checking up on the thoroughness of the cleaning operation. Such a list prevents oversight, as the supervisor is required to check off each item. There may be room on the form for comment on any points that occur to him, either in connection with the work, in changing the system, or in the quality of work compared to preconceived standards of cleanliness.

Formal Training

Cost is one of the very vital characteristics in cleaning—results being, of course, the ultimate. Therefore, the chief possibility of offsetting rising costs lies in training or teaching employees to perform their work better and faster.

There are many different methods of training. A definite course of instructions with the use of classroom technique, for concentrated instruction and for the sake of valuable discussion in which all may join, is particularly effective. Group meetings at the outset should be held at frequent intervals until the best possible results are obtained. After that, refresher meetings should be held as the need indicates. Audio-visual aids—films, slides, charts and practical demonstrations—should be used as much as possible in demonstrating new methods, new tools, and the technique of planning work.

Service manuals have been widely used by management as a guide to cleaning operation and are invaluable in speeding the training process, and covers the following subjects:

1. Compounds and materials used for different kinds of cleaning.
2. The frequency at which each operation is performed.
3. Cleaning organization and personnel.
4. Job specifications of various types of personnel.
5. Detailed instructions on how to perform each task.
6. Cleaning equipment for different purposes and how to care for it.

Scientific Cleaning

Today, outstanding cleaning programs have managed to double and even triple productivity. Costs have been cut from 30 to 50 per cent while quality has reached new heights. What are some of the characteristics of the scientific, closely controlled cleaning program?

Here are some of the fundamentals of these new cleaning programs, which are based squarely on modern management methods, and industrial cost control techniques:

1. Objective measurements of the total job.
2. Proven work standards (which comprise quality standards or degrees of cleanliness; standard cleaning methods; and standard time requirements for each job).
3. Continuous research and testing of new products and equipment.
4. Continuous personnel training, incorporating methods, engineering principles and morale factors.

The work measurement method as advanced by a national cleaning specialist, utilizes the proven practice of time and motion study. This method consists of

WORK LOAD DETERMINATION FORM

AREA _PROR MGMT. DEPT. 1570 SQ.FT._   QUALITY STANDARD _88_

ITEM TO BE CLEANED	CLEANING METHOD (DESCRIBE)	STANDARD TIME PER ITEM	AMOUNT OR NUMBER OF THE ITEM	TOTAL TIME (MINUTES)	CLEANING FREQUENCY	YEARLY TIME (HOURS)
WASTE BASKETS	EMPTY	17 SECONDS	15	4.3	DAILY	18.6
ASH TRAYS	EMPTY & DAMP WIPE	10 SECONDS	11	1.8	DAILY	7.8
STD. DESK GROUP— DESK, CHAIR, TELEPHONE, MAIL BASKET, FILE	DUST—WHISK UPHOLSTERED CHAIRS	42 SECONDS	12	8.4	DAILY	36.4
ASPHALT TILE FLOOR	DUST MOP	8 M/1000	1570 SQ.FT.	12	DAILY	52
ASPHALT TILE FLOOR	COMPLETE BUFFING	20 M/1000	1570 SQ.FT.	30	WEEKLY	25
PROJECT WORK	WAXING, FURNITURE WASHING, SPOT WASHING, ETC.	7 M/1000	1570 SQ.FT.	11	DAILY	47.6

TOTAL YEARLY TIME (Area Work Load):

Figure 1-5 / Workload determination form.

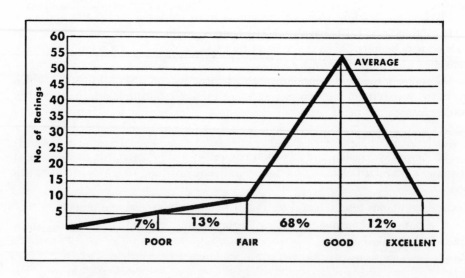

Figure 1-6 / Quality rating of cleaning performance.

standards for production for each of the major cleaning jobs; and standard frequencies for the performance of each job. These practices when properly applied to the building workload, establish the staffing required for cleaning.

The workload is determined by: (1) a complete inventory of work to be accomplished in each work area, and (2) time studies of each item of work.

Time studies are made by: (1) giving trained workers the necessary tools and materials, (2) having them perform the cleaning operation many times at a normal pace, and (3) clocking each complete operation, including make ready, transportation, and put away times. On job conditions such as soil load and traffic interference are taken into account.

The engineered approach to control of the cleaning program is based upon the principles of applying the best practices and methods available to the job operation. Establishing work standards—the setting up of measures for determining progress and results—is the basis for a cleaning system advanced by a firm of professional cleaning consultants who call it the "Work Standards System."

Figure 1-5 is typical of a form used by these analysts in setting up the workload for each integral area of a building.

The following factors are determined before arriving at the workload:

1. How clean the building is to be kept.
2. How much total space and equipment there is to clean.
3. What methods will be employed to clean it.
4. How much time each particular cleaning job takes.

Under this system, a building is objectively rated on its cleanliness and results are measured by means of a "Productivity Index". By multiplying the sanitation level of the area times the hourly square foot coverage of the cleaning worker, both quality and quantity of actual cleaning output can be computed.

The Quality of Cleaning

Quality of cleaning takes equal rank with cost considerations. A measuring stick for quality is something which the cleaning industry has lacked and engineers have developed. The new basis for measuring quality in industry is known as "statistical quality control". This plan reveals the actual performance as it normally occurs over a period of time. Statistical quality control is a sampling process used to determine the average performance and the occurrence at both extremes of the range of performance. Building managers and maintenance supervisors can apply this principle by sampling and rating performances in their cleaning operations.

For example, you are interested in determining the quality of cleaning on horizontal surfaces. Assume that four different grades should be used to measure quality such as: (1) poor, (2) fair, (3) good, and (4) excellent. Over a specified period of time, you will rate the quality of cleaning on horizontal surfaces. The results might appear this way:

Grades	Number of Ratings	Per Cent of Total
Poor	6	7
Fair	10	13
Good	55	68
Excellent	10	12
Totals	81	100

Figure 1-6 shows how these results appear in graph form.

Frequency Data

OFFICES

Dusting

Desk tops	
Ash trays	
Horizontal surfaces	1 × day
Sills	
Floor sweep	
Treated sweep	
Partitions	
Vertical surfaces	1 × week
Radiators	
Damp mop	1 × week
Carpet sweep rugs	3 × week
Vacuum rugs	2 × week
Buff	2 × month

Damp Wipe (Spot Wash)

Walls	
Doors	
Water fountains	
Partitions	1 × day
Partition glass	
Water bottles	
Sills	
Radiators	1 × week
Desk tops	
Door saddles	2 × month

Periodic Cleaning

Wash partition glass	1 × 2 weeks
Wash partitions	1 × month
Wash windows	1 × 2 months
Scrub or strip floors	2 × year
Mop floors (wet)	1 × 6 weeks
Refinish floors (1 coat)	1 × 3 months

Wash walls	1 × year
Wash furniture	1 × year
Polish furniture	3 × year
Dust blinds	1 × 3 months
Wash blinds	1 × year
Dust light fixtures	1 × 2 months
Wash light fixtures	1 × year
Clean anemostats (wash)	3 × year
Wash desks (entire)	2 × year
Wash desk floor pads	1 × month

CORRIDORS

Policing

Sand urns	
Floor	4 × day
Floor sweep	1 × day
Treated sweep	
Damp mop tile	1 × week
Terrazzo	1 × day

Damp Wipe (Spot Wash)

Ledges and sills	2 × week
Walls	
Doors	
Door saddles	1 × week
Radiators	
Water fountains	1 × day
Dust light fixtures	1 × 2 months
Wash light fixtures	1 × year
Dust walls	1 × 3 months
Scrub or strip floors (machine)	1 × 3 months
Mop floors (wet)	2 × week
Refinish (1 coat)	1 × 6 weeks
Metal polishing	1 × month
Wash partition glass	1 × month

STAIRWELLS

Damp Wipe (Spot Wash)

Floors	
Sand urns	
Walls	1 × day
Doors	
Handrails	
Treated sweep	
Vacuum clean carpet	
Ledges and sills	1 × week

Periodic Cleaning

Dust blinds	4 × year
Wash blinds	1 × year
Metal polish	1 × month
Dust light fixtures	1 × 3 months
Wash light fixtures	1 × 4 months
Dust walls	1 × 3 months
Mop and rinse steps	1 × day
Hand scrub steps	1 × week

LAVATORIES

Daily

Check soap	
Towels	
Tissues	3 × day.
Damp wipe surfaces (porcelain-chrome-stainless steel)	
Empty waste receptacle	1 × day
Spot mop floor	1 × day

Periodic Cleaning

Commodes	
Urinals	2 × day
Wash basins	

Damp Wipe (Spot Wash)

Partitions	
Receptacles	2 × day
Dispensers	
Ledges and sills	2 × week
Radiators	1 × week
Walls	
Doors	1 × day
Wash walls	1 × 4 months
Wash windows	1 × month
Dust blinds	1 × 2 months
Wash light fixtures	1 × year
Wash and rinse floor	1 × day
Machine scrub floor	1 × week

EXECUTIVE OFFICES

Dusting

Sweep
Dust mop

Treated sweep
Vacuum
Ledges and sills
Wall fixtures
Office furniture
Radiators   1 × day
Shelves
Water fountains or bottles
Doors
Walls
Partitions
Partition glass

Damp mop tile   1 × week

Buff   2 × week

Scrub and strip floor (machine)   1 × 2 months

Refinish (1 coat)   1 × month

Dust walls   1 × week

Periodic Cleaning

Dust blinds
Vacuum upholstered furniture   1 × week
Vacuum drapes

Wash furniture   1 × year
Polish furniture   4 × year
Wash blinds   1 × 6 months
Wash light fixtures   1 × year
Wash windows   1 × 2 months
Wash walls   1 × year
Wash partitions   2 × year
Wash partition glass   1 × 2 weeks
Shampoo carpets   2 × year

PUBLIC LOBBIES

Sweep
Dust mop
Treated sweep   1 × day
Damp mop and rinse
Buff

Machine scrub terrazzo   1 × week
Tile   1 × month
Refinish tile (1 coat)   1 × 2 weeks

Dusting

Radiators
Ledges and sills
Doors   1 × day
Signs
Sand urns

Damp Wipe (Spot Wash)

Miscellaneous furniture	
Doors	
Walls	
Water fountains	1 × day
Ledges and sills	
Radiators	

Periodic Cleaning

Wash walls	1 × 6 months
Dust light fixtures	1 × month
Wash light fixtures	1 × 3 months
Vacuum ceilings	1 × year
Wash ceiling	1 × 2 years
Paint ceiling	1 × 4 years
Wash furniture	1 × 6 months
Wash windows	1 × month
Dust blinds	3 × year
Wash blinds	2 × year
Door glass	1 × day
Polish metal	2 × week

ELEVATOR LOBBIES

Sweep	
Mop and rinse	1 × day
Treat sweep	

Dusting

Doors	1 × day
Walls	1 × week
Signs	1 × day
Wall fixtures	1 × week
Ledges and sills	1 × day

Periodic Cleaning

Wipe sand urns	1 × day
Wipe elevator doors	1 × week
Polish metal	1 × week
Wash walls	1 × year
Wash light fixtures	2 × year
Door glass	1 × day
Wash windows	1 × 2 months
Dust blinds	1 × week
Wash blinds	2 × year
Spot wash walls	1 × week
Spot wash doors	1 × 2 weeks

2 / ALUMINUM CLEANING

(*Source: Plant* magazine)

Architectural aluminum has few maintenance requirements and it adds immeasurably to a plant's appearance and structural longevity. Most aluminum surfaces are protected by a thin, tough film or oxide coating (it forms on exposure to the atmosphere) which guards against rust and corrosion that would quickly destroy other metals.

However, aluminum can get dirty just like any other material exposed to industrial atmosphere and hard usage. Aluminum on the exteriors of industrial structures is subjected to the worst conditions in this respect; smoke and fumes tend to discolor the surface and airborne dust combined with moisture lead to accumulations of dirt.

Ordinarily, this in no way harms the metal but, in most cases, some measure of upkeep is desirable to maintain the most prominent applications—such as entrances, sash, trim, grillework, handrails, similar items in the main reception and office areas—sparkling bright and new looking. While it is not economically feasible to clean the entire exterior of an aluminum clad plant, it is worthwhile to keep the office portion in good order for the purpose of good public relations.

Methods of Cleaning

Periodic cleaning and restoration of aluminum surfaces, even after years of neglect, can be simplified by utilization of proper methods and materials. Methods of cleaning vary with the type and severity of soiling, frequency of cleaning, and other factors. In general, three categories of cleaning techniques have been found acceptable and are described in the following paragraphs. For each specific plant, these methods should be tried in the order described on small but different types of typically soiled areas until satisfactory results are obtained. Once the choice of method has been established, the remainder of the surface can be cleaned accordingly.

1. Mild. Where surfaces are not too dirty or have been cleaned periodically, try the following procedures:

a. Wash with clean water and dry thoroughly. Or,

b. Wash with mild soap and warm water, rinse, and dry. Or,

c. Apply a non-etching chemical cleaner, diluted three parts of water to one part of cleaner, in accordance with the manufacturer's instructions.

2. Medium Severe. If a thick coating of dirt has accumulated, it may be found easier to first loosen the heavy crust with a solvent cleaner, and then try one of the following procedures:

a. Apply a wax base polish cleaner with a clean, soft rag or pad. Make certain the manufacturer's directions are followed closely. Or,

b. Apply a nonwax base polish cleaner. Follow same precautions as above. Or,

c. Apply an abrasive wax with same precautions as above, Or,

d. Apply a mild abrasive cleaner (scouring powder) with a clean, damp cloth. Be sure to rinse well and dry.

3. Severe. If the foregoing methods are not successful, try the following procedure.

Apply liquid or one of the above cleaners with a stainless steel wool pad (size 00 or finer). Mild steel wool can also be used as an applicator, but it is extremely important that no wool particles remain to rust-stain the aluminum surface.

Care should be exercised in using steel wool or abrasive waxes and cleaners as they might damage the appearance of the surface if the metal is scoured too long or too hard. Steel wool or abrasive cleaners should be rubbed in the direction of the metal's finish. A bristle brush, rather than a cloth or pad, is recommended for use with all cleaners on patterned surfaces.

Another precaution is that all cleaner deposits, with the exception of those from wax base preparations, should be removed with clean water followed by a thorough drying of the surface. Wax base cleaners leave a thin protective coating which need not be removed unless the surface is to be lacquered.

Heavy-Duty Cleaning

Should the foregoing methods fail to produce satisfactory results, and the surface still looks streaked and spotted, it will be necessary to resort to even more severe cleaning procedures. All that may be requird on parts that have been anodized is a heavy-duty cleaner put on with a damp clean cloth or stainless steel wool pad, rinsed with water, and dried thoroughly. Determination of whether or not a part has been anodized can be made by a check on the original building specifications; or by a "scratch" or "rub" test. If the surface scratches easily or if a rubber eraser leaves a bright spot, an anodic coating has not been applied.

Extremely dirty surfaces not having an anodic coating should be cleaned as follows:

Apply a suitable etching chemical cleaner (phosporic acid type), diluted three parts of water to one part of cleaner, with a clean sponge, rag or brush. Work a small area, just large enough to be covered and keep wet three to five minutes at a time. Be sure to start at bottom of panel and work up, so splashes or rundowns do not get onto uncleaned surfaces. Rinse surface with water before cleaner dries. Make certain that all cracks, grooves, etc. are rinsed. Dry surface thoroughly. Drying may be speeded by swabbing with a 50-50 solution of denatured or wood alcohol and water. When handling chemical cleaners, particular attention should be given to protection of the workmen's eyes and skin.

Preserving the Finish

After cleaning, a coating of liquid wax or clear lacquer can be applied if desired to preserve the restored finish and facilitate future maintenance.

Normally, waxed aluminum can be kept clean by wiping with a damp rag from time to time, or by rinsing with clean water. To apply a liquid wax, first clean the surface with a solvent cleaner, then spread the wax and polish with a soft cloth or pad. As mentioned previously, wax based cleaners also leave a satisfactory protective wax film.

However, after repeated applications of wax, the built-up coating may become soft or tend to yellow. When this occurs, the accumulation must be removed with a solvent or mild abrasive cleaner, and the surface re-waxed.

A good clear methacrylate lacquer coating will protect aluminum surfaces for several years without yellowing or cracking. For best results, the surface should be carefully prepared and a lacquer applied as follows:

1. If old lacquer has worn off in spots, the entire surface should be stripped with a lacquer remover, following the manufacturer's directions.

2. Clean the stripped surface thoroughly with a solvent cleaner.

3. For better lacquer adhesion on bare aluminum, it is advisable to provide a good "tooth" on the surafce by use of an etching type chemical cleaner. Follow the foregoing directions (under "Heavy-Duty Cleaning") on applying this type of cleaner.

4. Apply a thorough, wet coat of lacquer. Spray application is preferable, but brush coating is satisfactory if the lacquer is thinned with a slow evaporating solvent. The coating should be applied as uniformly as possible and after the first coat has dried, a second coat should be applied in the same manner.

Cleaning Schedule

Aluminum surfaces require cleaning more often in some areas than in others; a proper schedule may vary from two weeks to six months. If a plant is located in an area with a concentration of soot, factory fumes or salt sea mist, cleaning must be at more frequent intervals, to insure a bright, attractive appearance. As with any building product, the more aluminum is cleaned, the easier each successive job will be.

3 / ASPHALT MAINTENANCE

(Source: The Asphalt Institute, University of Maryland)

In general, asphalt pavements are easy to maintain, especially pavements constructed of asphaltic concrete or asphalt macadam, which require little or no repair for many years. Asphalt surfaces may be renewed to a smooth, waterproof surface by the application of a light seal coat. At intervals of three to five years, surface treatments may require an additional light treatment depending upon traffic and climatic conditions. Heavy duty surfaces should require no such treatments for at least ten years after initial construction.

One of the best methods of crash filling and rejuvenating of a weathered surface that is cracked or spalled, is to use an emulsified asphalt slurry seal or asphalt sealer (paint type).

Application

Before applying either product, all pot holes, rocking, and badly distorted areas should be properly repaired. Immediately prior to applying, the pavement surface should be thoroughly cleaned. In the application of slurry seal, the surface should be broomed and dampened with a light application of water, to insure coverage and proper bond. The slurry seal is then poured from the mixer into the mixing box and onto the pavement. The asphalt sealer can be applied by a brush for a small area or sprayed in larger areas.

4 / CARE OF CARPETS AND RUGS

(Sources: American Carpet Institute, New York; General Services Administration, Washington, D. C.)

Regular care is the secret of good carpet and rug maintenance. Clean carpets and rugs daily with a vacuum or carpet sweeper, to keep surface soil from sinking into the pile, where it is difficult to remove and accelerates wear. Light daily cleaning consists of three strokes over a given area. A thorough cleaning consists of seven strokes back and forth over a given area.

Carpet sweepers take up lint, crumbs and other foreign matter from the surface. They do not get at soil that has found its way down between the tufts. Brooms sweep dust from the carpet, tossing it into the air and causing it to fall back on the carpet or other furnishings. A light brooming is helpful in brushing up a matted area. Never use a metal broom or a very stiff brush which might damage looped pile or break carpet tufts. The practice of running a vacuum cleaner over the back of a rug is recommended to be done at least once a year.

Cleaning Carpets and Rugs

There are three types of cleaning which the building superintendent can have performed on carpets or rugs by his own personnel:

1. Powdered cleaners.
2. Sponging with a cleaning fluid.
3. Cleaning with a solution of detergent or shampoo.

Powdered cleaners. Several absorbent powdered cleaners are available for carpet or rug cleaning. These cleaners consist of solvent saturated or detergent saturated sawdust or other inert powdered material. The compound is brushed into the pile in a circular motion, and should be allowed to remain in the rug for several hours until dry. The length of time depends upon the quantity applied and the atmospheric conditions. The carpet or rug should then be vacuumed thoroughly, picking up all of the powder. This method will give the carpet a certain degree of surface brightening. Compounds that contain fine powder may be more difficult to remove from the carpet than a coarser type.

Sponging with a cleaning fluid. Rugs and carpets made of wool or man-made fibers should be sponged with a cleaning fluid, but it is not recommended for cotton rugs. The cleaning fluid dissolves the oil film which makes dirt particles adhere to carpet fibers and thus effectively brightens their colors. This cleaning material will not injure the carpet yarns or the dyestuff, and it evaporates quickly and completely, leaving no residue. Apply the fluid with a sponge, using a gentle wiping motion so that only the top portion of the carpet pile becomes wet. Excess fluid may leave rings or soak into the backing and soften the back sizing. Solvent type cleaners will not remove stains or soil due strictly to water soluble materials, such as sugars or starches. Several dry cleaning solvents are available which have a carbon tetrachloride base. While these solvents are friendly to your carpets, they may be flammable and toxic, or both. Therefore, follow the recommendations and precautions of the manufacturer, and take the following precautions:

1. Avoid inhaling fumes which are toxic.

2. Be sure to have windows open so that liquid evaporates quickly and lessens chance of inhaling fumes.

3. When working with a cleaner which is flammable, avoid having lighted cigarettes or operating electrical appliances near the cleaning operation.

Cleaning with a solution of detergent or shampoo. Wet cleaning is suitable for all types of carpets. Certain precautions must be taken, the most important of which is to avoid the use of soap, ammonia, washing soda or any of the common household cleaning agents intended for use on hard surfaces, such as woodwork, linoleum or tile. Soaps should be avoided, regardless of how pure and mild they are claimed to be, since all soaps are alkaline by nature. Alkaline materials cause dyestuffs to run and may damage carpet fibers. There are many neutral detergents used for dishwashing or home laundering which may be used, along with special shampoos. Two heaping tablespoons of detergent to a gallon of one of these materials in a pail of water will produce a cleaning solution which can be used to clean carpets with a minimum of hazard. Special shampoos generally cover 80 to 100 square feet per gallon of mixed solution, and are derived from sulfated alcohol or sulfonated hydrocarbons.

When cleaning rugs with any solution, guard against over-wetting. Equipment which can be used, is a rug shampoo machine, or a floor polisher with a 15 or 16-inch brush converted by means of a solution tank connected to the handle which has a connecting tube and center feed ring or perforated brush. For best results, use a brush which feeds the solution through its back. Pick up the lather with a vacuum promptly, before it disintegrates and takes the dirt back into the carpeting. If working alone, do not shampoo more than 20 square feet at a time. Use a dry automatic floor brush or a hand pile brush to raise the pile, and allow to dry eight to ten hours before vacuuming.

Professional Cleaning Services

For thorough cleaning that removes all of the soil imbedded in carpets or rugs, reliable professional cleaning should be employed. Professional cleaners' services generally include: (1) plant cleaning, (2) on the floor cleaning, (3) dry cleaning, (4) spot removal, (5) re-dyeing, and (6) repairs.

Plant cleaning. A rug or carpet can always be cleaned most thoroughly and most efficiently in a professional cleaning plant. The plant is equipped to use such processes as dry dusting, shampooing, thorough rinsing and complete drying. Special attention will be given to adhesive seaming or inserts, in order to avoid shrinking or buckling, and in most causes firmness can be restored during shampooing.

On the floor cleaning. When cleaning carpets on the floor, the professional cleaner usually proceeds as follows:

1. Removal of all furniture from the room or area.
2. Preliminary brushing to open the carpet pile and permit removal of imbedded soil by vacuuming.
3. Thorough vacuuming with commercial cleaner.
4. Application of a non-alkaline detergent solution by a rotary scrubbing machine, using a minimum amount of solution.
5. Brushing of the pile to restore it to its original condition.
6. Drying of the carpet by forced drying through the use of heating devices, electric fans, and blowers.

Dry cleaning. Dry cleaning is generally satisfactory, however there are not many dry cleaning plants equipped to handle room-size floor coverings. Dry cleaning is not recommended for rubber-backed floor coverings because the solvent will degrade the rubber. If the carpeting is dry cleaned, the shrinkage is practically nil.

The professional cleaner has the experience for removing such special stains as paints, varnishes, and indelible inks. He also has re-dyeing facilities and a repair department for replacing worn or torn bindings, replacing missing tufts; and repair of holes and tears.

Insect Control

Good housekeeping is the most effective method for protecting carpeting from insect damage. Daily vacuuming, air, and light are beneficial. Periodic cleaning in out of the way areas discourages pest damage. Cleaning the back of the carpet at least once a year is recommended.

Insects which might damage carpets include the larvae (nymphs) of the clothes moth and carpet beetle. They are found in warm, humid, dark areas—generally around baseboards, in cracks of old floors and under radiators. They feed on animal fibers such as wool, fur, hair, and woolen lint, but do not damage cotton and most manmade fibers. Carpets made of blends of wool and manmade fibers are not insect proof because of the wool content.

Insect sprays can offer effective temporary prevention of pest damage. They should be used sparingly due to the general content of an oil or water base. Oil may cling to the carpet and the water may cause dampness. The directions should be read carefully to protect against any effects of a toxic which may be present. When insect damage appears to be a serious problem, professional treatment should be secured. Cleaners have insect repellant which can be applied to carpets or rugs. If insect damage has already occurred, he may be able to make necessary repairs.

Factors to Be Considered in Cleaning

Shrinkage. Shrinkage is natural in wet cleaning, but can be controlled by the use of frames and other equipment designed to retain the original size of the floor covering during or following the drying period.

Shading. Shading refers to areas in carpeting that seem to vary in tone after they are on the floor for a period of time. Walking over carpet pile sometimes pushes the tufts in different directions, and the light reflects from the tufts with various degrees of intensity. There is less shading if a vacuum cleaner is driven in the direction of the pile. Light brooming of cotton rugs raises the pile and therefore corrects shading. Shampooing allows the fibers to relax while wet, and when they are all brushed in one direction and allowed to dry, the shadowing will generally disappear.

Sunlight. Give a carpet normal protection from direct sunlight which is given to any colored fabric.

Pile crushing and corner curling. When carpet pile is crushed because of furniture pressure or walking, it can be raised by means of a hot iron over a damp cloth, or with a steam iron. (Avoid high heat for nylon, saran, and acetate carpet.) Brush up the spot briskly after treatment.

Fluffing. Fluffing is sometimes referred to as shedding. It consists of loose bits of material left in the carpet during manufacture. As the vacuum cleaner or carpet sweeper is used, fluffing disappears. It does not affect the quality or life of the floor covering.

Sprouting. Occasionally a tuft will rise above the pile surface of a carpet.

Snip these high rising tufts off evenly with the pile surface. Do not pull them out.

Stair carpet suggestions. The edges of a stair step take the heaviest amount of wear. To protect the carpeting lay with an extra foot of length folded under against one or two risers at the top of the stairs. A shift downward can be made when required, to give the edges a rest. As these shifts are made, the excess carpet at the foot of the stairs will fold under against the lowest riser. Another recommendation is an underlay of carpet cushioning with particular attention to the stair step edges.

Humidity factor. During increased periods of humidity, carpets will increase in their size. Excessive humidity or damp weather may cause temporary buckling in the carpet. This will probably disappear with a dryer atmosphere, and if buckling persists, consult the carpet dealer or manufacturer. A carpet layer can sometimes solve the problem by restretching an installation. In dry weather carpet attached to the floors should be layed under tension. If chair pads are used on ground floors of concrete over dirt, they should be taken up periodically to prevent moisture buildup under them, which can cause mildew and rotting. This condition is evident with the use of plastic chair pads which create a vapor barrier.

Static electricity. The friction caused by rubbing almost any two different materials together will cause static electricity. The friction caused by walking across a carpet or rug sometimes generates a charge which is felt as a shock when a person touches a metallic object. Such electricity is not dangerous. The amount will depend upon the amount of friction and atmospheric conditions. Static can be reduced by adding moisture to the atmosphere through humidification; or application of antistatic agents. There are some chemical agents which immediately reduce any static charge generated. Some antistatic agents cause dirt to adhere to the carpet treated with them. This type of treatment should be considered after consultation with a professional cleaner.

Carpet labels. Remove carpet labels as they may be useful if replacement tufts or repair of tape bindings are necessary. Having the pattern number and grade name of the floor covering will be valuable in corresponding with the manufacturer.

Spot Removal

When spots or stains occur:

1. Act quickly to remove spots or stains before they dry or set themselves.

2. Have necessary cleaning equipment at hand.

3. Try to identify what caused the spot or stain, and remove it, using the correct material and procedure.

Often a spilled liquid will dry on a carpet and will not appear to leave a stain. Later, after cleaning the carpet, a brown stain may appear that cannot be removed. Most fruit juices and beverages contain a sugar called "reducing sugar" that is colorless when deposited on a fabric. Later after cleaning or exposure to direct sunlight, the stain will appear as a tan or brown discoloration.

Two cleaning materials that can be safely used for spot cleaning are: (1) One teaspoonful of a neutral detergent to a quart of warm water. To this add one teaspoonful of white vinegar which is a weak acid and will serve to neutralize any alkaline materials. (2) A dry cleaning fluid (solvent) is useful for some spots. (See precautions described under "Sponging With a Cleaning Fluid".)

GENERAL CLEANING PROCEDURE

Step 1. Remove excess materials. In the case of liquids, absorb with a clean white cloth or other absorbent material. If semisolid, scrape with a knife, spoon, or sponge.

Step 2. Apply solution of detergent, vinegar, and water. Use a clean cloth and wipe gently from the edge of the soiled area toward the center. At intervals, blot with a dry clean cloth to absorb excess solution.

Step 3. Dry the carpet.

Step 4. Apply a dry cleaning fluid again, wiping gently and working from the edges of a spot or stain toward the center.

Step 5. Dry the carpet and brush the pile gently to restore the original texture.

In using the general cleaning procedure, use judgment as to whether both types of cleaning solution are required. If one removes most of the stain, it would be wise to repeat application.

Be sure to dry a wet carpet quickly and completely. This will avoid mildew, or other damage. The cleaned area should be raised from the floor and dried with a fan or other forced circulation. A solvent cleaner will dry quickly, allow for ventilation until all of the fumes have disappeared.

REMOVAL OF SPOTS AND STAINS

Type of Stain	*Procedure*
Butter, grease, oil, hand cream, ball point pen ink, ammonia	Remove excess materials; apply a dry cleaning fluid; dry the carpet; repeat application of solvent if necessary; dry the carpet and gently brush pile.
Coffee, tea, milk, gravy, chocolate, blood, egg, ice cream, sauces, salad dressings, vomit	Remove excess material, absorbing liquids and scraping semisolids; apply solution of detergent, vinegar, and water; dry the carpet; apply dry cleaning solvent; dry the carpet and brush the pile gently.
Candy, soft drinks, alcoholic beverages, fruit stains, washable ink, urine, excrement	Blot up liquids or scrape off semisolids; apply solution of detergent, vinegar, and water; dry the carpet; apply the solution again, if necessary; dry carpet and brush pile gently.
Gum, paint, tar, heavy grease lipstick, crayon	Remove excess materials; apply a dry cleaning fluid; apply solution of detergent, vinegar, water; apply dry cleaning fluid again; dry carpet and brush pile gently.

Nail polish. Nail polish remover is a satisfactory spot remover for nail polish spilled on a carpet. However, both nail polish and nail polish remover will seriously damage any carpet containing acetate fibers. Such cases generally require professional service. Some dyestuffs are not completely fast to nail polish remover, so test it first by applying it sparingly on some inconspicuous area of the carpet, prior to attempting to remove the nail polish.

Cigarette burns. Cigarette damage cannot be completely remedied except by reweaving. An area of carpet charred in a superficial manner can be improved by this procedure:

1. Carefully clip off blackened ends of tufts using small sharp scissors.
2. Apply solution of detergent, vinegar, and water as described in "General Cleaning Procedure".

Acid substances. Strong acids are not in common use. However, carbolic acid disinfectants and some tile cleaning compounds do fit into this category. If any of these should be spilled on a carpet, the area should be flushed with water, then sponged up. This should be repeated several times until the acid has been diluted and washed away. Then sponge the area with a dilute alkaline solution prepared by adding one tablespoonful of baking soda to a quart of warm water, and rinse again.

Rust. If the stain is fresh, use the detergent, vinegar, and water solution. Generally rust stains require professional service, because the cleaning agents required are hazardous when not properly used.

Permanent ink. Permanent inks are strong fast dyes and cannot be removed by any spotting procedures. Prompt action in blotting up ink stains and washing with water may prove successful. When ink is spilled on a carpet, try to determine if the ink is a washable type. If so, see the procedure described previously.

Job Description

The job of rug cleaning is performed by using a central vacuum cleaning system, a portable type vacuum cleaner, or a domestic type vacuum cleaner.

Usually vacuum cleaning rugs is a part of the room cleaning assignment, except where the presence of a large number of rugs makes specific job assignments more appropriate.

Rugs normally are vacuum cleaned after desks and other articles in the room have been dusted, so that any materials such as paper clips, shavings, and tiny other items that may have fallen on the rug during the dusting operation will be picked up.

Equipment and Material

A. *Equipment:*

1. *Central Vacuum Cleaning System:*

    a. Elbow joint and valve
    b. Floor handle

    c. Floor tool
    d. Hose (two or more 25 ft. lengths)
    e. Rug tool

2. *Domestic Vacuum Cleaner:*

    Note: Operator should be instructed how to adjust vacuum for rugs with short or long nap in accordance with manufacturer's recommendations.

3. *Portable Vacuum Cleaner:*

    a. Elbow joint
    b. Floor handle
    c. Floor tool
    d. Hose (one or more 25 ft. lengths)
    e. Rug tool
    f. Vacuum cleaner (portable)

4. *Miscellaneous:*

    a. Corn broom
    b. Wedge

B. *Material:*

Wiping cloths (waffleweave)

Job Methods

Step 1

Operation Steps	Explanation
1. Obtain necessary equipment and materials.	a. Obtain (as required) necessary equipment.
	b. Check to see if vacuum dust bag is clean and properly installed.
	c. Inspect vacuum hose for breaks before connecting to machine or outlet.
2. Proceed to assigned work area.	All the equipment should be taken to the starting point of the assigned work area, to be used as needed.

Step 2

1. Prepare vacuum cleaner.	a. Attach hose to valve or elbow joint.
	b. Place tool on handle. Use proper tool for job (carpet or bare floor).
	c. When using either a central vacuum

Operation Steps	*Explanation*
	system or portable vacuum, use a wedge or doorstop to hold the door open, and pull hose into the room.
	d. Inspect plug before inserting the wall receptacle.
	e. Use *only one* 25 ft. hose for ¾ hp machine, and *never* more than two 25 ft. lengths for 1½ hp machine.
2. Prepare for vacuum cleaning.	a. Prepare room by moving as little furniture as necessary.
	b. Start machine by turning on switch and/or valve (in elbow joint).

NOTE

When using central vacuum system the shutoff valve should be closed except when equipment is actually in use.

Step 3

1. Vacuum clean bare floors.	a. Grasp handle with one hand and place tool parallel to floor.
	b. Use rug tool for bare floors around rugs.
	c. For large areas of bare floor, use bare floor tool.
2. Vacuum clean rugs.	a. Vacuum clean rugs by working tool back and forth with the nap of the rug.
	b. The last time over the rug operate the carpet tool in the direction that will lay the nap of the rug most evenly.
	c. Turn off switch and remove plug from wall or hose from outlet. Rewind cable and hose loosely.
	d. Remove machine or hose from room.

PRECAUTIONS

1. Avoid marring furniture or baseboards when operating with floor or rug tool.
2. Avoid marring furniture or baseboards with vacuum hose.
3. Avoid letting doors strike machine when moving machine into

room. Use doorstop or wedge to hold door open.

4. Place vacuum machine switch in OFF position before inserting or removing the plug from wall receptacle.

Operation Steps	*Explanation*
	Step 4
Replace furniture or equipment.	Replace, in their proper locations, any furniture or equipment which becomes disarranged during the vacuum cleaning operation.
	Step 5
Smooth nap on rugs.	Where required use corn broom in short even strokes to smooth nap of rug after vacuum cleaning is completed and furniture replaced in its original position.
	Step 6
Dispose of sweepings.	After each night's use, empty dirt receptacle of vacuum cleaner into paper parcel and place in trash.
	Step 7
Return equipment and materials to storage.	a. Disassemble equipment.
	b. Wrap vacuum hose loosely around machine.
	c. Store cleaning tools (handle with attached carpet tool and elbow joint) with the machine in gear or storage room.

Care of Equipment

A. *Dust Bags:*

In addition to removing sweepings from bags daily, clean and dust bags once a week. Where two or more machines are available use one machine to clean the bag of the other. Where another machine is not available clean the bag with a stiff brush.

B. *Electric Cable:*

1. Make sure cable connection is plugged all the way into electric outlet to avoid voltage drops.

2. Do not splice or replace electric cable. (This is a shop job.)

3. Do not pull on electric cord to remove plug from outlet.

C. *Hose:*

   1. Always operate machine with a cleaning tool on the end of a vacuum hose.

   2. Avoid sharp bends in hose when cleaning. Do not permit platform trucks or other vehicles to run over hose. Report any defects to your supervisor.

   3. Always remove vacuum hose from machine outlet at end of work day.

   4. Coil hose loosely on machine, or in case of central system, hang on hangers provided in gear or storage room.

D. *Machine:*

   1. Upon any signs of smoke or unusual odor stop machine immediately and notify your supervisor.

   2. To avoid damaging wheels, do not bump machine up and down stairs when carrying from one floor to another. Supervisors should make sufficient help available to move machines from floor to floor in buildings where there are no ramps or elevators.

   3. Wipe machine with a damp cloth when day's work is completed.

E. *Wiping Cloths:*

   Wash cloths as required and hang them to dry in proper place.

PRECAUTIONS

   1. *Never* oil or grease machines. (This should be done only by qualified personnel.)

   2. Never use "dry" vacuum unit to pick up liquids.

   3. *Do not tamper* with shutoff valve or other mechanism.

   4. Report needed repairs to your supervisor.

Performance Inspection Guide

A. *Rug Cleaning:*

   Rugs should be thoroughly clean and free from dust, dirt and other debris. Nap on rugs should be laid in one direction.

B. *Bare Floor Cleaning:*

   Bare floors around rugs should have been cleaned with rug tool. Large bare floor areas should have been cleaned with bare floor tool. No dirt should be left in corners, under furniture, or behind radiators or doors.

C. *Furniture and Equipment Replaced:*

   1. All furniture and equipment moved during the cleaning operation should be returned to its original position.

   2. All equipment used during the vacuum cleaning operation should be cleaned and properly placed in its assigned location.

   3. Portable and tank type machines should be wiped clean, dust bags emptied, and vacuum hose coiled loosely on machine or hung on racks provided for that purpose.

Equipment and Material Allocation and Replacement

Items	Allotment per Cleaner	Replacement or Reissue
Broom, corn	1	1 per year
Cloth (waffleweave)	1	4 per year
Vacuum cleaner with attachments (domestic) (or)	1	1 per 10 years*
Vacuum cleaner with attachments (portable)	1	1 per 10 years*
Wedge	To be obtained locally	As required

* Does not apply to replacement of vacuum cleaner attachments.

The allotment and replacement or reissue quantities are based on one rug cleaner working the entire eight hours of each working day on the job.

• Where other duties are assigned to such an employee to secure 100 per cent utilization of his time, consideration should be given to reducing the allotment and replacement quantities in relative proportion to the time spent per hour on other work.

5 / CORRIDOR AND LOBBY POLICING

Source: General Services Administration, Washington, D. C.

Job Description

The job of corridor and lobby policing includes collecting and removing from the assigned corridor and lobby area all loose paper, trash, rubbish, empty bottles and other discarded material; removing wads of gum, spots of tar and other sticky substances from the floors of such area; keeping the jardinieres and/or sand urns in a neat and presentable condition; tidying up as necessary any drinking fountains and glass surfaces that may be located within such area; mopping up any wet areas that may occur during bad weather, or caused by liquids being spilled; and proper care and maintenance of the equipment and material issued to the employee for use in doing the job. Employees assigned to this job are also instructed to notice when lights are out and other defective building items, and to report same to their supervisor.

Equipment and Material

A. *Equipment:*

1. *For normal policing:*

   a. Dustpan

   b. Dustpan broom

      c. Putty knife

      d. Wiping cloths

      e. Perforated scoop

  2. *For mopping wet areas:*

      a. Bucket with mop wringer

      b. Cotton mop

B. *Material:*

    For equipment care:

    Detergent

Job Methods

Operation Steps	*Explanation*
A. *Normal Policing:*	

Step 1

1. Obtain equipment needed.	Equipment needed for normal policing listed under "Equipment and Material".
2. Proceed to work area.	Proceed with the equipment to the assigned area where work is to start.

Step 2

1. Police corridor and lobby floors.	Start at the beginning of the work area and use the broom and dust pan to remove all loose paper, trash and other foreign material from the assigned corridor and lobby areas.
2. Remove gum, tar or other substances from the floor.	Use the putty knife to remove any wads of gum, spots of tar or other foreign substance from the corridor and lobby floors during the policing operation.
3. Police jardinieres and/or sand urns.	While policing the area, collect all cigarette butts, burnt matches, and other discarded material from around the jardiniere or sand urn units located within the corridors and lobbies. Use the perforated scoop to remove the rubbish from the urns, and to sift or stir fresh sand to the top of the unit.

Operation Steps	*Explanation*
4. Police drinking fountains and glass surfaces.	If drinking fountains and glass surfaces such as picture, door, display and directory board glass are located within the assigned area, check these items as they are reached during the normal policing operation and use a damp wiping cloth to remove any unsightly dirt smudges and in general tidy these articles as may be required.

B. *Mopping Wet Areas:*

Step 3

1. Obtain equipment needed.	Secure the mop, mop wringer and bucket from the equipment storage location.
2. Mop up wet spots.	Use the mop to dry thoroughly all wet spots in the entrances, lobbies, and corridors of the assigned area. Squeeze the excess water from the mop frequently.

NOTE

Step 3 is to be performed during periods of rain or snow, and at such other times as may be needed to keep the floors of the assigned area in a dry and presentable condition.

C. *Returning Equipment to Storage Locations:*

Step 4

1. Return all equipment to storage location.	Gather all pieces of equipment and proceed to the location where the items are stored when not in use.
2. Broom, dustpan, putty knife and scoop.	Clean all articles and return them to their proper storage places.
3. Mop and wiping cloths.	Rinse the mop and wiping cloths in clean water, wring or squeeze to remove excess water and put in proper place for drying and storage.
4. Bucket and mop wringer.	Empty the bucket, rinse, wipe dry

Explanation

and return the bucket and wringer to their proper storage places.

Care of Equipment

A. *Dustpan:*

1. Clean the dustpan of loose dirt and dust before storing.

2. Hang the dustpan by the handle so as not to allow any damaging weight to be put on it during storage.

3. In dumping the dustpan, avoid banging it with force against the waste container as such action results in damage to the sides and edge of the pan.

B. *Dustpan Broom:*

1. Comb the broom bristles periodically.

2. Wash a dirty or oily broom in a warm water and detergent solution. (Use one ounce of detergent per gallon of water.) Rinse in clean water and hang by the handle to dry. Allow the broom to dry thoroughly before using.

3. Hang the broom in a dry, clean place when stored, so that the weight of the broom is not upon the bristles.

C. *Putty Knife:*

1. Use the putty knife only for removal of gum and other foreign substances during policing. *Do not* use it as a screw driver or hammer.

2. Wipe the knife clean and dry and store it in a dry, clean place.

D. *Perforated Scoop:*

1. Wipe the scoop clean and store it in a dry, clean place, either on a shelf or hanging on a nail.

2. Store it so that no damaging weight is placed on the scoop.

E. *Wiping Cloths:*

1. Rinse all cloths used; or when dirty, wash them in a warm water and detergent solution (one ounce of detergent per gallon of water), rinse in clean water and wring or squeeze to remove excess water.

2. Spread or hang cloths to dry in their proper storage place.

3. Avoid leaving wet, dirty cloths piled together in the storage location.

F. *Mop:*

1. After each use and before storage, rinse the mop in clean water and wring or squeeze to remove excess water.

2. Wash dirty mops in a warm water and detergent solution (one ounce of detergent per gallon of water); rinse in clean water and wring or squeeze to remove excess water.

3. Fluff the mop strands by shaking the mophead.

4. Store the mop with the mophead up to allow better drying.

G. *Bucket and Mop Wringer:*

1. Rinse and dry the bucket and wringer thoroughly.

2. Wipe the outside of the bucket free of dirt.

3. Avoid striking the bucket and wringer against objects as such action tends to cause leaks in the bucket and shorten the life of the equipment.

4. Store in a dry, clean place so as to have no damaging weight bearing on the bucket or wringer.

Performance Inspection Guide

A. *Normal Policing:*

1. *Corridor and Lobby Floors*

   a. Corridor and lobby floors of the assigned area should be free of all loose paper, bottles, trash and other foreign materials.

   b. Wads of gum, spots of tar and other foreign substances that tend to stick to the floors should have been removed.

2. *Jardinieres and/or Sand Urns*

   a. Cigarette butts, burnt matches and other discarded material should have been removed from around jardiniere and/or sand urn locations.

   b. Jardinieres should be free of refuse and be presentable in appearance.

   c. Sand urns should be free of refuse and the top sand should present a clean and neat appearance.

3. *Drinking Fountains and Glass Surfaces*

   a. Drinking fountain surfaces should be free of discarded rubbish, ink stains, finger marks and other dirt smudges and should present a neat appearance.

   b. Glass surfaces located in doors, pictures, displays, directory boards and other such items within the assigned area should be tidy and free of finger marks, smudges and other dirt marks.

B. *Mopping Wet Areas:*

1. Entrances, corridor and lobby floors should be free of wet spots and footprints.

2. Wall surfaces and baseboards should be free of water marks resulting from the mopping operation.

C. *Equipment and Material:*

1. All pieces of equipment should be clean and properly placed in their assigned storage locations.

2. Any unused detergent should be returned to its assigned storage location.

Frequency and Production

A. *Frequency and Production Schedule:*

	Main Corridor and Lobby	*Secondary Corridor and Lobby*
Frequency	4 Times Daily	Daily
Production Rate per Man-day	300,000 sq. ft. of Corridor and Lobby Area	

B. *Qualifying Factors:*

1. *Frequency*

   a. The frequency of corridor and lobby policing in a building is dependent upon the amount of traffic, weather conditions and type of occupancy. Allowances should be made in the frequency of policing at the various locations so as to accomplish the most efficient and economical performance of this job.

   b. The frequencies given in the above schedule are those for a normal standard of corridor and lobby policing under average conditions.

2. *Production Rate per Man-day*

   a. The production rate given in the above schedule is based on the actual corridor and lobby area rather than the gross area.

   b. This rate as established may be subject to modification due to the varying types, sizes and locations of government operated buildings. It does, however, provide a standard from which such deviation (if any) should be figured.

Staffing

The man-day requirements of labor for corridor and lobby policing can be determined by use of the following formula:

$$\text{Man-days (of labor)} = \frac{\text{Quantity}}{\text{Production}} \times \frac{1}{\text{Frequency}}$$

where quantity is the actual area in square feet of corridors and lobbies to be policed; production is the square feet of corridors and lobbies policed per man-day; and frequency is the number of working days between operations.

If the frequency and/or production rate values as established in the Frequency and Production Schedule have been modified to meet the existing conditions at a particular location, then those modified values should be used in the above formula for the computation of the labor requirement.

SAMPLE CALCULATION

Assume a building with 16,000 square feet of main corridor and lobby area, 140,000 square feet of secondary corridor and lobby area, and with such existing conditions that the established values from the Frequency and Production Schedule may be used; then compute the man-days of labor as follows:

$$\text{Man-days} = \overset{\substack{\textit{Main Corridor} \\ \textit{and Lobby Area}}}{\frac{\text{Quantity}}{\text{Production}} \times \frac{1}{\text{Frequency}}} + \overset{\substack{\textit{Secondary Corridor} \\ \textit{and Lobby Area}}}{\frac{\text{Quantity}}{\text{Production}} \times \frac{1}{\text{Frequency}}}$$

$$= \frac{16,000}{300,000} \times \frac{1}{\frac{1}{4}} + \frac{140,000}{300,000} \times \frac{1}{1}$$

$$= 0.213 \qquad\qquad + 0.467$$

$$= 0.68 \text{ man-days of labor required (jobs)}$$

To this total requirement must be added a factor to compensate for leave in order to arrive at the total number of positions needed to accomplish the work.

Conversion factor including compensation for leave $= 1.15$
Conversion factor $\times$ jobs $=$ total positions required
$1.15 \times 0.68 = 0.78$ positions required

Leave: Average time lost on job through sickness, death in family, and personal absenteeism.

• Where the normal corridor and lobby policing duty does not require the full time of the employee, other duties such as utility work, sidewalk cleaning, and similar work should be assigned to the employee to secure 100 per cent utilization of his time.

Equipment and Material Allocation and Replacement

Items	Allotment per Cleaner	Replacement or Reissue
Bucket (26 qt.)	1	1 per 2 years
Detergent	1 pound	6 pounds per year
Dustpan	1	1 per 2 years
Dustpan broom (hearth size corn broom)	1	1 per year
Perforated scoop	1	1 per 2 years
Mop (1¼ lb.)	1	2 per year
Mop handle	1	1 per year
Mop wringer (squeeze type, size 2)	1	1 per 2 years
Putty knife (1¼″)	1	1 per 2 years
Wiping cloths (waffleweave)	2	24 per year

The allotment per cleaner and replacement or reissue quantities in this section are based on one cleaner having continuous corridor and lobby policing duty.

• Where the situation exists that other related jobs are assigned to the cleaner having this duty to secure 100 per cent utilization of his time, consideration should be given to a reduction in the replacement quantities in accordance with the actual amount of corridor and lobby policing duty assigned.

(*Sources:* Public Buildings Service, General Services Administration, Washington, D. C.; *Buildings* magazine, November 1958, November 1960)

Elevator inspection and maintenance is a highly technical field that requires the service of a trained technician. But by becoming familiar with some of the highlights of inspection and routine maintenance, you can be sure that your equipment is getting the careful attention it deserves.

Maintaining the elevators in a building is another executive responsibility of the building superintendent or plant manager. He must delegate this work to the most responsible employee. Inspections should not be limited to state, city or insurance companies. Inspection service by reputable elevator companies is available in many localities. Where it is not available, the building superintendent or plant manager oversees the inspections. Information as to what points should be inspected is available from the manufacturer, along with recommendations on how to perform preventive maintenance.

Most accidents happen at landings. Make a careful check of the condition of the floors and landing sills. The sills should be of nonslip material, and well illuminated. Particular attention should be given to main floor landings where the difference between outdoor and indoor lighting is severe. Hoistways should be checked frequently, cleaned and greased semimonthly. Vision panels (if present) should be cleaned daily. Counterweights should operate smoothly and sheaves should be properly aligned.

Inspection of the car should include a checkup for structural defects such as loose bolts and other fastenings, excessive play in guide shoes and worn flooring. Test each emergency by opening it. If panels are held in place by thumb screws, they should be removable without the use of pliers; if they are held in place by locks, the key should be in the elevator.

Test the car switch. It should return to neutral position when released, and lock there. If the car is cable operated, examine the cable lock. Check all switch contacts in the car. The glass cover over the emergency relief switch should be in place. To check the clearance of the governor flyballs, if used, lift them above the position at which the governor grips the rope and revolves them at this level. This not only proves them clear of obstruction, but also clears the spindle of congealed oil and dirt. Reliable service personnel should check all safety devices weekly.

All oil buffers lose some oil during normal usage. Oil levels should be checked at each inspection. Alignment and tightness of the bolts in the anchorage should be inspected. Spring buffers should be checked for alignment and for proper seating in cups and mountings. Springs should be examined for flaws and to see that they have not taken a permanent set.

Hoisting machines should be checked for misalignment and cracks. Oil level, motor brushes, commutator, couplings, bolts, set screws, and keys should be inspected. The gear housing should be checked for oil level, and at the same time look for worn teeth on gears. Oil should be removed from the brake drum.

Check pins and bearing surfaces for lubrication and wear. The brake shoes should be relined before rivet heads come in contact with the drum, just as you would reline brakes on an automobile.

Checklist for Elevator Maintenance

Warning: Always open the main line electric power switch to the elevator before cleaning, lubricating or making any adjustments to the moving parts. Make no adjustments or repairs without considering first—the effect on the equipment. Regular care and lubrication with the proper materials are essential to preserve the life of the elevator. The intervals for lubrication specified in the following instructions are based on average operating conditions. For extraordinary conditions consult your building engineer. *Always* renew all worn parts.

1. WORM GEARING   *Check monthly*

Use worm gear lubricant. Fill to top of standpipe gauge with machine at rest. With machine running, examine gear through hole in top of case to determine if carrying sufficient lubricant. (Do not tilt gauge to determine oil level.)

2. THRUST BEARINGS   *Check monthly*

Self-lubricated from gear case.

3. DRIP PAN   *Examine frequently*

The drip pan under worm shaft packing gland should be watched for excessive leakage. (Do not pour dripped oil back into gear case.)

4. SHEAVE SHAFT BEARINGS   *Check every two weeks*

Sleeve type (with grease cup—use cup grease).
Sleeve type (with oil reservoir—use bearing oil).

                                                       Check monthly

Roller or ball type (use ball and roller bearing grease).
Lubricate at least every six months. (Do not fill over one-half full.)

SHEAVE SHAFT THRUSTS

Self-lubricated from gear case.

5. A/C OR D/C MOTOR   *Check every two weeks*

Use bearing oil. *Bearings:* With machine at rest, pour in oil to gauge height, and see that oil rings are free to rotate with shaft. (Do not overflow reservoir.)

6. BRAKE   *Check monthly*

Magnet cores (D/C only): Use powdered graphite. Wipe clean (use powdered graphite on the core surface and in brass shell) at least every six months. *Pins and linkage:* Use bearing oil, lubricate sparingly.

                                                     Check every two months

A/C brake magnets: Use A/C brake magnet oil. Fill magnet case to within one-half inch of top of standpipe gauge. *Brake motor bearings (motor operated brakes):* Consult local building engineer for proper cleaning and lubrication. *Caution:* Avoid getting oil on brake linings.

7. MOTOR GENERATOR AND EXCITER SETS   *Check every two weeks*

Sleeve type bearings: Use bearing oil. With machine at rest, pour in oil to gauge height, see that oil rings are free to rotate with shaft. (Do not overflow reservoir.)

Ball bearings: Use ball and roller bearing grease. Lubricate at least every six months. (Do not fill over one-half full.)

8. DEFLECTOR SHEAVE   *Check every two weeks*

Shaft lubrication: Use cup grease. Auxiliary sheaves (overhead, compensating, 2:1 etc.). Sleeve bearings (grease cup, use cup grease). Sleeve bearings (oil cup, use bearing oil). Sleeve bearings (chain oiler, use traction machine oil). Ball bearings, use ball and roller bearing grease. Lubricate at least every six months. (Do not fill over one-half full.) Box bearings, use cup grease.

9. ROPES   *Check every two months*

Use wire rope lubricant. Lubricate only when ropes appear dry or show signs of corroding. (Do not oversaturate ropes.)

10. CAR AND COUNTERWEIGHT SAFETY DEVICES   *Check monthly*

Pins, actuating screws, tail rope drum bearings, use bearing oil. Lubricate annually. *Caution:* Do not tamper with safety nor make any adjustments. At least once a year arrange with building engineer for a safety operating test.

11. GOVERNOR   *Check monthly*

Gear and grease cup, use cup grease. (Do not use any grease on gear sector of rope jaws.) Oil ports, use bearing oil.

12. GUIDE RAILS   *Check monthly*

Use type "C" lubricator oils. *Important:* Consult building engineer for proper grade of oil to use on guide rails. *Gibs:* No rail lubrication required.

13. ROLLER GUIDES   *Check every two months*

Roller guides, no rail lubrication required. *Wheel bearings:* Lubricate annually, use ball and roller bearing grease. Stands (for cast shoes and gibs), use cup grease. Be certain that spindles are free and properly lubricated to permit easy action of the guide shoes.

14. CONTROLLER AND RELAY PANEL   *Check every two weeks*

Switch hinge pins, use bearing oil, lubricate sparingly (a drop of oil is sufficient). Time and overload relays and dashpots, use dashpot oil. Refill if necessary to proper gauge level; check oil level every three months. (*Use no other oil.*)

15. SELECTOR AND FLOOR CONTROLLERS   *Check monthly*

Screws and gearings, use cup grease. Pressure type fittings, use ball and roller bearing grease. Oil cups and oil ports, use bearing oil. Square guides, clean and apply coating of Slip-It. *Driving tapes:* Only when dry, use soft brush and apply bearing oil.

16. BUFFERS   *Check every three months*

Use buffer oil. *Important:* Use no other oil (be certain that buffers are filled to proper gauge level at all times).

17. PIT TENSION FRAMES   *Check every two weeks*

Sheave bearing grease cup, use cup grease. Sheave bearing oil port or cup, use bearing oil. Sheave bearing pressure fitting, use ball and roller bearing grease. Weight guides, clean and apply coating of Slip-It.

18. DOOR AND GATE OPERATORS   *Check monthly*

Type "A" gear unit, use worm gear lubricant. Type "O", "S" and "K" gear units, use traction machine oil. *Important:* Use only oil specified and fill to gauge height. Motor bearings, use bearing oil. Link and lever pins, use bearing oil.

19. CYLINDERS   *Check every two months*

Checking cylinders, use door closer oil. Door sill trips, use cup grease.

Note: Clean all of the equipment regularly. Accumulated dust, dirt and oil impairs its efficiency and operation.

6A / ELEVATOR CLEANING

Job Description

Elevator cleaning includes all cleaning work inside the elevator cab, such as vacuum cleaning; mopping or scrubbing; floor waxing and polishing; removing gum or other foreign substances; dusting doors, fans, lights, walls and grilles; cleaning and polishing metal and wood surfaces; cleaning threshold plate; and proper care and maintenance of the cleaning equipment used. Employees assigned to this job should be sure all elevator lights, fans and switches are turned off when the job is completed. They should be instructed to notice defects in flooring, loose railings, and similar service defects, and report them to their supervisors.

Equipment and Materials

A. *Equipment:*

   For elevator cleaning.

   a. Equipment carrier
   b. Vacuum cleaner and attachments
   c. Putty knife
   d. Dust cloths (polyethylene glycol treated cheesecloth)

    e. Wiping cloths
    f. Buckets
    g. Squeeze type wringer
    h. Cotton mops
    i. Steel wool
    j. Wax applicator
    k. Wood wedge

B. *Materials:*

    For cleaning elevator.

    a. Lemon oil polish
    b. Metal polish
    c. Detergent, soapless, synthetic
    d. Water emulsion, synthetic, or floor sealer (as directed)

Job Methods

Operation Steps	*Explanation*
Step 1	
1. Obtain equipment and materials.	Obtain equipment and materials needed for elevator cleaning. (Listed under "Equipment and Materials".)
2. Proceed to assigned work area.	Push equipment carrier with equipment and materials to the first elevator scheduled to be cleaned. Take the elevator out of service before starting to clean.
Step 2	
1. Clean elevator walls, doors, fans and lights.	Use vacuum cleaner with wall brush attachment to clean ceiling, walls, doors, fans and lights. Use treated dust cloth to supplement vacuuming as required.
2. Clean grillwork.	Use vacuum cleaner with radiator brush attachment to thoroughly clean grillwork.
Step 3	
1. Vacuum clean elevator floor.	Use vacuum cleaner with bare floor cleaning attachment to thoroughly sweep floor area and threshold plate.

Operation Steps	*Explanation*
2. Remove gum and foreign substances from floor.	Use putty knife to remove any gum or other foreign substances from floor.

PRECAUTIONS

1. Make sure all loose dirt is removed from corners of car during vacuum cleaning operation.
2. Do not pull against electric cord of vacuum cleaner when it is plugged into receptacle. Do not allow machine to run over cord.

Step 4

1. Wall spotting.	Use lemon oil polish, applied with a cloth to remove hand marks and stains from wood surfaces. Rub cleaned area briskly to match luster of the rest of wall surface.
2. Clean and polish metal surfaces.	Use clean cloths and metal polish, as directed, to clean and polish metal handrails, metal doors and other metal surfaces.
3. Clean and polish wood surfaces.	Use clean cloths and lemon oil polish as directed to thoroughly clean and polish wood surfaces.

PRECAUTIONS

Metal polish is not to be used on painted, lacquered, or other specially treated metal surfaces. Do not apply metal polish so heavily that it will clog switch key openings. For such materials as aluminum, stainless steel or white metal trim, special polishes are available and should be used.

Step 5

Mop elevator floor.	a. Mix one ounce of detergent per gallon of warm water in mop bucket.
	b. Use mop and detergent solution to thoroughly clean floor area. Dip mop into solution and wring out excess so mop does not drip. Push mop around edges of floor first, using care to remove all dirt from corners; then mop the rest of floor

Operation Steps	*Explanation*
	area. Avoid splashing walls. (If floors are extremely dirty, use scrubbing and polishing machine to scrub floor.)
	c. Wring mop and go back over mopped area to pick up excess cleaning solution.
	d. Use a second mop and clean water to rinse and mop floor. Frequently rinse and wring mop during this operation.

PRECAUTIONS

1. Do not use so much water that it will tend to splash or to run beneath floor covering.
2. Change the rinse water frequently.
3. Be careful not to splash the doors and walls or scar them with the equipment.

Step 6

Wax elevator floors.	Pour small quantity of wax into pan and use wax applicator to spread wax evenly over floor.

PRECAUTIONS

1. Use only water emulsion wax on rubber and asphalt tile floor coverings.
2. Be sure the floor is thoroughly dry before applying the wax.

Step 7

Polish elevator floor.	Use scrubbing and polishing machine to polish elevator floor. Start at rear of elevator and polish toward the door. Use cloth to polish corners by hand.

PRECAUTION

Do not polish the floor until after wax is thoroughly dry.

Step 8

Clean threshold plate.	Clean grooves of threshold with vacuum floor brush or cloth covered wood wedge. Use steel wool to clean

Operation Steps	Explanation
	nonskid surface. Clean with metal polish or other approved cleaner as directed.

NOTE

Return each elevator to service when cleaning is completed.

Step 9

1. Return equipment and unused materials to storage location.	Upon completion of assignment, place all equipment and materials on equipment carrier and proceed to proper storage location.
2. Clean and store equipment.	Clean all equipment and store on equipment carrier and proceed to proper storage location, for following cleaning.
3. Unused material.	Return all unused material to proper storage place.

PRECAUTION

Make sure that lids to polish, detergent, wax, and similar containers are on securely.

Care of Equipment

A. *Bucket and Mop Wringer:*

1. Thoroughly rinse and dry bucket and wringer after use.
2. Remove mop strands and other foreign matter remaining in wringer.
3. Wipe dirt from outside bucket.
4. Avoid striking bucket and wringer against objects, for this tends to cause leaks in the bucket and to shorten the life of the equipment.
5. Store in dry place in such a way that there is no weight on bucket or wringer.

B. *Dustcloths (polyethylene glycol treated):*

1. Thoroughly shake or vacuum dustcloths as required to remove loose dust.
2. Wash dirty cloths in warm detergent solution (mix one ounce of detergent per gallon of warm water). Rinse in clean water and wring or squeeze to remove excess water.
3. To treat new or washed cheesecloth spray or sprinkle approximately one fluid ounce of treatment (such as polyethylene glycol solution) to three parts water on each square yard of cheesecloth. Cloth should be treated the day before it is to be used.

C. *Equipment Carrier:*

1. Do not allow carrier to strike walls, furniture, or other equipment.

2. Wipe carrier clean of dirt and dust. Keep clean and orderly at all times.

3. Promptly report to the supervisor, any defects or equipment failure.

D. *Mops:*

1. After use and before storing, rinse mops in clean water and wring or squeeze to remove excess water.

2. Wash dirty mops in warm water. Rinse in clean water and wring or squeeze to remove excess water.

3. Fluff mop strands by shaking.

4. Store mops, with mop heads up, to dry.

E. *Polishing Machine:*

1. After each use, wipe machine and cord free of dirt and dust with a damp cloth, using detergent solution and water to remove spots. Wipe machine and cord dry, and rewind cord loosely on hooks provided.

2. Remove brush from the machine. Wash dirty brushes in detergent solution, rinse thoroughly, and shake free of excess water.

3. Wash and rinse wheels of the machine, and wipe with a dry cloth.

4. Use metal polish as directed to clean and polish the floor machine. Store machine and brush, with brush removed, in assigned storage space.

5. Report needed repairs to supervisor.

F. *Putty Knife:*

1. Use putty knife only to remove gum or other foreign substances during sweeping.

2. Store knife in a clean, dry place.

G. *Vacuum Cleaner and Attachments:*

1. Empty and wipe dirt receptacle clean after each use.

2. After use wipe machine and cord free of dirt and dust with a damp cloth, wipe dry, and wind cord loosely on hooks or other means provided.

3. Do not allow machine or attachments to strike walls or other objects.

4. After use, clean attachments and return them with machine to a clean dry storage area where they will not be damaged.

5. Report needed servicing or repairs to supervisor.

H. *Wax Applicator:*

1. Remove and thoroughly wash applicator pad in detergent. (Mix one ounce of detergent to one gallon of warm water.)

2. Rinse applicator pad in clean water.

3. Shake excess water from applicator pad and replace on block to prevent shrinkage.

4. Store applicator where there is free circulation of air and where there will be no weight against it.

I. *Wiping Cloths:*

1. Rinse all cloths used. When cloths are dirty, wash in warm detergent solution (mix one ounce of detergent to one gallon of warm water), rinse and wring out.

2. Spread or hang cloths to dry in their proper storage places.

J. *Wood Wedge or Scraper:*

1. Clean and dry wedge and return it to proper storage location.

Performance Inspection Guide

A. *Normal Policing:*

1. *Vacuum Cleaning and Dusting:*

Interior surfaces of elevator should be free of loose dirt and dust streaks.

2. *Cleaning, Polishing and Wall Spotting:*

a. Handrails, controls and other surfaces should be clean and polished.
b. Walls should be free of finger marks and other smudges.

3. *Mopping, Waxing and Polishing:*

Elevator walls should be free of splash marks. Floor, including corners and threshold plate, should be clean, and floor should be waxed and polished.

B. *Equipment and Materials:*

1. All pieces of equipment should be clean, and properly placed in their assigned storage locations.

2. All polish, wax, soap and other similar leftover materials should be returned to their assigned storage location.

Frequency and Production

A. *Frequency and Production Schedule:*

	Passenger Elevators	Freight Elevators
Frequency	Daily*	Weekly*
Production Rate per Man-day	25	25

* Or as directed by supervisor.

B. *Qualifying Factors:*

1. *Frequency*

a. The frequency of elevator cleaning is dependent upon the type of occupancy in the building, the amount of traffic, size of elevator car, and to some extent, the design of the car.

b. The frequencies given in the following schedules are for a normal standard of cleaning under average conditions.

2. *Production Rate per Man-day*

The production rate used in the schedule is the rate established for cleaning elevators of average size located in one building or in buildings reasonably close to each other. Due to the number of buildings which have only one or two elevators, and because of the varied types of elevators, the production rate as established may be subject to modification at various locations. It does, however, provide a standard from which deviation should be calculated.

Staffing

The man-day requirements of labor for elevator cleaning can be determined by use of the following formula:

$$\text{Man-days (of labor)} = \frac{\text{Quantity}}{\text{Production}} \times \frac{1}{\text{Frequency}}$$

where quantity is the actual number of elevators to be cleaned, production is the number of elevators cleaned per man-day and frequency is the number of workdays between operations.

If the frequency and/or production rate values, shown in the frequency and production schedule, have been modified to meet existing conditions at a particular location, then those modified values should be used in the above formula for the computation of the labor requirement.

SAMPLE CALCULATION

Consider a building that has 16 passenger elevators and three freight elevators of such design and subject to such traffic conditions that the average cleaning values from the frequency and production schedule may be used; and compute the man-days of labor as follows:

$$
\begin{aligned}
\text{Man-days} &= \overbrace{\frac{\text{Quantity}}{\text{Production}} \times \frac{1}{\text{Frequency}}}^{\textit{Passenger Elevators}} + \overbrace{\frac{\text{Quantity}}{\text{Production}} \times \frac{1}{\text{Frequency}}}^{\textit{Freight Elevators}} \\
&= \frac{16}{25} \times \frac{1}{1} + \frac{3}{25} \times \frac{1}{5} \\
&= .64 \\
&= .664 \text{ man-days of labor required (jobs)}
\end{aligned}
$$

To this figure must be added a factor to compensate for leave in order to arrive at the total number of positions needed to accomplish the work.

Conversion factor including compensation for leave = 1.15
Conversion factor × jobs = total positions required
1.15 × .664 = .764 positions required

• Where the normal elevator cleaning duty does not require the full time of an employee, other duties should be assigned to secure 100 per cent utilization of his time.

Equipment and Material Allocation and Replacement

Items	Allotment per Cleaner	Replacement or Reissue
Buckets	2	1 per 2 years
Cheesecloth	2 yds.	12 yds. per year
Detergent (soapless synthetic)	1 pound	50 lbs. per year
Equipment carrier	1	1 per 10 years
Lemon oil polish	1 pint	4 pts. per year
Metal polish (liquid)	1 pint	4 pts. per year
Mops (1¼ lb.)	2	4 per year
Mop handles	2	2 per year
Mop wringer (squeeze type)	1	1 per 4 years
Polyethylene glycol	1 pint solution	2 pts. glycol per year
Putty knife (1¼")	1	1 per 2 years
Scrubbing & polishing machine	1	1 per 10 years**
Steel wool No. 00	1 pound	6 pounds
Vacuum cleaner and attachments	1	1 per 10 years **
Wax applicator (complete)	1	1 per 2 years
Wax applicator refill pad	As required	3 per year
Wax:	As required	1 drum per year
Liquid spirit (55 gal. drum)		
or		
Water emulsion (55 gal. drum)		
Wiping cloths	2	12 per year
Wood wedge	To be obtained*	As required

* Obtain locally.
** Does not apply to replacement of polishing brushes or vacuum cleaner attachments.

6B / ESCALATOR CLEANING

Job Description

Escalator cleaning includes the cleaning of all surfaces of the escalator and its surroundings that can be reached from the normal walking surface, such as vacuum cleaning landings and treads; removing gum or other foreign substances; dusting fire apparatus doors and ledges; cleaning radiators and grills; cleaning handrails, glass surfaces, and other metal and wood surfaces; wall spotting; cleaning treads and risers; and properly maintaining the equipment used for cleaning the escalator. Mopping and/or scrubbing of the escalator landings should be performed by the regularly assigned corridor mopping and/or scrubbing crews. These crews should be cautioned to use only a damp mop on the access panels to prevent water running through and onto the machinery below.

Employees assigned to this job should be instructed to notice lights out, and similar service defects, and to report them to their supervisor.

Equipment and Materials

A. *Equipment:*

   1. *For cleaning escalator.*

      a. Bucket
      b. Chamois
      c. Dustcloths
        (treated cheesecloth)
      d. Vacuum cleaner and attachments
      e. Wood wedge
      f. Wiping cloths
      g. Wood scraper

B. *Materials:*

   1. *For cleaning escalator.*

      a. Detergent
      b. Lemon oil
      c. White soap (cake)
      d. Metal polish

Job Methods

Operation Steps	*Explanation*
Step 1	
1. Obtain equipment and materials.	Obtain equipment and materials as needed for escalator cleaning (listed under "Equipment and Materials").
2. Proceed to assigned work area.	Take equipment and materials to first escalator scheduled to be cleaned.
Step 2	
1. Vacuum landings and treads.	Start at top landing and use vacuum cleaner with hose and bare floor attachment to vacuum clean all landings and treads.
2. Remove gum, and foreign substances.	Use wood scraper to remove any gum or other foreign substances from landings and treads during vacuum cleaning operation.

Operation Steps	*Explanation*
3. Vacuum clean radiators and grills.	Use vacuum cleaner with radiator brush attachment to remove dirt and dust particles from radiators and grills in escalator areaway.

PRECAUTION

Make sure all loose dirt and dust is picked up with the vacuum equipment, and that no dirt or dust is knocked or brushed into the escalator mechanism.

Step 3

Damp wipe treads and risers.	Start at top landing and clean grooves in treads using a wood wedge, covered with a damp cloth, shaped to fit snugly between the grooves of the treads.

PRECAUTIONS

1. Do not wash treads and risers, but wipe them with a damp cloth.
2. Use separate cloths for treads and risers so that any oil or grease will not be transferred from one to the other.

Step 4

1. Dust with treated dustcloths.	Start at bottom landing and dust fire apparatus, doors, ledges, and grills in the escalator areaway. Use treated dustcloths to dust all surfaces, except walls, that can be reached by standing on landings or treads.

PRECAUTION

Avoid using treated dustcloths on painted wall surfaces.

Step 5

1. Clean glass surfaces.	Use a clean, damp chamois to clean all glass surfaces.
2. Clean handrails.	Use a damp cloth to clean handrails.
3. Clean and polish metal surfaces.	Use clean cloths, and metal polish as directed, to clean and polish metal work except as noted below.
4. Clean and polish wood surfaces.	Use clean cloths and lemon oil polish to clean and polish wood surfaces as directed.

PRECAUTION

Metal polish is not to be used on painted, lacquered or other metal surfaces that have been specially treated.

Step 6

1. Normal wall spotting.	Use a clean, damp cloth to spot clean the enclosure wall up as high as can be reached while standing on the landing or tread.
2. Remove stubborn spots.	Use white soap on damp cloth to remove any stubborn spots that cannot be removed by normal wall spotting. Carbon tetrachloride is helpful in removing spots from metal surfaces, but should be used only when and as directed.

PRECAUTIONS

1. This step is for spot removal only, and not for washing the entire wall.
2. After rinsing cloths in bucket of clean water, wring them thoroughly to avoid getting an excessive amount of water on the wall. Rinse clothes often.
3. Be sure to wipe any soap particles from wall with a clean damp cloth.

Step 7

1. Return all equipment and unused materials to storage location.	Gather all pieces of equipment and unused materials and proceed to proper storage location.
2. Clean and store equipment.	Clean all particles and return them to proper storage position.
3. Unused materials.	Return all unused materials to proper storage place.

PRECAUTION

Make sure that lids to polish and other containers are on securely.

Care of Equipment

A. *Bucket:*
 1. Rinse and dry bucket thoroughly after each use.
 2. Wipe outside of bucket free of dirt.

3. Avoid striking bucket against objects as this tends to cause leaks and shortens the life of the bucket.

4. Store in dry place, and in such a way that there is no weight on the bucket.

B. *Chamois:*

1. After each use rinse chamois in clean water and squeeze out excess water.
2. Stretch chamois to original shape before placing to dry.
3. Avoid getting any oil, polish or cleaning materials on chamois.

C. *Dustcloths (Polyethylene glycol treated):*

1. Thoroughly shake or vacuum dustcloths to remove loose dust.
2. Wash dirty cloths in warm detergent solution. (Mix one ounce of detergent per gallon of warm water.) Rinse in clean water and squeeze to remove excess water.
3. To treat new or washed cheesecloth, spray or sprinkle each square yard of cheesecloth with approximately one fluid ounce of polyethylene glycol solution (mix three parts water to one part polyethylene glycol). The cloth should be treated the day before it is to be used.

D. *Vacuum Cleaner and Attachments:*

1. Empty dirty receptacle and wipe clean after each use.
2. After use wipe machine and cord free of dirt and dust with a damp cloth. Wipe machine and cord dry, and wind cord loosely on hooks or other means provided.
3. Do not allow machines or attachments to strike walls or other objects.
4. After use, clean attachments and return them with machine to a clean, dry storage area where they will not be damaged.
5. Report needed servicing or repairs to supervisor.

E. *Wood Wedge or Scraper:*

1. Use wood scraper only for removal of gum or other foreign substances.
2. Wipe scraper clean and store it in a clean dry place.

Performance Inspection Guide

A. *Normal Policing:*

1. *Landings and Treads.*

   The landings and treads should be free of loose dirt, dust streaks, and gum or other foreign substances.

2. *Cleaning, Dusting, Polishing and Wall Spotting.*

   a. The walls and all objects in the area should be free of finger marks and other smudges.
   b. Handrails and glass should be clean. Wood and metal surfaces should be cleaned and polished.

B. *Equipment and Materials.*

1. All pieces of equipment should be clean and properly placed in their assigned locations.

2. All polish, soap and similar leftover materials should be returned to their assigned storage locations.

Frequency and Production

A. *Frequency and Production Schedule:*

Passenger Escalator

Frequency	Daily*
Production Rate per Man-day	20 Flights (floor to floor)

* Or as directed by supervisor.

B. *Qualifying Factors:*

1. *Frequency*

   a. The frequency given in the schedule is for a normal standard of cleaning under average conditions.

   b. Only about 40 per cent of the escalator treads are exposed when the escalator is stopped. Obviously only the exposed section can be cleaned. To assure that each section is cleaned in its turn, the escalator should be divided into three sections, and the beginning of each section numbered consecutively by means of small numbers on the risers. The escalator should be stopped at successive sections for cleaning on successive nights.

2. *Production Rate per Man-day*

   The production rate used in the schedule is the rate established for cleaning escalators under average conditions. Due to varying designs and conditions, the production rate as established may be subject to modification at various locations. It does, however, provide a standard from which such deviations should be calculated.

Staffing

The man-day requirements of labor for escalator cleaning can be determined by:

$$\frac{\text{Number of Flights (floor to floor)}}{\text{Production per Man-day}}$$

If the frequency and/or production rate values as given in the schedule have been modified to meet existing conditions at a particular location, then those modified values should be used for the computation of labor requirement.

SAMPLE CALCULATION

Consider a building that has 16 flights of escalators (floor to floor) and of such design and subject to such traffic conditions that the average cleaning values from the frequency and production schedule may be used, and compute the man-days of labor as follows:

$$\text{Man-days} = \frac{16}{20} = .80 \text{ Man-days of labor required (jobs)}$$

To this figure must be added a factor to compensate for leave in order to arrive at the total number of positions needed to accomplish the work.

Conversion factor including compensation for leave—1.15
Conversion factor × jobs = total positions required.
1.15 × 80 = positions required—.92

• Where the normal escalator cleaning duty does not require the full time of an employee, other duties should be assigned to secure 100 per cent utilization of his time.

Equipment and Materials Allocation and Replacement

Items	Allotment per Cleaner	Replacement or Reissue
Bucket (12 qt.)	1	1 per 2 years
Chamois	1	1 per year
Cheesecloth	1 yard	12 yards per year
Detergent (soapless synthetic)	1 pound	25 pounds per year
Lemon oil polish	1 pint	4 pints per year
Polyethylene glycol solution	1 pint	2 pints solution per year
Vacuum cleaner and attachments	1	1 per 10 years**
White soap (6 oz. cake)	1 cake	4 cakes per year
Wiping cloths	2	12 per year
Wood scraper	1	2 per year*
Wood wedge	1	2 per year*

* Obtained locally.
** Does not apply to replacement of vacuum cleaner attachments.

7 / EQUIPMENT CARE

(*Sources:* General Services Administration, Washington, D. C.)

This chapter covers instructions for the care, allocation and replacement of general equipment and materials commonly used in the building cleaning operations.

Applicator, Wax

1. Remove applicator pad from block and thoroughly wash.

2. Rinse thoroughly, shake excess liquid from applicator pad and replace on block to prevent shrinkage.

3. Store applicator where there is free circulation of air and where there will be no weight against it.

Bag, Canvas Shoulder Trash

1. Thoroughly empty bag or receptacle of trash and dirt after each day's use.
2. Avoid snagging or tearing the bag.
3. Store in a clean, dry location.

Bag, Wastepaper and Trash Collection

1. Do not empty contents of ash trays into this bag.
2. Avoid snagging the bag on sharp objects or getting it caught in the door.
3. Store neatly.
4. Launder as required.

Basket, Oak Splint

1. Clean the trash basket of trash and dirt after each day's use.
2. Store in such a manner it will not be damaged.

Belt, Safety

Note: The following is an excerpt from standards as they pertain to the care of safety belts:

1. Each safety belt shall be identified and a record of the date it was put in service shall be kept in the office of the building (or facility) superintendent and checked at frequent intervals to insure that proper inspection is made of belts which have been in service for a considerable period. A record shall also be kept of any repairs or replacements made to the belt.

2. Belts shall be maintained in good condition at all times.

3. All safety belts shall be examined by the supervisor at the beginning of each work shift. The person using this equipment shall also examine the belt at the beginning of each work shift and at other times during the day to make certain that no defects have developed.

4. All belts shall be stored, transported and handled so as to prevent corrosion or injury. Belts which have been damaged by mildew, by the action of an acid, by contact with sharp tools or equipment, or by any corrosive or deteriorating agent, shall not be used.

5. Impact carrying parts of safety belts shall be repaired *only by the manufacturer or his designated representative,* unless the regional safety engineer especially authorizes another individual to do so.

6. Persons responsible for supervising the use and care of window cleaning or window maintenance equipment shall make certain that all unsafe pieces of equipment are disposed of at once, and not left lying about where they can be picked up and used.

7. When a belt has been exposed to rain or snow, wipe it off with a clean rag and allow it to dry at room temperature.

8. Never expose belts to heat in excess of ordinary room temperature.

9. Belts shall never be dropped or thrown from one elevation to another, or otherwise mishandled.

10. For standard anchors and terminals a 9/16-inch plug gauge can be used to check wear on the terminals. If the belt terminal slot is so wide at any point that it will accommodate a 9/16-inch plug gauge, the terminal shall be replaced.

Boots, Rubber

1. Rinse off dirt and other matter and wipe dry after each day's use.

2. Store in a clean well ventilated place in such a manner that the boots will not be damaged.

Broom, Corn

1. Soak new broom overnight before using it for first time.

2. Never stand a broom on the straws when storing.

3. Store broom where there is free circulation of air.

4. Wash broom as required, using a warm synthetic detergent solution. Rinse in clear water and hang to dry.

5. Never use the broom for scrubbing or when it is wet.

6. Rotate the broom when using it so that it will wear evenly.

Broom, Dustpan

1. When broom becomes soiled, wash it in warm detergent solution, rinse in clear water and shake free of excess water.

2. Store broom so that its weight is not on the bristles.

Brush, Counter Dust

1. When brush becomes soiled, wash it in warm detergent solution.

2. Rinse in clear water and shake out excess water.

3. Hang up where air circulation is good so brush will dry.

Brush, Deck Scrubbing

1. Rinse brush in clean water, after each day's use and shake dry of excess water.

2. Place for drying and storage in a position so that the bristles do not bear the weight of the brush.

3. Avoid knocking the brush against objects as such action tends to split the brush block.

Brush, Floor Sweep

1. Clean brush daily by combing bristles.

2. Wash oily or very dirty brush as necessary in a warm detergent solution. Rinse in clear water, shake out excess water and hang to dry.

3. Store in a clean dry place so that the bristles do not bear the weight of the brush.

4. Once each week reverse the brush by placing the handle in the other hole of the brush block to increase brush life.

Brush, Radiator Dust

1. Clean brush daily by combing.
2. Store brush on a flat surface so that tufts will be flat and straight.
3. Avoid wetting the brush.

Brush, Sidewalk

1. Wash an oily or dirty brush in warm detergent solution and rinse in clean water. Shake free of excess water and hang to dry with bristles in a downward position and free of any weight.
2. Store in a clean dry place so that the bristles do not bear the weight of the brush.
3. Reverse the position of the handle in the brush block weekly to provide longer brush life.

Brush, Toilet (or toilet mop)

1. Wash daily in a solution of detergent or multipurpose cleaner.
2. Rinse thoroughly and shake out excess water.
3. Hang up to dry where air circulation is good.

Bucket

1. Rinse and dry the bucket inside and outside after each day's use.
2. In storing, place the bucket so that it will not be damaged.

Can, Ash (for collecting non-combustible material)

1. Empty container after each use.
2. Wipe interior and exterior with a damp wiping cloth to remove dirt, dust, etc.
3. Dry surfaces with a dry wiping cloth.
4. Replace container in assigned position so that it will not be damaged and will be ready for next day's use.

Chamois

1. Rinse chamois in clean water and squeeze out excess water after each day's use.
2. Stretch chamois to original shape before placing to dry.
3. Avoid contaminating chamois with oils, polish, etc.

Cloth, Drop

1. Brush or shake free of dust and dirt after each day's use.
2. If cloth becomes wet during use, hang overnight to dry.
3. Avoid snagging or tearing the drop cloth.
4. Fold and store in assigned storage location.

Cloth, Wiping

1. Rinse the wiping cloths in clean water after each day's use.

Dustcloth, Treated

1. Keep the cloth free from grime or oily material.
2. Wash the cloth weekly or as required in a warm detergent solution. Rinse in clear water and wring dry.

3. Treat with prescribed dustcloth treating compound as directed by supervisor.

4. Hang the cloth to dry where there is a good circulation of air.

Dustpan

1. Clean dustpan of dirt and dust before storing.

2. Hang dustpan by the handle so that it will not be bent or otherwise damaged.

Gloves, Rubber

1. After each day's use wash the gloves in warm multipurpose cleaner or detergent solution, rinse in clean water and shake free of excess water.

2. Store gloves in a clean dry place.

3. Always maintain gloves in first-class condition. Discard gloves when holes develop.

4. Be careful not to snag gloves on nails or other sharp-edged objects.

Goggles, Dust

1. Wipe goggles clean after each day's use.

2. Care should be taken not to drop or damage goggles.

3. Goggles should be maintained in first-class condition. When the lenses become chipped or otherwise damaged, the goggles should be replaced.

Hose, Water

1. Drain the hose of any remaining water and wipe the outside free of dirt and excess moisture.

2. Coil and/or properly store the hose in its assigned location.

Knife, Putty

1. Wipe the knife free of dirt and moisture after each day's use.

2. Store in a clean dry place.

3. Use only for the purposes specified. Do not use as a screwdriver or hammer.

Ladders (including platform type)

Ladders should be cleaned and inspected frequently and those which have developed defects should be withdrawn from service for proper repair, or disposal. In either instance, such ladders should be tagged or marked "DANGEROUS! DO NOT USE."

During routine inspections ladders should be carefully checked for the following defects:

1. All Ladders:

    a. Loose steps or rungs (consider step or rung loose if it can be moved at all with the hand).

    b. Loose nails, screws or bolts.

    c. Loose or missing shoes or antislip bases.

    d. Cracked, split or broken uprights, braces, steps or rungs.

    e. Slivers on uprights, rungs or steps.

Litterstick

1. Wipe the stick free of moisture and dirt after each day's use.

2. Place a cork or some similar object over the pointed end before storing.

Mop, Cotton Wet

1. Rinse a new mop before using.
2. After each day's use and before storage rinse the mop in clean water and squeeze or wring to remove excess water.
3. Wash dirty mops in a warm detergent solution, rinse in clean water and wring or squeeze to remove excess water.
4. Fluff the mop strands by shaking.
5. Store with the mophead up in a well-ventilated place to allow for better drying.

Mower, Hand Lawn

1. Wipe all parts free of dirt, moisture and grass cuttings after each day's use.
2. Store the mower in its assigned location and in such a position as to prevent its being damaged.
3. The mower should be kept properly lubricated and blades sharpened. Report all defects and/or necessary repairs to the supervisor.

Mower, Power Lawn

1. Brush off accumulated grass and wipe the entire machine, except the engine, with a dry cloth.
2. Remove any dirt or grass that has accumulated on the flywheel housing or between the cylinder fins of the engine with a brush.
3. The mower should be kept properly lubricated and blades sharpened. Report all defects and/or necessary repairs to the supervisor.

Overshoes, Rubber

1. Rinse or wipe off dirt and other matter and dry thoroughly.
2. Store in such a manner that they will not be damaged.

Polishing Machine, Floor

1. Remove brush and wash daily or as required.
2. Wipe the machine and cord free of dirt and dust with a damp cloth. A cloth dampened with detergent solution may be used to remove spots not otherwise removed. Wipe the machine and cord dry and rewind the cord loosely on the hooks provided.
3. Wash and rinse the machine wheels and wipe dry.
4. Use metal polish as directed to clean and polish the machine surfaces.
5. Store the machine and brush (with brush removed) in assigned storage space.
6. Report needed repairs to the supervisor.

Raincoat

1. Wipe the coat free of dirt and excess moisture after each day's use.
2. Store the coat by hanging on a hanger in a clean well ventilated place.
3. Avoid snagging on nails and other sharp objects.

Rake, Lawn

1. Wipe the rake free of moisture, dirt and other debris after each day's use.

2. Store by hanging in a safe and secure manner and so it will not be damaged.

Rake, Heavy Iron (for paper baling)

1. Wipe rake free of dirt and dust and dry thoroughly.
2. Remove any paper that might still be clinging to its spikes.
3. Store rake so the spikes will not be damaged or bent.
4. Avoid hitting the rake against metal or concrete during use.

Respirator, Dust

1. Wipe respirator clean daily.
2. Respirator should be maintained in first-class condition. If it becomes damaged in any way it should be replaced.

Scaffolding

1. Damp wipe scaffolding to remove solution spillage or other liquid.
2. Store the equipment in its assigned storage location. Avoid creating safety hazards in placing the scaffolding for storage.
3. Report defects or needed repairs to supervisor.

Scoop (perforated or sieve)

1. Wipe clean and store in a dry clean place.
2. Store so that no damaging weight is placed on the scoop or sieve.

Scrubber-Vacuum Machine

1. Drain and flush both the cleaning solution and the dirty water tanks.
2. Remove vacuum screen and clean.
3. Clean brushes after each day's use. On dual brush machine, reverse the brushes when replacing them. Install new brushes if required.
4. Clean guide wheel and under carriage.
5. Clean and replace brush shields.
6. If electric scrubber is used, clean and dry wipe electric cable.
7. Wipe dirt and other matter from all machine surfaces except gasoline engine.
8. Store machine in assigned storage position.
9. Report needed repairs to the supervisor. Do not attempt to repair the machine or accessories. (This is a shop job.)

Shovel

1. Wipe dirt and dust from shovel and dry thoroughly before storing.
2. Store shovel so it will not be damaged.
3. Avoid banging shovel against metal or concrete surfaces.

Sign, Warning or Caution

1. Wipe sign free of dirt and other matter.
2. Store in assigned storage position so it will not be damaged.

Snow Plow Attachments

1. Wipe the equipment free of dirt and moisture after each use.
2. Upon storing, coat the bare metal portions of the equipment with a rust

preventive compound as directed by the supervisor and otherwise maintain in a well lubricated and clean condition.

3. Report necessary repairs and defects to the supervisor.

Sponge

1. Rinse the sponge in clean water after each day's use.

2. When dirty, wash in warm detergent or multipurpose cleaner solution, rinse thoroughly and squeeze out excess water.

3. Store in a clean dry location.

Squeegee

1. Rinse the squeegee blade in clean water after each day's use.

2. Wipe dry and store in a clean dry location.

Sweep Mop, Treated

1. Treated sweep mops should be shaken or vacuum cleaned both during use and at close of operation each day. They should be kept free of grime or oily material.

2. Every two weeks or as required, remove the mophead, shake out as much dust as possible and wash mop in a warm detergent solution.

3. Treat the mop with prescribed mop treating material as directed by supervisor.

4. Replace the mophead on the frame and hang mop so that a good air circulation will be obtained to assist in drying the mop.

Sweeper, Power Sidewalk

1. Empty dirt pan.

2. Check vacuum intake housing and vacuum bag.

   a. Keep intake housing clean.

   b. Empty vacuum bag frequently by removing inner bag and shaking it to remove all the accumulated dust.

3. Clean sweeper after each day's use.

   a. Wipe entire sweeper except gasoline engine with dry cloth.

   b. Use a brush as required to reach areas that cannot be reached with cloth.

4. If sweeper is electric powered, return unit to battery charger, otherwise store sweeper in assigned location.

Tamper (for use in wastepaper baling)

1. Wipe tamper free of dirt and dust and dry.

2. Store the tamper so it cannot be damaged or damage other objects by falling.

Tank, Mop

1. Rinse mop unit compartments and wringer thoroughly and wipe dry after each day's use.

2. Remove any remaining mop strands and other matter from the mop unit and wringer.

3. Always leave mop wringer in released position.

4. Store in a clean dry location and otherwise maintain in a clean and orderly condition.

5. Report any defects or necessary repairs to the supervisor.

Tool, Ice Scraping

1. Wipe the tool free of moisture and dirt after each day's use.

2. Store in a safe manner in its assigned location.

Tools, Miscellaneous Shrubbery

1. Wipe tools free of dirt and moisture after each day's use.

2. Maintain tools in a well sharpened and lubricated condition as necessary.

3. Hang tools for storage in such a way that they will not be damaged or endanger personnel.

Truck, Four-wheeled Push

1. Clean the truck of dirt and trash after each day's use.

2. The wheels of the truck should be kept properly lubricated.

3. Report all necessary repairs or defects to the supervisor.

Truck, Stevedore

1. Clean thoroughly each week with a damp wiping cloth and dry thoroughly.

2. Avoid striking wall surfaces, radiators, etc. with truck.

3. Store truck out of the way of traffic to prevent anyone falling over it.

4. Arrangements should be made to have the wheels oiled regularly. Report any defects or repairs to the supervisor.

Vacuum Cleaner

1. Always operate vacuum equipment with a cleaning tool on the end of hose.

2. Avoid sharp bends in hose during operation. Do not permit platform trucks to run over hose. Report any defects to supervisor.

3. Always remove hose from machine outlet at end of work day.

4. Coil hose loosely on machine, or in case of central system, hang on hangers provided in gear rooms.

5. Remove sweepings from dust bag daily. In addition to removing sweepings daily, clean the inside of the bag once a week. Where two or more machines are available, use one machine to clean the bag of the other. Where another machine is not available, clean the bag with a stiff brush.

6. Wipe the machine with a damp cloth when day's work is completed.

7. Make sure the electric cable connector is plugged all the way into the electric outlet during operation of the machine.

8. Avoid pulling on the electric cable in removing plug from outlet.

9. Do not splice or replace electric cable. (This is shop job.)

10. Upon any signs of smoke or unusual odor stop machine immediately and notify supervisor.

11. To avoid damaging wheels, do not bump machine up and down stairs when carrying from one floor to another. Supervisors should make sufficient help

available to move machines from floor to floor in buildings where there are no ramps or elevators.

Wall Washing Machine

1. Empty the machine, rinse with clear water and wipe dry.
2. Rinse and drain machine hose and trowels, wipe dry and coil hose loosely on trowels.
3. Hang trowels on hooks on side of machine or other assigned location.
4. Store machine in clean dry location where no damage will be done to it.
5. Wash, rinse and place to dry all toweling used in the day's work.

Wedge and/or Scraper, Wood

1. Wipe wedge and/or scraper free of dirt and other matter after each day's use.
2. Store in assigned storage place so it will not be damaged or lost.

Wringer, Mop

1. Remove any mop strands and matter clinging to wringer.
2. Rinse and dry wringer thoroughly.
3. Store so that wringer will not be damaged.

8 / FENCE MAINTENANCE

A fence is generally erected to control access to a restricted area. The maintenance problem of this facility is to make certain that there are no holes in the fence, and that no washouts occur in the ground immediately adjacent to it. Regular inspection should be made, and repairs made when necessary. Also, insofar as appearance and protection against corrosion are concerned, a fence must be kept in a well painted condition unless it is constructed of noncorrosive material. In the interest of plant security, inspection ease, and appearance, the ground for a distance of one to two feet on both sides of a fence traversing an unlandscaped area should be periodically sprayed with a weed killer to prevent the growth of vegetation on or in the close proximity of the fence.

Selection of a paint or coating will depend on the material to be treated and the conditions of atmosphere and use to which it will be subjected. A reliable paint manufacturer or dealer is the best source of information in selecting the right paint for the job. He should be able to take into account the local atmospheric and meteorologic conditions that will affect the surface because of its location. Other conditions that warrant consideration are extreme heat or cold, bright sunlight, chemical fumes, dust abrasion, and salt water spray.

On a wire fence, a long braided fabric roller, dipped in a pan, is often used for painting and enables the painter to cover 100 per cent of the fence surface facing him, and also a considerable amount of the far side of the fence.

9 / **FLOORS AND FLOOR CARE**

(*Sources:* Public Buildings Service, General Services Administration, Washington, D. C.; *Buildings* magazine)

9A / **FLOOR FINISHES**

Floor finishes include those surface products that are applied regularly, such as wax and emulsified resins, that can be applied quickly and easily, that are prompt drying, and that can be readily removed when necessary. There are two types of wax—the solvent type, including both liquid and paste, and the water emulsion type. Water emulsion waxes are suitable for use on any type of floor except unsealed wood. Solvent waxes, although sometimes considered to be more durable, can be used only on wood, linoleum and cork.

Although not the only measure of quality, the proportion of carnauba wax contained in floor wax will largely determine how well the product beautifies and protects. Solvent waxes seldom exceed 12 per cent in solids. Most water waxes vary in solid content from 12 per cent to 18 per cent.

Many of the improved resin finishes now contain polyethylene or a similar synthetic. When originally developed, many resin floor finishes were easily scratched, and would not respond to buffing. They were also difficult to remove from the floor. Most resin finishes no longer present this problem.

Waxing Precautions

To obtain the best finish for your floor and maintain high quality levels with maximum economy, observe the following precautions when waxing:

1. Never wax an improperly cleansed floor. It only causes unsightly appearance, prevents wax from taking bond to floor. Soil and other impurities mixed with wax can upset the formula and cause a flaky or milky appearance to a new wax coat.

2. Never apply wax to a wet or damp floor. This can prevent bonding of the wax and cause a milky and cloudy appearance.

3. Never apply a heavy coat of wax.

4. Do not rewax every time floors become dull. They can usually be brought to a bright appearance by dry buffing. Dirt cannot be ground into or penetrate a good hard wax film. Therefore, for the most part, dirt appearing on a floor is surface soil and can ordinarily be removed by damp mopping—or if dry by steel wooling or buffing up with a standard buffing brush.

5. Never permit container of stored wax to stand open. Evaporation of vehicles will increase the solid content of the material, causing a heavier film to be applied. This will cause a faulty film on the floor and, in addition, less coverage per gallon.

6. Never apply wax that is under 70° F., nor apply it to a floor under this temperature. Cold floors or cold wax cause a heavier viscosity, which in turn makes a heavier film. The thinner the wax film, the better the results.

7. Never permit water waxes to freeze. Water waxes are neither an emulsion, nor a suspension, but rest on a point between these two chemical categories. The shock from freezing can unbalance the formulas causing the wax to be valueless.

8. Never use a dirty mop applicator, or receptacle to hold water waxes.

9. Never pour used wax into the original container with unused wax. Contamination can damage water waxes. Pour leftover used wax into a clean gallon or larger jug. This wax should be poured into a funnel that contains steel wool to act as a strainer. Be sure to keep all lids tight on storage containers to prevent evaporation.

Tile Floors and Their Care

Planned maintenance and a good knowledge of floor care is an important phase in a building maintenance program. Floor maintenance programs include a controlled cleaning and finishing schedule set to meet specific requirements under varying conditions. A well planned day-to-day maintenance schedule should take into consideration the type of flooring, amount and nature of traffic, atmospheric soil conditions, appearance and cleanliness level desired.

In order to perform proper maintenance on various types of floors, a knowledge of composition, limitations and adaptability of the floors should be known.

Asphalt tile. Asphalt tile is a mixture of asbestos fibers, pigments, and inert fillers bound together with an asphalt or resin binder. Colors are divided into four groupings, A, B, C, and D, with A as the darkest and D the lightest. A and B generally contain asphalt binders, C and D, resin binders. Asphalt tile is also furnished in a grade designated as greaseproof, obtainable at a slightly higher cost. It is normally the least expensive of the resilient floors, however some thin grades of vinyl-asbestos may be cheaper. With one or two exceptions where special adhesives are used, asphalt tile is the only resilient floor which can be installed on any smooth, solid subfloor, including below grade concrete. It is generally considered moisture proof and decay proof. It is the least resilient of the soft floors, and is easily indented by heavy or pointed objects. Natural enemies of asphalt tile are oils, greases, and such solvents as gasoline, naphtha, turpentine, carbon tetrachloride, and kerosene.

Cracks, checking and breaks in asphalt tile can be blamed directly on the use of alkaline or caustic cleaners which dry out the tile and makes it hard and brittle, eventually causing disintegration. The alkali in the cleaners used on this floor have emulsified the resins and plasticizers of the asphalt tile, causing this brittle, hard, shrinking surface. A drying out effect is obvious at the edges of the tile, indicating that water and alkaline salts have seeped into joints and cracks. In damp mopping that may follow, the wetting and re-wetting of the alkaline salts can cause an almost continuous swelling action. Pitting on asphalt tile is a sign that solvents have come in contact with it. Oil, greases, or solvents will soften and may eventually dissolve the tile. Strong caustic cleaners will also cause pitting.

Do not use varnishes, lacquers, shellacs, or other plastic finishes. These materials usually contain solvents that will permanently injure the floor. Never use oily sweeping compounds or dressings. Asphalt tile should not be installed in areas that are subject to extreme temperature changes.

Any good quality mild soap, neutral cleaner, or synthetic detergent may be used. The alkaline content of such cleaners should have a pH of more than ten. Solvent type cleaners, except alcohol, are detrimental to asphalt tile. After scrubbing with a good neutral cleaner, a thorough rinsing should follow, then a good water emulsion wax or emulsified resin type of floor treatment applied.

Vinyl tile. Vinyl tiles are commonly classified in four main types:

Vinyl asbestos, which is also referred to as semi-rigid or semi-flexible.

Homogeneous, which is also referred to as flexible tile, and better known as vinyl plastic.

Calendered vinyl mix or backed vinyl.

Rotogravure printed or vinyl coated gravure.

Vinyl asbestos, composed through full thickness, of vinyl resins, plasticizers, pigments, fillers and asbestos fibers formed under pressure while hot, is one of the most popular of all the resilient floors. It is more expensive than asphalt tile, which it closely resembles in appearance, but has the following advantages over asphalt:

1. It is practically immune to mineral solvent, oils, and greases, as well as to alkalies and acids.

2. Its indentation resistance is generally 25 lbs. per square inch.

3. Also decay and mildew-proof, it is easier to maintain than asphalt tile since generally, any kind of wax or cleaner can be used.

4. It can be installed on below grade concrete by use of special adhesive.

Vinyl plastic, composed through full thickness of vinyl resin, plasticizers, pigments and fillers formed under pressure while hot, is considered the best of the vinyls, and in most ratings one of the best of all resilient floors. It is also known as homogeneous vinyl tile. This tile is the most expensive. It possesses all the qualities of vinyl asbestos in being resistant to solvents, oil and other immunities, and is also more resilient, therefore is more comfortable and quieter on which to walk or work. It resembles rubber tile in appearance, and is flexible, colorful and glossy. It is more expensive than rubber tile, and has a load limit of approximately 200 pounds per square inch, which makes it eight times more resistant to indentation than asphalt or vinyl asbestos tile. It may be cleaned and maintained with any of the usual cleaners and waxes, and by use of a special adhesive, may be installed on below grade concrete.

Backed vinyl has a wearing layer composed of vinyl resins, plasticizers, pigments, and fillers, overlaid on a backing of various regular alkali resistant materials.

The four main types of vinyl are generally immune to grease, oil, and ordinary solvents, and resist ordinary acids and alkalies. Either water emulsion wax or spirit wax may be used. Water emulsion wax is more generally prescribed. All the vinyls can be maintained in much the same manner as asphalt and rubber tile, except that they will take solvent type cleaners, waxes, and sweeping compounds. Excess water or flooding will, however, create the danger of seepage between tiles, causing the adhesive to loosen. Some vinyl, when first installed, has a tendency to hold dirt, but ceases after a few months of regular maintenance.

Due to the smooth, dense surface, some vinyls will not take wax properly until after a period of use.

Rubber tile. A mixture of rubber, natural, synthetic, and/or reclaimed, with inert fillers and color pigments, rubber flooring varies widely in form and properties. It is available in tiles and sheets with many degrees of hardness and flexibility. Regular soaps are not recommended for cleaning rubber tile, since fats and oils are detrimental to rubber tile. Synthetic detergents derived from sulfanated hydrocarbons are approved for cleaning rubber tile. Mild alkaline cleaners (not TSP) may be used occasionally, but care should be taken to avoid the use of excess water. Do not wash too soon after installation, or use any substances containing gasoline, kerosene, naphtha, benzine, turpentine, mineral solvents, or harsh alkalies. Avoid the use of sweeping compounds containing oil, abrasives, or chemicals. Never use varnish or lacquer. When necessary to remove stubborn accumulations, mild abrasive cleaners may be used, or steel wool with a synthetic detergent. To remove hardened old wax coatings, steel wool pads and a good wax stripper are effective. Only water wax emulsions should be used on rubber tile. Solvent type, including paste wax, will cause the tile to soften and bleed. Do not install rubber tile in areas of bright sunlight, as the pigment will fade.

Linoleum or linoleum tile. Composed of oxidized linseed oil, fossil, other resins, or other oleo-resinous binder mixed with ground cork, wood flour, mineral fillers and pigments are pressed on burlap or saturated felt backing. It is supplied in rolls six feet wide and up to 90 feet in length, and is available in gauges from .0625" to .25" and in which latter class, the popular plain or battleship falls.

Linoleum is made in several classifications, including inlaid, marbleized, jaspe, spatter, etc. These classifications relate more to pattern than grade. Linoleum has a load limit of approximately 75 pounds per square inch and is rated about twice as resilient as asphalt and vinyl asbestos tile. The heavier grades are best adapted for institutional or commercial uses and linoleum should always be installed on suspended floors, never in direct contact with the ground, nor over damp concrete. Linoleum is available in tile form, in which case it is identical in quality with conventional linoleum. There is a special linoleum type tile of greater hardness and durability, having a load limit of approximately 200 pounds per square inch, and a resiliency of about the same as vinyl asbestos. It has a thickness of ⅛ inch and resembles asphalt tile on the floor.

All forms of alkali are injurious to linoleum and it may be stained by grease and oil. Highly alkaline materials will deteriorate the linoleum causing brittleness, and in some cases, result in color fading, whitening or disintegration. The use of excess water will undermine the adhesive and rot the backing. When clear water mopping is necessary, use a mop that is damp, not one that is soaking wet, and pick up rinse water immediately. Abrasives are not recommended, except on isolated stains. Wax accumulations may be removed by scouring with a non-alkaline cleaner. Be careful to wet only a limited section at a time. A nonalkaline wax stripper (neutral cleaner), used in conjunction with No. 1 steel wool or abradant pad is a good method. Either solvent type (including paste wax) water wax or emulsified resin finishes may be used.

Cork tile. Ground cork bark is molded and compressed to make cork tile.

The natural resins serve to bind the mass together when heat cured under hydraulic pressure. Different shades of color are obtained by varying the baking temperatures. Cork is available in tile or sheet form. It may or may not be waxed or otherwise factory finished.

Sweeping with a soft bristle brush and occasionally buffing with a floor machine should keep cork tile at its best. When discolored, dry clean with No. 0 steel wool or abradant pad. When water is used, it should be used sparingly. Avoid alkaline cleaners of all kinds. Use a neutral synthetic detergent for best results. Never clean cork tile with naphtha, gasoline or similar solvents, oily mops or sprays. When badly soiled, and abrasive cleaning with a cleaning solution does not restore the floor, sand lightly with No. 2 steel wool pad, screen type scouring pad or coarse nylon abradant pad. Then go over floor with vacuum. After treatment with a sealer or solvent type wax, maintain with a water type wax.

Other Types of Floors

Marble floors. Marble can be maintained with comparatively little effort. Routine maintenance includes sweeping or vacuuming or damp mopping which will remove minor soils. When cleaning marble use a neutral cleaner, a small amount should be used in the water when daily damp mopping. An acid cleaner will leave the surface of the marble dull and porous. Strong alkalies tend to penetrate the less highly polished marbles, such as the honed or sand finish types, and upon drying, expand and break the tiny cell walls of the marble, resulting in surface disintegration. Abrasive cleaners should never be used in removing stains or soils unless under recommendation of a floor treating expert. When abrasive cleaners are used, it is almost impossible under regular cleaning methods to remove the gritty residue which may scratch the surface under traffic. Soap type cleaners should never be used, as they are commonly responsible for the dull lifeless appearance of marble floors.

A pre-wetting of the marble will help prevent salts from being absorbed into the pores, and will also facilitate the rinsing procedure. The cleaning solution should be picked up and the floor rinsed thoroughly. Wiping the floor dry will prevent streaking. Seals and waxes are usually not applied to marble floors but in certain cases may be desirable to make a poor floor look better and easier to keep clean. When marble becomes porous or worn, it may be resurfaced by grinding and polishing. Do not try to clean with dirty water or dirty utensils. Oily sweeping compounds may discolor light-colored marbles, as may the continued use of ammonia.

Terrazzo floors. Made by a combination of marble chips and concrete, some floors are referred to as Gilbraltar floor, which utilizes a granite chip instead of a marble chip. The granite chip is extremely dense and does not permit the absorption of alkaline salts into the chip itself. With this type of chip, the alkaline salt present in a harsh cleaner will attack the grout or cement rather than the dense chip, leaving the granite chip protruding above the concrete portion of the floor. In normal Portland Cement terrazzo, this action would not be present. The marble chip used in it is not as dense as the granite chips and would absorb a certain amount of alkaline salt present in a harsh cleaner. The first action you might see would be a spalling and chipping of the marble chips, and possible exploding of the chips, leaving a crack or hole in the floor.

Considering that more than two-thirds of the surface is marble, it is useful to know that marble has natural enemies in the chemically opposite elements of acid and alkali. Being of limestone formation, marble is dissolved by acids— slowly by the milder acids such as citric, acetic (vinegar) etc., but quickly by muriatic, sulphuric and other corrosive acids. Suitable materials for treating or cleaning terrazzo floors will fill the original pores and have no effect on them. Harmful materials will increase the number of pores and enlarge the existing ones. Continued use of such harmful materials increases the maintenance problem and costs.

Terrazzo has a penetrating (not surface) seal which prolongs hydration of the cement to provide color density and longer life on new terrazzo, and reduces penetration of water, stains, and grime on old terrazzo. The urgency for the need of such penetration varies with the floor. Before a sealer is used, it should be tested on a remote area of the floor, as some are known to cause a yellowing effect, which detracts from the beauty of the floor. It is recommended that the use of pure surface waxes, lacquer, shellac, or varnish preparation be avoided. For cleaning, use a neutral cleaner. This type of floor should be moistened with clear water prior to cleaning (using cleaning solution) to avoid absorption of cleaning solution. After cleaning, the floor should be thoroughly rinsed and dried. A new terrazzo floor should be washed frequently to remove mineral salts which are a by-product of the settling and curing of the concrete bonding material. After several months, the floor will acquire a natural sheen and will require less work in its upkeep. An occasional scrubbing with a scouring powder added to the neutral cleaner will help in repolishing the floor. When badly worn, the floor may be resurfaced by grinding or polishing. Where the flooring has been mis-treated and blooming or dusting is a problem, terrazzo seal may be applied to densify the floor. Some authorities now recommend sealing new terrazzo floors depending on location and type of traffic over them.

Hard tile floors. Clay and ceramic floors are manufactured from different grades of clay, marble, slate, glass and flint. They may be glazed or unglazed and are the hardest, most durable floors available.

Tiles are alkaline in nature and, therefore, may bloom or dust just as concrete, terrazzo or marble flooring. It is usually not necessary to seal tile floors, but sealing is sometimes done to enhance the color of the tiles. However some authorities state that sealing is necessary to protect the concrete binder and help retain the original beauty of the tiles. Maintain by daily sweeping or vacuuming. Damp mop with a mild cleaning solution to remove slight soil. Always wet the floor before mopping. A 15 per cent solution of muriatic acid and water will remove heavy soils. Be sure to rinse the floor thoroughly. Due to the inherent slip hazard, keep floors dry at all times.

In the hard tile family, one of the most common types is quarry tile. The durable and permanent nature of this tile has probably been responsible for the idea that anything can be used to clean them. This is not true. The tiles in themselves do not depreciate due to lack of maintenance, but improper maintenance can destroy the grout around the tile and dull and discolor the attractiveness of the surface. The great density of quarry tile prevents nearly all absorption of a cleaner into the tile itself. A continued use of alkaline powders, however, has a marked tendency to set a crystalline expansion in the cement joints which causes them to crumble. This effect is not chemical but purely physical. The salt solution penetrates the surface, but in drying, only the water evaporates leaving the salt within. Crystals of salt form in pores and as they increase in size, pressure is exerted. Naturally the material which is more porous and weaker than the tile (in this case, concrete) will begin to crumble under such treatment within a short time. This expansion of crystalline salt often causes heaving of the floor.

Soap type cleaners leave a gummy sticky film of grease. Because soap is difficult to rinse, it keeps on building up a heavy coating of scum and dirt, and eventually the floors become dark, streaky, and uneven in color. This becomes extremely hard to remove and this condition exists in greater degree where the water is hard.

To properly maintain and safely clean hard tile floors the following materials are needed:

1. A neutral, nonalkaline chemical cleaner free from lye or caustics. This will provide safe cleansing action without hard scrubbing, prevent formation of harmful alkaline deposits, and prevent a slippery film.

2. A specialized penetrating finish seal. This will protect the tile surface and grout from water, stains, traffic wear, prevent efflorescence and bleeding, brighten colors, and give a desirable high gloss and antislip finish.

Wood floors. Wood floors can be scrubbed to death with harsh cleaners. They will slip, appear dried out and shrunken. These conditions are caused by fast, harsh cleaners, with powerful wetting agents which have carried strong alkalies deep into the celled structure of the wood, causing crystallization, splitting, and drying out of the natural oils.

When this occurs the wood cell structure is opened up and bacteria, molds, and dirt are carried into these voids by cleaners, floor oils, and harmful wetting. Serious damage and deterioration of wood fibers results, necessitating costly reconditioning, increased maintenance, or even expensive replacement.

To insure against such damage, a treatment must be used to fill and close all wood cells, binding them together so that even moisture cannot penetrate the surface. Because of the lateral sawing of lumber, the surface is the factor of concern (1/64 inch in depth). Proper sealing of this surface will protect the whole floor.

The following nine points can be used as minimum standards of a good floor finish product:

1. The seal must penetrate the top surface of the wood.
2. It must seal the pores so as to keep dirt out and resist soil stains.
3. The finish must reflect light so as to improve illumination.
4. The finish with its penetrating quality must not darken the wood.
5. The finish must be nonslippery.
6. The finish must not mar, scratch, nor flake off.

7. The finish must be of such quality so that if it becomes necessary to touch up worn spots, it can be accomplished without complete refinishing.

8. The finish (sealer) should be resistant to water.

9. The finish, after application, must not present a maintenance problem. It must insure economy and maintenance as to eliminate constant resanding and complete refinishing.

Concrete floors. Concrete floors are made of a mixture of portland cement, sand, stone, and water. If the materials are properly mixed and skillfully troweled, a concrete floor will give many years of service—depending on traffic conditions and maintenance. Proper sealing will greatly lengthen concrete floor life, prevent dusting, and make maintenance easier and more economical.

Unsealed concrete floors create a number of problems. In the first place, they encourage constant dusting which leads in time to gradual floor surface disintegration. Secondly, since dusting never stops once started—it is never entirely cleaned up, it is an unending maintenance headache, it gets into equipment and products, and it is a menace to the health of employees. And spillage seeps into the pores when there is no seal to stop it. Floors rapidly become unsightly because stain removal is difficult and often impossible. A sealed concrete floor helps eliminate these disadvantages.

However, free lime on the surface of new concrete will either attack or interfere with a bond of paints and seals. Therefore, in many cases the floor should be neutralized with a solution of muriatic acid before sealing. The recommended solution is one part of 30 per cent commercial muriatic acid added to fourteen parts of water. This solution should be mopped freely on the floor, and remain until bubbling or fizzing action is completed. The floor should then be rinsed and allowed at least six to eight hours of drying time. Only after thorough drying is the seal applied.

When the floor needs both cleaning and neutralizing, select a liquid detergent which when diluted with water and muriatic acid will both clean and neutralize in one operation.

Selection of the proper seal is important. Heavy traffic floors are best treated with a modified phenolic or epoxy resin floor seal. A first coat should be applied for maximum penetration so as to form a firm bond right in the pores of the concrete. A second coat should be applied to produce maximum wear resistance, and a smooth, easily maintained surface.

When a modified phenolic seal is used, there is no need to purchase a penetrating seal and a surface seal. A good modified phenolic seal is both because proper dilution with inexpensive mineral spirits or turpentine will produce the exact penetration required. Phenolic seals are available in several colored versions as well as in clear.

Where concrete floors are exposed to mineral oils and greases, mild acids and alkalies, use a chlorinated rubber-base seal. Where concrete is already saturated with oil, use a resin modified nitrocellulose-base primer before sealing. This locks in old oil, locks new spillage out, to provide a more easily maintained surface.

To clean sealed concrete floors use a neutral, synthetic, free-rinse liquid detergent. This will quickly emulsify oil and grease from stained surfaces without injuring the seal. Regular sweeping with a yarn broom treated with a liquid dust-control agents is all that is necessary to maintain sealed concrete floors. Such maintenance is easy—yet highly effective, efficient and economical.

Cleaning Materials

Regardless of the method used for floor maintenance, the end results will, to a great degree, depend on the quality of materials used. For example, the use of the wrong cleaner on resilient flooring can cause serious damage after only a few applications. There are a few general rules which can be of great assistance in choosing and applying the proper floor cleaners.

Always use a product specially designed for resilient floors. Most cases of serious floor damage are the result of using furniture polish, concrete cleaner, kitchen cleaners, soap and washing powders containing abrasives and free alkalies, rather than *floor* cleaners. There are hundreds of cleaners which have been formulated especially for resilient flooring. They are available from flooring manufacturers and their dealers, or by companies which specialize in floor maintenance materials. Both the Rubber Manufacturers' Association and the Asphalt and Vinyl Asbestos Institute have set up standards for resilient floor solutions and most floor cleaner manufacturers follow their recommendations.

Avoid excessive use of water or cleaning solution. Excessive use of water, especially hot water, may penetrate between tiles or seams to the adhesive and cause a loosening of the adhesive and eventually warp the floor. The use of excessive cleaning solution is not only uneconomical, but requires additional rinsing to prevent leaving a residue.

Do not use abrasive cleaners. Resilient floorings are relatively soft and may be permanently scratched by abrasives if used routinely. Abrasives may be used with care for removing deep seated stains.

Avoid harsh alkaline cleaners. Strong alkalies may attack the binder, filler or color pigments used in resilient flooring to cause embrittlement, fading or roughness of the surface. In addition to these general rules, solvents and oils should not be used on rubber or asphalt tile floors. On other resilient floorings, solvents may be used sparingly for removing spots or stains. However, excessive solvent may penetrate between tiles or seams and cause adhesive bleeding or loosening of the floor.

Types of Coatings

There are several types of coatings for floors which can be used to protect and beautify clean floors. The proper choice of material depends on the type of floor and the type of traffic to which it is subjected. The following finishes are available at local dealers:

1. *Liquid water emulsion wax.* A dispersion of wax and other modifying materials in water. This is the most widely used maintenance finish. It is suitable for use on all types of resilient flooring except natural cork. Products with excellent slip resistance are available. Water emulsion waxes dry with a gloss which

may be improved by buffing with a floor machine. Scuffs and traffic marks may be buffed out. Worn areas are easily patched.

2. *Paste water emulsion wax.* Similar to the liquid water emulsion wax except in paste form. The floor must be polished for luster. Suitable for use on all types of resilient floors except natural cork. Water emulsion paste wax is usually applied with a thin steel wool pad on a floor polishing machine. The wax is spread with the machine and allowed to dry. It is then polished to a high luster with a second, thick steel wool pad. The lubricating effect of the wax prevents the steel wool pad from scratching the floor.

3. *Liquid solvent wax.* A mixture of waxes and other ingredients in a solvent base. The floor must be polished for luster. Liquid solvent wax should not be used on rubber or asphalt tile, but may be used on other resilient floors. Care should be taken on thinner gauge floors since excess solvent may penetrate the seams and cause bleeding of the adhesive.

4. *Paste solvent wax.* Similar to liquid solvent wax except in paste form. Should not be used on asphalt tile or rubber floors, but may be used on other resilient floors and is recommended for natural and pre-waxed cork floors.

5. *Water emulsion resins.* A dispersion of natural or synthetic resins and modifying materials in water. They are usually plasticized to impart some buffing. Water emulsion resins may be used on all resilient floors with the exception of natural and pre-waxed cork. They show poor adhesion when applied over waxed surfaces and will rapidly wear off under this condition. Generally, the water emulsion resins produce hard or tough coatings with a high luster. Because of their hardness, they tend to scratch rather than scuff and the scratches are more difficult to buff out than is the case with water emulsion waxes. For this reason, these finishes should be avoided in areas subjected to large amounts of sand or gritty soil. Some of the water emulsion resins.have excellent resistance to oil and grease, and most of them are better in this respect than the waxes. Their high scuff resistance and luster make them well suited for prestige floors where good appearance is of paramount importance.

9B / **FLOOR MOPPING**

Job Description

The job of floor mopping pertains to the daily and/or periodic maintenance of floor surfaces in buildings by means of either damp mopping or wet mopping or a combination of both.

Damp mopping. Damp mopping is performed during inclement weather, to remove dirt and water from floors of building entrances and at intervals for cleaning hard floors such as marble, tile, and terrazzo in lobbies, halls and washrooms; and in other areas where lightly imbedded dirt is not adequately removed by the sweep mop and where a cleaning solution is not required.

Wet mopping. Wet mopping involves the use of a cleaning solution for thorough cleaning of hard floors where the damp mop procedures are inadequate, and where the building area and/or soil is insufficient to warrant the use of power scrubbing equipment on a regular basis. Wet mopping when performed as an adjunct to other jobs such as floor waxing is considered in the production rates for such jobs. The method used however is the same as described in this section.

Procedure. Floors should be swept with a treated sweep mop before wet mopping and before damp mopping as required. This work may be performed by the mop man or by room cleaners where assigned in the area to be mopped.

Employees assigned to this work are responsible for reporting any defective building items noticed in the work area during the performance of their duties.

Job Methods

Operation Steps	*Explanation*

A. *Damp Mopping:*

Step 1—Prepare for Work

1. Obtain equipment needed.	a. Bucket (12 qt.)
	b. Mop
	c. Mop unit (bucket and wringer, small mopping unit or mop tank)
	d. Putty knife (1¼″)
	e. Sweep mop, treated (as required)
	f. Warning signs
	g. Water hose (approx. 6 feet)
2. Proceed to work area.	Proceed to the work area where damp mopping is to start.

Step 2—Damp Mop the Floor

1. Prepare the work area.	a. Generally, it is not required that the floor area be cleared of movable furniture and equipment for this work.
	b. The area should be swept before damp mopping, if necessary, to remove visible debris and dirt.
2. Place warning signs.	Warning signs of wet floors should be placed in conspicuous locations.
3. Remove tar, gum and other substances.	Remove wads of gum, tar, and similar substances from the floor surface with putty knife.

Operation Steps	*Explanation*
4. Damp mop floor.	Immerse the mop in clean water and wring as dry as possible. Draw the mop parallel to baseboards and furnishings to avoid splashing these items before mopping the open areas. Turn the mophead over every four or five strokes to facilitate the cleaning. Rinse and wring the mop frequently. Change the water often enough to maintain a clean mop.
5. Mop strokes.	The mopping stroke should be one which gives the greatest coverage and speed with the least amount of fatigue. Where possible, use an approximately nine foot side-to-side sculling stroke, stopping about four inches of the baseboards and furnishings. Random or forward and backward strokes can be used under and/or around furnishings.

NOTE

1. New mops should be rinsed before use.
2. Mopping equipment should be kept ahead of the work in the area next to be mopped.

Step 3—Return Equipment to Storage

1. Replace moved pieces of furniture.	Replace any pieces of furniture moved during the damp mopping operation.
2. Warning signs.	When floor has dried remove the warning signs.
3. Final inspection.	Before leaving the work area, make a final inspection to see that the work has been performed as required.
4. Return to gear room location.	Gather up all equipment items and return to the gear room where items are to be stored.
5. Clean and store equipment.	Empty the mop unit and clean all equipment items before placing in their respective storage positions. (See "Equipment Care".) Hang wet mops to facilitate drying.

Operation Steps   *Explanation*

B. *Wet Mopping:*

Step 1—Prepare for Work

1. Obtain equipment and materials needed.

   a. Bucket (12 qt.)
   b. Deck scrub brush
   c. Detergent (may be prepackaged)
   d. Floor squeegee and water pickup equipment (optional)
   e. Measuring cup (if detergent is not prepackaged)
   f. Mop tank (three-compartment or mop tank, two-compartment and mop bucket or small mop units
   g. Mops, cotton (2 pounds)
   h. Overshoes, rubber (1 pair per man)
   i. Putty knife (1¼")
   j. Scouring powder
   k. Sweep mop, treated (as required)
   l. Warning signs
   m. Water hose (approx. 6 feet)
   n. Wiping cloths

2. Prepare cleaning solution.

   Prepare the cleaning solution in one compartment of the mop tank using the type of detergent and in the proportions specified by the supervisor.

3. Fill rinse water compartment of mop tank.

   Add clean rinse water, as required, to another compartment of the mop tank, if a three-compartment tank is used, otherwise use a separate mop bucket. The wringer side is left empty to receive the waste liquids picked up from the floor.

4. Proceed to work area.

   Move the equipment and materials to the area where the work is to be done.

NOTE

Parts 2 and 3 of this step may be postponed until the equipment is moved to the work area.

Operation Steps   *Explanation*

Step 2—Prepare the Area

1. Prepare space to be mopped.

   The area to be mopped should have been swept and any items located in the immediate path of the cleaning operation moved.

2. Place warning signs.

   Caution signs warning of slippery floors should be placed in conspicuous locations.

3. Remove tar, gum, and other substances.

   Use the putty knife to remove gum, spots of tar and other adhesive materials from the floor surface before mopping.

Step 3—Apply Cleaning Solution

1. Wet the mop.

   Saturate the mop with cleaning solution in the mop tank. Let surplus solution drain from the mop back into the tank to prevent splashing.

2. Put down cleaning solution.

   Draw the mop parallel to baseboards and furnishings to avoid splashing these items with the solution. Then spread the solution over a portion of the floor to be cleaned using side-to-side strokes where possible. Apply cleaning solution to an area approximately nine by twenty feet in sufficient quantity so that the floor does not dry before solution is picked up but not so much as to run under doors, and on floor coverings.

3. Mop strokes.

   The mopping stroke should be one which gives the greatest coverage and speed with the least amount of fatigue. Where possible, use an approximately nine foot side-to-side sculling stroke, stopping about four inches short of the baseboards and furnishings. Forward and backward strokes can be used under and around furnishings. Turn the mophead over every four or five strokes to further distribute the solution.

Operation Steps   *Explanation*

Step 4—Clean the Floor

1. Agitate cleaning solution.

After a portion of the floor area has been wet with the solution, swing the mop over the covered area putting a downward pressure on the heel of the mop to remove heavily imbedded dirt.

2. Clean inaccessible areas.

Areas inaccessible to the mop such as corners may be cleaned by means of mop strands grasped in the hand.

3. Use scrub brush for hard-to-clean spots.

Use the deck scrub brush and scouring powder to clean areas that do not respond to the mop cleaning.

4. Pick up cleaning solution.

Wring the cleaning solution mop as dry as possible and pick up the used cleaning solution. Pass the mop over the wet floor area in side-to-side and/or forward and backward strokes turning the mophead over from time to time until it is saturated. During this pickup work continually wring the mop into the empty compartment of the mop tank provided for this purpose. Dry the floor of cleaning solution as thoroughly as possible.

NOTE

1. Optional equipment such as floor squeegee and pickup pan or wet vacuum equipment may be used for this water pickup work.
2. New mops should be rinsed before use.
3. Mopping equipment should be kept ahead of the work in the area next to be mopped.

Step 5—Rinse Floor (optional or as required)

1. Wet the floor.

Use a clean rinse mop, fully wet, to apply rinse water to the mopped area before the floor surface dries.

2. Pick up rinse water and dry mop floor.

Rinse and wring the mop as dry as possible and mop the floor dry. Change the rinse water as often as required to maintain a clean mop.

1. Take care not to splash baseboards, walls, or any articles nearby with cleaning solution and/or rinse water.
2. Be sure that corners and other hard to reach areas are properly cleaned.
3. Do not allow the mop wet with cleaning solution to stand in contact with the floor either in the cleaned areas or in those portions still to be cleaned as the concentration of solution may spot the floor surface at that point.
4. Keep the wet mops and solutions away from electric floor outlets to avoid possible short circuits.
5. Use a damp cloth to wipe spatterings or other water marks from walls, furnishings, and wherever necessary.
6. Avoid using an excessive amount of cleaning solution or rinse water during mopping or rinsing.

Operation Steps	*Explanation*
Step 6—Return Equipment and Materials to Storage	
1. Replace moved furniture.	Replace any furnishings moved during the cleaning operation. Remove the caution signs that warned of slippery floors. Before leaving the work area, make a final inspection to see that the work has been performed as required.
2. Return to gear room location.	Gather up all equipment and materials and return to the gear room where items are to be stored.
3. Clean and store equipment.	Empty compartments of mop tank and clean all equipment items before placing in their respective storage positions. (See "Care of Equipment".) Hang all wet mops, cloths and brushes to facilitate drying.
4. Store usable materials.	Replace all unused materials in proper storage location.

NOTE

In small buildings without elevators where there is a need to carry the equipment up and down stairs, mop buckets or small portable mopping units should be furnished.

Care of Equipment

A. *Deck Scrub Brush:*

1. Rinse in clean water after each day's use and shake dry of excess water.
2. Place for drying and storage in a position so that the bristles do not bear the weight of the brush.
3. Avoid knocking the brush against objects as such action tends to split the brush block.

B. *Floor Squeegee (optional equipment):*

1. Rinse the squeegee blade in clean water after each day's use.
2. Wipe squeegee dry and store in a clean dry location.

C. *Measuring Cup:*

1. Wipe the cup free of detergent, and dry off all moisture.
2. Store so that the cup will not be damaged.

D. *Mop, Cotton:*

1. After each day's use and before storage, rinse the mop in clean water and squeeze or wring to remove excess water.
2. As required, wash dirty mops in a warm detergent solution, rinse in clean water and wring or squeeze to remove excess water.
3. Fluff the mop strands by shaking.
4. Store with the mophead up in a well-ventilated place to allow for better drying.

E. *Mop Tank, Bucket and/or Mop Unit:*

1. Rinse tank compartments, buckets, and wringer thoroughly and wipe them dry after each day's use.
2. Remove any remaining mop strands, strings, etc., from the compartments and wringer.
3. Store in a clean dry location with the wringer in a released position and otherwise maintain in a clean and orderly condition.
4. Report any defects or necessary repairs to the supervisor.

F. *Overshoes, Rubber:*

1. Rinse off dirt and other matter and wipe dry.
2. Store in such a manner that overshoes will not be damaged.

G. *Putty Knife:*

1. Wipe the knife free from moisture after each day's use.
2. Store in a clean dry place.
3. Use only for the purpose specified. Do not use as a screw driver or hammer.

H. *Sweep Mop, Treated:*

1. Shake out or vacuum the treated sweep mop during and at the close of operations each day. Keep free of grime or oily material.

2. Every two weeks or as required, remove the mophead, vacuum or shake out as much dust as possible and wash mop in a warm detergent solution. Rinse thoroughly in clear water and wring dry.

3. Treat the mop with prescribed mop treating material as directed by supervisor.

4. Replace the mophead on the frame and hang mop so that a good air circulation will be obtained to assist in drying the mop.

I. *Wet Vacuum Equipment (optional equipment):*

1. Rinse and dry water compartment after each day's use.
2. Wipe equipment free of dirt and moisture.
3. Coil hose and electric cord loosely and hang in proper storage positions.
4. Store eqiupment in clean dry location.
5. Report any defects or necessary repairs to the supervisor.

J. *Warning Signs:*

1. Wipe the signs free of dirt and/or moisture.
2. Store in assigned storage position so that they will not be damaged in any way.

K. *Water Hose:*

1. Drain the hose of water.
2. Wipe outside free of dirt and/or moisture.
3. Store in a dry space and in such a manner that the hose will not be damaged.

L. *Wiping Cloths:*

1. Rinse the wiping cloths in clean water after each day's use.
2. Wash dirty cloths as required in a warm detergent solution, rinse thoroughly and wring or squeeze out excess water before spreading them to dry.

Performance Inspection Guide

A. *Preparation for Mopping:*

1. Cleaning solutions, where used, have been mixed thoroughly and in the proportions specified without undue spillage of either solution or rinse water.

2. Proper precautions should have been taken to advise building occupants of wet and/or slippery floor conditions.

3. Taking care to prevent damage to furnishings, etc., the space to be mopped should have been properly prepared for the mopping operation by sweeping the floor area as necessary and otherwise clearing it of visible debris.

B. *Floor Mopping:*

1. The mopping work should have been performed in such manner as to properly clean the floor surface, care having been taken to see that the correct type and mixture of cleaning solution, if required, has been used.

2. All mopped areas should be clean and free from dirt, streaks, mop marks and strands, etc.; properly rinsed, if required, and dry mopped to present an overall appearance of cleanliness.

3. Wall, baseboards, and other surfaces should be free of watermarks, scars or marks from the cleaning equipment striking the surfaces and splashings from the cleaning solution and rinse water.

4. Care should have been taken throughout the mopping operation to prevent the liquids and equipment from coming into contact with electric outlets located in the floor areas or baseboards.

C. *Equipment and Materials:*

1. All equipment items used in the floor mopping work should be in a clean and well cared for condition and properly placed in a neat and orderly manner in assigned storage locations.

2. All unused materials should be properly stored in the assigned location.

Frequency and Production

A. *Frequency and Production Schedule:*

	Main Corridors	Secondary Corridors
Frequency	Daily	Weekly
Production Rate per Man-day	20,000 sq. ft.	

B. *Qualifying Factors:*

1. *Frequency*

   a. The frequencies given in the Frequency and Production Schedule are for a normal standard of cleaning under average conditions. These frequencies may be modified to meet local conditions.

   b. Main corridors are those located on the first or ground floor of a building or those that serve as primary access and/or exit areas. Secondary corridors are those less frequently used and usually located on upper floors and in the basement.

   c. Frequencies for other types of areas mopped should be established as required locally.

2. *Production Rate per Man-day*

   The production rate per man-day as established may be subject to modification at the various locations due to type of occupancy, floor condition, and traffic. They provide, however, a standard for certain buildings from which such deviation, if any, should be made.

Staffing

The man-day requirements of labor for floor mopping can be determined by use of the following formula:

$$\text{Man-days (of labor)} = \frac{\text{Quantity}}{\text{Production}} \times \frac{1}{\text{Frequency}}$$

where a quantity represents the square feet of floor area to be mopped at a given frequency; production is the square feet of floor area mopped per man-day, and frequency is the number of work days between operations.

If the frequency and/or production rate values as established in the Frequency and Production Schedule (under Floor Mopping) have been modified to meet existing conditions at a particular location, then those modified values should be used in the above formula for the computation of the labor requirement.

SAMPLE CALCULATION

Assume a building having a total of 5,000 square feet of main corridor area plus 25,000 square feet of secondary area, and with such existing conditions that the established values from the frequency and production schedule may be used; then compute the man-days of labor as follows:

$$
\begin{aligned}
&\quad\quad\quad\quad\quad \textit{Main Area} \quad\quad\quad\quad\quad\quad \textit{Secondary Area} \\
\text{Man-days} &= \frac{\text{Quantity}}{\text{Production}} \times \frac{1}{\text{Frequency}} + \frac{\text{Quantity}}{\text{Production}} \times \frac{1}{\text{Frequency}} \\
&= \frac{5,000}{20,000} \times \frac{1}{1} + \frac{25,000}{20,000} \times \frac{1}{5} \\
&= \quad .250 \quad\quad\quad\quad\quad + \quad\quad .250 \\
&= .500 \text{ man-days of labor required (jobs)}
\end{aligned}
$$

To this total requirement must be added a factor to compensate for leave in order to arrive at the total number of positions needed to accomplish the work.

Conversion factor including compensation for leave = 1.15
Conversion factor × jobs = total positions required
1.15 × .500 = .575 positions required

• Where the floor mopping duty does not require the full time of the employee, other duties should be assigned to secure 100 per cent utilization of his time.

Equipment and Materials Allocation and Replacement

Items	Allotment per Cleaner	Replacement or Reissue
Bucket (12 qt.)	1	1 per year
Deck scrubbing brush	1	1 per year
Deck scrubbing brush handle	1	1 per 2 years
Detergent, synthetic or powdered	As required*	As required
Floor squeegee (18″) (optional)	1	2 per year
Measuring cup	1	1 per year
Mop handle	2	2 per year
Mop, cotton (2 pounds, four-ply yarn)	2	6 per year
Mop tank or unit	1	1 per 5 years
Overshoes, rubber	1 pair	1 pair per year

Putty knife (1¼″)	1	1 per year
Scouring powder	1 pound	As required
Sweep mop frame and handle, and	1	1 per 3 years
mophead (optional)	1	1 per year
Vacuum equipment (optional)	1 unit	1 per 10 years
Warning signs	As required	As required
Water hose (approx. 6 feet)	1	1 per year
Wiping cloths	2	6 per year

* Recommended as a general purpose cleaner and in the proportions of one ounce per gallon of water or as instructed.

The allotment per cleaner and replacement or reissue quantities are based on one cleaner assigned floor mopping duty 100 per cent of his time.

• Where the situation exists that other related jobs are assigned to the cleaner to secure 100 per cent utilization of his time, consideration should be given to reduction in the replacement quantities in accordance with the actual amount of floor mopping duty assigned.

*p*H Scales
of Cleaning Products for Safety

This *p*H is safe for these surfaces (at normal temperatures and for normal exposure times):

For glass, glazed china, glazed ceramic tiles	0.0–13.0
(Ditto, in very hot solutions)	0.0–12.0
(*Exception:* chemicals containing hydrofluoric acid)	
For rubber, both natural and synthetic, and	
polyethylene and most plastics	0.0–13.0
For stainless steel	3.0–14.0
For bronze and brass	5.0–13.0
For aluminum and its alloys, magnesium	5.0–10.0
For common steel and cast iron	8.0–14.0
For stainless steel	3.0–14.0
For marble and unfinished concrete	7.0–12.0
For sealed or varnished concrete	2.0–10.0
For unfinished wood floors	3.0–11.0
For sealed, varnished or well waxed floors	2.0–10.0
For linoleum (battleship type)	2.0– 9.5
For asphalt tile, vinyl tile, rubber tile	2.0–10.5

9C / FLOOR WAXING AND BUFFING

Job Description

The job of floor waxing and buffing pertains to the scheduled periodic maintenance of floor surfaces by such procedures as cleaning to remove dirt and old wax, application of a thin wax film and polishing. Spot refinishing of heavy traffic areas, damp mopping and separate buffing work, as required, are also included as part of this job.

The floor waxing and buffing methods as outlined in this chapter are broken down into several component parts such as:

1. *Preparation for Work:* Consisting of preparation of the equipment and materials for the job, including cleaning solutions, and movement to the work area to commence work.

2. *Space Preparation:* Preparing the area to be waxed and buffed by movement of furniture, turning back edges of rugs, etc.

3. *Wet Cleaning* (as applicable): Including sweeping the floor, as required, removal of gum and other adhesive substances, removal of dirt and old wax film, scrubbing with machine if required, pickup of used cleaning solution, rinsing and dry mopping.

4. *Waxing:* Application of a thin film of the proper wax to the floor surface in the correct manner and allowing to dry.

5. *Buffing:* Polishing the floor area to an acceptable degree of luster either after the wax application or as a separate job after damp mopping in lieu of rewaxing.

6. *Space Readjustment:* Turning down all rug edges previously turned back and replacement of all moved furniture to its original location without damage to the furniture or wall areas.

7. *Return of Equipment and Materials to Storage:* Return of all equipment and unused materials to storage locations, cleaning and proper storage of equipment used and the replacement of unused material to storage.

Employees assigned to this work are responsible for reporting any defective operating equipment. They should also report burned out lights, floors in need of repairs and other defective items noticed in the work area during the performance of their duties.

Job Methods

Operation Steps	Explanation

A. *Using Water Emulsion, Spirit Wax* * *and Rotary Type Polishing Machine*

Step 1—Preparation for Work

1. Obtain necessary equipment and materials.	a. Bucket (12 qt.)
	b. Mops, cotton
	c. Mop tank, three compartment; or mop tank, two compartment and mop bucket
	d. Mop unit (2 bucket with wringers)
	e. Polishing machine and accessories
	f. Putty knife
	g. Water hose (approx. 6 feet)

Operation Steps   *Explanation*

                                    h. Detergent (may be prepackaged)
                                       or floor cleaning solvent **

                                    i. Steel wool No. 00

                                    j. Warning signs

                                    k. Wax (water emulsion or spirit)

                                    l. Wax applicator (optional)

                                    m. Wiping cloth

* Spirit waxes should be used on wood floors or linoleum floors. Spirit waxes and solvents should never be used on asphalt, rubber and similar type floors.

** Approved wax strippers may be substituted for use in lieu of prescribed cleaning solutions as authorized by supervisors.

2. Prepare floor cleaning solution.   Prepare the floor cleaning solution in one compartment of the mop tank using the type cleaning material and proportions as specified by the supervisor. Add clear rinse water, if required, to another compartment of the mop tank. If rinse water is not required in the cleaning operation then the two compartment tank is adequate for this work. The wringer compartment of the tank, or the mop bucket with wringer is left empty to receive the waste liquids picked up from the floor.

3. Proceed to the work area.   Move the required equipment and material to the area where work is to start.

Step 2—Space Preparation

1. Move furniture.   a. Clear the floor area that is to be waxed of all wastebaskets, chairs and other light movable pieces of furniture. Move these items in an orderly fashion so that they can be replaced easily in their original positions.

                                        b. Duplicate numbered tags may be utilized to assist in replacement of the moved equipment.

2. Turn back edges of rugs.   Where floors are covered with rugs, turn back the edges of rugs so that

Operation Steps	*Explanation*
	the floors for a distance of approximately one foot beneath the rug edges may be cleaned and waxed.
3. Place warning signs.	Erect warnings signs in the areas that are being cleaned and/or waxed to caution occupants about the wet floors.
4. Remove tar, gum, etc.	Use the putty knife to take up wads of gum, spots of tar, tape and other adhesive materials from the floor surface.

PRECAUTIONS

1. Take care not to scar the furniture or walls.
2. Replace all moved equipment items in their proper locations upon completion of the waxing work.
3. Do not place chairs, wastebaskets, and other items on top of desks and tables.

Step 3—Wet Cleaning

1. Wet the mop.	The area to be cleaned and waxed should have been swept to remove loose dirt and visible debris. (This floor sweeping work is usually performed by the room cleaner.) Saturate the mop in the cleaning solution in the mop tank. Let surplus solution drain from the mop back into the tank to prevent splashing.

NOTE

New mops should be rinsed before being put into use.

2. Put down cleaning solution.	With first strokes, cut in section to be cleaned. Draw the mop parallel to baseboards and furnishings to avoid splashing these items with solution. Then outline an approximate area of nine by twelve feet, and mop inside this area with side to side strokes. Use enough cleaning solution so that the floor stays damp during the in-

Operation Steps   *Explanation*

terval it remains on the floor surface to permit maximum cleaning action. (Solution should not be allowed to remain on floor longer than ten minutes.)

3. Mop strokes.

The mopping stroke should be one which gives the greatest coverage and speed with the least amount of fatigue. Where possible, use an approximate nine foot side-to-side stroke, stopping about four inches short of the baseboards and furnishings. Forward and backward strokes can be used under and around furnishings. Turn the mop over every four or five strokes to further distribute the solution.

4. Agitate the cleaning solution.

Starting at the point where the cleaner was first applied, agitate the solution on the floor surface with a saturated mop to loosen the dirt and old wax film. Clean small hard to reach areas by means of several mop strands grasped in the hand.

NOTE

Where the use of mechanized scrubbing equipment will result in more efficient performance for this agitation then such a machine should be used where possible.

5. Removal of spots and stains.

Spots and stains may require the application of No. 00 steel wool and/or mild abrasive powder.

6. Very dirty floors.

In cases of very dirty floors, agitation may be performed by means of the polishing machine and scrubbing brushes or fine grade steel wool pads.

7. Pick up the cleaning solution.

Immediately after agitation wring the mop as dry as possible and proceed with picking up the used cleaning solution. Pass the mop over the wet floor area in side-to-side and back-

Operation Steps   *Explanation*

ward and forward strokes, turning it over from time to time until it is saturated. Continually wring the mop during this pickup work. Dry the floor of cleaning solution as thoroughly as possible.

8. Rinse and dry mop the floor.

    a. On floors where rinsing is required, use a clean rinse mop and rinse water to thoroughly rinse the cleaned floor area before the floor surface dries.

    b. Wring the mop as dry as possible, and go over the floor removing all rinse water. Change the rinse water often enough to maintain a clean mop during this operation.

NOTE

1. This step applies only to those types of floors that are not harmed by the application of water.

2. Avoid use of water solutions on wood flooring.

Step 4—Waxing

1. Arrange equipment for waxing.

Pour an adequate amount of wax into the mop bucket. Place equipment in best location to start the waxing operation. Where practical, start at a point farthest from the exit, and work toward the exit.

2. Wetting the mop with wax.

    a. Although the instructions relate specifically to the use of a mop for this waxing work, an applicator with pad may be substituted for the mop with equally satisfactory results.

    b. Thoroughly saturate the lower two-thirds of a clean mop with wax. If water emulsion wax is used, wet the mop with water and wring before saturating with wax. Wring excess wax from the mop leaving just sufficient wax in the mop to

Operation Steps	*Explanation*
	deposit the desired wax film upon the floor.
3. Apply wax to floor.	Using long sweeping strokes from side-to-side with slight overlap on each stroke, spread a thin film of wax evenly over the cleaned floor area. If polishing is to follow the waxing operation, an approximately four-inch space at the baseboard area is not waxed as buffing will spread over enough wax to cover this area of little or no traffic. Repeat wetting the mop with wax as needed to spread the desired wax film onto the floor.
4. Rinsing the wax mop (when water emulsion wax is used).	When water emulsion wax is used, rinse the wax mop periodically to remove wax accumulations from the mop.
5. Keep traffic from waxed area.	Where possible, keep all freshly waxed areas blocked off from traffic to allow proper drying.

NOTE

Where paste wax is used in place of liquid wax use pads of folded cloth to spread the wax onto the floor area. This type of wax application should be limited to very small areas where liquid wax is undesirable.

PRECAUTIONS

1. Be sure that the buckets and mops are clean before using.
2. The floor area should be clean and dry to touch before applying wax.
3. Take care to avoid splashing baseboards and furniture with the mop or wax.
4. Be careful not to leave puddles or streaks of excess wax on the waxed floor during the wax application.
5. Keep only enough wax in the wax bucket to sufficiently wet the mop.

Step 5—Buffing

1. Set up machine.	Inspect the brushes to see that they are in satisfactory operating condi-

Operation Steps	*Explanation*
	tion. Snap the brush plate onto the machine.
2. Connect machine.	See that the OFF-ON switch on the machine is in the OFF position. Insert the cable plug into the electric outlet.
3. Start the machine.	Raise the brushes from the floor before starting or stopping the machine. Place the switch in the ON position and lower the brushes to the floor to start the polishing operation.
4. Polish the floor.	Starting in an area farthest from the room exit, polish the waxed floor. Where possible, guide the machine from side-to-side, covering the greatest area with the fewest possible steps by the operator.

NOTE

If necessary, the use of a felt carpet, or lamb's wool pad fitted beneath the brush is effective in removing high lights from the floor after the tampico brush buffing is completed.

PRECAUTIONS

1. Where possible, allow the wax or floor surface to dry to the touch before starting to buff.
2. Avoid damaging or scarring the furniture and baseboards with the buffing machine.
3. Erect signs or take other precautionary measures to warn occupants against possibilities of slipping on the wet floors.

Step 6—Space Readjustment

1. Turn down edges of rugs.	When the waxing and buffing work is completed in the space, turn down all folded up edges of rugs.
2. Replace furniture.	Replace all furniture to its original location taking care to avoid damage to furniture and walls.
3. Final inspection.	When all work has been completed in an area, make a final inspection to see that the work has been performed

Operation Steps	*Explanation*

as required and that all moved articles have been replaced correctly.

Step 7—Return Equipment and Materials to Storage

1. Gather up equipment and materials.	Gather together all pieces of equipment and materials being careful to leave the floor areas in a clean condition.
2. Return to gear room.	Upon completion of work, return equipment and unused materials to their respective storage locations.
3. Clean and store equipment and usable materials.	Clean all equipment (mops, mop tank, buckets, etc.) before placing in their respective storage locations. Hang all wet mops and brushes to facilitate drying. Replace all unused cleaning materials in their proper storage locations.

PRECAUTIONS

Any wax remaining in the wax bucket upon completion of the waxing operation *should not* be poured back into the new wax container but stored in a separate container. If poured back into a new wax container it will contaminate the new wax and generally results in spoilage of the wax supply.

B. *Damp Mopping and Buffing:*

NOTE

Damp mopping and buffing may sometimes be used in place of or in between the regular waxing operation.

Step 1—Preparation for Work

| 1. Obtain necessary equipment. | a. Bucket (12 qt.)
b. Mops, cotton
c. Mop tank or mop bucket unit
d. Polishing machine and accessories
e. Putty knife
f. Warning signs
g. Wiping cloths |
| 2. Proceed to work area. | Move the required equipment to the area where the damp mopping and buffing work is to start. |

Operation Steps   *Explanation*

Step 2—Space Preparation

1. Move furniture.

Clear the floor area that is to be damp mopped and buffed of wastebaskets, chairs and other light movable pieces of furniture. Turn back edges of rugs. Move the furnishings in an orderly fashion so that they can be replaced easily in their original positions.

2. Place warning signs.

If necessary, place caution signs in conspicuous locations to warn occupants of slipping or tripping hazards.

NOTE

The area to be buffed should have been swept to remove loose dirt and other waste material. This floor sweeping work is usually performed by the room cleaner.

Step 3—Damp Mopping and Buffing

1. Damp mop the floor.

Using the clean mop dampened in clean cold rinse water and wrung as dry as possible in the wringer, go over the floor area to be buffed in much the same method as that used for wet mopping. Rinse and wring the mop frequently. Change the water often enough to maintain a clean mop. Use putty knife to remove gum, tape, etc. from floor surface.

2. Polish the floor.

Follow the same procedure in buffing after damp mopping as that outlined for buffing after waxing.

PRECAUTION

Avoid scarring furniture, walls or baseboards with the polishing equipment.

Step 4—Space Readjustment

1. Replace furniture.

Replace all moved pieces of furniture taking care to avoid damage to furniture and walls. Turn down all folded up rug edges. Arrange these replaced articles so that each is placed in its original location as nearly as possible.

Operation Steps	Explanation
2. Final inspection.	When all work has been completed in an area, make a final inspection to see that the work has been performed as required.

Step 5—Return Equipment to Storage

1. Return to gear room.	Upon completion of work, return all equipment to their respective storage locations.
2. Clean and store equipment.	Clean all items of equipment before placing in their respective storage positions. Hang all wet mops and brushes to facilitate drying.

Care of Equipment

A. *Applicator, Wax:*

1. Remove and thoroughly wash applicator pad in detergent solution, or in floor cleaning solvent if spirit wax is used.

2. Rinse thoroughly and shake free of excess liquid.

3. Replace pad on block and store applicator where there is free circulation of air and where there will be no weight against it.

B. *Cloths, Wiping:*

1. Rinse wiping cloths in clean water after each day's use.

2. Wash dirty cloths, as required, in warm detergent solution and rinse thoroughly.

3. Wring or squeeze excess water from the cloths before spreading to dry.

4. *Do not* leave wet dirty cloths piled together in the storage location.

C. *Cup, Measuring:*

1. Wipe cup free of detergent and other matter. Dry off all moisture.

2. Store so that it will not be damaged.

D. *Hose, Water:*

1. Wipe free of dirt and moisture.

2. Store in a dry place and in such a manner that the hose will not be damaged.

E. *Mops, Cotton:*

1. After each use and before storage, rinse mops in clean water and wring or squeeze to remove excess water.

2. Mops used for waxing should be cleaned within a few minutes after their use before the wax remaining in the mop has set.

3. Wash dirty mops in warm detergent solution; rinse in clean water and wring or squeeze dry.

4. Fluff the mop strands by shaking.

5. Store mops with mopheads up in well-ventilated area to allow for better drying.

F. *Mop Tanks,* G. *Mop Unit, Buckets and Wringers:*

1. Rinse tank compartments, buckets and wringers thoroughly and dry them after each use.

2. Remove any remaining mop strands and other foreign matter from compartments, buckets and wringers.

3. Avoid any damage to the equipment such as would tend to shorten its life.

4. Store in a dry place and otherwise maintain in a clean and orderly condition.

5. Report any defects or equipment failure to the supervisor.

H. *Polishing Machine and Accessories:*

1. Remove the brush or brushes from the machine. Wash dirty brushes in a warm detergent solution, rinse thoroughly and shake free of excess water. Hang brushes or lay with bristles up to facilitate drying.

2. After each day's use, wipe the machine and cord free of dirt and dust with a damp cloth. A cloth dampened with detergent solution may be used to remove spots otherwise not removed. Wipe the machine and cord dry and rewind the cord loosely on the hooks provided.

3. If cylindrical type polishing machine is used, remove dust bag, empty and replace. Clean the fan at the direction of the supervisor.

4. Wash and rinse the machine wheels and wipe dry.

5. Use metal polish as directed to clean and polish the machine.

6. Store the machine and accessories with the brush removed in assigned storage space.

7. Report needed repairs to the supervisor.

I. *Putty Knife:*

1. Wipe the knife free of dirt or moisture.

2. Store in clean dry place.

3. Use only for purpose specified. Do not use as screw driver or hammer.

J. *Warning Signs:*

1. Wipe the signs free of dirt and other matter.

2. Store in assigned storage positions so that they will not be damaged in any way.

Performance Inspection Guide

A. *Preparation of Floor Area for Waxing:*

1. The floor area should be free of dirt and dissolved wax particles, cleaning material residue, streaks, mop strands, and otherwise be thoroughly cleaned.

2. Walls, baseboards, furniture bases and other surfaces should be free of

watermarks, marks from the cleaning equipment, and splashings from the floor cleaning solutions.

3. All cleaned surfaces should be wiped dry and the floor ready for application of the wax.

B. *Waxing:*

1. The surface waxed should have had the proper type of wax applied in accordance with best operating practices.

2. The wax should have been applied thinly, uniformly and evenly in such a manner as to avoid skipping of areas, and has been allowed to properly dry before being polished.

3. Walls, baseboards, furniture and other surfaces should be free of wax residue and marks from the equipment.

4. The waxed area should be free of streaks, mop strand marks, skipped areas and other evidence of improper wax application.

C. *Buffing:*

1. The waxed or damp mopped surface shall have dried to the touch before being buffed.

2. Baseboards, furniture and equipment should not be disfigured or damaged during the buffing work.

3. The finished area should be polished to an acceptable, uniform lustre and free of extreme highlights from the brushes of the machine.

D. *Furniture Arrangement in Waxed Area:*

1. All rug edges should be replaced to their proper position.

2. All moved items of furniture and office equipment should be returned to their original positions.

3. Care should have been exercised to avoid damage to building/and/or office equipment during movement of the furniture, etc.

E. *Equipment and Materials:*

1. All items of equipment used in the waxing and/or buffing work should be clean and properly placed in a neat and orderly manner in their assigned storage locations.

2. All remaining materials should be returned to their assigned storage locations.

3. Left over wax, if kept, should not be returned to the original wax container with the new wax, but stored in a separate container securely covered.

Frequency and Production

A. *Frequency and Production Schedule:*

1. Clean floor, apply wax, polish, using rotary type polishing machine:

	Office Area	Open Area
Frequency	Every 66 days	
Production Rate per Man-day	3,000 sq. ft.	5,000 sq. ft.

2. Damp mopping and buffing; using rotary type polishing machine:

	Office Area	*Open Area*
Frequency	As required	
Production Rate per Man-day	30,000 sq. ft.	40,000 sq. ft.

NOTE

Polish floor without applying additional wax.

B. *Qualifying Factors:*

1. *Frequency*

   a. The frequencies given in the Frequency and Production Schedule are for a normal standard of cleaning under average conditions. These frequencies may be modified to meet local conditions.

   b. Frequencies for other types of areas should be established as required locally.

2. *Production Rate per Man-day*

   The production rates as established may be subject to modification at the various locations due to type of occupancy, floor condition, etc. They provide, however a standard, from which such deviation, if any, can be made.

Staffing

The man-day requirements of labor for floor waxing and buffing can be determined by use of the following formula:

$$\text{Man-days (of labor)} = \frac{\text{Quantity}}{\text{Production}} \times \frac{1}{\text{Frequency}}$$

where quantity represents the square feet of floor area waxed and/or buffed at a given frequency; production is the square feet of floor area waxed and/or buffed per man-day for the type of job method utilized; and frequency is the number of work days between operations.

If the frequency and/or production rate values as established in the Frequency and Production Schedule of this section have been modified to meet existing conditions at a particular location, then those modified values should be used in the above formula for the labor requirement computation.

SAMPLE CALCULATION

Assume a building having a total waxing and/or buffing area of 239,400 square feet of office space and 30,200 square feet of open space with existing conditions such that the established values from the Frequency and Production Schedule for the rotary type polishing machine may be used.

Assume also that the 30,200 square feet of open area is to be damp mopped and buffed two times in-between the regular every 66 day waxing operation, or eight times per year. The following chart shows a typical schedule for this work:

SCHEDULE FOR WAXING, DAMP MOPPING
AND BUFFING

Waxing Frequency (Days)		66			66		
Damp Mopping and Buffing Frequency Interval (Days)	22	22	22	22	22	22
Operation to Be Performed	Wax	Buff	Buff	Wax	Buff	Buff

For purpose of computing the man-day requirements for this damp mopping and buffing work in the open area, the frequency value to be used is 33 days as the area would be buffed twice in the 66 day interval between waxing operations.

Then the total man-day requirement is computed as follows:

$$\text{For normal waxing} = \underset{\textit{Office Area}}{\frac{239,400}{3,000} \times \frac{1}{66}} + \underset{\textit{Open Area}}{\frac{30,200}{5,000} \times \frac{1}{66}} = 1.301$$

$$\text{For damp mopping and buffing} = \frac{30,200}{40,000} \times \frac{1}{33} = \frac{.023}{1.324}$$

Total man-days
of labor required
(jobs)

To this total requirement must be added a factor to compensate for leave in order to arrive at the total number of positions needed to accomplish this work.

Conversion factor including compensation for leave = 1.15
Conversion factor × jobs = total positions required
1.15 × 1.324 = 1.52 positions required

• Where the floor waxing and buffing duty does not require the full time of the employee, other duties should be assigned to secure 100 per cent utilization of his time.

Equipment and Materials Allocation and Replacement

Items	Allotment per Wax Crew	Replacement or Reissue
Applicator, complete wax (optional)	1	1 per 2 years (refill pads as required)
Basket (12 qt.)	1	1 per year

Items	Allotment per Wax Crew	Replacement or Reissue
Cloth, wiping	3	12 per year
Cup, measuring	1	1 per year
Detergent, synthetic	As required	As required
Handle, mop	3	3 per year
Hose, water (6 feet)	1	6 feet per year
Mop, cotton, wet (2 pounds)	3	12 per year
Mop unit (2 buckets with wringer)	1	1 per 5 years
Polishing machine (with accessories)	type and quantity As required	As required As required
Putty knife (1¼")	1	1 per year
Solvent, floor cleaning	As required	As required
Steel wool No. 00	As required	As required
Tank, mop	1	1 per 5 years
Warning sign	As required	As required
Wax, liquid	As required	As required
Wax, water emulsion (16 per cent)	As required	As required

9D / FLOOR SCRUBBING

Job Description

The daily or periodic maintenance of marble, terrazzo, and other floor surfaces in buildings is accomplished by scrubbing with mechanized scrubbing equipment.

The job method involves preparation for the scrubbing work by readying the equipment and preparing the floor cleaning solution; preparation of the area to be scrubbed; scrubbing the floor area; and care, maintenance and proper storage of the equipment and materials used for this work.

Employees assigned to this work are responsible for reporting any defective operating equipment. They should also report burned out lights and other defective items noticed in the work area during the performance of their duties.

Job Methods

A. *Electric Floor Polishing Machine (Used for Scrubbing):*

Operation Steps	*Explanation*

Step 1—Prepare for Work

1. Obtain necessary equipment and materials.	a. Buckets (12 qt.) b. Detergent (may be prepackaged) c. Floor polishing machine, electric, with scrub brushes. (Check

Operation Steps	*Explanation*

brushes for wear; if bristles are less than one-half inch long, install new brushes.)
d. Measuring cup (if detergent is not prepackaged)
e. Mop tank, three compartment; or mop tank, two compartment and mop bucket.
f. Mops, cotton (2 pounds)
g. Overshoes, rubber
h. Putty knife (1¼")
i. Warning signs
j. Water hose (approx. 6 feet)
k. Wiping cloths

2. Prepare cleaning solution.

Prepare the cleaning solution in one compartment of the mop tank using the type of detergent and the proportions specified by the supervisor.

3. Proceed to work area.

Move the equipment and materials to the area where the work is to start.

NOTE

Parts 1 and 2 of this step may be postponed until the equipment is moved to the work area.

Step 2—Apply Cleaning Solution

1. Prepare space.

The area to be scrubbed should have been swept if necessary and any items located in the immediate path of the cleaning operation moved. Caution signs warning of slippery floors should be placed in conspicuous locations.

2. Wet the mop.

Saturate the mop in the cleaning solution in the mop tank. Let surplus solution drain from the mop back into tank to prevent splashing.

3. Put down cleaning solution.

Spread the solution over the area to be scrubbed using side-to-side strokes where possible. Draw the mop parrallel to the baseboards and furnishings to avoid splashing these items

Operation Steps	*Explanation*
	with solution. Apply sufficient solution so that the floor does not dry before the solution is picked up.
4. Mop strokes.	The mopping stroke should be one which gives the greatest coverage and speed with the least amount of fatigue. Where possible, use an approximately nine foot side-to-side stroke, stopping about four inches short of the baseboards and furnishings. Forward and backward strokes can be used under and around furnishings. Turn the mophead over every four or five strokes to further distribute the solution.
5. Remove gum, tar and similar substances.	The putty knife is used during this step to remove wads of gum, tar and similar foreign substances from the floor surface.

NOTE

Solution tanks are also available for attaching to the polishing machine so that the cleaning solution may be put down at the same time the floor is scrubbed.

Step 3—Scrub Floor

1. Attach brush.	Check the brush for wear and put on new one as required. Attach the brush or brush plate by placing the polisher on its side and securing the brush on the plate or shaft by hand. Do not attach brush by running machine over it and allowing it to lock in place by starting the motor.
2. Connect machine.	Make sure the OFF-ON switch on the machine is in the OFF position. Insert the cable plug into the electric outlet and secure cable at this point to prevent damage by pulling on plug and/or outlet.
3. Operate scrubbing machine.	Most scrubbing machine brushes rotate in a counterclockwise direction.

Operation Steps	*Explanation*
	The movement of the concentrated weight machine is controlled by raising the handle to move to the right and lowering the handle to move to the left. The divided weight machine is operated by moving the machine in a straight forward or backward direction. The scrubbing operation should start with the machine directly in front of the operator.
4. Proceed with scrubbing.	Press down on the machine handle to start with the brush off the floor. Place the OFF-ON switch in the ON position and begin scrubbing. Use machine to provide maximum coverage and speed with the least amount of fatigue.
5. Mop areas inaccessible to machine.	Areas inaccessible to the machine may be scrubbed by hand with the deck scrub brush. In all cases the machine or brush is directed in such a manner that the cleaning solution is moved in the direction in which the scrubbing is being done.
6. Pick up cleaning solution.	Immediately after scrubbing, wring the mop as dry as possible and pick up the used cleaning solution. Pass the mop over the wet floor area in a side-to-side and/or forward and backward strokes, turning the mophead over from time to time until it is saturated. During this pickup work continually wring the mop into the empty compartment of the mop tank provided for this purpose. Dry the floor of cleaning solution as thoroughly as possible.

PRECAUTIONS

1. Take care not to splash baseboards, walls, and other property with cleaning solution.

2. Do not permit the machine to strike and scar the furnishings during the scrubbing operation.

3. Do not let the machine stand on the scrubbing brushes except when in use as this tends to flatten the bristles and make the brushes useless for the purpose intended.

4. Do not allow the wet mops and/or scrub brushes to rest on the floor either in cleaned area or in those portions still to be cleaned.

5. Be sure that corners and other hard to reach areas are cleaned during this operation.

Operation Steps	*Explanation*

Step 4—Rinse Floor (*optional or as required*)

1. Wet the floor.	Use a clean rinse mop, fully wet, to apply warm rinse water to the scrubbed area before the floor surface dries.
2. Pick up rinse water and dry mop floor.	Rinse and wring the mop as dry as possible and go over the floor removing all moisture. Change the rinse water as often as required to maintain a clean mop.

Step 5—Return Equipment and Materials to Storage

1. Replace moved furniture.	Replace any pieces of furniture moved during the scrubbing operation. Remove the caution signs that warned of slippery floors. Before leaving the work area, make a final inspection to see that the work has been performed as required.
2. Return to gear room location.	Gather up all pieces of equipment and materials and return to gear room where items are to be stored.
3. Clean and store equipment and usable materials.	Empty compartments of mop tank and clean all equipment items before placing in their respective storage positions. (*See* "Equipment Care".) Hang all wet mops, cloths and brushes to facilitate drying. Replace all unused materials in proper storage locations.

Care of Equipment

A. *Bucket:*
1. Rinse and dry the inside and outside after each day's use.
2. In storing, place the buckets so that they will not be damaged.

B. *Floor Polishing Machine:*

1. Remove the scrubbing brush from the machine and wash as specified under H.

2. After each day's use, wipe the machine and cord free of dirt and dust with a damp cloth. A cloth dampened with detergent solution may be used to remove spots not otherwise removed. Wipe the machine and cord dry and rewind the cord loosely on the hooks provided.

3. Wash and rinse the machine wheels and wipe dry.

4. Use metal polish as directed to clean and polish the machine surfaces.

5. Store the machine and brush (with brush removed) in assigned storage space.

6. Report needed repairs to supervisor.

C. *Measuring Cup:*

1. Wipe cup free of detergent and other matter. Dry of all moisture.

2. Store so that it will not be damaged.

D. *Mops, Cotton:*

1. After each use and before storage, rinse mops in clean water and wring or squeeze to remove excess water.

2. Wash dirty mops in warm detergent solution. Rinse in clean water and wring or squeeze to remove excess water.

3. Fluff the mop strands by shaking.

4. Store mops, with mopheads up, in well-ventilated place to allow better drying.

E. *Mop Tank and/or Mop Bucket:*

1. Rinse tank compartments, buckets and wringers thoroughly and wipe dry after each day's use.

2. Remove any mop strands or other foreign matter from compartments, buckets and wringers.

3. Always leave wringer in released position.

4. Avoid damage to the equipment.

5. Store in a dry place and otherwise maintain in a clean and orderly condition.

6. Report any defects or equipment failure to the supervisor.

F. *Overshoes, Rubber:*

1. Rinse off dirt and other matter and wipe dry.

2. Store in such a manner that they will not be damaged.

G. *Putty Knife:*

1. Wipe the knife free of dirt and moisture.

2. Store in clean dry place.

3. Use only for purpose specified. Do not use as screw driver or hammer.

H. *Scrubbing Brushes:*

1. Remove scrubbing brushes from floor polishing machine after each day's use.

2. Wash all scrubbing brushes in warm detergent solution. Rinse thoroughly and shake free of excess water.

3. Store brushes so that the bristles are free to straighten out.

I. *Scrubber Vacuum Machine:*

1. Drain and flush both the cleaning solution and the dirty water tanks.

2. Remove vacuum screen and clean.

3. Clean and reverse brushes. Install new brushes if required.

4. Clean guide wheel and under carriage.

5. Clean and replace brush shields.

6. If electric scrubber is used, clean and dry wipe electric cable.

7. Wipe dirt and other matter from all machine surfaces except gasoline engine.

8. Store machine in assigned storage position.

9. Report any needed repairs to supervisors. Do not attempt to repair the machine or accessories.

J. *Warning Signs:*

1. Wipe the signs free of dirt and other matter.

2. Store in assigned storage positions so that they will not be damaged.

K. *Water Hose:*

1. Wipe free of dirt and/or moisture.

2. Store in a dry space and in such a manner that it will not be damaged.

L. *Wiping Cloths:*

1. Rinse wiping cloths in clean water after each day's use.

2. Wash dirty cloths as required in warm detergent solution and rinse thoroughly.

3. Wring or squeeze the excess water from cloths before spreading to dry.

4. Hang up cloths to dry. Do not leave wet dirty cloths piled together in the storage location.

Performance Inspection Guide

A. *Preparation for Work:*

1. The machine and other equipment should have been checked and readied for work in a careful and thorough manner.

2. Additions of motor oil, where required, should have been accomplished in a safe and careful way so as to avoid spillage and overfilling.

3. Cleaning solutions should have been mixed thoroughly and in proportions specified without undue spillage of either solution or rinse water.

B. *Operation of Machine:*

1. The mechanized equipment should have been operated only by authorized personnel having sufficient instruction as to its proper and efficient operation.

2. The scrubbing machine should have been started and operated in a safe and reasonable manner.

3. Care of the mechanized equipment should have been exercised at all times during its operation to avoid damage to personnel, the building and equipment.

C. *Floor Scrubbing and Rinsing:*

1. Proper precautions should have been utilized to inform the building occupants of wet and/or slippery conditions during the scrubbing operation.

2. The scrubbing work should have been performed in such manner as to properly clean the floor surface with care taken to see that the proper cleaning solution has been used.

3. All areas, including areas inaccessible to the machine and which are cleaned by means of deck scrubbing brushes and/or mops, should be clean and free of dirt, water streaks, mop marks, and string; properly rinsed; and dry mopped to present an over-all appearance of cleanliness.

4. Walls, baseboards, and other surfaces should be free of watermarks, scars from the cleaning equipment striking the surfaces, and splashings from the cleaning solution and rinse water.

D. *Equipment and Materials:*

1. All items of equipment used in the floor scrubbing work should be in a clean and well cared for condition and properly placed in a neat and orderly manner in their assigned storage locations.

2. All supplies of motor oil should be stored in approved safety containers in a safe and orderly manner.

3. All unused materials should be properly stored in the assigned locations.

Frequency and Production

A. *Frequency and Production Schedule:*

	Main Corridors	Secondary Corridors
Frequency	Daily	Weekly
Production Rate per Man-day	20,000 sq. ft.	

B. *Qualifying Factors:*

1. *Frequency*

   a. The frequencies given in the Frequency and Production Schedule are for a normal standard of cleaning under average conditions. These frequencies may be modified to meet local conditions.

   b. Main corridors are those located on the first or ground floors of a building or those that serve as primary entrance and/or exit areas. Secondary corridors are those less frequently used and usually located on upper floors and in the basements.

   c. Frequencies for other types of areas scrubbed should be established as required locally.

2. *Production Rate per Man-day*

The production rate per man-day as established may be subject to modification at the various locations due to narrow or angular corridors, difficult access to water and drains, and very dirty floors that must be gone over more than once. They provide, however, a standard for normal operated buildings.

Staffing

The man-day requirements of labor for floor scrubbing can be determined by use of the following formula:

$$\text{Man-days (of labor)} = \frac{\text{Quantity}}{\text{Production}} \times \frac{1}{\text{Frequency}}$$

where quantity represents the square feet of floor area scrubbed at a given frequency; production is the square feet of floor area scrubbed per man-day for the type of job method utilized; and frequency is the number of work days between operations.

If the frequency and/or production rate values as established in the Frequency and Production Schedule have been modified to meet existing conditions at a particular location, then those modified values should be used in the above formula for the labor requirement computation.

SAMPLE CALCULATION

Assume a building having a total of 45,000 square feet main corridor area plus 225,000 square feet of secondary area and with such existing conditions that the established values for the electric floor polishing machine may be used.

Then the man-day requirement is computed as follows:

$$
\begin{aligned}
&\qquad\qquad\quad \textit{Main Area} \qquad\qquad\qquad\quad \textit{Secondary Area} \\
\text{Man-days} &= \frac{\text{Quantity}}{\text{Production}} \times \frac{1}{\text{Frequency}} + \frac{\text{Quantity}}{\text{Production}} \times \frac{1}{\text{Frequency}} \\
&= \frac{45,000}{20,000} \times \frac{1}{1} + \frac{225,000}{20,000} \times \frac{1}{5} \\
&= 2.25 \qquad\qquad\qquad\qquad + \ 2.25 \\
&= 4.5 \text{ man-days of labor required (jobs)}
\end{aligned}
$$

Since this is normally performed by a two-man crew (machine operator and mop man), this represents a requirement of 2.25 man-days for the machine operator and 2.25 man-days for the mop man.

To this total requirement must be added a factor to compensate for leave in order to arrive at the total number of positions needed to accomplish the work.

Conversion factor including compensation for leave = 1.15
Conversion factor × jobs = total positions required
1.15 × 4.5 = 6.75 positions required

• Where the floor scrubbing duty does not require the full time of the employee, other duties should be assigned to secure 100 per cent utilization of his time.

Equipment and Materials Allocation and Replacement

Items	Allotment per Crew	Replacement or Reissue per Crew
Bucket (12 qt.)	2	1 per year
Detergent, synthetic	As required	As required
Measuring cup	1	1 per year
Mop, cotton	3	12 per year
Mop handle	3	4 per year
Mop tank	1	1 per 5 years
Overshoes, rubber	2 pair	2 pair per year
Putty knife (1¼")	2	1 per year
Scrub brush, deck	1	2 per year
Scrubbing machine or floor polishing machine with accessories	1	1 per 10 years (brushes as required)
Warning signs	*	As required
Water hose (approx. 6 feet)	1	1 per year
Wiping cloths (waffleweave)	2	12 per year

* As many as necessary.

The allotment and replacement or reissue quantities in this standard as established are based on a two-man floor scrubbing crew having continuous floor scrubbing duty.

9E / FLOATING FLOORS

Floating floors are a new flooring concept for proposed or existing structures that provide:

1. Subfloor access for power lines and other services.
2. Unlimited flexibility for rearrangement of machine layout.
3. Subfloor space for heating and ventilating.

The floor is laid several inches (six to ten) above existing or new subfloor; it is easy to lay, rearrange, or to remove with a flexibility heretofore impractical with conventional techniques. The installation generally consists of 36½" x 36½" modules, which are carried on an adjustable pedestal. Pedestal heads are so designed that the modules are self-locking as they fall into place, without need for adjustment or tightening. The screw flange base of the pedestals rest freely on the subfloor and do not have to be bolted down. The pedestal is readily adjustable to raise or lower the floating floor to compensate for unevenness in the subfloor. This adjustment makes it possible to provide either more or less space between the two floors. Access to the subfloor is obtained by lifting out a panel.

Cutouts in individual floor plates permit entry of electrical wiring or pipe lines from the subfloor area for connection to machinery. Plates can be cut for installation of air registers or duct work whenever needed. The subfloor area can be utilized as a pressurized plenum chamber for heating or cooling. A radiant heating or cooling effect can be achieved in this manner. Floating floor installations have been made in offices that have computing machines which require a maze of power and feeder cables for operation.

10 / **HIGH CLEANING**

(*Source:* Office of Buildings Management, General Services Administration, Washington, D. C.)

Job Description

High cleaning is a specialized job and consists of planned and scheduled periodic cleaning of lights, transoms, pipes, high files; dusting venetian blinds and other objects high enough to require a ladder (or scaffolding), and too high for the room cleaner to reach while standing on the floor. High cleaning is performed in all areas in buildings where such work is required; and the assignment also includes proper maintenance and care of equipment and materials used for this type of work.

Employees assigned to these jobs should be instructed to turn out lights not in the immediate area being cleaned, close any windows found open, and should report any defective items noticed such as: burned out lights, broken venetian blind cords, slats, and other items to their supervisor.

Job Methods

Operation Steps   *Explanation*

Step 1—Prepare for Work

1. Obtain necessary equipment, materials and supplies.

    a. Ammonia
    b. Brush, wall, dust
    c. Buckets (12 qt.)
    d. Chamois
    e. Cloths, dust
    f. Cloth, wiping
    g. Detergent
    h. Gloves, rubber
    i. Ladder platform, safety (of proper height), or scaffolding
    j. Soap, white, cake
    k. Sponges, cellulose

Operation Steps	*Explanation*
	l. Sweep mop
	m. Truck, platform (push type)
	n. Vacuum cleaner with attachment for cleaning venetian blinds and overhead pipes
2. Proceed to assigned work area.	All equipment, materials and supplies should be taken to the starting point of the work area, to be used as needed.

Step 2—Dust Surfaces

1. Use vacuum cleaner, sweep mop and/or dustcloth to dust.	a. Wall surfaces b. High moldings around ceilings and walls, doors and windows c. Tops of high partitions d. Overhead piping e. Venetian blind slats and tapes f. Clocks, pictures, and plaques g. Wall or ceiling ventilators h. Tops of high bookcases and lockers i. Other high surfaces as directed
2. Dust wall and overhead fans and door checks.	a. Wall and overhead fans and door checks requiring ladders to reach should be dusted with cloths that are kept separate, and used for this purpose only, to avoid oil smears on other surfaces. b. Use ladder or scaffolding as required in a safe manner in the performance of this work.

Step 3

Damp wipe surfaces as required.	Use a water and ammonia solution (mixed as directed), sponge and chamois as required to damp wipe and dry high surfaces, such as transoms, clock glass, picture frames and glass, smudged areas surrounding air grilles and ventilators.

NOTE

Do not damp wipe picture surfaces not covered by glass.

Operation Steps	*Explanation*

Step 4

1. Clean light fixtures.	Due to the many variables connected with this phase of high cleaning, specialized job methods to cope with the type of fixture, degree of dirt accumulation, fixture height from the floor, and any other fixture problem, will need to be formulated and instituted at the various locations for the accomplishment of this work.
2. Group light replacement.	Where a group light replacement procedure is followed in a particular location, then the scheduled cleaning of these fixtures should be incorporated as a part of the replacement schedule.
3. Formulation of specialized methods.	a. Set up work platform (ladder, scaffolding, and other equipment) at point most convenient to clean fixture.
	b. Place cleaning material and equipment on platform.
	c. Remove light fixture parts as required, clean and set aside while remainder of fixture is cleaned.
	d. Replace fixture parts and move work platform to next fixture location.

PRECAUTIONS

1. Lights should be turned off in time for the fixture to cool before being cleaned.
2. Liquids or damp rags should be used with care around fixtures to avoid shock hazards.
3. Make sure that fixtures are dry before turning on lights.
4. Care should be exercised to see that the fixture is properly secured in place after cleaning so there will be no danger of it falling.

Step 5

| Return equipment and unused materials to storage. | a. Replace any furniture items moved during the high cleaning operation. |

Operation Steps   *Explanation*

Before leaving the work area, make a final inspection to see that the work has been performed as required. Gather up all equipment and materials and return to the gear room where items are to be stored.

b. Clean equipment and store equipment and unused materials in proper storage position.

PRECAUTIONS

1. Caution should be taken that liquids are not dripped on furniture and/or rugs.

2. Any dirt and dust resulting from the work performance should be cleaned up and removed.

3. Defective items such as burned out lights, broken venetian blinds, cords, and slats, broken plaster, and others should be noted and reported to the supervisor.

Care of Equipment

A. *Brush, Wall, Dust:*
1. Comb bristles and use vacuum cleaner to remove remaining dust.
2. Store in proper manner.

B. *Bucket (12 qt.):*
1. Rinse and dry the inside and outside of the bucket.
2. In storing do not place heavy objects on the bucket.

C. *Chamois:*
1. Rinse chamois in clean water and squeeze out excess water after each use.
2. Stretch chamois to original shape before placing to dry.
3. Avoid contaminating chamois with oils, polish or cleaning materials.

D. *Cloths, Dust and Wiping:*
1. Keep the cloths clean and free from grime or oily material.
2. Wash the cloths once a week or as required in a warm synthetic detergent solution. Rinse in clear warm water.
3. Hang the cloths to dry where there is good circulation of air.

E. *Gloves, Rubber:*
1. After each use, wash gloves in a warm detergent solution, rinse in clear warm water and wipe dry.

2. Always maintain gloves in first-class condition. When holes develop the gloves should be discarded.

3. Be careful not to snag gloves on nails or other sharp objects.

4. Gloves should be stored in a clean dry place.

F. *Ladder or Scaffolding:*

1. Ladder or scaffolding should be wiped free of dirt and moisture and returned to proper storage area.

2. Equipment should be cleaned and inspected frequently and that with defects withdrawn from use.

G. *Sponge:*

1. Rinse the sponge in clean warm water after each day's use. Wash a very dirty sponge in a warm detergent solution, rinse in clean water and squeeze out excess. Store in clean dry place.

H. *Sweep Mop:*

1. Sweep mop should be shaken or vacuum cleaned both during use and at the close of operations each day. Keep clean and free from grime or oily material.

2. Wash mophead frequently enough to maintain a clean and usable mop.

3. Replace mophead on the frame and hang to dry where there is a good circulation of air.

I. *Truck, Platform:*

1. Do not allow truck to strike wall surfaces, radiators, etc.

2. Clean truck daily of dirt and dust.

3. All defects and damage to the truck should be reported immediately to the supervisor. Arrangements should be made to have the wheels oiled regularly.

J. *Vacuum Cleaner and/or Equipment:*

1. Empty dirt receptacle. Wipe machine after each day's use with a dry cloth. Wind cord loosely on the hooks provided.

2. Do not run machine over electrical cords or pull against cord when it is plugged into receptacle.

3. Do not allow machine to strike walls, furniture, radiators, or other objects.

4. After use, return hose, and attachments, to assigned space in storage room.

Performance Inspection Guide

A. *Transoms:*

1. Both sides of glass should be clean, and surrounding woodwork should be free of dust.

B. *Clock:*

1. Face should be clean and free of streaks.

2. Edge should be wiped free of dust.

C. *Molding Around Ceiling:*

1. Should be free of dust accumulations.

D. *Tops of Partitions:*

1. Should be free of dust.

E. *Overhead Pipes:*

1. Should be free of dust. If very dirty, pipes should be washed.

F. *Wall Fans:*

1. Should be free of dust. (Thorough cleaning should be done by electrician.)

G. *Venetian Blinds:*

1. Slats should be free of dust, both sides.
2. Window frame and adjoining area should be free of dust.

H. *Pictures, Placques, and Similar Objects:*

1. Glass should be clean and free of streaks.
2. Frames should be free of dust.

I. *Wall or Ceiling Ventilators:*

1. Should be free of dust.
2. Framework around ventilator should be wiped clean.

J. *File Cases and Bookcases:*

1. Tops of file cases and bookcases should be free of dust.

K. *Lockers:*

1. Tops should be free of dust.

L. *Walls:*

1. Should not be streaked and surfaces free of dust.
2. Cobwebs should have been removed.

M. *Light Fixtures:*

1. Should be free of dust.
2. No dirt should be left on furniture underneath fixture or on rug, or floor.
3. If washed, should be clean and wiped dry.
4. Fixtures should be properly reassembled.
5. No water drippings should appear on rugs, floors, or furniture.

N. *Equipment Care:*

1. All pieces of equipment should be clean and properly placed in their assigned storage locations.

2. Soaps, detergents and other materials left over should be returned to their storage location.

Frequency and Production

A. *Frequency and Production Schedule:*

	Office Building Area
Frequency	Every four months
Production Rate per Man-day	10,000 sq. ft.

B. *Qualifying Factors:*

The job of high cleaning is not limited to offices but covers all areas in the building where such work is needed. Due to the many variables connected with high cleaning work, the development and application of specialized methods and work zones at the individual locations may be required for its efficient accomplishment. These detailed procedures should follow as closely as possible the general guidelines presented herein.

Staffing

The man-day labor requirements for high cleaning can be determined by use of the following formula:

$$\text{Man-days (of labor)} = \frac{\text{Quantity}}{\text{Production}} \times \frac{1}{\text{Frequency}}$$

Where quantity represents the square feet of floor area in which the work is to be performed, production is the square feet of floor area high cleaned per man-day; and frequency is the number of work days between cleanings.

If the frequency and/or production rate values as established have been modified to meet existing conditions at a particular location, then those modified values should be used in the above formula for the labor requirement computation.

SAMPLE CALCULATION

Assume a building having a total of 400,000 square feet of office building area plus 30,000 square feet of post office workroom area with existing conditions such that the established frequency and production rate values may be used.

Then the man-days requirement is computed as follows:

$$
\begin{aligned}
&\qquad\qquad \textit{Office Building Area} \qquad\quad \textit{Post Office Workroom Area} \\
\text{Man-day} &= \frac{\text{Quantity}}{\text{Production}} \times \frac{1}{\text{Frequency}} + \frac{\text{Quantity}}{\text{Production}} \times \frac{1}{\text{Frequency}} \\
&= \frac{400,000}{10,000} \times \frac{1}{66} \quad+\quad \frac{30,000}{7,000} \times \frac{1}{21} \\
&= 0.61 \qquad\qquad\qquad + 0.21 \\
&= 0.82 \text{ man-days of labor required (jobs)}
\end{aligned}
$$

To this figure must be added a factor to compensate for leave in order to arrive at the total number of positions needed to accomplish the work.

Conversion factor including compensation, for leave $= 1.15$
Conversion factor $\times$ jobs $=$ total positions required
$1.15 \times 0.82 = 0.94$ positions required

- Where the high cleaning duty does not require the full time of the employee, other duties should be assigned to secure 100 per cent utilization of his time.

Equipment and Materials Allocation and Replacement

Items	Allotment per Cleaner	Replacement or Reissue
Ammonia, household	As required	As required
Brush, wall, dust	1	1 per year
Brush, handle, wall, dust	1	1 per year
Bucket (12 qt.)	2	1 per year
Chamois	1	2 per year
Cloth, dust	2	24 per year
Cloth, waffleweave	2	24 per year
Detergent cleaner, synthetic	As required	As required
Gloves, rubber	1 pair	6 pair per year
Ladder, safety platform (with shoes or scaffolding)	1	As required
Polyethylene glycol or other dust mop and cloth treating compound	1 pint solution	1 quart compound per year
Soap, white (cake)	1	6 per year
Sponge, Cellulose	As required	As required
Sweep mophead	1	4 per year
Sweep mop, handle and frame	1	1 per year
Truck, platform (push type)	1	1 per 5 years
Vacuum cleaner and attachments	As required	1 per 10 years (Does not apply to attachments)

11 / LAWNS

(*Source: Plant* magazine, April 1960)

A good lawn is a must to welcome and impress customers or visitors of a building or plant. Fortunately good lawn turf is easy to grow, providing you know what is required. A lawn that is fertilized, mowed, watered, and protected will make a good impression on all clients and visitors.

The choice of grass is governed by the climate and sunlight intensity. Kentucky bluegrass and red fescues are logical choices in the north. Bentgrasses make beautiful lawns, but requires specialized management. Kentucky bluegrass or improved Merion is the proper choice for full sunlight. Red fescue strains are the best grasses for dry soil either in sun or shade. Creeping red fescue spread rather quickly. Under moist shade conditions, Kentucky bluegrass (poa pratensis) should be included.

Some seed mixtures contain redtop or rye grass to give faster initial cover. This practice is questionable since these grasses can persist for several seasons and may crowd out the more desirable types. A mixture of 60 per cent Merion or Kentucky bluegrass, and 40 per cent fescue is ideal for most industrial lawns where shade as well as sun can be expected.

In the south, improved Bermudas are preferred in the open. Zoysia and St. Augustine thrive in the shade where Bermuda will fail.

Most lawn soils are amply endowed with potash. Sand and peats may be the exceptions. Phosphorous levels are often low at the time of planting. Both of these elements along with the lime needs, should be checked every three to five years by means of soil testing. Many state experiment stations and some fertilizer firms provide this service. These samples should be taken in the late winter or early spring at a depth of approximately two inches below the surface of the ground.

Upon the completion of the soil analysis, the proper amounts of fertilizer should be applied. If large amounts of lime and fertilizer are required, two or three small feedings are recommended over a single feeding. This will eliminate nitrogen burn and excessive watering. Then lawn fertilizer becomes a matter of supplying enough nitrogen to maintain color, density and freedom from weeds.

There are many good fertilizers to choose from. Melorganite is a common choice for supplying nitrogen, phosphorous and the vital trace elements needed by grass. The amount of fertilizer which should be used depends upon the length of the growing season and the kind of grass. For the cool season, bluegrasses and fescues, 17 to 20 pounds for each 1,000 square feet for every month of good growing weather, are required. Double this rate is advocated for the ravenous Bermuda in the south. Lesser amounts will do some good, but the rate suggested is for the ultimate in turf quality.

Lawns must be protected from insects, diseases, weeds, and improper mowing practices. They should be mowed whenever the growth of the grass justifies cutting. For best results, no more than one-third of the total leaf length should be removed in any one cutting. Bermuda and bentgrass demand close one-half to three-quarter inch cutting. All others should be mowed one inch or better. The matting of clippings can do damage to a lawn. This can be eliminated by the collection of clippings, generally accomplished by rakings. It is a good practice to vary the cutting pattern with each mowing. The mower should be kept sharp at all times.

Some insects feed on grass roots, others attack the above ground leaves. Both can be controlled with chlordane, Aldrin, Dreldrin, BHC, DDT, and lead arsenate.

Root zone control of fungus, grubs, crabgrass, will last three years or longer. This should be incorporated with fertilizing to reduce labor cost. Surface feeding insects like cutworms and webworms seldom contact poisons in the soil. Several surface applications of insecticide each season may be needed to keep these caterpillars in check, especially in the south.

Broadleaf dandelion and plantain control is standard with 2,4-D. The proprionic form of 2,4,5-T is good on yarrow, chickweed and clover. Crab grass can be controlled with disodium methyl arsonate or potassium cyanate after it emerges or before germination with lead arsenate, calcium arsenate or chlordane. All weed authorities agree that the best control of all is prevention by growing a thick stand of grass.

Disease attacks can be bad on lawn turf. Merion bluegrass resistance to leaf spot is one reason it is preferred over common Kentucky bluegrass in the north.

Best defense in the battle against weeds is a lush, well-fertilized stand of grass. But, until a good, thick lawn has been established, the following chemical controls are recommended:

Use 2, 4-D on:

DANDELION   PLANTAIN   SORREL   BUCKHORN

Newer proprionic form of 2, 4, 5-T is good on:

CHICKWEED   KNOTWEED   GROUND IVY   MONEY WORT

Figure 11-1

Everybody's pest:

CRAB GRASS

Figure 11-2

Lawn grasses can also be hit by brownpatch, dollar-spot, snowmold, and other diseases. There are several good fungicides available to control them.

Lawn grass must have an ample supply of moisture. However, the tendency has been to use too much rather than too little water. This creates conditions favorable for diseases and weeds, and wastes fertilizers. Lawns will grow well with an application of one to one and one-half inches of water per week during dry summer periods. A properly designed and installed irrigation system takes this into account. The secret of good watering is a thorough soaking applied as infrequently as possible.

Even on the best turf, there will usually be some spots where the grass is too thin, and which requires some patching. In the latitude of the Middle Atlantic States, the best time for doing this is during the month of September. This operation involves the use of a top dressing, consisting of top soil, peat moss, and sand, which is applied to the area to be patched at the time the seed is sown.

12 / LIGHTING MAINTENANCE

(*Source:* The Port of New York Authority, New York)

Methods and Procedures

The in-service foot candle levels that are to be maintained in any lighting installation are determined by a study of the conditions under which the system will operate. This study generally includes the foot candles required, the system and luminaire to be used, the reflection of the walls, ceiling, floors, and the resulting coefficient of utilization. The maintenance cost of a lighting system is a prime factor in annual operating charges, which must be given equal consideration along with initial cost and life expectancy of the various types of luminaires.

In maintenance of a lighting system, original design should give consideration to accessibility of the light source, to facilitate cleaning and lamp replacement. The fixture itself should be designed for easy removal of dust and dirt from its lenses, louvers, lamps, and reflectors. In special problem areas, consideration should be given to the feasibility of providing disconnecting and lowering hangers, which would permit lowering the light fixture for maintenance. No matter how efficiently the lighting system may have been designed initially, its adequacy in operation can be assured only by a well-planned maintenance program. A maintenance program must be established with the goal of keeping illumination up to original design.

In the operation of any lighting system, three maintenance factors effect the amount of light obtained:

1. The decrease in the output of light from the lamp as it ages. The average lumen output throughout the life of a lamp is approximately 12 to 27 per cent lower than initial output.

2. Loss of light through accumulated dust and dirt on the transmitting or reflecting surfaces of the fixture or lamp itself. Fixtures should be washed once per year. If a large amount of dust accumulates during interim periods, additional dusting may be required.

3. Loss of light through the accumulation of dirt on walls and ceilings. Walls and ceilings should be cleaned once per year.

When a lighting system is installed, a fixed amount of capital is committed for payment of installation and fixtures. Depending upon the hours of usage, the following costs are also committed: power costs, lamp costs, labor charges to replace the lamps, and the expense of cleaning the fixture and lamp in order to obtain the maximum amount of light.

When instituting a maintenance program, it must be decided who is going to do the work. Employees selected should be able to properly identify different types of lamps. They should be trained in methods of washing and dusting fixtures, safely replacing lamps from a ladder or ladder cart, and changing lamps in explosion proof fixtures. It is recommended that the repair of any troubles such as faulty ballasts or damaged sockets, be handled by trained electrical personnel. The plant or building should be divided into areas, considering similar fixtures, height, and types of lamps to be installed or cleaned. This will aid in securing maximum performance from employees, and in setting work standards.

Records and Forms

A signal system designed to cover the frequency of operation should be established. This will include the design of a work card with the designation of each month across its top.

Figure 12-1

A tab system, whereby a signal is placed on the month during which certain work is to be performed. For example in Figure 12-1, after the work which was designated for March has been accomplished, the signal would be moved to the next scheduled maintenance date, possibly June. Varied colored tabs may be used to designate frequency such as red for bimonthly, inspect for burnouts and replacements; yellow for semiannually, dust fixture; blue for annually, wash fixtures and lamps.

Records can also be maintained on punch cards. Special reporting cards can be marked with an electrographic pencil, as work is performed, or as additions or deletions are made in the system. These are forwarded to the data processing department for keeping the system up to date and accurate for the next report. Reports and schedules are submitted to the building superintendent or plant manager on predetermined dates by the data processing department, indicating work to be scheduled during that month, quarter, or year.

An area lighting maintenance card should be maintained by the building superintendent or plant manager, in his master card file. This card should cover information on the fixtures, lamps, area, and work accomplished. It should also cover other pertinent data essential to the operation of a good maintenance program. This will be an accurately posted record of the history and performance of each lamp and fixture. It will also denote the frequency of certain types of inspection, and will alert him to pull the area work card. (See Figure 12-2.)

JAN.	FEB.	MAR.	APR.	MAY	JUNE	JULY	AUG.	SEPT.	OCT.	NOV.	DEC.

AREA LIGHTING MAINTENANCE   Card No. *L-12*

Bldg. OFFICE   Area ILLUSTRATING - DRAFTING

Type Fixture RECESSED FLUORESCENT, 2-40 WATT, ALBALITE GLASS
CHROME FRAME   Rated Lamp Life 7600 HRS.

Manufacture WILHELM   Location SCRANTON

No. of Fixtures 98   No. of Lamps 196   Type Lamp F-40 T12 WW

Ballast Cat. No. 89 P707   Area Time Standards   Group Cleaning 16HRS-20MIN,   Group Cleaning 22HRS and Relamping 52MIN

Average Daily Useage 14 HRS.   Average Lamp Cost $.80   Average Hourly Rate $1.65

INSTRUCTIONS

Type Relamping GROUP-REPLACE LAMP-WASH FIXTURES- INSPECT AND REPLACE MONTHLY

Cleaning ANNUAL-DUST TUBE, WASH FIXTURE

Remarks GROUP REPLACE AFTER 39 BURNOUTS OR 80% OF RATED LIFE, WHICHEVER COMES FIRST

Date	Lamps Chg'd.	Fixture Cleaned	No. Lamps Used	Time	Total Cost
3/30/61	196	98	196	21 HRS.	$193.45

MAINTENANCE REPAIR and REPLACEMENT RECORD

Date	Mechanic	Clock #	Description of repairs-part replaced	Hrs.	Cost
1/14/61	MATTHEWS	76	LEAKING BALLAST-NEW BALLAST $8.00	3/4	$9.34

Figure 12-2 / Area lighting maintenance card. Information on the fixtures, lamps, area and work done. Kept in the office Master File.

The area work card should be numbered to correspond with the area lighting maintenance card, as shown in the illustrations, both cards are numbered L-12. The area work card should be pulled from the file and given to the foreman in charge of lighting maintenance, or to the person in charge. Every card which schedules work for a particular month should be given to the foreman at the beginning of the month, in order to aid him in scheduling and laying out his work in a proper and efficient manner. It may be required in some areas, that an inspection for replacements be held once a month, while in other areas where peak lighting is not compulsory, inspection for replacement may be held on a two or three months' basis. The practice of going over three months for inspection is not recommended under any circumstances. Since burnouts will be fewer immediately after relamping, inspections may be held every two months for the first four months after the relamping. After that, it would be advantageous to revert to monthly inspections. By using the signal system, a record can be maintained without continually changing the context of the card. A study should be made of operations covered on the area work card by the foreman, and notes made from it. The employee should be informed of the work standard, and a demonstration made of the method of performance desired to obtain the standard. (See Figure 12-3.)

AREA WORK CARD				Card No. L-12 Schedule-Monthly			
Bldg. OFFICE			Area or Room ILLUSTRATING-DRAFTING				
Type Fixture RECESSED FLUORESCENT, 2-40 WATT							
ALBALITE GLASS, CHROME FRAME							
No. of Fixtures 98		No. of Lamps 196		Rated Lamp Life 7600 HRS.			
Type Lamp F-40 T-12 W W				Ballast Cat. No. 89P707			
INSTRUCTIONS							
GROUP RELAMPING X AND WASH FIXTURE, INSPECT & REPLACE MONTHLY							
SPOT REPLACEMENT ___							
GROUP REPLACE AFTER 39 BURNOUTS OR 80% OF RATED LIFE							
GROUP CLEANING- ANNUAL WASH FIXTURE, DUST TUBE							
SPOT CLEANING							
Remarks: FIXTURES TO BE WASHED WHEN LAMPS ARE CHANGED							
Standards Per. Fixture	Replace Only 4 MIN.		Group Cleaning 4 MIN.		Group Cleaning and Relamping 14 MIN.		
Lamps Changed	Date	Time Required	Fixtures Cleaned	Date	Time Required	Total Burnouts	Date
196	3/30/61	13 HRS.	98	3/30/61	16½ HRS.	2	3/30/61
6	12/1/61	24 (MIN.)	—	—	—	8	12/1/61
8	2/6/62	32 (MIN.)	—	—	—	16	2/6/62
4	3/21/62		98	3/21/62	16 HRS.	20	3/21/62

Figure 12-3 / Area work card. Work cards are given to the lamp changer foreman or person doing the work, to show the work to be done in the area.

Each person who is changing lamps will record the amount of time spent in each area, and the work done, on a daily lighting maintenance card. This information is transferred to the area work card, and from the area work card to the area lighting maintenance card in the master file. (See Figure 12-4.)

| DAILY LIGHTING MAINTENANCE CARD | | | | | |
| Name B. Matthews   Clock No. 76   Date 3/30/61 | | | | | |
Area	Lamps Replaced	Fixtures Washed	Starters Replaced	Time Start	Time Finish
ILLUSTRATING	36	18	———	8:00 AM	12:00 AM
ILLUSTRATING	34	17	———	1:00 AM	5:00 PM

Figure 12-4 / Daily lighting maintenance card. Lamp changers record time spent and the work done on this card. This information is transferred to the Area Work Card, then to the Area Lighting Maintenance Card (Master File).

Whether a system of spot relamping and cleaning, group relamping and cleaning, or a combination of both, is the best method for lighting maintenance, depends upon the particular installation. The *type* of lamp replacement used in each area, depends upon the *economics* of maintaining the area, weighed against the *requirements*.

Spot Replacements

Spot replacement is the replacing of burned out lamps as they fail. This can prove to be a tedious process, as time spent in locating such burned out lamps makes this type of replacement very costly. Where appearance is not a factor, a modified spot replacement program is used, with maintenance crew inspecting and replacing burnouts weekly. With a spot relamping program, the continual occurance of burned out lamps, and new lamps installed next to old ones, results in lower lighting levels, interferes with work performance, and creates a poor appearance. A formula for calculating spot replacement cost vs. group replacement is shown in Figure 12-5. If a spot replacement program is used, it is recommended that the fixtures be washed a minimum of once per year. Suggested procedure is covered in this chapter under Standard Work Methods.

In most operations, large or small, costs can be reduced by using a program of group relamping, over a spot replacement program.

Group Relamping

Group relamping is the systematic replacement of lamps before they burn out. This results in higher lighting levels with no extra cost for electricity. Better lighting reduces fatigue and increases productivity. The numerous visual operations of

Figure 12-5 / Spot replacement cost vs. group replacement.

employees are quickened, made easier and more accurate. Quality of work will improve with less waste, fewer accidents and better morale. Maintenance calls for lamp replacements during working hours are eliminated. Group relamping can be done at a convenient time—during vacation shutdowns, after working hours, or on Saturdays. Programs can be varied slightly, to fit into schedules when they will result in less work interruptions. This prevents wasted time, as employees will not be distracted by the maintenance crew while they are changing light bulbs.

Another advantage of group replacement is that savings are realized by eliminating damage and burning out of starters and ballasts caused by blinking and slow start in aged lamps. It has been estimated that the life of a ballast can be reduced as much as 45 per cent from conditions such as these.

In establishing the proper time interval for group relamping, the main consideration is the life of the fluorescent lamps. One of the methods for determining group replacement, is to use the percentage of failures. The number of failures in a group indicates the portion of average life delivered by the group. Figure 12-6 shows that when fluorescent lamps have reached 70 per cent of their average life when 13 per cent have burned out, and 80 per cent of average life when 21 per cent have burned out. After 80 per cent of average life, the rate of failure

FLUORESCENT LAMPS

Figure 12-6 / **Average mortality curve—fluorescent lamps.**

increases rapidly. Relamping after 20 per cent of failures is one of the most accepted standards in determining when to relamp. When an area is group relamped at 80 per cent of average life, 20 per cent of the best remaining lamps are retained as individual replacements during the interim period, before the next relamping. These should be lamps with the best appearance from the standpoint of brightness and clean ends. When this supply is exhausted, it is a signal that group relamping is again required. The cycle is then repeated. If it is decided that the lamps will be used beyond 80 per cent of their average life, it is not recommended that these be used for interim replacement. Only new lamps should be used for replacements under these conditions. This would also be true of filament lamps after 85 per cent of their rated life. (See Figure 12-7.)

Another method is to determine the minimum amount of foot-candles recommended for a particular area. When this minimum is reached, it is time to replace lamps. Replacement inspections should be scheduled with this type of program, as previously described.

If previous experience does not include a group relamping program, the following criteria may determine the frequency of group relamping in your plant or building:

Single-shift operation   *Relamp every two years*
Two-shift operations   *Relamp every year and a half*
Three-shift operations   *Relamp once every year*

In most installations the group replacement program will prove to be more efficient and economical over the spot replacement program. Tables covering a particular fluorescent lamp mortality curve can be secured from the lamp manufacturer.

Figure 12-7 / **Average mortality curve—filament lamps.**

Planned Fixture Cleaning

Planned fixture cleaning is a necessity. The considerable expenditure of money in new lighting installations for maintenance, fixtures, and installation are sometimes soon forgotten. Dust continually accumulates on fixtures, and after a period of approximately twelve months without maintenance, installations are known to produce less than 50 per cent of their initial output. From this fact, it would be more practical and less expensive to install only half as many fixtures, and to keep them clean. Another example would be a plant or building designed for 40 foot-candles, but due to dirt they are producing 20 to 25 foot-candles. This is almost similar to hiring forty men when twenty-five can do the job.

Equipment

The purchase of special equipment, or the modification of a regular ladder, will increase the efficiency and justify the cost in a short time. Some special types of equipment available are:

1. Electric fork lift trucks.
2. Platform ladder with cart attached.
3. Pressure containers for spray water will eliminate the need for dropcloths and buckets.
4. Floor cart with two tanks, one holding cleaning solution and the other rinse water, for washing louvers.
5. Special louver trucks designed so that the louvers have space between them.
6. Movable scaffolds (telescopic or sectional type).

Greater efficiency is achieved if such equipment is designed to pass over obstructions such as desks, machines, or other equipment. Filament lamps can sometimes be changed from the floor with a lamp changing device. Equipment should be purchased with its versatility kept in mind, for other operations between lighting maintenance programs.

Relamping and Cleaning

1. Have the employee start the job completely equipped. *For example*, this should include a ladder cart combination of light construction, with platform to hold one pail of water with detergent, and one pail of clear rinse water. One box of new lamps and one empty carton to hold the old lamps should be attached to the front of the cart. Hooks on both sides of the cart will hold a clean louver on one side, and the dirty one on the other side. He will also need the following items: two flat sponges, one louver truck, if louvers are to be replaced, dropcloths if required, a supply of electrical repairs needed tags (Figure 12-8), and

Electrical Repairs Needed slips (Figure 12-9). The ladder cart combination should be of such construction that it be movable on rubber casters, and so that the two casters on the step portion of the ladder will be retractable when the ladder is positioned.

2. Turn off lamp in the area to be serviced.

3. Check to see that all equipment is in a safe position, and accurately position the ladder truck.

4. Glass Type (A): Unlatch the glass and remove the lamps from the fixture and place in spare, empty box. Put on rubber gloves, and thoroughly clean the entire fixture with a detergent solution. Rinse the fixture with sponge and clear water, wipe dry, and remove gloves.

Louver Type (B): Unlatch the louver and hang along the side of the ladder cart. Remove lamps from the fixture and place in spare empty box. Put on rubber gloves, and thoroughly clean the entire fixture with a detergent solution. Rinse the fixture with a sponge and clear water, wipe dry, and remove gloves.

5. Install new lamps taken from carton attached to truck.

6. Latch glass into position, or replace clean louver taken from side of truck.

7. Dismount ladder and reposition it. If louvers are being replaced, remove dirty louver from the side of the ladder and replace it with a clean one. If the louvers are being washed in conjunction with the lamp changing, it may now be washed in a special portable tank.

If spare louvers are maintained, or if several are taken down prior to starting a large area, from a remote section, which is to be serviced last, group washing will aid your efficiency.

8. Repeat the above operation for the duration of the shift, leaving sufficient time to wash dirty louvers and other equipment, replacing the equipment to its proper location for storage. Remove discarded lamps to proper location, and secure a new supply of lamps for the next shift. Make out required reports.

A red Out of Order tag should be used to coordinate the work between the person changing lamps and the electricians. The tag should be of sufficient size to be easily seen. (See Figure 12-8.) The tag should be numbered and have a corresponding notice of electrical repairs needed slip, which should be filled out by the person changing the lamps, with the corresponding number of the red tag recorded on it, and the location. These should be printed to cover the required information, date, number, building, floor, room, lamps changed, type of lamps, brief description, and your signature. This slip should be turned in to the foreman at the end of the shift. (See Figure 12-9.) This will result in a maintenance order and is a method of keeping the system in good repair.

Maintenance of Luminous Ceilings

The maintenance of luminous ceilings starts with preliminary recommendations prior to installation. Specifications should include the following:

1. All surface areas above the ceiling should be sealed. Use aluminum foil or white paint. This will aid in light reflection.

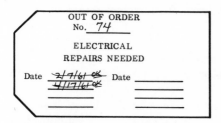

Figure 12-8   /   **Electrical repairs needed (tag).**

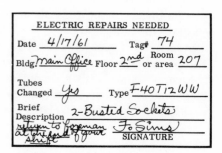

Figure 12-9   /   **Electrical repairs needed (slip).**

2. Loose mortar should be chipped off the ceiling and walls.

3. All windows or holes above the ceiling must be completely sealed off.

4. Do not install ceiling panels until immediately prior to occupancy. This will prevent dust problems.

The average luminous ceiling should be washed once a year, along with the fixture and dusting of lamps. To clean and destaticize plastic panels or fixtures, use a normal household detergent in warm water. *Do not wipe dry.* Allow plastic to air dry in order to avoid accumulating static charge. Two tanks and a rack cart are recommended for cleaning plastic ceiling panels.

Tank #1—Warm water for washing with detergent, and brushes installed on both sides of the tank, and a drain valve at the bottom.

Tank #2—Warm water for rinsing with a waxing agent which will destaticize the plastic, so that it will repel dust.

Rack Cart—Multi-sectioned cart so that the panels can stand on edge to drain properly, and to air dry. A trough should catch all water and a drain valve attached.

During the past several years, many cities are now served with lighting maintenance companies. Where the value of group replacement and planned maintenance programs are recognized, lighting maintenance companies are employed to do the work. Due to their specialized work, they should be equipped with the most efficient equipment and best methods. Through their efficiency they should be able to perform the work at a lower cost. These firms are usually willing to provide free estimates on the costs of their services.

Voltage Line Check—Incandescent Lamps

A voltage check should be made on line voltage at various locations throughout the building on 120-volt incandescent lamps. In purchasing 120-volt lamps, the voltage should not exceed this rating. It has been discovered recently, that in some installations the voltage has been exceeding 120 volts. A 120-volt lamp operated at 122½ volts loses approximately 25 per cent of its rated life. If a 125-volt lamp is operated at 122½ volts, it gains approximately 35 per cent of its rated life. Lamp life burning at a lower than rated voltage does not materially affect the light output or efficiency relative to power consumption. By changing to 125-volt lamps, life expectancy would be about 170 per cent of that obtained from 120-volt lamps. With extended life of incandescent lamps as explained, this would decrease the number of lamps to be replaced by 40 per cent, and thus reducing the work required. The 120-volt lamp is considered standard, and most manufacturers will furnish a 115-volt or 125-volt lamp at the same price as the 120-volt lamp.

New Developments a Challenge

New developments are constantly taking place in the lighting field which will require constant attention, in order to qualify one in planning a maintenance program. Research studies are now being made to combine a single panel element that will provide control of temperature and light at the same time. Increased use of lighting design to accommodate air conditioning systems with the use of a capacitive ballast, which would eliminate most of the wattage which loads an air conditioning system and much of the luminaire weight. Designs in lighting are being made to be included in the heating system in order to take the heat from the fixtures and pipe it to the heating ducts. An ultraviolet lamp is being developed for the annihilation of dangerous bacteria in heating and air conditioning ducts. Flat electroluminescent light panels that will emit practically no heat and consume a minimum amount of current will completely diffuse the light without special fixtures or baffles. It is also reported that a light control system has been developed to measure daylight, and will balance the electric light to assure constant room illumination.

With these developments in mind, maintenance responsibility increases, demanding constant development of know-how in the field of lighting maintenance methods and procedures.

A lighting maintenance program should be installed in every plant or building, or improved upon. All methods of education and reading must be explored to keep one qualified as a building superintendent or plant engineer. It has been an established practice to spend huge sums of money for research and development of new equipment, with only token offerings for maintenance. It is recommended that in the purchase of new equipment, the purchase order contain the requirement of a parts catalog, operating instructions, and all maintenance manuals. A building superintendent or plant manager is charged with the responsibility of protecting and getting full utilization of capital expended for fixtures and equipment. These catalogs and manuals will assist him in performing his job in a more efficient and economical manner for his employer.

13 / **LOBBY AND ENTRANCE CLEANING**

(*Source:* Buildings Management Division, General Services Administration, Washington, D. C.)

Job Description

Lobby and entrance cleaning includes all cleaning work in building lobbies and entrances, except floor scrubbing which is done by a scrubbing crew, and entrance door and glass cleaning which is done as a part of sidewalk cleaning and grounds maintenance.

The job of lobby and entrance cleaning consists of sweeping, dusting, polishing metal and wood surfaces, wall spotting, cleaning drinking fountains, mopping, and also the proper care and maintenance of the cleaning equipment and materials. Employees assigned to this job are instructed to notice lights out, defective door equipment and similar service defects, and to report them to their supervisor.

Equipment and Materials

A. *Equipment:*

    1. For sweeping and dusting.

        a. Dustpan
        b. Floor sweep mop
        c. Radiator dust brush
        d. Putty knife
        e. Dust cloths (polyethylene glycol treated cheesecloth)

    2. For polishing, wall spotting and mopping.

        a. Cheesecloth
        b. Cellulose sponge
        c. Cotton mop
        d. Buckets with wringer

    3. For equipment and materials transportation.

    Equipment carrier

B. *Materials:*

    1. For polishing, wall spotting and mopping.

        a. Detergent (mopping) solution
        b. Lemon oil polish
        c. Liquid metal polish
        d. White soap (cake)

2. For treating dust cloths.

 Polyethylene glycol solution

Job Methods

Operation Steps   *Explanation*

Step 1

1. Obtain equipment and materials.

Equipment and materials needed are listed under "Equipment and Materials".

2. Proceed to work area.

After placing equipment and materials on equipment carrier, move to area where work is to start.

PRECAUTION

Do not allow the equipment carrier to strike the walls, radiators or furniture.

Step 2

1. Dust radiators.

Use the radiator dust brush to clean radiators and grilles located within the assigned area as required.

2. Sweep lobby and/or entrance.

Use the floor sweep mop to sweep the lobby and/or entrance floor area, collecting the sweepings from such area into the dustpan. Dispose of the sweepings as directed by the supervisor.

3. Remove gum, tar and other foreign substances.

Use the putty knife to remove any gum, tar or similar substances from the floor areas during the sweeping.

PRECAUTIONS

1. Make sure all loose dirt is removed from baseboard areas and corners in the process of sweeping.

2. Be careful when using the putty knife not to gouge the floor surfaces.

Step 3

1. Dust with treated dust cloths.

Use the polyethylene glycol treated cloths to dust radiator tops, grilles,

Operation Steps	*Explanation*
	door frames and mouldings, ledges and all other surfaces that are to be dusted.
	Start the dusting at the highest surfaces that can be reached while standing on the floor and work downward toward the floor.

PRECAUTION

Avoid using the treated dust cloths on painted wall surfaces.

Step 4

1. Clean and polish metal surfaces.	Use clean cheesecloth, and metal polish as directed, to clean and polish metal doorknobs, push bars, kickplates, railings and other metal surfaces.
2. Clean and polish wood surfaces.	Use clean cheesecloth and lemon oil polish to clean and polish wooden handrails, doors and other wood surfaces as directed.
3. Clean drinking fountains.	Use warm water, white soap and a sponge to clean the bowls of all drinking fountains. Wipe remainder of fountain with a clean damp cloth. Wipe all chromium fixtures with a clean dry cloth.

PRECAUTION

Metal polish is not to be used on painted, lacquered, chrome-plated or other metal surfaces that have been specially treated.

Step 5

1. Place mop buckets for mopping.	Place the buckets of detergent (mopping) solution and rinse water in convenient positions for the beginning of the mopping operation.
2. Mop the lobby and/or entrance floors.	Use mop and detergent solution to thoroughly clean the floor areas. After dipping the mop into the solution, wring out enough excess solution so that the mop does not drip. Push the

Operation Steps

Explanation

mop close to the baseboards, taking care to remove all dust from corners. In open areas swing the mop from side to side in long arcs, being careful to cover all the floor and to keep from splashing the baseboards or walls. After wringing the mop, go back over the mopped area to pick up the excess cleaning solution.

3. Rinse and dry the mopped areas.

Use a second mop and clean rinse water to thoroughly rinse and dry the mopped floor. Frequently rinse and wring the mop during this operation.

PRECAUTIONS

1. Avoid using an excessive amount of cleaning solution or rinse water during the mopping or rinsing.

2. Change the rinse water frequently.

3. Be careful not to splash or scar the walls or baseboards with the equipment.

4. As may be appropriate, suitable warning should be given to the building occupants against the danger of slipping on the wet floor.

Step 6

1. Return all equipment and unused materials to storage location.

Gather all pieces of equipment and unused materials, place them in the equipment carrier and proceed to storage location.

2. Clean and store equipment.

a. Shake cloths to remove excess dust and dirt; rinse out if required, and when dry, treat with polyethylene glycol solution. Place for drying and storage.

b. Wipe the pan and knife free of dust and dirt and place for proper storage.

c. Clean the dust and dirt from the brush, comb the bristles and place in its proper storage position.

d. Rinse the mops, sponge and wiping cloths in clean water, squeeze or

Operation Steps	*Explanation*
	shake dry of excess water, and place for drying and storage.
	e. Empty buckets, rinse, wipe dry and return buckets and wringer to their proper storage positions.
	f. Wipe the carrier free of any moisture, dust and dirt, and place it in its proper storage location.
3. Store unused materials.	Return all unused materials to their proper storage places.

PRECAUTION

Make sure that lids are replaced securely on the containers for the cleaning and polishing materials.

Care of Equipment

A. *Dust Pan:*

1. Clean the dust pan of loose dirt and dust before storing.

2. When dumping the dust pan, avoid banging it with force against the waste container as such action tends to damage the sides and edges of the pan.

3. Hang by the handle so as not to allow any damaging weight to be put on the pan during storage.

B. *Floor Sweep Mop:*

1. Treated sweep mops should be shaken or vacuum cleaned, both during use and at the close of operations each day. They should be kept clean and free from grime or oily material.

2. Once every two weeks, remove mop head, shake out as much dust as possible and wash mop in a warm solution of synthetic detergent. Rinse in clear warm water.

3. Wring out as much water as possible and treat with polyethylene glycol (mix thoroughly three parts of water with one part of glycol). Spray mixture on mophead. Quantities required are approximately one ounce for three-quarter pound mop; one and one-half ounces for 1 pound mop; two ounces for one and one-quarter pound mop.

4. Replace the mophead on the handle and hang the mop so that a good air circulation will be obtained to assist in drying the mop. Let the mop dry for at least eight hours before using.

C. *Radiator Dust Brush:*

1. Comb the bristles periodically to clean the brush.

2. Store the brush either by laying it flat or by hanging it so that the bristles stand free of surrounding objects.

3. Do not use the radiator dust brush for any other purpose than for dusting radiators and grilles.

D. *Putty Knife:*

1. Use the putty knife only for the removal of gum, tar and other foreign substances during sweeping. *Do not* use as a screw driver or hammer.

2. Keep the putty knife clean and in good condition at all times.

3. Wipe free of dust and dirt after each use and store in a clean, dry place.

E. *Dust Cloths (polyethylene glycol treated cheesecloth):*

1. Thoroughly shake, or, if vacuum facilities are available, vacuum the dust cloths to remove loose dust.

2. Wash dirty cloths in warm detergent solution, (mix one ounce of detergent per gallon of warm water); rinse in clean water and wring or squeeze to remove excess water.

3. To treat new or washed cheesecloth, spray or sprinkle approximately one fluid ounce of polyethylene glycol solution (mixed in proportion of three parts of water to one part of polyethylene glycol) per square yard of cheesecloth. The cloth should be treated at least eight hours before using.

F. *Cheesecloth:*

1. Rinse all cloths after each use.

2. Wash dirty cloths in a warm detergent solution, (mix one ounce of detergent per gallon of water), and rinse in clean water.

3. Wring or squeeze to remove excess water and spread or hang the cloths to dry in their proper storage places.

4. Avoid leaving wet, dirty cloths piled together in the storage location.

G. *Cellulose Sponge:*

1. Rinse the sponge after each use.

2. Wash the sponge in detergent solution, as necessary, to remove dirt, and rinse in clean water.

3. Squeeze, *do not* wring, the sponge to remove excess water and place in proper storage position.

H. *Cotton Mops:*

1. After each use and before storage, rinse mops in clean water and wring or squeeze to remove excess water.

2. Wash dirty mops in warm detergent solution, (mix one ounce of detergent per gallon of warm water); rinse in clean water and wring or squeeze to remove excess water.

3. Fluff the mop strands by shaking.

4. Store the mops with the mopheads up to allow better drying.

I. *Buckets and Mop Wringer:*

1. Rinse and dry the buckets and wringer thoroughly after each use.

2. Remove any mop strands and other foreign matter remaining in the wringer.

3. Wipe the outside of the buckets free of dirt.

4. Avoid striking the buckets and wringer against objects as such action tends to create leaks in buckets and shorten the life of the equipment.

5. Store in a dry place and in such positions as to have no damaging weight bearing on the buckets or wringer.

J. *Equipment Carrier:*

1. Do not allow the carrier to strike the walls, furniture, or other equipment.

2. Wipe the carrier clean of dirt and dust at least once a week; maintain in a clean and orderly condition at all times.

3. Report promptly any defects or equipment failure to the supervisor.

Performance Inspection Guide

A. *Sweeping and Dusting:*

1. Lobby and entrance floors should be clean and free of dirt streaks and there should be no dirt remaining under radiators, in corners, behind doors or where the dirt was picked up with the dustpan after the sweeping operation.

2. Wads of gum, tar, and other sticky substances should have been removed from the area.

3. Radiators, grilles and woodwork should be dust-free after dusting. Dust should have been removed rather than merely pushed around.

4. There should not be any spots or smudges on the painted wall surfaces, caused by touching the wall with the treated dustcloth.

B. *Polishing and Wall Spotting:*

1. Doorknobs, push bars, kick plates, railings, doors and other surfaces should be clean and polished to an acceptable lustre.

2. Any drinking fountains located within the assigned area should be clean and free of stains. The wall surfaces around the drinking fountains should be free of water spots and streaks.

3. Wall surfaces up to a standing height should be free of finger marks, smudges and other dirt spots of any kind.

C. *Mopping:*

1. Lobby and entrance floors should be free of loose and/or caked dirt particles and should present an over-all appearance of cleanliness after the mopping operation.

2. Walls, baseboards and other surfaces should be free of watermarks, scars from the cleaning equipment striking the surfaces, and splashings from the cleaning solution and rinse water.

3. All surfaces should be dry and the corners and crevices clean after mopping.

D. *Equipment and Materials:*

1. All items of equipment should be clean and properly placed in a neat and orderly manner in their assigned storage locations.

2. All metal and furniture polish, soap and other materials left over from the cleaning operation should be returned to their assigned storage locations.

Frequency and Production

A. *Frequency and Production Schedule:*

	Sweeping and Dusting	Polishing and Wall Spotting	Mopping
Frequency	Daily *	Weekly *	Daily *
Production Rate per Man-day		16 main (large) lobbies or entrances 32 secondary lobbies or entrances	

* Or as directed by the supervisor

B. *Qualifying Factors:*

1. *Frequency*

   a. The frequency of lobby and entrance cleaning is dependent upon weather conditions, type of building and location, type of occupancy, and amount of traffic through the lobby and/or entrance.

   b. The frequencies given in the Frequency and Production Schedule are for a normal standard of cleaning under average conditions.

2. *Production Rate per Man-day*

   a. The main (large) lobbies or entrances are those that serve as the principal access to the buildings.

   b. The secondary lobbies or entrances are those of lesser importance, smaller in size and usually less frequently used.

   c. Due to the various types and sizes of lobbies and entrances, the production rate as established may be subject to modification at the various locations.

Staffing

The man-day requirements of labor for lobby and entrance cleaning can be determined by use of the following formula:

$$\text{Man-days (of labor)} = \frac{\text{Quantity}}{\text{Production}} \times \frac{1}{\text{Frequency}}$$

where quantity is the actual number of lobbies and entrances to be cleaned in the building; production is the number of lobbies and entrances cleaned per man-day; and frequency is the number of work days between operations.

If the frequency and/or production rate values as given in the Frequency and Production Schedule in this chapter have been modified to meet the existing conditions at a particular location, those modified values should be used in the above formula for the computation of the labor requirement.

SAMPLE CALCULATION

Assume a building with two main lobbies and/or entrances, plus ten secondary lobbies and/or entrances, and subject to such conditions that the average cleaning values from the Frequency and Production Schedule may be used.

$$\text{Man-days} = \frac{2}{16} \times \frac{1}{1} + \frac{10}{32} \times \frac{1}{1}$$
$$= 0.13 \quad\quad + 0.31$$
$$= 0.44 \text{ man-days of labor required (jobs)}$$

In order to determine the total number of positions needed to accomplish the work, this figure is multiplied by a conversion factor to compensate for leave allowances.

Conversion factor including compensation for leave = 1.15

Conversion factor × jobs = total positions required

1.15 × 0.44 = 0.51 positions required

Where the normal cleaning duty does not require the full time of the employee, other duties such as toilet cleaning, stairway cleaning, or some other job should be assigned to the employee to secure 100 per cent utilization of his time.

14 / CARE OF OUTSIDE AREAS

(*Source:* Buildings Management Division, General Services Administration, Washington, D. C.)

The care and maintenance of outside building and garage areas as outlined in this chapter has been broken down into the following duties: (A) Area policing; (B) sweeping; (C) outside entrance cleaning; (D) hosing sidewalks; (E) area scrubbing; (F) lawn maintenance; and (G) snow removal. These duties pertain to areas outside of the buildings except where garages and driveways are located within the building confines.

Job Description

In general, this job consists of keeping the specified areas policed of paper, trash and other debris; periodic sweeping of sidewalks and other paved areas as scheduled; wet cleaning sidewalks, steps, exterior portions of garages, and other required areas either by hosing down and spot scrubbing with a deck brush where necessary by mopping, or by machine scrubbing; cleaning exterior portions of building entrances; maintaining the lawn areas in a presentable condition by mowing and trimming the grass, trimming shrubs, raking leaves, watering grass and shrubbery; and, assisting in the removal of snow and ice as necessary.

It is suggested that the advice and experience of local county agents and other recognized experts on lawn and shrubbery care for your area be utilized as an aid in the achievement of satisfactory results.

All employees assigned to this work are responsible for reporting defective operating equipment and building items encountered during their tour of duty.

Job Methods

Operation Steps	*Explanation*

A. *Area Policing:*

Step 1—Prepare for Work

1. Obtain equipment needed.	a. Canvas shoulder bag or other approved trash container b. Dust pan, long handle c. Gloves d. Sidewalk brush (24″) e. Litterstick with sharp point (for picking up paper)
2. Proceed to work area.	Proceed to the assigned location where area policing is to start.

Step 2—Wastepaper and Trash

1. Pick up wastepaper and trash.	Go over the assigned outside areas and pick up loose wastepaper and/or trash. Place collected paper and trash in the trash room, or dispose of it as directed by the supervisor.
2. Litter sweeping.	During the policing operation use the brush to sweep up litter, loose accumulations of dirt, leaves, etc. from the hard surfaced areas as required. This litter sweeping should not substitute for the regularly scheduled sweeping job.

Step 3—Return Equipment to Storage

1. Return to storeroom location.	Gather all policing equipment and return it to the storage location.
2. Clean and store equipment.	Clean the equipment as directed and place in the assigned storage location.

Operation Steps	*Explanation*

B. *Sweeping:*

Step 1—Prepare for Work

1. Obtain equipment needed.	a. Dust pan, long handle b. Gloves c. Sidewalk brush (24") d. Trash basket (3 bushel oak splint) or other suitable trash container
2. Proceed to work area.	Proceed to the assigned location where sweeping is to start.

Step 2—Sweep the Assigned Area

1. Sweep with brush.	Sweep the assigned area using short push strokes of two and one-half to three feet, and pressing down slightly on the brush bristles when sweeping rough surfaces. Overlap the brush strokes as necessary to avoid leaving fine dirt behind.
2. Pick up string, pieces of paper, etc.	Pick up pieces of paper, string, and other trash which cannot be pushed forward with the brush and place them in the trash container.
3. Dispose of trash.	Empty the collected sweepings and trash into designated containers in the trash room, or dispose of as otherwise directed by the supervisor.

Step 3—Return Equipment to Storage

1. Return to storeroom location.	Gather all pieces of equipment used during the sweeping operation and return them to the storage location.
2. Clean and store equipment.	Clean the equipment as directed. Place all items in their proper storage positions.

C. *Outside Entrance Cleaning:*

Step 1—Prepare for Work

1. Obtain equipment and materials needed.	a. Ammonia b. Bucket (15 qt.)

Operation Steps	*Explanation*

c. Cheesecloth
d. Deck scrub brush
e. Detergent
f. Dustpan
g. Lemon oil
h. Metal polish
i. Mop unit (2-compartment mop tank or mop buckets with wringer)
j. Mop, Cotton
k. Putty knife (1¼")
l. Sidewalk brush (24")
m. Sponge
n. Squeegee, floor
o. Squeegee, window
p. Water hose (length as required)

2. Proceed to work area.

Proceed with the equipment and materials for work to be performed to the area where the entrance cleaning is to start.

Step 2—Sweep the Entrance

1. Sweep with brush.

Sweep the entrance area, using short push strokes, and pressing down slightly on the brush bristles when sweeping rough surfaces. Overlap the brush strokes as necessary to avoid leaving fine dirt behind.

2. Pick up string, pieces of paper, and other waste material.

Pick up by hand pieces of paper, string and other trash which cannot be pushed forward with the brush, and dispose of same with the other sweepings.

3. Remove gum and other foreign substances.

Use putty knife to remove wads of gum, spots of tar, or other foreign substances from the floor area.

Step 3—Wet Clean the Entrance

1. Hose down the entrance.

If practical, use a hose to wet clean the entrance steps, doors and areaway. As necessary, use the mop and/or deck brush and detergent solution (mix one ounce per gallon water) to remove grime and dirt.

Operation Steps	*Explanation*
	Thoroughly rinse after detergent solution is used.
2. Pick up excess water.	Squeeze off or mop up all excess water remaining after the cleaning operation. Rinse and wring the mop frequently in clean water.

NOTE

This work should be performed during periods of minimum traffic through the building entrances to avoid inconveniencing the building occupants and visitors. As necessary, warning signs should be conspicuously placed near the work area.

Step 4—Polish Glass, Wood and Metal

1. Clean entrance glass.	Use a sponge, clean water and window squeegee to thoroughly clean both side (inside and out) of glass surfaces in the entrance. As necessary, ammonia may be added to the water to loosen oil and grime adhering to the glass. Wipe up water drippings from the glass cleaning operation with the sponge.
2. Clean and polish metal surfaces.	Use clean cheesecloth, and metal polish as directed, to clean and polish metal doorknobs, push bars, kick plates, railings and other metal surfaces.
3. Clean and polish wood surfaces.	Use clean cheesecloth and lemon oil polish to clean and polish wooden handrails, doors and other wood surfaces as directed.

PRECAUTIONS

Metal polish is not to be used on painted, lacquered chrome-plated or other metal surfaces that have been specially treated.

Step 5—Return Equipment and Materials to Storage

1. Return to storeroom location.	Gather up all equipment and unused materials and return them to the storage area.
2. Clean equipment and store equip-	Clean all equipment items as directed.

Operation Steps	*Explanation*
ment materials.	Store equipment and unused materials in their assigned storage locations.

D. *Hosing Sidewalks:*

Step 1—Prepare for Work

1. Obtain equipment and materials needed.	a. Rubber boots or overshoes b. Squeegee, floor c. Water hose (length as required) d. Water hose nozzle e. Wiping cloths
2. Proceed to work area.	Proceed with the equipment to the assigned area where work is to start.

Step 2—Clean the Assigned Area

1. Hose down the area.	Connect the water hose to a convenient water outlet and hose down the sidewalk and other designated areas. Play the water stream from side to side as required to clean the hard-surfaced areas.
2. Remove excess water.	Use the squeegee to remove water remaining on the cleaned surfaces.
3. Wipe up spatterings.	Use the wiping cloth to clean water marks or spatterings from nearby wall surfaces, door, hand railings, and other places, if necessary.

PRECAUTION

1. Use as little water as possible to properly clean the area.
2. Avoid directing the water stream on surrounding plants, shrubs and buildings.
3. This work should be performed at times of least inconvenience to occupants.

Step 3—Return Equipment to Storage

1. Return to storeroom location.	Disconnect water hose from water outlet, drain water from hose, and return it and other equipment items to the storage area.
2. Clean and store equipment.	Clean the equipment items as directed. Store the items in assigned storage locations.

Operation Steps	*Explanation*

E. *Area Scrubbing:*

Step 1—Prepare for Work

1. Obtain equipment and materials needed.

   a. Bucket (15 qt.)
   b. Deck scrub brush
   c. Detergent
   d. Mop unit (2-compartment mop tank or mop buckets with wringer)
   e. Mops, cotton
   f. Putty knife
   g. Rubber boots or overshoes
   h. Scouring powder
   i. Squeegee, floor
   j. Water hose (length as required)

2. Proceed to work area.

   Proceed with the necessary equipment and materials to the assigned area where work is to start.

Step 2—Wet Cleaning

1. Mop or scrub the assigned area.

   Wet clean assigned areas, such as garage, driveway, and portico by the most practical of the following prescribed methods:

2. Clean with water hose and deck scrub brush.

   a. Use water hose to wet the area to be cleaned. Scrub with deck scrub brush and detergent solution (mix one ounce detergent per gallon water). Use scouring powder as necessary to remove embedded dirt and grime.

   b. Thoroughly rinse cleaned area with water hose, and use floor squeegee to remove excess water. As necessary, a mop may be used to remove excess water and to dry the floor.

3. Clean with mop and detergent solution.

   Job methods for wet cleaning floors as outlined in Section 9B, Floor Mopping, may be followed in the performance of this work.

4. Clean with power scrubbing ma-

   Where using a power scrubbing ma-

Operation Steps	*Explanation*
chine.	chine will result in more efficient performance, one should be used for this work.
5. Remove grease and oil spots, wads of gum and tar, noticed in area.	Use the putty knife and/or scouring powder and deck scrub brush to remove grease and oil spots and stains, particles of tar and gum, and other embedded dirt not otherwise removed.
6. Rinse the cleaned area.	Use clean rinse water and mop, or water hose, to thoroughly rinse the cleaned area. As applicable, the floor squeegee may be used to remove excess rinse water.

PRECAUTIONS

1. Before hosing down areas, check the drains to see that they are open to carry off the wash water.

2. Avoid splashing dirty water on surrounding equipment, walls, etc.

3. Thoroughly rinse all areas where detergent solution or scouring powder has been used.

Step 3—Return Equipment and Materials to Storage

1. Return to storeroom location.	Gather all equipment items and unused materials and return them to storage area.
2. Clean equipment, and store equipment and materials.	Clean all equipment items as directed. Store equipment and materials in their assigned storage locations.

F. *Lawn Maintenance:*

Step 1—Prepare for Work

1. Obtain necessary equipment.	a. Edger b. Gloves c. Hand truck (as necessary) d. Lawn mower (hand or power machine) e. Lawn rake (as necessary) f. Power equipment accessories (if power equipment is used)

Operation Steps	*Explanation*
	g. Shrubbery tools (shears, knife, and others)
	h. Trash basket (3 bushel oak splint), or suitable containers for trimmings and leaves.
	i. Water hose (length as required)
	j. Wiping cloths
2. Proceed to work area.	After obtaining the necessary equipment required for the particular job to be done, proceed to assigned area where work is to start.

Step 2—Grass Cutting

1. Grass cutting season.	In general, the first spring grass cutting should be delayed until the grass has had an opportunity to grow, to allow for greater root development. The last cutting in the fall should take place at such time to allow the grass to grow back to a length of two to three inches as a protection against the winter season.
2. Cutting frequency.	For purposes of staffing the cleaning standard establishes the frequency for grass cutting as once every five days. However, this work should be performed as the growth of the grass requires. A good general schedule to follow is to cut the grass whenever it reaches a height of three inches, one and one-half inches since the last cutting.
3. Grass clippings.	Usually grass clippings may be left on the lawn. They act as a mulch, reduce moisture evaporation from the soil, help keep the soil cool, and contribute to the feeding of the soil. However, long clippings that lie on top of the grass rather than filtering down onto the soil should be raked up and disposed of to prevent smothering or killing the grass, and to eliminate the unsightly appearance of

Operation Steps	*Explanation*
	dried, discolored clippings on the lawn.
4. Cutting height.	Generally a minimum cutting height of one and one-half inches is recommended. At this height the turf is less likely to suffer, even when the grass is frequently cut, and the grass tips can be kept uniformly trimmed so that the lawn has a well-groomed appearance.
5. Cutting procedure.	Cut up and down the lawn or in a circular direction, overlapping the previous swath by about two inches. When using power equipment, use the longest uninterrupted run practicable. When cutting the crown of a terrace mow up and down the slope, as cutting crosswise may result in scalping the crown. Trim the grass areas adjoining sidewalks, shrubs, and other areas, as required during the lawn mowing operation.
6. Mower blade maintenance.	Well set, sharp mower blades provide a fast, clean cutting action. This prevents the bruising of grass blades, which occurs when dull blades chew off the ends rather than shearing them evenly. For safety, police the lawns before cutting the grass to remove stones, broken glass and other debris. This helps keep the mower blades from becoming nicked and avoids damage and serious breakdowns of the equipment.
7. Rolling, aeration, feeding, weed and insect control.	Various other duties pertinent to lawn maintenance, such as lawn rolling, soil aeration, feeding, elimination of weeds, and pest control should be handled on a local basis as required.

GENERAL GRASS CUTTING RULES FOR PROPER LAWN MAINTENANCE:

1. Delay the first spring cutting until the grass has made some new growth.

2. Cut the grass at a minimum height of one and one-half to two inches, using well-set sharp mower blades.

3. Remove the clippings if extra long and during wet weather when the clippings are heavy enough to mat.

4. Stop cutting the lawn early enough in the fall to insure a growth of two to three inches before winter.

Step 3—Pruning Shrubbery

NOTE

The pruning information outlined in this step is of a general nature. The advice of recognized pruning experts should be followed in the performance of this work in the various localities.

Operation Steps	*Explanation*
1. When to prune.	Generally, early blossoming shrubs which bloom on the previous year's growth should be pruned just after they bloom. Late blossoming shrubs which bloom on the same year's growth should be pruned in late winter or early spring. Late summer pruning is unsafe because the new growth of wood that occurs rarely becomes hardened enough to withstand severe winter weather.
2. Pruning tips.	Pruning is performed to remove surplus or undesirable growth at the proper time of the year. All cuts must be made cleanly with a sharp knife, saw or shears, leaving no projecting stubs or branches. Cut surfaces should be treated with creosote or other suitable recommended materials and coated to prevent decay. Branches should never be broken off and left untreated.

Step 4—Watering

1. Watering frequency.	Water lawn only often enough to keep it alive. Loam and clay soils hold more water and longer than sandy and gravel soils and so need not be watered as frequently. A method for determining the dryness of the soil

Operation Steps	*Explanation*
	in some areas is to examine it to a depth of two to three inches. Dryness of the upper part of the soil generally indicates need for watering.
2. Amount of water.	If the lawn must be watered, thorough soaking to a depth of six inches is much better than light sprinklings. Light sprinklings in quantities that do not allow thorough penetration of the soil tends to draw the grass roots to the surface of the ground. Because of surface runoff and greater moisture loss, special consideration should be given to steep slopes and slopes facing in a southerly direction. Apply the water only as fast as the soil can absorb it to prevent surface runoff and consequent water loss.

NOTE

When watering lawns, care should be taken to prevent muddy water splashing from bare ground areas onto nearby building walls, foundations, and walks.

Step 5—Return Equipment to Storage

1. Return to storeroom location.	Gather all equipment items and return them to the storage location.
2. Clean and store equipment.	Clean all pieces of equipment as directed, and store in their assigned storage positions.

G. Snow Removal:

Step 1—Prepare for Work

1. Obtain equipment and materials needed.	a. Bucket (15 qt.) b. Gloves c. Hand truck d. Ice scraper e. Plow attachments for power equipment (type and quantity as required) f. Raincoat

Operation Steps	*Explanation*
	g. Rubber boots (or overshoes)
	h. Sand and/or chemical compound
	i. Snow shovel
2. Proceed to work area.	Move the required equipment and materials to the assigned area where work is to start.

Step 2—Removal of Snow and Ice

1. Clean sidewalks, entrances, and driveways of snow and ice.	Use shovels, ice scrapers, and/or plows attached to power equipment to clear areas of snow and ice. Pile the snow and ice on lawns and around trees rather than pushing into streets and gutters.
2. Sand sidewalks, walks and driveways.	Use an approved chemical snow and ice remover compound or sand on areas as required to control hazards to occupants and visitors.

NOTE

Chemical snow and ice remover compound is preferable to sand for use at building entrances and on adjoining sidewalk areas where possible. Use of sand in such areas results in trackage of the sand into buildings, which necessitates additional cleaning. Where sand is used, provision should be made for its pickup and proper disposal, as directed, as soon as is practical after it has served its purpose.

Step 3—Return Equipment and Materials to Storage

1. Return to storeroom location.	Gather all equipment and unused materials and return them to the storage location.
2. Clean and store equipment; store materials.	Clean all pieces of equipment as directed. Store equipment and unused materials in their proper storage positions.

Care of Equipment

A. *Canvas Shoulder Trash Bag or Other Approved Receptacle:*

1. Thoroughly empty bag or receptacle of trash and dirt after each day's use.
2. Avoid snagging or tearing the bag.
3. Store in a clean, dry location.

B. *Cheesecloth:*

1. Rinse all cloths after each day's use.

2. Wash dirty cloths as required in a warm detergent solution, rinse thoroughly and wring or squeeze out excess water before placing them to dry.

C. *Deck Scrub Brush:*

1. Rinse in clean water after each day's use and shake dry of excess water.

2. Place for drying and storage in such position that the bristles do not bear the weight of the brush.

3. Avoid knocking the brush against objects for this tends to split the brush block.

D. *Dustpan:*

1. Clean dustpan of dirt and dust before storing.

2. Hang dustpan by the handle so that it will not become bent or otherwise damaged.

E. *Gloves:*

1. Shake or wipe free of dirt and dust after each day's use.

2. Avoid snagging gloves on nails or other sharp objects.

3. Store gloves in a clean, dry location.

F. *Hand Lawn Mower:*

1. Wipe all parts free of dirt, moisture and grass cuttings after each day's use.

2. Store the mower in its assigned location and in such a position as to prevent its being damaged.

3. The mower should be kept properly lubricated and sharpened. Report all defects and/or necessary repairs to the supervisor.

G. *Hand Truck:*

1. Clean the truck of dirt and trash after each day's use.

2. The wheels of the truck should be kept properly lubricated. Report all necessary repairs or defects to the supervisor.

H. *Ice Scraping Tool:*

1. Wipe the tool free of moisture and dirt after each day's use.

2. Store in a safe manner in its assigned location

I. *Lawn Rake:*

1. Wipe the rake free of moisture, dirt and other debris after each day's use.

2. Store by hanging in a safe and secure manner so it will not be damaged.

J. *Litterstick:*

1. Wipe the stick free of moisture and dirt after each day's use.

2. Place a cork or similar protective object over the pointed end before storage.

K. *Mop, Cotton (2 lb.):*

1. Before storing after each day's use rinse the mop in clean water and squeeze or wring to remove excess water.

2. Wash dirty mops in a warm detergent solution, rinse in clean water, and wring or squeeze to remove excess water.

3. Fluff the mop strands by shaking.

4. Store, with the mophead up, in a well-ventilated place to allow for better drying.

L. *Mop Unit (2-compartment mop tank or mop buckets with wringer) and Bucket (15 qt.):*

1. Rinse bucket, mop unit compartments and wringer thoroughly and wipe dry after each day's use.

2. Remove any remaining mop strands and other matter from the bucket, mop unit and wringer.

3. Always leave mop wringer in released position.

4. Store in a clean dry location and otherwise maintain a clean and orderly condition.

5. Report any defects or necessary repairs to the supervisor.

M. *Power Sidewalk Sweeper:*

See instructions for equipment care under *H* in the following section "Performance Inspection Guide."

O. *Putty Knife:*

1. Wipe knife free of dirt and moisture after each day's use.

2. Store in a clean dry place.

3. Use only for the purpose specified. Do not use as a screw driver or hammer.

P. *Raincoat:*

1. Wipe raincoat free of dirt and excess moisture after each day's use.

2. Store by hanging on a hanger in a clean and well-ventilated place.

3. Avoid snagging on nails and other sharp objects.

Q. *Rubber Boots:*

1. Rinse off dirt and other matter, and wipe dry after each day's use.

2. Store in a clean, well-ventilated place in such a way that the boots will not be damaged.

R. *Shrubbery Tools:*

1. Wipe tools free of dirt and moisture after each day's use.

2. Maintain tools in a well-sharpened and lubricated condition as necessary.

3. Hang tools for storage in such a way that they will not be damaged or endanger personnel.

S. *Sidewalk Brush (24"):*

1. Wash an oily or dirty brush in a warm detergent solution and rinse in clean water. Shake free of excess water and hang to dry with bristles in a downward position and free of any weight.

2. Store in a clean, dry place so that the bristles do not bear the weight of the brush.

3. Reverse the position of the handle in the brush block weekly to assure longer brush life.

T. *Snow Plow Attachments:*

1. Wipe equipment free of dirt and moisture after each use.

2. Upon storing, coat bare metal portions of the equipment with a rust preventive compound as directed by the supervisor, and maintain in a well lubricated, clean condition.

3. Report necessary repairs and defects to the supervisor.

U. *Sponge:*

1. Rinse sponge in clean water after each day's use.

2. When dirty, wash in warm detergent solution, rinse thoroughly, and squeeze out excess water.

3. Store in a clean, dry location.

V. *Squeegees:*

1. Rinse squeegee blade in clean water after each day's use.

2. Wipe dry and store in a clean, dry location.

W. *Trash Basket:*

1. Clean trash basket of trash and dirt after each day's use.

2. Store in such a way that it will not be damaged.

X. *Water Hose:*

1. Drain hose of any remaining water and wipe outside free of dirt and excess moisture.

2. Coil and properly store hose in its assigned location.

Y. *Wiping Cloths:*

1. Rinse wiping cloths in clean water after each day's use.

2. Wash dirty cloths as required in a warm detergent solution, rinse thoroughly, and wring or squeeze out excess water before spreading to dry.

Performance Inspection Guide

A. *Area Policing:*

1. Lawn areas, sidewalks, driveways and other assigned areas should be free of trash, paper and other debris after the policing work has been performed.

2. Sidewalks and building entrances should be kept free of cigarette butts, loose sand, string, paper, and other debris, and be presentable in appearance at all times.

B. *Sweeping:*

1. Sidewalks, entrances, garages and other portions of the assigned areas should have been swept clean, as scheduled.

2. Loose trash, such as paper, string, sticks, and other litter should have been cleared away in the sweeping process.

C. *Entrances:*

1. Entrance steps and areas should be policed, and kept free of dirt and other debris.

2. Entrance glass, metal and wood surfaces should be clean and, where applicable, polished to an acceptable lustre.

D. *Hosing Sidewalks:*

1. Sidewalks and other designated paved areas should have been hosed down and cleaned as scheduled.

2. Excess water should have been squeegeed off the cleaned areas.

3. Water spatterings should have been wiped from railings, entrances, and other surrounding surfaces as required.

E. *Area Scrubbing:*

1. Paved sidewalks, entrances, garages, and other paved areas should have been wet cleaned as scheduled.

2. Grease spots and stains should have been removed and the areas left in a clean and presentable condition.

F. *Lawn Maintenance:*

1. All grass and shrubbery should present a well-groomed appearance at all times.

2. Grass should not have been cut to a height of less than one and one-half inches except for those plant varieties that may be mowed closer.

3. In season, leaves should be raked up and removed from the lawn areas as necessary.

G. *Snow Removal:*

1. Sidewalks, entrances, drives and other such areas should be as free as possible from accumulations of snow and ice.

2. As required, such areas should be kept sanded or chemically treated to provide safe footing or traction.

H. *Equipment Care:*

1. All equipment used in performing this work should be clean and properly cared for.

2. All equipment and materials should be stored in assigned storage locations when not in use.

Frequency and Production

A. *Frequency and Production Schedule:*

	Frequency	Production per Man-day
1. *Area policing.* Includes entrances, parking areas, garages, ramps, sidewalks, lawn areas, driveways.	Daily	300,000 sq. ft.

	Frequency	Production per Man-day
2. *Sweeping.* Includes parking areas (hard-surfaced), garages, ramps, driveways, and sidewalks.	Every 5 days	Hand— 50,000 sq. ft. Machine— 100,000 sq. ft.
3. *Outside entrance cleaning.* Includes daily sweeping, wet cleaning weekly, and cleaning and polishing glass, metal and wood surfaces as required.	Daily	Main—16 Secondary—32
4. *Hosing sidewalks.* Includes hosing down sidewalk and other designated paved areas periodically and removing resulting water puddles from such surfaces.	As required	30,000 sq. ft.
5. *Area scrubbing.* Includes wet mopping or scrubbing of exterior portions of garages, ramps, driveways, and other specified paved areas.	As required	Mopping— 20,000 sq. ft. Scrubbing Machine 25,000 to 50,000 sq. ft.
6. *Lawn maintenance.* Includes cutting and edging of grass areas, watering, care of shrubbery, raking leaves, etc., as required.	Every 5 days	100,000 sq. ft.
7. *Snow removal.* Includes removing snow and ice from entrances, sidewalks, parking areas, driveways, and ramps, and spreading sand or snow and ice remover compound to reduce safety hazards.	As required	Performed by special crews from maintenance force.

B. *Qualifying Factors:*

The values for frequency and production given in the above schedule are for a normal standard under average conditions. These values may be subject to modification at certain locations due to climatic conditions, type of occupancy, terrain, and other reasons. However, they provide a standard for buildings from which such deviations, if any, should be made.

Staffing

The man-day requirements of labor for this work can be determined by use of the following formula:

$$\text{Man-days (of labor)} = \frac{\text{Quantity}}{\text{Production}} \times \frac{1}{\text{Frequency}}$$

Where quantity represents the square feet of area maintained at the given frequency; production is the square feet of area maintained per man-day for the type of equipment and the job method utilized; and frequency is the number of work days between operations.

If the frequency and/or production rate values established in the Frequency and Production Schedule, have been modified to meet existing conditions at a particular location, then those modified values should be used in the above formula for the labor requirement computation.

SAMPLE CALCULATION

Assume a building location having the following areas to be maintained, under such conditions that the established values from the Frequency and Production Schedule may be used:

Sidewalks	=	16,700 sq. ft.
Driveways, garages and parking areas	=	22,900 sq. ft.
Lawn area	=	23,200 sq. ft.
Main entrances	=	4

Then the area to be policed is 16,700 sq. ft. + 22,900 sq. ft. + 23,200 sq. ft., or 62,800 sq. ft.; sweeping area is 16,700 sq. ft. + 22,900 sq. ft., or 39,600 sq. ft.; sidewalk hosing area is 16,700 sq. ft. based on a weekly basis; area scrubbing is 39,600 sq. ft. based on a quarterly basis; and lawn maintenance area is 23,200 sq. ft. Therefore, the man-days (of labor) are computed as follows:

$$\text{For Area Policing} = \frac{62,800}{300,000} \times \frac{1}{1} = .21$$

$$\text{For Sweeping} = \frac{39,600}{50,000} \times \frac{1}{5} = .16$$

$$\text{For Sidewalk Hosing} = \frac{16,700}{30,000} \times \frac{1}{5} = .11$$

$$\text{For Entrance Cleaning} = 4/16 \times \frac{1}{1} = .25$$

$$\text{For Area Scrubbing} = \frac{39,600}{25,000} \times \frac{1}{66} = .02$$

$$\text{For Lawn Maintenance} = \frac{23,200}{100,000} \times \frac{1}{5} = \underline{.05}$$

$$\text{Total Jobs} \qquad\qquad\qquad .80$$

To this total requirement must be added a factor to compensate for leave in order to arrive at the total number of positions needed to accomplish this work.

Conversion factor including compensation for leave = 1.15
Conversion factor × jobs = total positions required
1.15 × .80 = positions required–.92

Where this work does not require the full time of the employee, other duties should be assigned to secure 100 per cent utilization of his time.

Equipment and Materials Allocation and Replacement

Items	Allotment per Cleaner	Replacement or Reissue
Boots, rubber	1 pair	1 per 5 years
Brush, deck scrub	1	1 per year
Brush handle, deck scrub	1	1 per 2 years
Brush, radiator	1	1 per year
Brush, sidewalk (24")	1	2 per year
Brush handle, sidewalk	1	1 per year
Bucket (15 qt.)	1	1 per year
Cheesecloth	2 yards	8 yards per year
Cloth, wiping	2	6 per year
Detergent *	1 pound	50 pounds per year
Dustpan	1	1 per 2 years
Gloves	1 pair	2 pair per year
Hose, water	As required	As required
Ice scraping tool	1	1 per 5 years
Lawn edger, sprinkler, and Lawn equipment (miscellaneous)	As required	As required 1 per 5 years
Lawn mower, hand	1 (as required)	
Lawn mower, power †	As required	As required
Litterstick	1	2 per year
Mop, cotton	1	6 per year
Mop handle	1	1 per year
Mop unit	1	1 per 5 years
Putty knife (1¼")	1	1 per 2 years
Raincoat	1	1 per 5 years
Rake, lawn	1	1 per 2 years
Sand or chemical compound	As required	As required
Scouring powder	1 pound	25 pounds per year
Shrubbery tools	As required	As required
Sidewalk sweeper, power †	As required	As required
Snow plow attachments	As required	As required
Snow shovel	1	As required
Sponge	1	2 per year
Squeegee, floor (18")	1	2 per year
Squeegee, window	1	1 per year
Trash bag, canvas shoulder or other approved receptacle	1	As required
Trash basket (3 bushels)	As required	As required
Truck, hand	1	1 per 5 years

* Recommended as a general purpose cleaner. Has proven satisfactory for general floor cleaning in proportions one ounce per gallon of water.

† Mechanized equipment should be provided with safety features, such as fire extinguisher, fill and vent fitting, and others as prescribed to insure compliance with safe operating practices and regulations.

The allotment per cleaner and the replacement or reissue quantities in this section are based on one cleaner spending 100 per cent of his time on this work.

• Where the situation exists that other duties are assigned to the cleaner to secure 100 per cent utilization of his time, consideration should be given to a reduction in the replacement quantities in accordance with the actual amount of this work assigned.

Operation of Gasoline-Powered Grass Cutting Machine

Operation Steps   *Explanation*

NOTE

Although these instructions pertain specifically to the operation of power lawn mowers, they also have application to power trimmers, edgers and leaf mulchers.

Step 1—Preparation for Work

1. Obtain equipment and materials needed.
   - a. Approved safety gasoline can
   - b. Engine oil (S.A.E. 30)
   - c. Gasoline (white, unleaded)
   - d. Lawn mower, gasoline-powered
   - e. Radiator brush
   - f. Wiping cloths

2. Check oil level in crankcase.
   - a. Remove oil filler plug and check to see if crankcase is full of oil.
   - b. If oil is low, add enough oil to bring it up to proper level.

3. Check gasoline tank.
   - a. Remove filler cap of gasoline tank.
   - b. When necessary fill gasoline tank with white (unleaded) gasoline *after* machine has been taken outdoors.
   - c. Be sure that vent hole in filler cap is open.

PRECAUTIONS

1. Always wipe any accumulated dirt from gasoline filler cap, oil filler cap, oil filler plug, and the area around them before they are removed for checking or refilling.

2. Be sure dirt and water do not enter the gasoline tank or engine crankcase.

3. Be sure there is no lighted cigarette, cigar, pipe, or match nearby when handling gasoline.

4. Do not fill gasoline tank while engine is running.

5. Avoid spilling gasoline on hot engine.

6. Always fill gasoline tank outdoors.

7. When using a rotary blade mover, be sure that guard is in place to prevent possible injury from the blade, flying stones, and other debris.

Operation Steps	*Explanation*
4. Procedure to start engine.	a. Open gasoline shut-off valve located near bottom of gasoline tank.
	b. Open gasoline throttle slightly.
	c. Close choke on carburetor.
	d. Crank engine with rope starter, foot pedal starter, or hand crank provided.
	e. When engine starts gradually open choke valve until engine runs smoothly with choke open.

NOTE

1. When engine is difficult to start, operator should check the following:
   a. No fuel in gasoline tank.
   b. Improper choking.
   c. Throttle valve stuck or improperly adjusted.
   d. Throttle rod loose.
   e. Loose cr defective wiring.
   f. Cracked spark plug.
2. If operator cannot start engine he should notify his supervisor.

5. Proceed to work area.	a. Open throttle to speed engine up slightly.
	b. Engage the propelling clutch.
	c. Control forward speed of mower by opening or closing throttle.

PRECAUTIONS

1. Be sure all clutches are disengaged before starting engine.

2. The engine exhaust contains carbon monoxide gas which although colorless and odorless is a deadly poison. Be sure that engine is permitted to run only in well-ventilated areas.

3. Do not wrap starting cord around hand or wrist, or place thumb on opposite side of crank handle from palm of hand when cranking engine. This will avoid injuries which might result if the engine should backfire.

Operation Steps	*Explanation*

Step 2—Cut Grass

1. Start machine and operate.	a. Engage reel or rotating blade clutch, if mower is equipped with one.
	b. Engage propelling clutch.
	c. Control forward speed of mower by opening or closing gasoline throttle.
	d. Overlap previous swath about two inches.
2. Stop machine.	a. Disengage propelling clutch.
	b. Disengage reel clutch, if any.
	c. Close gasoline throttle.
	d. Press grounding spring against top of spark plug and hold in this position until engine has stopped.

PRECAUTIONS

1. Be sure to pick up stones or other solid objects in the path of the mower before mowing grass.

2. Always stop engine before cleaning or working near the reel or rotating blade.

3. Be careful to avoid letting foot slip under guard of rotating blade while blade is in motion.

4. Always stop engine and leave propelling clutch engaged if there is any possibility of mower moving when it is out of gear and operator is away from the controls.

5. Do not permit mower to run into or strike against any object.

6. Check oil and gasoline every four hours.

7. Be sure to remove wire from spark plug before attempting to make adjustments or haul the lawn mower.

Step 3—Returning Equipment and Materials to Storage

Return all equipment and unused materials to storage location.	a. Gather all pieces of equipment and materials and proceed to designated gear room.
	b. Brush off accumulated grass and wipe power lawn mower, except the engine, with a dry cloth.
	c. Use radiator brush to remove any dirt or grass that has accumulated

Operation Steps　　　　　　　　　*Explanation*

on fly-wheel housing or between the cylinder fins of engine.

d. Comb tufts of radiator brush out straight. Store on a flat surface so that tufts will be flat.

e. Rinse out wiping cloths used (or, if dirty, wash in warm detergent solution), wring and place for drying.

f. Return all unused oil and gasoline, and other materials to their proper storage.

PRECAUTIONS

1. Make sure gasoline is kept and stored in approved safety cans.
2. Oil must be stored in closed metal containers with covers securely in place.
3. Be sure to close gasoline shut-off valve.
4. Notify supervisor when lawn mower, or engine, is in need of adjustment, servicing or repair.
5. When not in use, park machine in a well-ventilated area that is clear of combustibles.

15 / **PAINTS**

(*Sources: Buildings* magazine, November 1958, 1959, 1960; "Guide to Paint Selection and Application" by J. E. Spector, *American Machinist* magazine, March 20, 1961)

Color and light can do much to build efficiency in an office or plant. Good color and lighting can relax tensions, improve morale, stimulate output, decrease absenteeism. Colors should not be distracting or disturbing. Such colors will pull the employee's attention from his work and leave him staring at the wall. It usually costs no more to use a color correctly.

Paint Formulation

The two basic ingredients in paint are pigment and vehicle. The pigment consists of small particles of several types of opaque materials which perform a number of functions including color, hiding power, and protection from deterioration from the sunlight.

The binder or vehicle is the liquid portion of the paint and contains two basic components, the thinner and solvent. The thinner is the volatile part of the paint. After application, it evaporates, leaving behind the solid paint film. The purpose of the thinner is to reduce the viscosity of the paint so that it can be spread easily and uniformly. In solvent based paints, the thinners are organic materials, such as turpentine, mineral spirits or naphtha. These materials are largely responsible for the odor associated with paint.

The binder has the important function of binding the pigment particles into a uniform paint film. The nature and amount of binder determines the important properties of the paint, such as washability, toughness, adhesion, aging stability and resistance to abrasion, scrubbing, weathering and corrosive chemicals. Linseed oils, soya oil, dehydrated castor oil, and alkyd resins or varnishes are commonly used binders in solvent thinned paints. Some of the binders used in latex paints are butadiene-styrene, polyvinyl acetate and acrylic resins. These binders are not actually dissolved in the thinner, but are dispersed in the form of tiny particles.

Emulsion Paints

Water emulsion paints are easy to apply and are quick drying. Of these, acrylic and polyvinyl acetate are probably the most widely used.

Drying time: Both acrylic and polyvinyl acetate paints are dry to the touch and ready for the second coat in less than an hour. Therefore, two coats can be applied to a large room in less than a day.

Color Stability: Color retention is good for both indoor and outdoor applications. Much of this color stability is due to the light resistant nature of both binders. Since the binder is colorless, the true pigment colors come through with exceptional clarity.

Odor Characteristics: Both of these paints have a mild odor which dissipates as soon as the film is dry.

Moisture Permeability: This property enables the paint film to breathe. Therefore moisture, one of the common causes of failure due to blistering and peeling, can pass through the paint film.

Application Conditions: Both paints can be applied without difficulty under unfavorable atmospheric conditions, including high humidity. A freshly dried coat will be impervious to water spotting in case of rain.

Surfaces

Preparation. Any material that will interfere with the adhesion of paint to the surface should be removed. On new work, the dirt should be brushed off, then dusted. To prepare a surface for repainting, all dirt, grease, loose or peeling paint and other foreign matter should be removed. The surfaces should be clean and dry. Rust must be removed from metal and a proper primer used. Wax must be removed from floors, as it interferes with the adhesion of the paint, and will delay the drying. Peeling paint on exterior wood surfaces is generally due to moisture getting behind the paint. Proper treatment requires the removal of all loose paint, and correction of the moisture condition, or the peeling will likely recur.

Wood. The first coat of paint for wood should be chosen primarily for adhesion and for a base for further coats. For interior use, enamel under-coaters are very satisfactory, giving an excellent surface for finish coats. For exterior use, where wood may be expected to swell and shrink with moisture changes to a greater extent than inside, house paint primers should be used.

Metal. The first coat of paint for metal should act to prevent corrosion of the metal, as well as furnish a base for future paint coats. When repainting, remove any rust with steel wool or a wire brush. For iron and steel, anti-corrosive primers containing red lead or zinc yellow, acts to prevent the spread of corrosion, if the paint is damaged mechanically. Other primers, usually containing iron oxide are used when corrosive conditions are less severe.

Old aluminum should be cleaned of any dirt and loose oxide by brushing or sanding. Follow this with a coat of zinc chromate metal primer and then with exterior metal primer followed by exterior metal enamel. To keep the original metal color, use a clear varnish or one of the special metal lacquers. *New aluminum* should first be treated with a phosphoric acid compound containing grease solvents.

Copper, brass and *bronze* do not rust, but rain water running down from these metals will stain the masonry or paint below. It is easier to give the metals a protective coat of lacquer or varnish than to remove the stains later.

Zinc dust-zinc oxide paints do best on galvanized metal. These primers are also very satisfactory on iron and steel in special cases and are often used on the interior of water tanks.

Masonry. On brick, concrete, stucco, plaster, and similar masonry surfaces, the principal problem is the free alkali which attacks and softens oil base coatings. A suitable primer which seals the alkali primer permits the use of any desired finished coat. Certain masonry paints are made of an oil or varnish base, fortified with resin, and these give excellent results where conditions are not too severe. However, when the maximum alkali resistance is called for, paints based on a solution of a synthetic rubber resin, or portland cement based paints are preferred.

Bituminous coatings. Asphalt or coal-tar pitch tend to dissolve in most paint solvents, "bleeding" into the succeeding coats and discoloring them. For this reason, bituminous coatings are preferred for such surfaces unless the desired color cannot be obtained with bitumens. In this case, a water dispersed primer, usually a latex, is necessary, since the solvent does not dissolve the bitumen.

Asbestos cement. Painting asbestos-cement shingles, siding and sheeting presents a problem because the alkali in the cement often combines with oil paint to make a soluble soap that harms the paint film. The following methods are recommended:

1. Solvent thinned resin coating with the resin being a derivative or modification of rubber. Chlorinated rubber paints are an example of this type. Solvent thinned resin coatings have the advantages of extreme water resistance,

stain resistance, protection of metal fittings from corrosion, good abrasion resistance and excellent hiding power.

2. The use of specially formulated resin coating as a primer, followed by conventional oil or alkyd resin base topcoats. They are sold as asbestos shingle primer, alkali resistant primer, etc.

3. The use of two coats of exterior latex paint. The principal advantages of the latex paints are ease of application, rapid dry satisfactory application on damp surfaces, easy cleaning of painting equipment in water, and transmission of interior water vapor so that blistering of the paint film is uncommon.

There are oil vehicle masonry paints containing modified linseed or other oils that reduce the alkali sensitivity of the oils. On weathering asbestos-cement siding, they will give satisfactory performance, but if there is doubt as to the degree of weathering, a solvent thinned primer should be used as a base.

Walls and ceilings. For walls and ceilings flat paints are usually chosen because of better hiding power and more uniform distribution of reflected light. Flat paints are usually based on alkyd resins, which are thinned by paint solvents, or on emulsions (styrene butadiene, polyvinyl acetate, or acrylic) which are water thinned. The choice between alkyd and latex is largely a matter of personal preference. The alkyd paints usually have slightly better hiding power and are more washable, especially early in the life of the film. Latex paints have slightly less odor during and, being water thinned, cleanup of tools, drips, etc. is easier.

Where a high degree of washability and resistance to abrasion and marring is required, semigloss finishes are usually used. Diet kitchens and washrooms are best finished in such coatings. Gloss finishes have the best washability and resistance to abrasion and water. Semigloss finishes have a higher hiding power and less tendency to show up defects in the underlying surfaces.

The color of walls, ceilings and trim is a matter of personal preference. The light reflection of such surfaces is part of the lighting of the room and must be taken into consideration. The lighting has usually been designed for surfaces of a certain reflection and, unless repainting is kept within the same range, the light distribution of the room will be thrown out of balance.

Wall coatings are sometimes done in multicolor paints. One or more colors can be applied in a single operation. Most of these are sprayed on, but some formulations can be applied with rollers. These multicolor paints give an extremely tough chip and scratch resistant textured finish, and because of the random distribution of color flecks, do not show dirt and other marks. They can withstand repeated scrubbings.

Ceilings (acoustical). Emulsion type coatings are recommended. They should be brushed so as not to fill the small diameter holes. Since they are flat, they do not add any glare for the lighting.

Exteriors. Where long life and little or no exposure to abrasion or standing water is likely to be encountered, the conventional house paints, based on mixed pigments, are the best selection. Where industrial fumes are prevalent, a lead free paint will avoid staining from hydrogen sulfide.

Paints to be used above or next to brick surfaces should be of a nonchalky type to prevent staining of the brick.

Trim paints are used where high gloss and extreme color retention are required, and exterior enamels are preferred for outdoor furniture and for metal surfaces, over a good primer.

If a suitable sealer is used on masonry, any good exterior paint will usually give satisfactory service as a finish coat, but it is usually safer to use a finish coat, latex or synthetic rubber, designed for exterior masonry. Cement water paints are also excellent.

Where a clear coating for brick or stone is required, water repellent solutions, usually silicones are available.

Natural coatings for exterior wood are usually varnishes, oils or stains. None of these have a life comparable with conventional pigmented coatings, but, if refinished at suitable intervals, will give satisfactory service.

Special insecticides in powdered form are available for adding to paint, making it effective for killing insects such as ants, flies, roaches, mosquitoes, etc., that come in contact with the surface.

Roofs. Roofs of most general concern will be either of galvanized metal or of an asphalt-felt composition. Galvanized metal requires a special zinc dust-zinc oxide primer, which can be followed by any tough paint. It should be remembered that any pastel colors or natural aluminum will help reduce under-roof temperature by reflecting sun heat.

Since the solvent in conventional paints will often attack the asphalt roofing, they should not be used. There are a number of special roofing paints formulated for this purpose which will give protection to roofing material from the sun, heat, and moisture. Colored aluminum roofing paints can also be used. Many of the exterior latex products can be used over this type of roof. Light colors, which will have to be renewed more frequently, will also reduce heat absorption.

Interior surfaces. Interior surfaces to be painted must be clean and free of any foreign matter that will prevent the paint film from bonding with the surface.

Procedures for preparing an interior surface for painting and for applying the paint itself vary with the type of paint. The best recommendations are those provided by the manufacturer for using his product. The following tips are applicable for most interior paint types under normal conditions.

Interior Paints and Their Qualities

1. *Cumar:* Alkali and acid resisting, this paint will not "burn" aluminum powder flakes, and is often preferred as an aluminum heat-resisting and interior coating.

2. *Ester Gum:* This is a good water and fade resistant paint.

3. *Alkyd:* Color and gloss retention are two of alkyd's outstanding qualities. It is also weather and water resistant.

4. *Phenolic:* Phenolic is fast drying, and has good weather, water and chemical resistance, although it usually chalks easily and often yellows in white formulation.

5. *Epoxy:* Outstanding hardness and chemical resistance are attributed to epoxy. However, it is often low on elasticity and weather resistance.

6. *Maleic:* This fast drying paint is usually harder than ester gum and holds color better than cumar.

7. *Silicone:* Silicone has outstanding water resistance and slickness, but it is often difficult to make subsequent paint coats adhere.

8. *Latex:* This paint has outstanding washability and color stability but usually needs about thirty days for complete curing.

9. *Synthetic Rubber:* Excellent resistance to chemicals, alkali, acids and abrasion are the desired qualities in this paint, but usually has little resistance to petroleum solvents.

High temperatures. Where temperatures in the 200 degree range are encountered, the acrylic enamels should be used. They should be applied over a clean, non-primed surface since no moisture will ever be present and because acrylics, due to the hot solvent in them, will not tolerate a conventional primer under them.

For temperatures above 400 degrees, such as engine exhaust manifolds, mufflers and boiler stacks, a silicone type coating is recommended. The service life of such material is sometimes considered in direct proportion to the cleanliness of the surface to which it is applied. Generally where such surfaces are sandblasted, they average two years of service life.

Water storage tanks. The tanks should be sandblasted and coated with vinyls or red lead primer in a phenolic resin with a compatible finish coat of aluminum. If this painting can be accomplished before the tank is put into service, the effective life will, in most cases, exceed fifteen years. Although the expense is high initially, it more than pays for itself over the years due to reduced maintenance cost.

Cooling towers. Cooling tower piping should be sandblasted and coated prior to installation. Assuming that the cooling tower piping has been sandblasted, several coatings can be used. The best is zinc enriched inorganic coating. Next to the zinc enriched coatings are the polyamid epoxies which, when properly applied with a film thickness of eight to fourteen mils, will insure a performance life of several years. Where a tower cannot be shut down, merely get the pipe as dry as possible, then rig a tarpaulin as a wind and spray breaker and apply a red lead primer followed by an asphalt mastic. If desired, apply a finish coat of aluminum or any other color, after the mastic has had sufficient time for the entrapped solvent to evaporate.

Primers. The use of primers in buildings for maintenance painting is generally regulated to equipment located in the basement or on the roof, with very little other metal being involved. In general, wherever a highly corrosive condition is encountered, such as moisture and constant dripping, a red lead or slow drying primer is recommended, preferably two coats, followed by the desired finish color on alkyd resin. Otherwise the corrosion is not a problem and a quick drying primer is usually satisfactory when applied in two coats with a finish coat of the desired color.

Thinners. Usually no difficulty is experienced with the use of thinners, except when too much is used in a given quantity of paint. Paint containers invariably show the thinner to be used. Contract painters should not be allowed to over-thin a material in order to stretch out the square footage, subsequently giving a thinner film and a shorter satisfactory service life.

Application. Paint may be applied by brush, spray, or roller. The method to be used depends on the type of surface, the area involved, the type of paint, and the problems of cleanup. Certain types of paints including lacquers and the fast drying coatings are designed for spray application only. This is also true of most multicolor finishes. Small areas and irregular surfaces are usually done best with a brush. Rollers work best on large and fairly uniform surfaces.

Storage. The storage of paints is not difficult, especially if the building is air-conditioned. Extremes of heat and cold should be avoided, and paints should not be stored near fires or open flames. When paint is stored, it should be maintained in temperatures of 60° F. to 90° F. Emulsion type paints will take several freezing cycles before they are unfit for use. Some types of coatings, particularly those with a phenolic resin, will have chemical reaction take place in the container when they are stored in temperatures exceeding 115° F.

Unopened containers should be inverted periodically, to avoid breaking up any skin which may have formed.

Some paints, particularly dark colors, tend to lose drying properties in storage, and material which has been on hand for some time should be tested for drying properties before use. If the paint does not dry readily, the addition of a small amount of drier will correct the difficulty.

Brushes and rollers should be cleaned with a suitable solvent after use. If they are not to be used within a short period of time, they should be washed out with soap and water, wrapped in paper and stored, either laying on their sides or hanging up. If brushes or rollers are to be used presently, they may be suspended in a suitable solvent. Under no circumstances should brushes stand on the bristles.

Rags and drop cloths should be spread out to dry, particularly if they are soaked with oil, or stored in a tightly closed container. Wadded up rags will heat up, from oxidation of the oils, and under favorable conditions, may ignite.

Glossary of Paint Terms

Acid. Any chemical compound containing one or more hydrogen atoms available for reaction with active metals or alkaline solutions.

Acid number. The number of milligrams of potassium hydroxide required to neutralize the free fatty acid in one gram of fat, oil, wax, or resin.

Acrylic acid. Colorless, organic liquid which polymerizes to a hard solid when heated.

Acrylic resins. Family of synthetic resins made by polmerizing esters of acrylic acid.

Alkali. Substance that neutralizes acids; highly destructive to oil paint films.

Alkyd. Generic name indicating a family of synthetic materials formed from a complex organic acid and an alcohol.

Alligatoring. Condition of a painted surface caused by improper buildup.

Barium sulphate. Heavy, white crystalline extender pigment.

Binder. The non-volatile portion of a paint vehicle which serves to bind or cement the pigment particles together.

Bleeding. When coloring material from either the wood or undercoat works up into succeeding coats and imparts to them a certain amount of color.

Blistering. Formation of bubbles on the surface of paint film, usually caused by moisture. Also caused by excessive heat.

Bloom. Condition of clouding or fogging of paint film, usually caused by reactive materials in paint film coming into contact with dust, oil, deposits from gases in the air or soluble matter in rain.

Blushing. Applied to lacquers when they become flat or opaque and white on drying. Usually occurs when applied in a humid atmosphere.

Brushability. Adaptability of paint to application with a brush.

Body coat. Intermediate coat of paint between priming and finishing.

Calcimine. A paint composed essentially of calcium carbonate or clay, and glue.

Casein. Protein obtained from milk, soluble in alkaline water solution.

Casein paints. Paint in which casein solution has replaced binder.

Chalking. Presence of loose powder on surface of paint.

Checking. Formation of short narrow cracks in surface of film.

Coagulation. Precipitation of colloids into single mass; usually caused by excessive heat or catalytic agents.

Coating. All material which has been spread as film over surface while in fluid condition and which remains upon surface.

Cohesion. Attractive force between polymers of similar nature which tends to hold them together.

Colloid. Composed of ultramicroscopic particles of solid, liquid or gas dispersed in a different medium.

Color-in-oil. A paste formed by mixing a color pigment in linseed or other oil. Used for tinting.

Copolymer. Product obtained when two different monomers are polymerized or linked together chemically to yield a resin.

Copolymerization. Simultaneous polymerization of two compounds which have properties different from polymer obtained with either monomer separately.

Cracking. Form of paint failure in which breaks in film extend through all coats down to building material.

Crazing. Hairline cracks in paint film.

Cure. Toughening or hardening of paint film.

Dimer. Formed by chemical combination of two similar molecules.

Dispersed. Finely divided or colloidal in nature.

Dispersing agent. Material used to aid in holding finely divided matter in dispersed state.

Dispersion. Generic term describing any heterogeneous system of solids gases or liquids.

Drier. Composition of certain metals that accelerates drying action of oil when added to paint or varnish.

Drying oils. Vegetable or animal oils which, when applied as film, absorb oxygen and dry to a relatively tough, elastic coating.

Efflorescence. A deposit of water soluble salts on the surface of masonry or plaster caused by the dissolving of salts present in the masonry.

Emulsifier. Material which, when added to mixture of dissimilar materials will produce stable emulsion.

Emulsion. A preparation in which very fine particles of liquid such as oil, are suspended in another, such as water.

Enamel. Special type of paint made with varnish or lacquer as the vehicle.

Extender. Pigment of low hiding power; may contribute desirable properties to paint products, such as improved flow and sheen control.

Fade-o-Meter. Mechanism used to artificially reproduce effect of sunlight on paint.

Failure. Commonly used to describe condition of paint film at end of useful life.

False body. Describes characteristic of paint which becomes viscous on standing but thins down on stirring.

Flaking. Detachment of small pieces of paint film.

Flashing. Nonuniform appearance on surfaces in which coating dries with spotty differences of color or gloss.

Flash point. Lowest temperature at which mixture in an open vessel gives off enough vapors to produce momentary flash of fire when small flame is passed near surface.

Flatting agent. In oil paints, a soap added to paints to reduce gloss.

Floating. Separation or layering of pigment in mixture of pigment.

Flocculate. Agglomeration of undispersed pigment particles.

Ghosting. Patches of lighter color showing in dry coat.

Hiding power. Ability of paint to obscure surface.

Holidays. Unintentional missing of areas of surface being painted.

Incompatible. Describes material which cannot be mixed with another material without damaging original properties.

Intumesce. To foam, swell, froth or bubble up as a result of heat, liquid, air or chemical action.

Lacquer. A material that dries by the evaporation of the thinner or solvent.

Latex. Generic term describing any of many relatively stable dispersions of submicroscopic, insoluble resin particles in a water system.

Lifting. Buckling of finish coat when applied over previous coat which is not yet dry, or when solvents in second coat are too strong.

Mil. Unit of thickness, 1/1000 inch.

Monomer. Organic compound capable of polymerizing or linking together.

Pigment Volume Concentration (P.V.C.). This represents value obtained by dividing volume of pigment by total volume of solids in dry film.

Polymer. High molecular weight material composed of large number of repeating units of monomer linked together.

Polymerization. Type of reaction resulting in linkage of monomers to form high molecular weight polymers.

Polyvinyl Acetate Latex (PVA). Latex composed primarily of vinyl acetate.

Rain spots. Describes defects on paint film caused by rain.

Resin. A solid or semi-solid organic material of either natural or synthetic origin.

Sagging. Wet paint film which tends to flow downward and become thicker in some areas.

Sheen. Special type of gloss measured in terms of reflected light at an angle of 30 degrees or less.

Solvents. Defines products used to dissolve film-forming constituents; volatilize during drying and do not become part of film.

Spreading rate: Area of surface over which unit volume of paint will spread, usually expressed in square feet per gallon.

Varnish. Any homogeneous, clear liquid which forms film on curing.

Vehicle. Liquid portion of paint.

Water-based paints. Misnomer; no paint employs water as a permanent, film-forming base.

Applying Paint to Metal

The accompanying chart is applicable to most of all problems of applying paint to metal, and can be used as a basic guide.

Special problems, especially those involving high production painting, should be carefully worked out with a paint manufacturer's representative to insure maximum surface life, ease of application and minimum cost.

APPLICATION OF PAINT

Items	Surface Preparation	Primer Coat	Type of Finish Coat
Constant Exposure—Outdoors			
1. *Top Abuse.* Cutting, pushing, lifting, scuffing, etc.	Remove all loose scale, rust, and foreign matter.	Polyamide Epoxy	Polyamide Epoxy
2. *Medium Abuse.* Guard rails, covers, housings, etc.	Remove all loose scale, rust, and foreign matter.	Epoxy	Epoxy
3. *Occasional Abuse.* Switch panel doors, light standards, etc.	Wire brush, remove all loose matter.	Containing Keytoxine compounds	Industrial enamel
4. *Weathering only.* Iron grillwork, metal canopies, light hoods, etc.	Wire brush, remove all loose matter.	Containing Keytoxine compounds	Industrial enamel
5. *Construction equipment.*	Wire brush or sandblast.	Enamel undercoat	Alkyd enamel
Marine Equipment			
1. Metal parts on shore, exposed to salt spray.	Remove all loose scale, rust, and foreign matter.		

APPLICATION OF PAINT (*continued*)

Items	Surface Preparation	Primer Coat	Type of Finish Coat
2. Metal parts exposed to fresh water.	Wire brush, and remove all loose material.	Rubber base	Rubber base
3. *Boats.* Submerged or exposed parts.	Wire brush surface as clean as possible.	Chlorinated rubber	Chlorinated rubber

Number of Coats				
Prime	Finish	Method of Application	Drying Time (Hours)	Approx. Life Expectancy (Years)
1	1	Brush, roller, spray	2-4	5
1	1	Brush, roller, spray	2-4	5
1	1	Brush, spray	4-6	2-3
1	1	Brush, spray	4-6	2-3
1	2	Brush, spray	4-6	1-2
1	2	Brush, spray	4-6	1-2
1	1	Brush, spray	1-2	1-2

Items	Surface Preparation	Primer Coat	Type of Finish Coat
Indoor Plant and Office Equipment and Furnishings			
1. Storage facilities, lockers, closets.	Wire brush, remove loose particles.	Enamel undercoat	Alkyd enamel
2. Materials handling equipment, rough use.	Wire brush, remove loose particles.	Enamel undercoat	Alkyd enamel
3. Floor trucks, cranes, other powered equipment.	Wire brush, remove loose particles.	Enamel undercoat	Alkyd enamel
4. Components subject to scuffing—elevator doors, kick plates, shelf surfaces, metal stair treads.	Remove loose matter, wash with mineral spirits.	Epoxy	Epoxy
5. Machine tools.	Wire brush, remove loose particles.	Enamel undercoat	Alkyd enamel
6. *Large surfaces.* Grillwork, metal partitions, canopies.	Remove loose matter, wash with mineral spirits.	Epoxy	Epoxy

Number of Coats				
Prime	Finish	Method of Application	Drying Time (Hours)	Approx. Life Expectancy (Years)
1	1	Brush, spray	4-6	3-5
1	2	Brush, spray	4-6	2-3

APPLICATION OF PAINT (*continued*)

Number of Coats		Method of Application	Drying Time (Hours)	Approx. Life Expectancy (Years)
Prime	Finish			
1	1	Brush, spray	4-6	3-5
1	1	Brush, roller, spray	2-4	2-3
1	1	Brush, spray	4-6	3-5
1	1	Brush, roller, spray	2-4	2-3

Items	Surface Preparation	Primer Coat	Type of Finish Coat
Atmospheric Abuse			
1. *General acid.* Plating rooms, textile finishing, electrolytic processes.	If possible, sandblast.	100 per cent Solids epoxy	Cut top coat 20 per cent
2. *Alkali.* Salt spray.	If possible, sandblast.	100 per cent Solids epoxy	Cut top coat 20 per cent
3. *Fine abrasive particles.* Grinding, milling.	If possible, sandblast.	100 per cent Solids epoxy	Cut top coat 20 per cent
4. *Petroleum.* Petro-chemicals, coal and coke products, organic residues.	If possible, sandblast.	100 per cent Solids epoxy	Cut top coat 20 per cent
Fabricated Metal Products			
1. Severe outdoor exposure.	Degrease and chemical etch.	Rust inhibitor, zinc chromate or chromate-oxide	Alkyd or alkyd-melamine
2. Expendable containers.	Remove visible dirt and grease.	None	Alkyd or alkyd-urea
3. Flat surfaces.	Degrease	None	Alkyd-urea or alkyd-melamine
4. Deep-drawn and curved surfaces, precoated. Deep-drawn and curved surfaces, after coated.	Degrease	None	Alkyd-urea or alkyd-melamine

Number of Coats		Method of Application	Drying time (Hours)	Approx. Life Expectancy (Years)
Prime	Finish			
1	1	Brush, spray	2-4	3-4
1	1	Brush, spray	2-4	3-4
1	1	Brush, spray	2-4	3-4
1	1	Brush, spray	2-4	3-4

APPLICATION OF PAINT (*continued*)

Number of Coats Prime	Finish	Method of Application	Baking Time (Temperatures or Hours)	Approx. Life Expectancy (Years)
1	1	Spray, flow, dip, roller, curtain	275-350°F.	2-5
1		Spray, flow, dip, roller, curtain	275-350°F.	1 plus
1		Spray, flow, dip, roller, curtain	275-350°F.	Indefinite
1		Spray, flow, dip, roller, curtain	275-350°F.	Indefinite

Items	Surface Preparation	Primer Coat	Type of Finish Coat
Fabricated Metal Products (*continued*)			
5. *Sanitary products.* Often-cleaned surfaces in restaurants, kitchens, laboratories.	Degrease and chemical etch.	Epoxy or phenolic rust inhibiting chromate-oxide	Epoxy, vinyl, polyurethane, polyester
6. *Rigid metal goods.* Castings, forgings.	Degrease and chemical etch.	Rust inhibiting chromate-oxide	Alkyd-melamine, alkyd-urea, or epoxy
7. High temperature exposure.	Degrease and chemical etch.	Silicone-alkyd or straight silicone	Silicone-alkyd or straight silicone
8. Low temperature exposure.	Degrease and chemical etch.	Vinyl rust inhibiting type	Vinyl
9. High-gloss surface.	Degrease and chemical etch.	Sanding type rust inhibiting chromate-oxide	Alkyd-melamine or alkyd-urea
Consumer Goods			
1. *Toys*, for non-toxic finish.	Degrease	None	Lead free alkyd or lacquer
2. *Toys*, for scuff and bruise resistance. *Expendables:* pails, mops, inexpensive tools.	Wash and clean as well as possible.	None	Lead free alkyd enamel
3. *Metal furniture*, indoor, outdoor.	Wire brush. Remove rust, and loose matter.	None	Lead free alkyd enamel

APPLICATION OF PAINT *(continued)*

Number of Coats Prime	Finish	Method of Application	Baking Time (Temperatures or Hours)	Approx. Life Expectancy (Years)
1	1	Spray, flow, dip, roller, curtain	275-350°F.	2-5
1 (Spot Fill)		Spray, dip	275-300°F.	Indefinite
(Intermediate)	1 or 2	Spray, flow, dip, roller, curtain	375-450°F.	Indefinite
1	1	Spray, dip, roller, curtain	250-275°F.	Indefinite
1 or 2	1	Spray, curtain	250-300°F.	Indefinite
			Bake or Force Dry	
1		Spray, dip, roller, curtain	2-4	Indefinite
2		Brush, spray	2-4	1-2
2		Brush, spray	2-4	1-2

16 / **PARKING LOT LAYOUT**

Several factors must be taken into consideration in laying out a parking area. Some of these are:

1. Dimensions of the parking area.
2. The route by which the cars will enter and exit.
3. The average length of time each car is parked in the lot.
4. The number of times per day of car "turnover."

The installation of fences, gates, light standards, and over-the-walk driveways must all conform to the parking pattern selected.

Lots that are 76 feet and wider are usually laid out for angular parking. This is preferred because it is easier to park at an angle, and the circulation of cars are easier to control. The width of the driveway will determine the parking angle, which can vary from a 90° angle to a sharp 45° angle.

To design a good functional parking area, there should be little or no waste of pavement. The proper type of fences, gates, lighting, signs, reflective parking lines, directional arrows, and locations of entrances and exits should be given careful consideration. To eliminate damages by a car to any of these items, concrete stops are recommended to be located at the end of each space. These stops also aid as a guide in keeping the parking uniform.

The schematic drawing illustrates 60-degree diagonal parking on a lot approximately 100 feet by 150 feet. The dimensions shown in the table for 45, 55, 60 and 90-degree parking are the ones most used.

DIMENSION TABLE

Dimensions when parking at any of these angles:

		45°	50°	55°	60°	90°
Offset	A	18'	15'8"	13'4"	11'	1'6"
Car Space	B	12'	11'4"	10'8"	10'	8'7"
Stall Depth	C	16'	16'8"	17'4"	18'	18'6"
Stall Depth	D	18'	18'4"	18'8"	19'	19'
Overhang	E	2'	2'1"	2'2"	2'3"	2'9"
Driveway	F	13'	14'6"	16'	17'6"	25'
Turnaround	G	17'	16'	15'	14'	14'
Extra	H	6'	5'	4'	3'	0

To determine the number of cars that can be parked in each of the four banks:

1. Deduct the area lost in parking the first car. (Dimension "A" in the illustration.)

2. Then divide the car space (dimension "B") into the total length of each bank of cars, plus the extra factor "H", if there is any extra space.

Lot Layout
Economical Use of Parking Blocks

Figure 16-1

The shaded space of the parking lot may be used for planting. Dotted lines illustrate two large cars in parking position with alternate wheels against block—bumpers separated. Light standards are shown in drawing by "X".

Planting Seasons

Off season planting should be avoided whenever possible. Great care should be taken to move trees or shrubs successfully at seasons ordinarily regarded as unfavorable. Often when they are set out during the wrong season, they will survive only after a heavy cutting back, and will remain in a very depleted condition, giving little or no leaf effect until the following natural spring growing season. Therefore, nothing is gained, and the expense is increased by the necessity of utilizing more carefully and laborious moving methods and by the lengthening of the period of artificial watering.

Trees

A good maintenance program will include: (1) pruning, (2) spraying, (3) fertilizing, (4) mulching, (5) leaf disposal, and (6) drainage.

Pruning. The shaping of a tree, and the removal of excess growth is generally called pruning. This is only done to the degree necessary to balance the top of the tree to the root system. The roots must have the ability to supply moisture to the leaf area, or it may die or drop its leaves. A tree should be kept to its natural shape as much as possible. All pruning should be done vertically to the direction of growth.

Figure 17-1

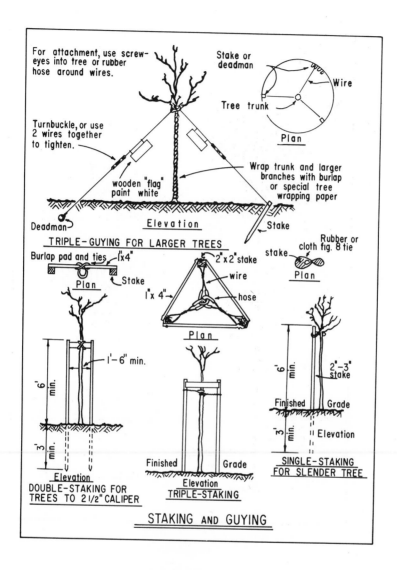

Figure 17-2

Pruning equipment should be kept sharp and clean. When moving from one tree to another, the equipment should be cleaned with alcohol to prevent the transmittal of possible disease.

Spraying. In the early spring, a dormant spray should be applied before the tree is in bud, and when the temperature is higher than 40°. Generally one or two additional sprays are required during the growing season for the control of insects.

Fertilizing. Either a liquid or solid fertilizer is used in the spring of each year. Good leafage and rapid wooded growth are the results of fertile soil.

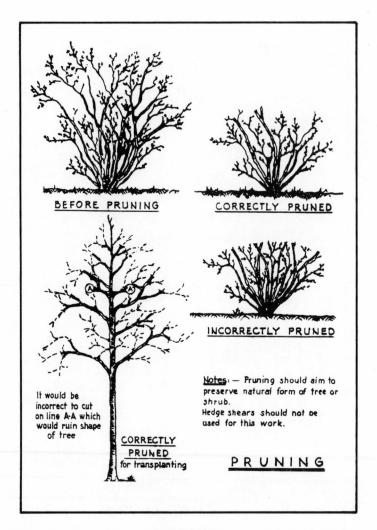

Figure 17-3

Where tree roots are located under lawns, they should be fertilized. Fertilizers containing a large proportion of nitrogen are desirable because nitogen is the element contributing most to the leaf growth.

Mulching. Mulching is the practice of covering the ground around the tree trunk with a substance to prevent weed growth, washing away of soil, and to retain moisture. Materials used for mulching are peat moss, peanut shells, and leaves. *Leaves* contain plant food where the others do not, and they are known to furnish some nutritive elements.

Drainage. Most plants will die if the soil about them remains saturated for any great length of time. If plants are not capable of enduring such conditions, drainage must be provided.

Figure 17-4

Shrubs

A good maintenance program will include: (1) spraying, (2) fertilizing, (3) mulching, (4) trimming, and (5) snow protection.

As indicated in the recommendations for trees, a dormant spray should be used, and either a liquid or solid fertilizer applied in the early spring. The amount of fertilizer used is based on the size and kind of shrub. The ground around the shrub should have leaf mulch or peat moss to prevent weed growth.

Depending upon the type of shrub, from one to three trimmings may be required each growing season. Trimming equipment should be kept sharp and clean. When moving from one shrub to another, the cutters should be cleaned with alcohol to prevent the transmittal of possible disease.

In areas that receive snow, shrubs should be bound with chicken wire or similar material in the late fall of the year. This will prevent the shrubs from becoming broken or spread apart by the snow.

(*Source:* U. S. Department of Health, Education and Welfare, Washington, D. C.)

18A / **CONTROL OF INSECTS**

Domestic Flies

Domestic flies are pests and may transmit diarrhea, dysentery, typhoid, and other human diseases. Some bite man. Fly larvae may infest human flesh or intestines, and stored food.

Environmental Control: Wrap drained garbage, and store in rustproof cans with tight lids. Collect garbage at least twice weekly, using covered trucks. Dispose of all refuse in sanitary landfills or efficient incinerators. Eliminate privies and animal shelters from city limits. Screen houses and restaurants.

Chemical Control: Where adult flies congregate, use residual sprays (5 percent DDT indoors, 5 percent malathion-12½ percent sugar outdoors at 1 gal./950 ft.²); space sprays (0.1 percent synergized pyrethrum or allethrin indoors at 8 oz./10,000 ft.³; 5 percent DDT, 1 percent lindane, or 3 percent malathion outdoors at 2.5 gal./acre). Install insecticide impregnated cord (10 percent parathion or 25 percent diazinon cord; at 30 linear ft./100 ft.² of floor; purchase cords ready made, do not attempt to manufacture), or larvicide (2 percent chlordane, 1 percent lindane, or 2.5 percent diazinon).

Mosquitoes

Mosquitoes suck blood and may transmit encephalitis and malaria in the United States. Yellow fever, filariasis, and other mosquito-borne diseases might be introduced without warning.

Environmental Control: Empty water from gutters, catch basins, rain barrels, tree holes, etc. Bury cans, jars, old tires, etc., in sanitary landfill. Drain or fill areas where water stands. Maintain a clean, weed-free shoreline on permanent standing water. Screen houses, schools, and workplaces.

Chemical Control: Use mosquito repellents (diethyltoluamide, indalone, Rutgers 612, or 622), residual sprays (5 percent DDT, 3 percent malathion at 1 gal./950 ft.²), space sprays (0.1 percent synergized pyrethrum or allethrin indoors at 8 oz./10,000 ft.³; 1 percent lindane or 3 percent malathion outdoors at 2.5 gal./acre), or larvicide (1.25 percent DDT or 0.625 percent malathion solution mists at 2 gal./acre). Higher concentrations endanger fish.

Cockroaches

Cockroaches are pests, produce unpleasant odors, and may nibble on sleeping children. They can transmit diarrhea, dysentery, tapeworms, and possibly other diseases. They destroy stored foods.

Environmental Control: Reduce structural harborage by eliminating cracks, crevices, dead spaces, etc. Store food and other products properly. Store, collect, and dispose of refuse in a sanitary manner. Watch for and destroy cockroaches and their egg-cases being introduced with groceries, furniture, firewood, plants, etc.

Chemical Control: Pin-stream spray insecticides (2.5 percent chlordane, 1 percent lindane, 2 percent malathion, or 0.5 percent diazinon emulsion) into cracks and crevices in walls, baseboards, furniture, fixtures, cabinets, and other places cockroaches hide. Blow finely-powdered silica gel, 5 percent chlordane dust, or 3 percent malathion dust into dead spaces, or on electric wires, fuse boxes, and other items which sprays might damage.

Lice

Lice bite severely causing skin irritation and sometimes a generalized toxic reaction. Body lice may transmit epidemic typhus, relapsing fever, and trench fever. Head and crab lice do not transmit disease. Rat lice, dog lice, and other nonhuman lice do not bite man. Disinfect louse bites immediately. If reaction is severe, consult a physician.

Environmental Control: Bathe frequently with hot soapy water to limit (but not eliminate) infestation. To control body lice, launder clothing, and press with a hot iron (ineffective against head or crab lice).

Chemical Control: Dust individuals with 10 percent DDT or 1 percent lindane. If dust is inadvisable because it marks infested individuals, use 12 percent benzyl benzoate shampoo or proprietary lindane ointment. Repeat treatment in seven days to destroy late-hatching lice as all eggs are not killed by initial treatment.

Bedbugs and Kissing Bugs

Bedbugs and Kissing Bugs may cause severe skin inflammation and distress. Kissing bugs may transmit Chagas disease, but bedbugs are not proven vectors of any human disease. Disinfect bites immediately. If bite reaction is severe, consult a physician.

Environmental Control: Watch for and eliminate bedbugs introduced with luggage, bedding or furniture. Eliminate cracks and crevices where bedbugs and kissing bugs harbor. Avoid bedroom furniture with wood-to-wood joints. Use pillows and mattresses with flat or French (not rolled) seams. Keep building free of rodents and other hosts of kissing bugs. These techniques will limit but not eliminate bedbug and kissing bug infestations.

Chemical Control: Spray infested dwellings with 5 percent DDT emulsion, giving special attention to cracks and crevices in and near beds and upholstered furniture. Thorough application is essential. Use 1 percent lindane on bugs which have become resistant to DDT.

Fleas

Fleas suck blood and may transmit murine typhus, plague, rat tapeworm, and dwarf tapeworm to man. Disinfect bites immediately.

Environmental Control: Vacuum clean floors weekly if pets are allowed in building. If pets get on upholstered furniture, vacuum clean it weekly. Change or wash animal bedding weekly. Keep premise free of domestic rodents and other small mammals.

Chemical Control: Dust infested houses, yards, and animals (except cats) with 5 percent DDT or 3 percent malathion. Dust cats with 3 percent malathion or 1 percent rotenone. Spray infested houses or yards with 5 percent DDT or 2 percent malathion emulsion. Always treat house thoroughly before leaving it empty for an extended period. Routine preventive dusting of pets will aid in keeping large infestations from developing.

Ticks

Ticks suck blood and may transmit spotted fever, tularemia, relapsing fevers, and other diseases to man. Toxic tick saliva may cause paralysis in man. Hard ticks harbor on and under vegetation, soft ticks, in or near the host's nest. Either may infest homes. Remove attached ticks with care. Disinfect the bite. In disease areas, or if bite reaction is severe, consult a physician.

Environmental Control: Fill cracks and crevices where soft ticks hide. Keep rodents and other mammals out of buildings. In hard-tick infested areas wear impregnated protective clothing; check each two hours for attached ticks; clear vegetation from paths and yards.

Chemical Control: Impregnate clothing (twenty-five percent benzyl benzoate emulsion; soak clothing; then air dry). Use diethyl-toluamide repellent. Residual spray (five percent DDT, two percent chlordane, 0.5 percent dieldrin, or 0.5 percent diazinon at one gallon per 950 ft.) or dust (ten percent DDT, four percent malathion at twenty pounds per acre) infested building and areas. Treat four-foot swaths along walkways. Dust pets (three percent malathion, one percent lindane, or one percent rotenone). Do not use lindane on cats.

Mites

Mites suck blood, causing severe skin irritation. Grocer's itch, straw itch, chigger dermatitis, and scabies result from mite attacks. Mites may transmit rickettsialpox to man in the United States. Scrub typhus and possibly epidemic haemorrhagic fever are important mite-borne diseases in Asia. Non-biting clover mites may infest houses in great numbers. If mite dermatitis is severe or associated with illness, consult a physician.

Environmental Control: Wear impregnated protective clothing in mite-infested areas. Keep birds, bats, and rodents from harboring in or near buildings. Clear vegetation from infested areas. Destroy mite-infested foods.

Chemical Control: Control chiggers and other field mites with residual sprays (five percent aramite, five percent ovex, two percent dieldrin, two percent malathion, or two percent chlordane at one gallon per 950 feet.), or dusts (ten percent aramite, ten percent ovex, two percent dieldrin, five percent chlordane, or five percent malathion at 20 pounds per acre). Use diethyl-toluamide repellent. Impregnate clothing as for ticks.

Scorpions, Spiders, and Centipedes

Scorpions, Spiders, and Centipedes inject venom. The only deadly spider in the United States, the black widow, is shiny black with an orange or red hour-glass on its underside. The bite of the brown spider, *Loxosceles,* may severely damage tissues. No deadly scorpions are found in the United States except in southern Arizona. Centipedes rarely bite man, and the reaction is usually mild. However, since venom reaction varies, consult a physician if stung by any scorpion or bitten by any spider or centipede.

Environmental Control: Remove boards, cardboard, and loose rocks, from basements and yards (wear gloves). Fill small holes, cracks, crevices, and other openings which might conceal these animals. Use ducks to eliminate scorpions. Sweep spider webs from porches, or wherever found weekly. Teach children to stay away from scorpions, spiders, and centipedes.

Chemical Control: Spray spiders and webs with one percent lindane or two percent chlordane. Spray two percent chlordane or 0.5 percent dieldrin where scorpions or centipedes hide.

18B / TERMITES AND THEIR CONTROL

(*Source:* General Services Administration, Washington, D. C.)

If termites are working in a building, it is most important that they be discovered and checked. The damage they create in their attack on wooden structures is seldom discovered until replacement is necessary. It is therefore recommended that all buildings be surveyed at least once a year.

Termites eat the interior of wood. They eat only the inside, however, leaving the outside shell to protect themselves. Working under cover in this way, their presence in a building may not be suspected until the winged forms appear. These winged forms, which swarm in great numbers in the spring and fall, are kings and queens—the "colonizing adults." After mating they shed their wings and retire to cracks and crevices in the ground to establish colonies. They are mostly black or brown, with whitish wings. (In the spring, and occasionally at other times, some species of ants also produce swarms of winged forms which might be mistaken for the winged termite. Ants can be distinguished from termites, however, by their slender wasp-like waists. Termites have such thick waists that the sides of their bodies are nearly parallel.)

Inspection

In the subterranean or ground-nesting termites, contact with the ground must be maintained in order for colonies to survive. If there is no wood in contact with the ground, shelter tubes made of earth are constructed by the termites, through or over the termite-proof materials, for the passage of worker termites from the nest in the ground to the woodwork of the building. If these tubes are broken or sealed up, their contact with the ground is broken and the termites in the wood will die.

Each termite colony consists of three forms or castes: the colonizing (winged) kings and queens; second and third form (wingless) kings and queens; and sterile workers and soldiers (also wingless). The colonizing king and queen work together in caring for and feeding their young until the workers are grown. It then becomes the workers' job to feed the rest of the colony on predigested food from their own bodies, consequently their appetites are enormous. The workers also must build the shelter tubes and excavate new galleries. They are practically colorless, rarely if ever exposed to light. The termite soldier's job is to defend the colony against invaders, the most frequent of which is the ant.

As soon as termites are discovered in a building the extent of infestation should be determined. The principal food of termites is cellulose, obtained from wood and other plant tissues. If they are attacking at isolated points (such as through cracks, or around pipe openings in a basement) spot treatment may be sufficient. If the soil from which they are attacking can be reached it should be saturated with soil poison, and any scraps of wood in the soil should be removed. Termite shelter tubes should be destroyed, and the cracks and openings sealed. Once work is started to control termites, inspections should be made at frequent intervals to make certain these tubes are not replaced.

Termites are destructive to the woodwork of buildings, telephone poles, fence posts, or any other wood in contact with the ground.

Structural Changes

If the infestation appears to be general, steps should be taken to block the termites from the building. The most effective and permanent means of accomplishing this objective is to make structural changes which will insulate all woodwork from the ground, and allow proper ventilation of all unexcavated areas enclosed by the foundation. All wood that has been structurally weakened should be replaced, preferably with wood that has been pressure-treated with pentachlorophenol. (Lumber dealers should be able to furnish treated wood.) Wood members that were formerly in contact with the soil should be placed on poured concrete bases. Voids, cracks or expansion joints in concrete or masonry under wood should be filled with cement grout, coal-tar pitch, or coal-tar plastic cement.

If the building has termite shields, they should be inspected to see that they are continuous, without breaks, and in good condition.

Soil Treatment

Chemicals toxic to subterranean termites can be used advantageously to check infestations present in the soil. They are useful in treating new building sites where termites have become established, as well as serving as a valuable adjunct to structural changes for checking infestation in buildings. Chemical treatments lack permanent value, however, and should not be considered as equivalent to proper structural methods. Satisfactory control in buildings cannot be expected where the chemicals are applied to or about wood that is left in contact with the ground.

Where large-scale soil poisoning is thought necessary, the soil about walls and piers, especially those of masonry construction, and about pipes, should be poisoned deeply enough to cover all possible points of termite entry. The treated barrier should be from eight to twelve inches wide.

The following steps should be taken in applying soil poisons to the soil adjacent to masonry foundations which extend more than thirty inches below the surface of the ground:

1. First dig a trench the width of a shovel and at least thirty inches deep. The chemical should be applied to the bottom of the trench until the soil appears saturated. As the earth is replaced, the same procedure should be followed at about six-inch intervals.

2. Under some conditions a combined "trench and bar-hole method" is advisable. In such cases a shallow trench twelve to fifteen inches deep is sufficient. Auger or rod holes, spaced at intervals of twelve to fifteen inches apart, are then extended down through the remaining soil to the footing. Soil poison is then poured in each hole to bring about complete saturation.

Chemical Control Methods

Caution: Be careful in handling soil poisons. (See General Safety Precautions and First Aid.)

1. *Sodium Arsenite.* An odorless, white powder, which, mixed one pound to a gallon of water, is allowed to soak into the soil as previously described. The solution is highly toxic to vegetation if allowed to come into contact with it. As sodium arsenite is water soluble, precautions should be taken against any possibility of poisoning wells, for it is also extremely poisonous to man and animals.

2. *Pentachlorophenol.* Used as a wood preservative and a soil poison for termite control. It is applied as a five per cent solution in a fuel oil type of carrier, and has a slight odor. The hands should be protected with rubber gloves when handling it, and precautions should be taken against any possibility of fire. Prepared five per cent solutions, as well as concentrates, are available on the market.

3. *Coal-tar Creosote.* A poison that is best applied by the trenching method, because the poison must be mixed thoroughly with the earth. Coal-tar creosote in light fuel oil (one part of creosote to one or two parts of fuel oil) may be used when odor or discoloration are not factors to be considered. It should be handled with caution as it is an irritant of skin and eyes. This also is made up commercially and can be purchased from local exterminators.

4. *Orthodichlorobenzene and Trichlorobenzene.* Two organic poisons which have vaporizing properties that enable them to permeate soils readily. They are particularly useful when applied by the bar-hole method where trenching is impractical. Both of them have a distinct odor, resembling that of paradichlorobenzene (clothes moth crystals), and are excellent penetrants. The vapor from these chemicals is irritating to the nose and eyes and, if sufficiently concentrated, may act as an anesthetic. They are usually diluted with three parts of fuel oil to one part of orthodichlorobenzene or trichlorobenzene. So far only light sandy soil have been treated by this method, and at present its use is restricted to such soils.

It is estimated that about one gallon of any of the above mentioned chemicals is required per linear foot of trench for treating foundations with deep footings, and one-half gallon for shallow footings.

General Safety Precautions and First Aid

Persons who handle termite poisons should protect themselves by wearing respirators, rubber gloves, and rubberized clothing. They should not allow the poison to come in contact with their eyes or skin, and if their clothing is accidentally wet with the poison they should have a change available. With the exception of sodium arsenite, which is dissolved in water, the poisons are dissolved in inflammable solvents. Thus, precautions against fire must also be observed until the solvents have evaporated. When working with these poisons in confined places, ventilation should be provided, as prolonged breathing of the fumes must be avoided.

All poisons should be kept under lock and key, with a responsible person in charge, and should be properly labelled.

If a poison is actually swallowed, *call the doctor immediately. Tell the doctor what poisons has been taken.*

Induce vomiting by giving the victim warm salt water in the proportion of one tablespoon of salt to one glass of warm water or warm soapy water (mild soap flakes shaken up in warm water to make good suds). If these substances do not cause vomiting, a cup of warm water containing one teaspoon of dry mustard may be given.

Vomiting should be induced repeatedly until the fluid coming from the stomach is clear. If it is necessary to induce vomiting after the person has had several glassfuls of the emetic, tickle the back of his throat.

It is most important to keep the victim warm and quiet while giving first aid. *If he stops breathing give artificial respiration at once.*

After everything possible has been done to dilute and remove the poison, a soothing drink, such as the raw whites of two or three eggs in a little water, one or two glasses of milk, or a thin paste of starch or flour and water should be given if the victim can swallow. A stimulating drink such as hot coffee may be helpful.

Note: Since prompt action is of greatest importance and because of the availability of warm water in most instances, the preparation of the above emetics may be greatly facilitated by previous packaging of the solid part of the emetics into amounts equivalent to one tablespoon (in the case of salt) or one teaspoon (in the case of dry mustard). Sufficient mild soap flakes should be packaged to make a good suds in a large glass of water (warm). These packages (at least six of each type) should be included in the equipment carried by persons engaged in the extermination work.

Wood Treatment

When termite-damaged wood is replaced, it is usually advisable to use lumber that has been pressure treated with pentachlorophenol or creosote. If pressure-treated lumber is not available the wood should at least be painted with two heavy coatings of pentachlorophenol or creosote. Wood in contact with the ground should be thoroughly impregnated to a retention of not less than ten pounds per cubic foot of wood. Wood which is not in contact with soil may be treated by immersion or by painting. Painting or immersion will not give the protection of pressure-treated wood, but will add years to the period of service.

In California, and in certain other parts of the country, wood is subject to attack by dry-wood species of termites. These insects unlike the subterranean species, are able to live in wood that has no contact with the ground. They do not build shelter tubes, and cannot be controlled by cutting off ground moisture, but must be attacked directly. When wood is found to be infested with them, a volatile chemical should be painted or sprayed on the surface. Chemicals suitable for this purpose are pentachlorophenol, creosote, trichlorobenzene or orthodichlorobenzene. If greater penetration of the wood is desired, small holes may be bored, connecting with the termite tunnels, through which the chemical may be injected. If preferred, a solid chemical such as paradichlorobenzene may be injected, and the holes plugged with wood putty or similar material. In regions where dry-wood termites are prevalent, building openings through which the flying termites might enter should be screened. Special attention should be given to attic openings, as the attic timbers of buildings frequently become infested by dry-wood termites.

Wood decay is caused by fungi, minute plants consisting of many microscopic threads. Termite damage can be distinguished from the decay caused by fungi without difficulty, as the termites follow the grain of the wood, eating out definite tunnels and leaving thin partitions between the tunnels, while fungi soften the wood and cause it to crumble. If both termites and decay fungi are at work in the same wood, the fungi softens the partitions between the termite tunnels.

The term "dry rot" is a misnomer, for most species of fungi cannot exist in wood unless there is some moisture present. Fortunately there are only two species of fungi that have the ability to carry their moisture with them when they go from moist to dry wood. If well-seasoned wood is used in buildings and it is protected from moisture, there is little likelihood of damage by fungi. Basically, protection measures against fungi are the same as those against termites.

18C / **CONTROL OF DOMESTIC RODENTS**

(*Source:* U. S. Department of Health, Education and Welfare, Washington, D. C.)

Public health workers of today do not experience the great outbreaks of plague which once brought suffering and death to millions of humans. Only rarely do they encounter murine typhus which was once widespread in the southern United States.

Rodent-Borne Diseases

Rodent-borne diseases are with us still—in our slums as well as in our finest homes, apartments, ships, trains, and aircraft. Rodents cause the following diseases: Salmonellosis, plague, murine typhus, leptrospirosis, rat-bite fever and tetanus, rickettsialpox, lymphocytic choriomeningitis, and listeriosis. In addition, rodents attack our stored food (three hundred million dollars worth annually), devouring some, contaminating and spoiling much more.

Salmonellosis. Bacterial food poisoning, can be initiated by rodent feces deposited on suitable foods. This is probably the commonest disease transmitted by domestic rodents in the United States at the present time.

Plague. A highly-fatal bacterial disease of mammals caused by *Pasturella pestis,* is transmitted from field rodent to field rodent by the bites of infected fleas. When the rodent disease-rate is high, plague may spill over into domestic rodents and thence to man. In heavily infected areas, occasional transmission may occur directly from field rodents to man.

Murine typhus. A rickettsial disease of rodents (especially rats) caused by *Rickettsia typhi,* is transmitted from rodent to rodent and to man by scratching infected flea feces into the skin. Occasional human cases occur when the domestic rat population is maintaining the disease at a moderately high rate.

Leptospirosis. Weil's disease, an acute systemic spirochetal disease of rodents caused by *Leptospira icterohaemorrhagiae,* is transmitted from rodent to rodent and to man by contact with infected urine. Cases occur in humans handling rodents or working in a wet environment; soldiers in combat, fish handlers, children playing in contaminated water.

Rat-bite fever. Is common in areas where domestic rodent populations are high. Danger of secondary infection and tetanus should be minimized by proper disinfection and treatment. Rat-bite fever, a bacterial disease of rodents caused by *Streptobaccillus moniliformis,* is transmitted from rat to rat and to man by biting.

Rickettsialpox. A febrile disease exhibiting a chicken-pox type rash, is caused by *Rickettsia akari* and transmitted from mouse to mouse and probably from mouse to man by a rodent mite (*Allodermanyssus sanguineus*). When mouse and mite populations are high, the disease may be carried into the human population in epidemic proportions.

Lymphocytic choriomeningitis. A virus infection of a house mouse, may occur in man with a marked variation in clinical symptoms. Transmission from mouse to mouse and to man is by means of food or dust contaminated with respiratory droplets or powdered feces of infected animals.

Listeriosis. Is a bacterial disease of rodents, ruminants, fowl, and man caused by *Listeria monocytogenes.* Transmission can probably occur from infected rodents to man through food and air contaminated with powdered rodent feces, although the epidemiology of the disease is still relatively known.

Control Methods

(*Source:* General Services Administration, Washington, D. C.; Fish and Wildlife Service, U. S. Department of the Interior, Washington, D. C.)

Measures for the permanent riddance of rats should be taken whenever practicable. They usually must be combined with destruction of the animals, and many times continual killing is the only practical method of control. Numerous materials and contrivances have been designed for rat destruction, but relatively few of them have proved to give complete satisfaction.

The most efficient known means of destroying rats, and the one most generally recommended, is poisoning. Success in poisoning rats depends largely upon the baits used and the methods of mixing and distributing them. The important requirement is to set out food that the rats will eat. Usually it is almost as difficult to get the animals to eat unpoisoned foods as those that are properly prepared and poisoned. For this reason the procedures recommended herein should be carefully followed. The fact is emphasized that all of the poisons considered herein are effective if properly used.

Preventive measures. The permanent exclusion of rats from a building is the ideal solution to the problem of rodent control, but unfortunately this can seldom, if ever, be achieved. Nevertheless, if not too costly, any measures directed to this end are worthwhile.

The first step to be taken in any rat control program is a thorough survey of the building premises. If the building has a masonry foundation it should be possible to close all openings by which rats might enter through the foundation. Concrete, metal sheeting, and ¼-inch hardware cloth are useful materials for this purpose. Doors that might otherwise be left open at night should have self-closing devices. Special attention should be given any cracks and crevices, such as the small openings around pipes. Such openings should be examined and closed with gratings. Exterior doors which are made of wood should, wherever possible, be covered with sheet metal or metal cloth to a height of 12 to 15 inches. All modern buildings and many of the older ones of permanent type construction can usually be treated in this way at very little cost.

Even after all openings, crevices, and cracks in a building have been closed, it is still possible for rats to enter a building. They can, for instance, enter the building in shipments of supplies. Once inside, the rats will remain and multiply if they are able to obtain food and find a nesting place.

The removal of food supply is an important measure in rat control. It places a limit on the number of rats which can exist in a building, and makes poisoning much easier, since rats take poisoned bait far more readily when hungry. Food stored within the building should either be in rat-proof containers or in rat-proof rooms. Garbage in or near the building should be kept in covered containers.

Materials which are stored in a building should be far enough off the floor to permit cleaning of floor space and other space which might be used for nesting by rats and other vermin. Spaces between walls and underneath floors can sometimes be made rat-proof by closing a few holes. The rat-proofing of interior walls is not recommended, however, unless it can be done economically.

Even after all these precautions have been taken, it is usually necessary to destroy rats within a building. Poisoned baits provide an efficient method for rat extermination. However, the use of poison has two disadvantages: it is dangerous to humans; and it sometimes causes rats to die in inaccessible places from which they cannot readily be removed. Danger to humans can be minimized by careful handling, or by use of the one rat poison (Red Squill) which is comparatively non-toxic to humans. To counteract unpleasant odors arising from the inaccessible remains of a dead rat, naphthalene flakes may be used. If a dead rat is known to be behind a wall, a small hole drilled through the wall at the approximate location of the rat will permit the pouring of naphthalene flakes through a funnel onto or in the immediate area of the remains. The hole should then be closed.

Either naphthalene flakes or a wick type room deodorant, placed in the vicinity of the objectionable odor, will help to mask the odor. Since the remains of the rat seldom give off an odor for more than three days after death, only temporary measures are necessary. Dead rats, whenever possible, should be disposed of in an incinerator or burned in a furnace.

If fumigation of rat burrows outside of a building becomes necessary, it is suggested that a licensed exterminator be employed.

Types of Poisons

Red Squill. Red Squill is a rat poison which has the advantage of being relatively harmless to humans and domestic animals. This is due to its acrid taste, and also to the fact that it acts as an emetic when taken internally in dangerous amounts. However, since rats do not vomit, Red Squill is a specific poison for them.

Red Squill is marketed in both liquid and powdered form, both of which are effective. The powder is easier to use, is less expensive, will keep better, and can be more readily mixed with a wide variety of baits. Red Squill should be stored in sealed containers in a cool, dry place. A large stock of it should not be kept on hand, as it may deteriorate with age. Follow manufacturer's instructions.

The simultaneous use of three or more kinds of bait will increase the chances of a thorough clean-up of any premises. Separate baits, mixed with Red Squill, should be prepared from at least three of the following classes:

1. *Fish.* Fresh fish ground in a meat chopper, or a cheap grade of canned salmon, canned mackerel, or sardines in oil may be used. Mix one and one-half ounces of powdered Red Squill with a little water to form a thin paste free of lumps. Add one pound of fish, and mix thoroughly.

2. *Meat.* Mix one and one-half ounces of powdered Red Squill with a little water to form a thin paste free of lumps. Add one pound of fresh ground meat, and mix thoroughly. (Meats suitable for this purpose include canned dog food containing horse meat, and unseasoned hamburg steak.)

3. *Cereal.* Mix one and one-half ounces of powdered Red Squill and one pound of cereal meal such as oatmeal, graham flour, corn meal or bran. (Mix cereals together while dry.) Add one pint of sweet milk or water and stir to a mushy consistency.

4. *Fruits and vegetables.* Using a pepper shaker, dust powdered Red Squill over thin slices of fresh fruit or vegetables, and stir or shake as the powder is applied to insure even distribution. A small muskmelon, for example, should be cut into sixteen slices and each slice cut into three sections. This will require about one and one-half ounces of powdered Red Squill and will make forty-eight baits. Two medium sized tomatoes, sweet potatoes, or bananas, each cut into about sixteen sections, may be similarly used for each ounce of Red Squill powder.

In order to be certain of effecting a complete clean-up of all rats, prebaiting is recommended. This is accomplished by exposing three or more varieties of the above baits, prepared as directed, but without the use of poison. If these baits are taken freely the first night, poisoned food should be substituted after an interval of one or two nights. Otherwise clean baits should be exposed at two or three-day intervals (being picked up the following morning), until the rats consume them without hesitation.

A teaspoonful of the prepared Red Squill mixture is sufficient for the average rat bait. Put the baits in places frequented by rats, preferably where they have been observed to feed. In public places where there is a possibility of their being disturbed, baits should be placed in paper envelopes or on small squares of paper and labeled "POISON". Baits should be distributed in the evening and those uneaten should be picked up early the following morning and destroyed by burning. It is better to put out too many baits than too few. Should the baiting be unsuccessful, it is well to wait two weeks before repeating.

Note: In order to obtain a product of known toxicity, only fortified Red Squill should be purchased. The following specification should be used: Fortified Red Squill powder, standardized to the potency established by the Fish and Wildlife Service, of the U. S. Department of the Interior; 500-600 mg/kg.

Safety Precautions: Red Squill or any poison used should be handled with great care. During the mixing and preparation of the bait, a respirator approved for protection against the inhalation of toxic dust should be worn. The poison should not be allowed to come in contact with the users eyes or skin as it causes a sensation similar to a nettlesting. To avoid such contact wear glasses, and use rubber gloves extending over long shirt sleeves or rubber gloves and rubber-coated sleeves during the mixing and preparation of the bait.

A change of clothing, to be removed after the bait has been prepared, should be an integral part of the personal protective equipment of the exterminator. Hands should be thoroughly washed after each contact with the poison. Poisons and prepared baits should be kept in a well-made container distinctly marked with the word: "POISON". All of the materials, including the change of clothing, should be kept under lock and key with a responsible person in charge of their use and disposal. Destroy unused baits in an incinerator or furnace.

First Aid: In case of accidental poisoning *call the doctor immediately.* Tell the doctor what poison has been taken. Further the emetic effect of "Red Squill" by giving the victim warm salt water in the proportion of one tablespoon of salt to one glass of warm water or warm soapy water (mild soap flakes shaken up in warm water to make good suds).

If these substances do not cause vomiting, a cup of warm water containing one teaspoon of dry mustard may be given.

Vomiting should be induced repeatedly until the fluid coming from the stomach is clear. If it is necessary to induce vomiting after the person has had several glassfuls of the emetic, tickle the back of his throat.

It is most important to keep the victim warm and quiet while giving first aid. *If he stops breathing, give him artificial respiration at once.*

After everything possible has been done to dilute and remove the poison, a soothing drink, such as the raw whites of two or three eggs in a little water, one or two glasses of milk or a thin paste of starch or flour and water should be given if the victim can swallow. A stimulating drink such as hot coffee may be helpful.

Note: Since prompt action is of the greatest importance and because of the availability of warm water in most instances, the preparation of the above emetics may be greatly facilitated by previous packaging of the solid part of the emetics into amounts equivalent to one tablespoon (in the case of salt), or one teaspoon (in the case of dry mustard). Sufficient mild soap flakes could be packaged to make a good suds in a large glass of warm water. These packages (at least six of each type) should be incorporated in the equipment carried by any person engaged in work of extermination.

Antu. Antu is the common and shortened name of the organic chemical *alphanaphthylthiourea.* It is a greyish powder, insoluble in water, and stable at ordinary room temperatures. It has no odor, but its taste varies with individuals from tasteless to intensely bitter.

Antu is much more toxic to the Norway rat (the common brown rat) than to other species. Young Norways are more resistant to Antu than are adults.

A small sublethal dose of Antu will cause rats to develop a tolerance to future quantities. This tolerance is very marked for several days, but is lost after about two weeks. Rats that have survived this poison will refuse for several weeks to eat baits containing it. Therefore it should be used only once every four weeks.

In order to effect a complete cleanup of all rats in one baiting, prebaiting is recommended. If the baits without poison are taken freely the first night, poisoned food should be substituted after an interval of one or two nights. Otherwise clean baits should be exposed at two or three-day intervals (being picked up the following morning), until the rats take them without hesitation.

Unused baits containing poison should not be put in garbage that is fed to animals, but should be disposed of in an incinerator or burned in a furnace. Dead rats should be disposed of in like manner to prevent other animals from feeding on the remains and also becoming poisoned.

In Norway rat habitats, the use of only one per cent of Antu in the baits is adequate. Where other species are present, five per cent should be used. The bait and the poison should be mixed as evenly as possible. The directions for the preparation of Red Squill may be used as a guide, except that the quantity of poison will vary. Follow the manufacturer's instructions. Any palatable food attractive to rats may be used including those previously described.

Safety Precautions: Because of its high toxicity to humans and to animals such as cats and dogs, Antu must be handled with extreme caution. A type respirator approved for protection against the inhalation of toxic dust should be worn along with rubber gloves and either rubberized sleeves or long shirt sleeves. This respirator should be worn AT ALL TIMES both during the preparation of all baits and during the actual baiting period where dry baits are used (corn meal, oatmeal, and other cereals). Persons engaged in the preparation of bait with Antu should wear a change of clothing which should be removed when the preparation of the bait has been completed. Hands should be thoroughly washed after each contact with the poison. The poison and prepared baits should be kept in a well-made container distinctly marked with the word "POISON". All the materials, including the change of clothing, should be kept under lock and key with a responsible person in charge of their use and disposal. Destroy all unused baits in an incinerator or furnace.

First Aid: In case of accidental poisoning *call the doctor immediately.* Tell the doctor what poison has been taken. Induce vomiting by giving the victim warm salt water in the proportion of one tablespoon of salt to one glass of warm water, or warm soapy water (mild soap flakes shaken up in warm water to make a good suds).

If these substances do not cause vomiting, give a cup of warm water containing one teaspoon of dry mustard, thoroughly mixed.

Vomiting should be induced repeatedly until the fluid coming from the stomach is clear. If it is necessary to induce vomiting after the person has had several glassfuls of the emetic, tickle the back of the throat.

It is most important to keep the victim warm and quiet while giving first aid. *If he stops breathing give artificial respiration at once.*

After everything possible has been done to dilute and remove the poison, a soothing drink, such as the raw whites of two or three eggs in a little water, one or two glasses of milk, or a thin paste of starch or flour and water should be given if the victim can swallow. A stimulating drink such as hot coffee may be helpful.

Warfarin. Warfarin is a stable, odorless and tasteless substance suitable for permanent baiting of rats and mice. It differs from all previously used rodenticides in two respects. Its remarkable killing power is effective only after it is consumed repeatedly over a period of four to ten days. Death results in five to ten days from general internal hemorrhage. It causes no bait refusal or bait shyness in rats or mice that are being poisoned by it. The animals show no indication of pain or other acute physiological response.

Warfarin may be obtained commercially in ready-mixed, ready-to-use form, or in a concentrated form which must be mixed with a bait such as corn meal or oatmeal. One part of this concentrate is usually mixed with nineteen parts of corn meal or oatmeal. Warfarin is sold under various trade names, and directions on the package should be followed.

If precautions are used in the handling of Warfarin, the risk to the handler is very slight. No allergic manifestations have been observed in anyone through inhalation or skin absorption, and it can only be harmful if taken internally over a period of time and in sufficient quantity. Warfarin was discovered and patented by the Wisconsin Alumni Research Foundation and appears to be an outstanding success.

Safety Precautions: Handle this poison with extreme caution. Because of its high toxicity to humans as well as animals a type respirator approved for protection against the inhalation of toxic dust should be worn. This respirator should be worn *at all times*, both during the preparation of the bait and during the actual baiting period where dry baits are used. To avoid contact, rubber gloves and rubber-coated sleeves or long shirt sleeves should also be worn. A change of clothing, to be removed after the bait has been prepared, should be worn by the person engaged in the preparation of baits containing Warfarin. Hands should be thoroughly washed after each contact with the poison. The poison and prepared bait should be kept in a well-made container distinctly marked with the word "POISON". All the materials including the change of clothing, should be kept under lock and key with a responsible person in charge of their use and disposal. Destroy unused baits in an incinerator or furnace.

First Aid: See First Aid as outlined previously in this section for "Antu".

Note To Physician: Blood transfusions combined with intravenous injections and oral doses of Vitamin K are indicated as in the case of hemorrhage caused by overdoses of dicoumarol.

Strychnine poisoned sunflower and flax seed. *Safety Precautions:* Handle all poisoned seeds with care. To avoid contact rubber gloves should be worn. Wash hands thoroughly after each contact with the poisoned seeds. Keep the poisoned seeds in a well-made container distinctly marked with the word "POISON". All strychnine materials should be kept under lock and key with a responsible person in charge of their use and disposal.

First Aid: If seeds are accidentally swallowed *call the doctor immediately.* Tell the doctor what poison has been taken. *The prevention of convulsions before the arrival of the doctor is the principal object of the first aid treatment.* Give the victim *one tablespoonful* of *bone black* (powdered active charcoal) stirred into water. Keep the victim very quiet in a dark room remote from all noises. *Do not* give an emetic or a stimulant because doing this is apt to bring on convulsions.

Note: Bone black (powdered active charcoal) should be packaged in amounts equivalent to one tablespoonful. At least three of these packages should be incorporated in the equipment carried by any person engaged in the work of extermination.

Outline of Procedures

RED SQUILL AND ANTU

Operation	*Explanation*	*Safety Precautions and First Aid*
Inspect building for best spots to place baits.	Look for signs of rats, such as droppings, gnawings and greasy places near holes where rats could pass through. Find places where rats feed or where they might be nesting.	
Pre-bait by putting out food *without poison.*	Any wholesome food may be attractive to rats, but food which has not been available to them is usually the most attractive. Fish, meat, cereal, fruits and vegetables may be used. Scatter the food at likely spots, putting about a teaspoonful at each location.	
Inspect building next day for results of pre-baiting and pick up baits.	Note whether baits were taken freely and which food was preferred. If not taken freely, wait one or two days and repeat pre-baiting.	
Mix poison bait.	Assemble mixing pan, tablespoon, teaspoon, bait and poison. A scale for weighing bait and the poison may be necessary. Exact procedure will depend somewhat upon the bait used. For example, oatmeal may be mixed with Red Squill or Antu and then moistened with enough water to make it hold together. Fresh vegetables, such as tomatoes, may be sliced and the poison sprinkled upon the slices. Use either Red Squill or Antu as the poison.	Handle these poisons with extreme caution. Wear approved respirator. Avoid contact with skin. Wash hands thoroughly after each contact with poison. In case of accidental poisoning: *Call the doctor immediately.* Tell the doctor what poison has been taken. Administer proper emetic (water solutions of either salt, soap or mustard.) If necessary stick finger down victim's throat. Keep victim warm and quiet. Administer artificial respiration if necessary.

RED SQUILL AND ANTU

Operation	Explanation	Safety Precautions and First Aid
		After diluting and removing poison administer soothing drink (whites of eggs, milk or thin paste of starch).
Storage of poison and baits.	Meat, fruits, vegetables and fish which are not of the canned varieties and are to be used as baits must be kept in a refrigerator to prevent spoilage. Foods in a deteriorated condition do not make suitable baits.	Poisons and prepared baits should be kept in well-made container distinctly marked with the word "POISON". All of the materials shall be kept under lock and key with a responsible person in charge of their use and disposal.
Proportions to be used.	*Red Squill:* To one pound of bait, add six level tablespoons or one and one-half ounces of Red Squill. *Antu:* To one pound of bait, add three level teaspoons or one-quarter ounce of Antu. (Five times this amount for the black rat.)	Destroy unused baits in an incinerator or furnace.
Put out poisoned bait.	Place poisoned baits in spots where rats took pre-baits freely. Should poison baiting fail to give results, wait for two weeks before repeating, or if using Antu, four weeks.	In public places put poisoned bait on small squares of paper labeled "POISON".
Inspect for results next day.	Pick up dead rats and unused poisoned baits and destroy in furnace or incinerator.	The dead rats should be handled with gloves and care taken to prevent lice and mites from transferring to the clothing. These lice and mites carry the typhus germ and usually try to leave the rodent shortly after it dies.

WARFARIN

Inspect building for best spots to place baits.	Look for signs of rats, such as droppings, gnawings, and greasy places near holes where rats could pass through. Find places where rats feed or where they might be nesting.	
Mix poison bait. (If ready-to-use bait is available,	Assemble mixing pan, cup, tablespoon, teaspoon, bait, and poison. Any convenient	Handle this poison with extreme caution. Wear approved respirator. Avoid contact with

Operation	*Explanation*	*Safety Precautions and First Aid*
disregard this section.)	utensil such as a cup may be used to measure pioson and bait. Use nineteen parts of bait, such as corn meal or oatmeal, to one part of Warfarin. Stir until it is mixed thoroughly.	skin. Wash hands thoroughly after each contact with poison. In case of accidental poisoning: *Call the doctor immediately.* Tell the doctor what poison has been taken. Administer proper emetic (water solutions of either salt, soap or mustard). If necessary stick finger down victim's throat. Keep victim warm and quiet. Administer artificial respiration if necessary. After diluting and removing poison administer soothing drink (whites of eggs, milk or thin paste starch).
Put out poisoned bait.	Place poisoned baits in spots previously selected. Baits should be examined regularly and replenished before completely eaten. Baiting should be continued as long as feeding is observed. As Warfarin is a slow-acting poison, baits should be kept before rats for from five to fifteen days or until no new rat signs are observed.	Poisons and prepared baits should be kept in a well-made container distinctly marked with the word "POISON". Keep all materials under lock and key with a responsible person in charge. In public places put bait on small squares of paper labeled "POISON".
Inspect for results.	Pick up dead rats and inspect baits daily. If necessary to replace baits, destroy unused baits in furnace or incinerator. Also destroy dead rats by the same means.	The dead rats should be handled with gloves and care taken to prevent lice and mites from transferring to the clothing. These lice and mites carry the typhus germ and usually try to leave the rodent shortly after it dies.

STRYCHNINE

Inspect for ratruns as above, and place seed.	Sunflower seed poisoned with strychnine alkaloid is a poisoned rat bait which comes ready for use. Places where rats will be likely to pick it up should be selected and a teaspoonful placed at each point. It is not necessary to pick up the seed as it does not spoil if kept dry. Neither need it be con-	Handle poisoned seed with care. Avoid contact with skin. Wash hands after each contact with seeds. Mark seeds "POISON (STRYCHNINE)". Keep under lock and key. In case of accidental poisoning *Call the doctor immediately.* Tell the doctor what poison has been taken. Give victim one tablespoonful of

Operation	Explanation	Safety Precautions and First Aid
	sidered a hazard since it is attractive only to rodents and birds. The seed should be inspected from time to time and replenished when necessary. If placed in small cups, either paper or metal, it can be picked up while the floor is being swept, and then replaced. Use poisoned flax seed in the same manner for the control of mice.	*bone black* stirred into water. *Do not give an emetic.* Keep victim in dark quiet room remote from all noises.
Set traps in rat-runs.	Ordinarily traps are not used as it is difficult to catch rodents in them especially rats. Occasionally occupants of an office are strongly prejudiced against poisons. In these circumstances it may be a good policy to use traps although they are not as effective as poisons. Electric rat traps have not been found suitable, but the common spring type of trap has proved satisfactory. It is usually necessary to tie the bait to the trigger of the trap to prevent the rodent from stealing the bait. Meat and cheese are preferred trap baits as they are easier to fasten to the trigger.	The primary safety precaution to be observed in handling traps is care in setting them. The fingers and hands can be severely bruised if caught in the jaws of the trap.

18E / CONTROL OF BIRDS AND FLYING INSECTS

Birds

On many occasions pigeons, sparrows and starlings deface buildings, trees and shrubs. Birds which nest in or on buildings are sometimes infested with mites and lice. Their nests often attract insect pests such as carpet beetles, and spider beetles. Roosting starlings may cause so much noise that occupants of the building may be annoyed.

Public relations problems must be recognized with any bird control program. A preventive program may accomplish your desires, without the risk of violating laws. Birds can be prevented from entering windows, belfries, attics, or ornamental portions of a building by screening them with aluminum or copper screen. If screening would interfere with the appearance, three-quarter inch chicken wire is recommended.

The use of sloaping boards, sheet metal (installed at a 45° angle) or wire on ledge if possible prevents the birds from gaining a foothold. These problems should be taken into consideration when remodeling or planning new construction.

Deliberate feeding usually results in nuisance problems, as birds generally rest where they are fed. Moving strips and spirals of bright metals or cloth, are sometimes effective in moving birds. The use of phonograph records recently have met with considerable success in moving birds. If an extreme problem is encountered, electric wiring similar to stock (cattle) fencing can be placed in areas of trouble. The wires carry a low voltage current that gives a mild shock. This equipment will be expensive, but effective.

Outdoor Flying Insects

Black light grid panels attract and electrocute flying insects outdoors at night. The panels should be placed near the area you desire to keep the insects away from, or they can be installed on windows if a special problem is encountered. A black light fluorescent tube is installed on both sides of grid panel that has electrified wires strung about a quarter inch apart in rows. Black light is attractive to night insects, especially houseflies and mosquitos. As the light seeking insects pass between these wires, the moisture of their bodies creates a short circuit which kills them instantly. Black light is barely visible to the human eye. A container of screen or some other similar material should be located directly under the panel to catch the insects as they fall. This container should be emptied on a daily basis.

18F / DICTIONARY OF INSECTICIDES AND THEIR USE

(*Source:* "Dictionary of Insecticides and Their Use," by Professor Glen E. Lehker, *Modern Sanitation and Building Maintenance*, March 1958)

Acrylonitrile. A grain fumigant, used especially for spot treatment in elevators, mills and food processing plants. It is formulated and sold under the name of Acrylon, a preparation which contains 33.3 per cent acrylonitrile and 66.7 per cent carbon tetrachloride. In most cases spot treatments can be made without the use of a gas mask.

Aldrin. A chlorinated insecticide related to dieldrin and used primarily to control grasshoppers and soil insects. It is more volatile than dieldrin, DDT or toxaphene and therefore has a shorter residual action when sprayed upon plants. Common formulations include two and four pounds per gallon concentrates, 50 per cent wettable powders, 75 per cent seed treaters, 2.5 per cent dusts, 2.5 to 25 per cent granular mixtures, and 0.1 to 1.0 per cent fertilizer mixtures. Aldrin is of moderately high toxicity to humans with a rating of 0.107.

Allethrin. A synthetic pyrethrum contained in household, livestock and garden sprays, often in combination with a synergist. Common formulations include 0.1 to 0.6 per cent aerosols, one per cent dusts, and oil solutions. Allethrin, with a rating of 1.088 is of moderately low toxicity to humans.

Anthracene oil. A contact material to be mixed with equal parts of kerosene for the control of mites in poultry houses.

Aramite. A chlorinated miticide widely used to control plant feeding mites. The common formulation is a fifteen per cent wettable powder, although two pounds per gallon concentrates, three to five per cent dusts, and ten per cent pressurized sprays are also available. Aramite, with a rating of 10.080, is of low toxicity to humans.

Azobenzene. A greenhouse fumigant sold as Benzofume to control mealybugs and red spider on floriculture crops. It has been replaced to a large extent by other materials and is now seldom used except on gardenias, where it remains one of the best treatments.

Baver 21/199. A systematic insecticide, added to the feed, being tested for the control of cattle grubs. Not yet registered or approved for use.

Benzene hexachloride. A chlorinated insecticide commonly called BHC. It has a persistent, disagreeable odor which may impart off-flavor to food crops. The purified form, with little odor, is known as lindane. BHC has been used widely to control spittlebugs and animal parasites. Common formulations include one pound and two pounds per gallon concentrates, 12 to 36 per cent wettable powders and one to three per cent dusts. BHC, with a rating of 0.960, is of moderate toxicity to humans.

Calcium arsenate. An arsenical insecticide used to control chewing insects. It is more toxic to plants than lead arsenate and is therefore often used in dust formulations. Calcium arsenate, when swallowed, is of high toxicity to humans. It has a rating of 0.032.

Calcium cyanide. A granular fumigant used for the destruction of rodents in their burrows, ants in lawns, bees in buildings, and for fumigating greenhouses. The material liberates hydrogen cyanide gas. Both the granules and gas are of very high toxicity to humans and should not be used indoors without a gas mask.

Calomel. A mercurous chloride compound sometimes used for the control of root maggots. Common formulations include 99.6 per cent powders for use in water and four per cent dusts.

Carbon disulphide. A fumigant that is explosive when mixed with air. It is used as a grain fumigant and as a spot treatment for soil insects. It is often formulated with carbon tetrachloride to reduce the fire hazard. Carbon disulphide is of moderately high toxicity to humans.

Carbon tetrachloride. A non-inflammable fumigant commonly used as an ingredient in proprietary grain fumigants. It has excellent nonabsorptive properties.

Chlordane. A widely used chlorinated insecticide for the control of many household pests, termites, soil insects and plant feeding pests. Resistance to chlordane has been developed generally by house flies, and by German roaches, brown dog ticks, fleas in some areas, and by certain animal parasites. Common formulations include four to eight pounds per gallon concentrates, 40 per cent wettable powders, five to ten per cent dusts or granules, 0.5 to two per cent fertilizer mixtures, and one to three per cent pressurized sprays or oil solutions for household use. Chlordane, with a rating of 0.732, is of moderate toxicity to humans.

Chlorbenside. A phosphate miticide sold as Mitox for the pre-bloom control of mites on fruit trees. Common formulations include two pounds per gallon concentrates and 40 per cent wettable powders. It is of moderately low toxicity to humans.

Chlorobenzilate. A chlorinated miticide for use on plants. It is effective against parathion resistant mites. Common formulations include two pounds per gallon concentrates, 25 per cent wettable powders, four per cent dusts and ten per cent pressurized sprays. Chlorobenzilate, with a rating of 7.690, is of low toxicity to humans.

Chloropicrin. A fumigant for industrial use in grain storages and warehouses, and also for treating soil. Chloropicrin is a tear gas and the fumes are extremely disagreeable. Use indoors with a gas mask.

Chlorthion. A phosphate insecticide and miticide for use on nonfood plants to control a variety of insects and mites. Common formulations include four pounds per gallon concentrates, 25 per cent wettable powders, and three per cent dusts. Chlorthion, with a rating of 2.410, is of moderately low toxicity to humans.

Crag fly repellent. A prophylene glycol fly repellent for use on livestock, especially against stable flies and horse flies. It is used as an ingredient in commercial fly sprays, often in combination with pyrethrins or other toxicants. It is also available in formulations for use in automatic treadle sprayers. Crag repellent is of low toxicity to humans.

Creosote. A wood preservative which will kill plants and is caustic to the skin. Impregnated timbers such as telephone poles and railroad ties resist wood rots and insect damage. Cresote is not recommended for treating buildings to control or prevent termites.

Cryolite. A fluorine stomach poison not extensively used, except to control blister beetles and rose chafers. Common formulations include 20 to 100 per cent dusts and a 100 per cent material for making sprays. Cryolite, if swallowed, is of moderate toxicity to humans. It has a rating of 0.325.

DD mixture. A soil fumigant consisting of a mixture of dichloropropane and dichlorophropene. It is used mainly for the control of nematodes.

DDT. A widely used chlorinated insecticide for the control of plant feeding insects, animal parasites and household pests. Resistance to DDT has been developed by house flies generally and also by fleas, codling moth, bedbugs, brown dog tick, and other insects in some areas. Common formulations include two pounds per gallon concentrates, 50 per cent wettable powders, five to ten per cent dusts, ten per cent aerosols and five to six per cent oil solutions for household use. DDT, with a rating of 0.400, is of moderate toxicity to humans.

Demeton. A systemic phosphate insecticide and miticide sold as Systox and used largely to control aphids and mites on fruit trees, shade trees, shrubs, and commercial vegetables. The common formulation is two pounds per gallon concentrate. Demeton, with a rating of 0.014, is of very high toxicity to humans. It should not be used without a respirator.

Diazinon. A phosphate insecticide and miticide used mainly to control DDT resistant flies, but also registered for use on certain fruits. Common formulations include two pounds per gallon concentrates, 25 per cent wettable powders, and a four per cent dust. Diazinon, with a rating of 0.200, is of moderate toxicity to humans.

Dieldrin. A chlorinated insecticide more stable than aldrin to which it is related. It is used as a soil insecticide, seed treater, and for the control of certain fruit and vegetable insects, grasshoppers, chinch bugs, mosquitoes, termites, box-elder bugs, and certain household pests. Resistance to dieldrin has been developed by the German cockroach in some areas. Common formulations include 1.5 pound per gallon concentrates, 50 per cent wettable powders, 1.5 per cent dusts, five to fifteen per cent granules, 50 to 75 per cent seed treaters, up to one per cent fertilizer mixtures, and 0.5 per cent oil solutions for household use. Dieldrin, with a rating of 0.130, is of moderately high toxicity to humans.

Diethyl toluamide. A new insect repellent effective against mosquitoes, biting flies, ticks, chiggers and related pests. It is of low toxicity to humans.

Dilan. A chlorinated insecticide with a limited use on vegetable crops. Common formulations include two pounds per gallon concentrates, 25 per cent wettable powders and 1.5 per cent dusts.

Dimethyl phthalate. A mosquito and insect repellent. It is of low toxicity to humans.

Dimite. A miticide for use on plants. The common formulation is a two pound per gallon concentrate. Dimite is of moderately low toxicity to humans.

Dinitrocresol. A dinitro compound used largely as a dormant spray to control aphid eggs and scale insects on trees and shrubs. Common formulations include a 19 per cent liquid concentrate, a 30 per cent liquid concentrate and a 40.3 per cent wettable powder. Dinitrocresol, with a rating of 0.042, is of high toxicity to humans.

Diphenylamine. A material formerly used in screwworm smears which have now been largely replaced by Smear EQ335 containing lindane.

Dipterex. A phosphate insecticide used in fly baits for the control of resistant house flies. It has a rating of 0.800, and is of moderate toxicity to humans.

Dorlone. A nematicide with limited use for the control of soil nematodes. It is formulated as a 93.2 per cent liquid.

DN-111. A dinitro miticide for use on fruit trees. The common formulation is a 20 per cent wettable powder.

DN-289. A dinitro insecticide and miticide for use as a dormant spray on trees to control aphid eggs and scale insects.

Dylox. A systemic phosphate insecticide related to dipterex but designed for use on plants. Formulations include 50 per cent soluble powders, five and ten per cent dusts, and two and one-half and five per cent granules. Dylox, with a rating of 0.720, is of moderate toxicity to humans.

Endrin. A chlorinated insecticide related to aldrin and dieldrin and used to control certain tobacco and vegetable pests and also cutworms in small grains. It is especially effective against certain caterpillars. Common formulations include a 1.6 pound per gallon concentrate and a 1.5 per cent dust. Endrin, with a rating of 0.040, is of high toxicity to humans.

EPN. A phosphate insecticide and miticide used principally on fruit trees, shade trees, shrubs, and certain vegetables. Common formulations include a 25 per cent wettable powder and one to three per cent dusts. EPN, with a rating of 0.024, is of high toxicity to humans.

ET-57. A systemic insecticide, applied as a spray, being tested for the control of cattle grubs. It is also effective against the nasal botfly of sheep when injected into the nostrils. It is not registered or approved for use.

Ethylene dibromide. A fumigant used to control nematodes and wireworms, and also as an ingredient in certain grain fumigants as well as in spot fumigants used in food processing plants. Common formulations include five per cent of the toxicant in grain fumigants, ten to twenty-five per cent in spot fumigants and 40 to 80 per cent in soil fumigants.

Ethylene dichloride. An ingredient contained in commercial grain fumigants. It is also used to control certain tree borers.

Ethyl hexanediol. A mosquito and insect repellent commonly known as Rutgers 612. It is of low toxicity to humans and safe for use on synthetic fabrics.

Genite. A miticide for early season use on fruit trees. The common formulation is a 4.8 pound per gallon concentrate.

Guthion. A phosphate insecticide now being tested against a wide variety of plant feeding pests. Formulations include two pounds per gallon concentrates, 25 per cent wettable powders and two and one-half and five per cent dusts and granules. Guthion, with a rating of about 0.024, is of high toxicity to humans.

HCN. A powerful liquid hydrogen cyanide fumigant for use by commercial operators to control insects and other pests in sealed enclosures. HCN is stored in steel containers and pumped into the areas to be treated or used to impregnate paper discs, which are stored in sealed cans. These discs liberate the gas when exposed to the air. Hydrogen cyanide is of very high toxicity to humans and should only be used while wearing a gas mask.

Heptachlor. A chlorinated insecticide related to chlordane and used for the control of many soil and plant feeding pests. It is more volatile than chlordane and therefore has a shorter residual action when sprayed upon plants. Common formulations include two pounds per gallon concentrates, 25 per cent wettable powders, 1.5 to 2.5 per cent dusts, five to twenty-five per cent granules and 1.5 per cent fertilizer mixtures. Heptachlor, with a rating of 0.144, is of moderately high toxicity to humans.

Hercules 528. A phosphate miticide now registered for use on cotton, but being tested against mites on other plants. The common formulation is a 33 per cent concentrate. Hercules 528, with a rating of 0.064, is of moderately high toxicity to humans.

Indalone. A mosquito and insect repellent of low toxicity to humans.

Karathane. A fungicide primarily, but of some value as a miticide. Common formulations include a twenty-five per cent wettable powder and one, five and ten per cent dusts.

Kelthane. A new miticide for the control of plant feeding mites. Formulations include twenty-five per cent concentrates and wettable powders, and four per cent dusts. Kelthane, with a rating of 0.920, is of moderate toxicity to humans.

Korlan. A phosphate insecticide also known as ET-59. It is being tested for the control of household pests and animal parasites. Formulations include two and four pounds per gallon concentrates, twenty-five per cent wettable powders, five per cent dusts, and one-half pound per gallon oil solutions. Korlan, with a rating of about 4,000, is of moderately low toxicity to humans.

Fumazone. A nematicide with limited use to control soil nematodes. It is formulated as a forty-seven per cent liquid.

Lead arsenate. An arsenical stomach poison widely used for the control of chewing insects. As a spray, it is normally mixed with water at the rate of six teaspoonfuls per gallon or three pounds in one hundred gallons. Repeated applications must be safened with equal parts of lime or with other safeners to prevent plant injury. Lead arsenate is highly poisonous if swallowed.

Lime-sulphur. A fungicide and insecticide used for many years as a dormant spray to control scale insects, and also the maple bladder gall mite. The normal dilution is one gallon in eight gallons of water. It is also available as dry lime-sulphur, of which four pounds equals one gallon of the liquid. Lime-sulphur will stain paint.

Lindane. A purified form of the gamma isomer of benzene hexachloride with little or no objectionable odor. It is widely used to control many plant pests, animal parasites, certain household pests and also as a seed treatment. Resistance to lindane has been developed by house flies generally and by fleas in certain areas. Common formulations include 1.6 pound per gallon concentrates, twenty-five per cent wettable powders and one to three per cent dusts. Lindane, with a rating of 0.200, is of moderate toxicity to humans.

Malathion. A relatively safe phosphate insecticide and miticide related to parathion. It is widely employed to control insects and mites affecting fruit, shade trees, shrubs and flowers. It is likewise excellent for aphid control on field crops, and also for the control of resistant roaches, house flies, and fleas and ticks on cats and dogs or in and around buildings. It is likewise used for clover mite control. A high degree of resistance to malathion has been developed by mites in greenhouses and fruit orchards. Common formulations include five pounds per gallon concentrates, twenty-five per cent wettable powders and four to five per cent dusts. Malathion, with a rating of 1.600, is of moderately low toxicity to humans.

Malrin. A patented combination of malathion and perthane having synergestic action upon each other, and used for the control of chlordane resistant roaches, and certain other structural pests. The common formulations are fifty-five per cent concentrates.

Metacide. A phosphate insecticide and miticide very closely related to parathion and sometimes used to control flea beetles, aphids and mites. Common formulations include two pounds per gallon concentrates, and one to two per cent dusts. Metacide, with a rating of 0.024, is of very high toxicity to humans.

Metaldehyde. A material used commonly in slug and snail baits, often in combination with calcium arsenate or other stomach poisons. These baits, if swallowed, are of high toxicity to humans.

Methoxychlor. A chlorinated insecticide related to DDT but less likely to accumulate in milk and the fatty tissues of animals. It is widely used to control plant feeding pests and animal parasites. Resistance to methoxychlor has been developed generally by house flies and by bedbugs and fleas in some areas. Common formulations include two pounds per gallon concentrates, fifty per cent wettable powders, five to ten per cent dusts and two to three per cent aerosols, oil solutions and pressurized formulations. Methoxychlor, with a rating of 9.600, is of low toxicity to humans.

Methyl bromide. A fumigant having excellent properties for penetration and used widely by commercial fumigators in vacuum chambers, mills, warehouses and box cars. It is also widely used to treat fresh and dried fruits, green vegetables, nursery stock and ornamentals. It is also an ingredient in certain grain and soil fumigants. Methyl bromide is a gas at ordinary temperatures and is therefore kept under pressure in sealed containers. The common formulations are a ninety-eight per cent compressed gas and a twenty-six per cent liquid. Methyl bromide is of high toxicity to humans and a gas mask is necessary if the operator is exposed to the fumes.

MGK-repellent-11. An insect repellent for general use including applications to dairy cattle. It is normally used at a two per cent strength in combination with other insecticides. MGK-repellent-11 is of low toxicity to humans.

Naphthalene. A weak fumigant and insect repellent commonly encountered as "moth balls". It is a crystalline material which volatilizes slowly and is used for the prevention and destruction of clothes moths and carpet beetles.

Nemagon. A fumigant injected into the soil for the control of nematodes. Common formulations include twenty-five, fifty and seventy-five per cent liquid concentrates and solutions and also ten and twenty-five per cent granules.

Neotran. A miticide for the control of plant feeding mites. The common formulation is a forty per cent wettable powder. Neotran has a rating of 4.000, and is of moderately low toxicity to humans.

Nicotine. A contact insecticide widely used to control chicken lice and soft bodied plant feeding insects. The common formulation is forty per cent nicotine sulphate. Nicotine dusts, soaps, roost paints and preparations for greenhouse use are also available. Nicotine, with a rating of 0.088, is of high toxicity to humans.

Ovex. A miticide for the control of plant feeding mites. It is especially effective against the eggs and young mites. Common formulations include one pound and five ounces per gallon concentrates, forty to fifty per cent wettable powders and five to ten per cent dusts. Ovex is of low toxicity to humans.

Paradichlorobenzene. A slow acting fumigant most often encountered as "moth crystals". It is used for the prevention and control of clothes moths and carpet beetles and to some extent, peach tree borers.

Parathion. A phosphate insecticide and miticide widely used for the control of plant feeding pests. A high degree of resistance to parathion has been developed by mites in orchards and greenhouses. Common formulations include two pounds per gallon concentrates, fifteen and twenty-five per cent wettable powders, one and two per cent dust's and ten per cent aerosol formulations. Parathion, with a rating of 0.005, is of very high toxicity to humans. It should not be used without a respirator.

Paris green. An arsenical insecticide composed of copper acetoarsenite. It is no longer widely used except in poison baits to control grasshoppers and cutworms and sometimes as a mosquito larvacide. The common formulation is a ninety-nine per cent powder. Paris Green, if swallowed, is of high toxicity to humans. It has a rating of 0.035.

Pentachlorophenol. A wood preservative and insecticide commonly referred to as "penta". Impregnated wood is highly resistant to insect attack and decay. It is used for the control of powder post beetles and to a lesser extent as a soil treatment for termites. Common formulations include a fifty per cent concentrate and a five per cent ready-to-use solution. Pentachlorophenol is irritating to the skin, will kill plants and is of moderately high toxicity to humans. It has a rating of 0.123.

Perthane. A chlorinated insecticide for use on certain fruits, vegetables and livestock. Common formulations include fifty per cent wettable powders and ten per cent dusts. A patented combination of perthane and malathion, known as malrin, is used to control resistant roaches. Perthane, with a rating of 9.600, is of low toxicity to humans.

Petroleum oils. Petroleum oils of certain specifications are used as insecticides. Dormant and summer spray oils are used to control scale insects and mites on plants. In addition, petroleum oils are widely used as carriers for other insecticides, especially in household and livestock sprays. Common formulations include miscible and emulsifiable oils as well as pure oils for tank mixing, or as solvents for other insecticides.

Phosdrin. A phosphate insecticide and miticide of short residual action for the control of plant feeding pests. Common formulations include two pounds per gallon concentrates, ten per cent wettable powders, one-quarter to two per cent dusts and one to five per cent granules. Phosdrin, with a rating of 0.021, is of high toxicity to humans. It should not be used without a respirator.

Phosphorus. An insecticide and rodenticide used in cockroach baits and pastes and also as a rat poison. It is of high toxicity to humans.

Pyrenone. An activated pyrethrin containing either piperonyl butoxide or piperonyl cyclonene. It is contained in wheat and grain protectants, and used as an ingredient in many pyrethrin sprays, dusts and aerosols. Concentrates are also available for fly control, and for use in fog machines and in food processing plants. Pyrenone is of low toxicity to humans.

Pyrethrins. A common insecticide of plant derivation, widely used and often with a synergist in household sprays and aerosols, garden sprays and dusts, and in fly sprays for use on livestock. It is also widely used in spray or aerosol form to control insects in milk houses, barns and food processing plants. Dusts are available for fruit fly control on tomatoes. Common formulations include 0.05 to 0.4 per cent oil solutions, 0.1 to 0.6 per cent pressurized sprays and aerosols, 0.5 to 2.5 per cent dusts and 0.5 to 20 per cent concentrates. Pyrethrins are of low toxicity to humans.

Rotenone. An insecticide of plant derivation widely used in garden sprays and dusts and for the control of cattle grubs, ticks, lice and fleas. Common formulations include 0.75 to 1.5 per cent dusts, two to three per cent concentrates, and five per cent wettable powders. Rotenone is of low toxicity to humans.

Ryania. An insecticide of plant derivation sometimes used to avoid residues in control of the codling moth and the European corn borer. Common formulations include forty to one hundred per cent dusts and wettable powders. Ryania, with a rating of 1.200, is of moderately low toxicity to humans.

Sabadilla. An insecticide of plant derivation sometimes used for the control of hard to kill hemipterous insects. It is a sneeze powder and for this reason a respirator is desirable when it is applied. The common formulation is a ten to twenty per cent dust. Sabadilla, with a rating of 6.400, is of low toxicity to humans.

Schradan. A systemic phosphate insecticide and miticide, also known as OMPA, used for the control of certain sucking insects and mites on nonfood plants. Common formulations include two to four pounds per gallon concentrates and ten per cent aerosols. Schradan, with a rating of 0.021, is of high toxicity to humans. It should not be used with a respirator.

Sevin. An experimental insecticide being tested for the control of apple and vegetable insects. It is most commonly available as a fifty per cent wettable powder. Sevin, with a rating of 3.500, is of moderately low toxicity to humans.

Sodium arsenite. An arsenical insecticide not safe for use on plants, but found in commercial ant baits and moth-proofing preparations, and used as a soil poison for termites. Sodium arsenite, if swallowed, is of high toxicity to humans.

Sodium and potassium cyanide. A fumigant which produces hydrogen cyanide gas. It is used by commercial pest control operators for the control of structural pests and also by greenhouse operators. The common formulation is a crystalline material. Sodium and potassium cyanide are of very high toxicity to humans, and should not be used without a gas mask. Small quantities are also used for making insect killing bottles.

Sodium fluoride. A fluorine insecticide used for killing cockroaches and for louse control on poultry. The common formulation is a powder. Sodium fluoride, if swallowed, is of moderate toxicity to humans. It has a rating of 0.325.

Sodium fluosilicate. A fluorine insecticide used for making cutworm and grasshopper baits and also moth proofing solutions. If swallowed, it is of moderate toxicity to humans.

Sodium selenate. A selenium compound sometimes used as a systemic poison for the control of aphids, whitefly, thrips, and mites on floriculture crops. Common formulations include a one hundred per cent powder and a commercial preparation known as P-40. Sodium selenate, if swallowed, is of high toxicity to humans. Food crops must not be grown on treated soil.

Strobane. A chlorinated insecticide used primarily for the control of household pests, often in combination with other materials. Finished sprays and aerosols usually contain from two to five per cent of the active ingredient. Other formulations include eight pounds per gallon concentrates, fifty per cent wettable powders and ten and twenty per cent dusts. Strobane, with a rating of 0.123, in concentrated form is of moderately high toxicity to humans.

Sulfotepp. A phosphate insecticide and miticide used largely in aerosol form to control insects in greenhouses. It is of high toxicity to humans.

Sulphenone. An insecticide and miticide for the control of certain fruit and greenhouse pests. Common formulations include fifty per cent wettable powders and ten to twenty per cent dusts.

Sulphur. A well-known fungicide also effective against chiggers, psyllids and certain mites. Common formulations include wettable sulphurs, dusting sulphurs, pastes and candles. Sulphur produces sulphur dioxide when burned. This is a weak fumigant in the concentrations normally used. Sulphur is of low toxicity to humans, but irritating to the eyes.

Tabutrex. An insect repellent now registered for use against house flies, cattle flies, ants and roaches. It can be used on dairy cattle, and in dairy barns, homes and commercial buildings. Formulations include twenty per cent concentrates, one per cent oil solutions and five per cent pressurized sprays alone or combined with other insecticides and synergists. Tabutrex is of low toxicity to humans.

Tartar emetic. A stomach poison formerly used in combination with brown sugar as a spray for thrips. The common formulation is a one hundred per cent powder. Tartar emetic, if swallowed, is of high toxicity to humans.

TDE. A chlorinated insecticide also known as DDD. It is related to DDT and used for the control of many plant feeding insects and animal parasites. It is particularly effective against leafrollers. Common formulations include two pounds per gallon concentrates, fifty per cent wettable powders and five per cent dusts. It has a rating of 5.450, and is of moderate toxicity to humans.

Tedion. A chlorinated miticide for experimental use. It is of low toxicity to humans.

Tepp. A phosphate insecticide and miticide related to parathion. It has a shorter residual action than parathion and is used for the control of aphids and certain other plant feeding pests. Common formulations include twenty to forty per cent concentrates and two to five per cent dusts. Tepp, with a rating of 0.002, is of very high toxicity to humans. It should not be used without a respirator.

Thallium sulphate. A material used in the preparation of commercial ant and rodent baits. If swallowed, it is of very high toxicity to humans.

Thimet. A systemic phosphate insecticide and miticide now used on cotton, but which shows considerable promise as a seed treatment to control other insects including the spotted alfalfa aphid and hessian fly. The common formulation is a forty-four per cent concentrate. Thimet, with a rating of 0.006, is of very high toxicity to humans. It should not be used without a respirator.

Thiocyanates. A group of related compounds used as fly sprays and also in greenhouses and nurseries for insect control. The thiocyanates are often contained in pyrethrin preparations. Their toxicity to humans ranges from moderately low to moderately high, with ratings of 1.600 for thanite, 0.800 for Lethane 60, and 0.144 for Lethane 384.

Thiodan. A phosphate insecticide and miticide being tested for the control of a wide range of insects. Formulations include 25 per cent wettable powders, two and three per cent dusts and five per cent granules. Thiodan, with a rating of about 0.144, is of moderately high toxicity to humans.

Toxaphene. A chlorinated insecticide with a long residual action. It is used for the control of a variety of insects including grasshoppers, armyworms, corn borer and cutworms, and also certain animal parasites. It is less toxic to honeybees than most other insecticides. Common formulations include four, six and eight pounds per gallon concentrates, 50 per cent wettable powders and ten to twenty per cent dusts. Toxaphene, with a rating of 0.110, is of high toxicity to humans.

Trithion. An experimental phosphate insecticide and miticide for use on plants. Formulations include four pounds per gallon concentrates, twenty-five per cent wettable powders and one, two and five per cent dusts. Trithion, with a rating of 0.043, is of high toxicity to humans.

Vapam. A nematicide and soil insecticide to control nematodes and certain soil pests, including those in vegetable plant beds. The common formulation is a thirty-one per cent liquid.

19 / PAVEMENT MAINTENANCE (CONCRETE)

The best possible provision for maintenance of a concrete pavement is to use good materials and the best methods of construction, so that repairs will be infrequent. The defects in a concrete road can almost always be traced to some fault in the materials, in preparing or placing the concrete, or to neglect of some important features in preparing the subgrade.

Next in importance to employing good materials and insuring thorough workmanship, is taking care that all imperfections in the road should receive attention as soon as they are discovered. If this is not done, small breaks will become large holes, and expensive repairs will be necessary. The edges of cracks are constantly battered by the tires and in time the cracks are enlarged into chuckholes. Prompt repairs are therefore essential. The road should be inspected annually, and hot bitumen should be poured into all cracks. This repair work is generally done at a small cost, and it constitutes the only charge for upkeep on concrete pavements besides that of taking care of the shoulders along the road.

The major repairs that are likely to be necessary to concrete pavements will fall mostly into three general classes: (1) the replacement of the pavement where it has been cut through to lay or repair underground pipes; (2) the repair of depressions or chuckholes caused either by original faulty construction or by the normal effects of wear; and (3) repairs along expansion joints or self-formed cracks in the pavement. Repair patches that are properly made should prove as durable as the original pavement, and such patches should not be noticeable after being exposed to traffic for a short time.

(*Source:* "How to Care for Your Built-up Roof," by G. E. Hann, reprinted by special permission of *Factory Management and Maintenance*, September 1952, copyright by McGraw-Hill Publishing Company, Inc.)

Roofs need regular upkeep and care just like any other part of the plant. But in many plants they get little if any attention—until they leak.

If you want to keep building maintenance costs down, do not wait for the roof to leak and cause water damage. That means you are too late—and you are in for some expensive remedies. Routine upkeep of a roof is always cheaper than more extensive emergency repair.

Your roof contractor may be responsible for the repair of a bonded roof, but he is not responsible for repair of roof copings and parapets. Many guarantees also do not include roof flashings. And no guarantee ever covers repair of walls, ceiling, equipment, or product damaged by water. Remember, too, some guarantees expire when the contractor retires from business or goes bankrupt. Be sure you read every guarantee clause before you sign the contract.

A reliable roofing contractor can be a big help in planning and carrying out a good roof maintenance program. But, whether the repairs are made by the contractor or by your own plant maintenance crew, the prime responsibility for roof care rests on the plant owner. And it usually falls on the shoulders of the plant engineer or maintenance superintendent. Therefore, the engineer or superintendent should acquaint himself with the principles and practices of proper roof care.

The majority of manufacturing plant buildings are topped with a built-up roof, therefore, we shall only discuss this type of a roof. Many of the maintenance techniques, however, are equally applicable to other types of roofs and should be helpful in inspiring good care of roofs, no matter what their design.

Built-up Roofs

A typical built-up roof consists of a supporting base or deck, and a laminated surface application or mat.

Deck. The roof deck may be of wood, steel plate, poured concrete, precast concrete slabs, gypsum slab, or other structural material. The ideal deck is leakproof against common roofing materials such as asphalt or tar. It does not depend on the first layer of sheathing paper to prevent seepage, and it is structurally firm.

Mat. The mat is composed of one or more thicknesses of roofing felt. This felt is made of a fabric impregnated with tar or asphalt which provides the waterproof qualities. The fabric acts only as a reinforcement to hold the waterproofing in place.

Roofing fabrics are normally made of paper, rag, or asbestos fabrics, or combinations of these. Roofing is estimated and sold in squares. A square of roofing is the amount required to cover 100 square feet. Single-ply felts usually run fifteen pounds per square. Double-ply runs thirty pounds. Special felts may run as high as ninety pounds. Size and area of one roll vary according to brand. The more common widths are thirty-two and thirty-six inches.

In a built-up roof, several layers of roofing felt are applied to the roof with a hot bonding agent. There are two main agents, tar and asphalt. Each has its advantages.

Tar will stand up under water better than asphalt. But it has a low melting point and needs a binder of gravel to keep it from running when softened by hot weather. Hence tar is better for flat than steep grades. Gravel helps to insulate the roof against solar heat and retards drying out. It can take the brunt of foot traffic. It helps protect the roof against fire from sparks and embers. (See Figure 20-1.)

Asphalt can be used on any grade. An asphalt roof has a smooth surface, hence dirt gets washed off easily by wind and rain. You can spot flaws in an asphalt roof more readily. And it is easier to maintain.

Construction and Repair

Laying roof deck. The roof deck must be leakproof against the hot bonding agent. If it is not, apply a preliminary layer or capsheet of 30-pound felt with a two-inch overlap. This layer is nailed on along the seams. The roof plies are then applied over a mopping of tar or asphalt between layers.

The number of plies a roof has is fixed by the width of overlap of each layer of felt. An overlap of half the width of a roll gives two plies. Overlap of two thirds give a three-ply mat.

The felt is laid starting at the lowest point, parallel to the gutter. In a typical five-ply roof using a two-ply capsheet the first gutter strip is cut one-third the width of the roll. Another two-thirds strip is added, then a full width strip, all touching the edge at the gutter. Ensuing full width strips are then laid, with a two-thirds overlap, to the crown of the roof. Here partial width strips are again used, as at the gutter. There are several ways to use different weight capsheets or roof layers with varying overlaps to obtain a given number of plies.

Drainage. A good roof drains well, usually into gutters. It doesn't have any hollows that will hold stagnant water, which rots an asphalt mat. All low points have drains with properly sized downspouts. Valleys between monitors or saw-teeth are pitched to an outlet at either end, or to a center drain.

Parapet and coping. Many buildings have outer walls or parapets that extend above the roof deck. If not properly constructed and joined to the roofing mat, they can be a prolific source of leaks. (See Figure 20-2.)

The outer face of the parapet is usually an extension of the face masonry of the building. The inside face or back-up, however, may be made of common brick, building tile, concrete block, or even poured concrete. In between faces, if they do not meet, you may find loosely filled mortar and rubble, or hollow tile.

Most important part of a parapet in preventing water leakage is the coping, and the cap flashing that seals the top. Copings are made of units of clay tile,

Figure 20-1 / Typical built-up roof is laid with overlapping felt strips so thickness of mat is same at all points. Here a 5-ply mat consists of one 2-ply capsheet and three 1-ply strips. Each layer is mopped over with hot asphalt or tar to make it waterproof.

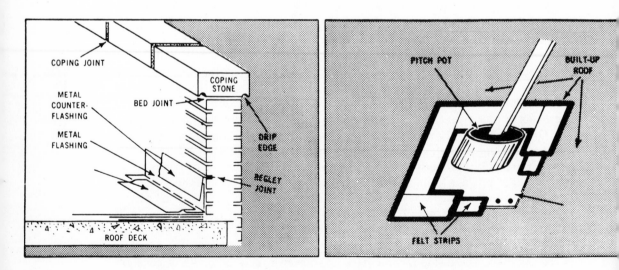

Figure 20-2 / Good construction of parapet wall and coping adds to life of roof. Flashing keeps water out of corner. Anchors or eyes for cables or signposts will not harm roof if properly sealed off. The pitch pot method is one good way.

metal, cement, brick, or continuous concrete. Joints may be made of cement or mastic. To do a good sealing job, copings themselves must be waterproof, and the joints must stay leakproof.

Flashings. The angle where the roof deck meets the parapet wall is a critical joint that has to be protected against water leakage by a special treatment known as flashing. Different roofing contractors have different ways of installing it. In principle, a good flashing keeps water on the roof from getting under the edge of the roof mat. It also keeps out water that flows down the parapet. This usually requires two kinds of flashing—base flashing and counterflashing.

One common method of *base flashing* is to turn the roof mat up against the vertical surface. Sometimes a separate angle strip is cemented to the roof mat. This is called angle or gutter flashing. In either case, the turned-up portion must extend high enough to exceed the depth of any flow of water along the wall.

Counterflashing hangs downward from a tight joint in the inside parapet wall, known as a reglet joint, and laps over the base flashing. Sometimes it extends through the whole width of the parapet from a point just below or near the coping. Then it is known as a cap flashing or wall flashing.

Flashings are made of various materials—roofing felt, sheet metal, or saturated fabric membrane.

Other roof structures. Every vertical roof structure that interrupts the plane of the roof surface needs joint treatment in the form of flashing.

Some structures are an integral part of the roof, such as elevators penthouses, monitors, skylights, and expansion joints. Other structures—chimneys, stacks, exhaust vents, and other ventilators—pierce through the roof deck. In both types, the aim of the treatment is the same—to keep water out of the joint by use of flashing and counterflashing or their functional equivalents.

Where anchors or eyes for rods or cables are fastened to the roof structure, the anchor is often sealed off by surrounding it with a metal collar known as a pitch pot. The collar is filled with mastic, and treated with flashing around the outside surface. Another way is to use a fabric covering or skirt covered with asphalt or tar.

Elements That Can Ruin Your Roof

Sun. Most roofs do not wear out—they dry out. Hot sunshine on a roof causes the volatile ingredients of tar or asphalt to evaporate. The asphalt oxidizes and becomes brittle. Slowly the roof mat loses its elasticity—the surface coating becomes checked and flakes off, exposing the felt. What you have left is a dried up roof felt that acts like dry paper—brittle, easily torn, and in the last stages, ready to absorb rather than repel moisture. Thus it is susceptible to easy damage from wind, rain, and foot traffic. And it loses the elasticity to respond to temperature change stresses, so it cracks.

Water. When water seeps into a dry roof, or steals through a crack, it causes a leak. But worse damage is yet to come with freezing weather, which turns the moisture into ice. This tears and heaves the roof, leaves it wide open.

Wind. A strong wind takes advantage of any weakness in the roof mat or structure. It drives rain into defective joints in the mat or parapet; it tears at loose seams; and it sways roof structures.

Temperature changes. Expansion and contraction are at work all the time. Often expansion strains in a new wood or concrete structure cause the roof mat to tear. Seasonal changes in temperature expand and contract mortar in the coping joints, and provide an opening wedge for water to do its worst. The various forces of expansion and contraction in the roof deck and building walls wrestle at the angle joint and strain the flashings. Expansion of hot stacks loosens the roof joints.

Settlement. Settlement of roof or wall structures is not unusual. It will cause trouble wherever the horizontal and vertical surfaces meet. As walls settle, or as roof timbers dry and shrink, extra strains are exerted on flashings. Or the roof may settle below the level of the drain pipe. This will cause either a backup of flood water, or a leak through the crack around the drain.

Outside interference. Roof mats are not designed for extra accessories such as signs and electric wires. Nor are they intended for regular foot traffic. Many agencies are not careful, when installing such services, to provide the extra precautions of flashing and mastic waterproofing. Sign supports or braces are spiked or bolted to any convenient spot on the roof, regardless of its structural relationship. Anchorage planks are spiked or lagged to the deck, piercing both the mat and deck, and causing serious leakage.

Inspection

Take frequent looks at your roof. Good care of a roof begins with regular inspection of the roof premises for signs of weakness or repair. The biggest step in holding down maintenance expenses is to catch your roof troubles before they are born, or while they are still young.

You can expect any person to find the bad leaks, but it takes a qualified person to spot the small leaks. Your inspector has to know what to inspect and what to look for. Competent inspection includes many points—copings, parapets, flashings, skylights, ventilators, inside and outside walls, ceilings, and so on.

Semiannual inspections. Inspect the roof every six months, preferably in the early fall to anticipate winter weather, and in the early spring in preparation for the hot summer sun.

Special inspections of the roof should be made after a violent rain or windstorm, or after a nearby fire, or after "outside-interference" workmen have been on the roof.

Use a roof plan. A schematic drawing or plot plan of the roofs of all buildings in your plant can be a big help in making roof inspections.

To be of value, show on this plan the location of each roof, and when installed. Also state who did the job, guarantee (if any) and approximate dimensions. Set up an inspection chart. After each inspection enter brief notes on the condition of the roof and the general nature and cost of repairs. This data will prepare you for the next inspection, and guide you on future repairs and choice of new materials and methods to be used.

One helpful technique is to note any weak points on the roof you feel do not need repair at least until after the next inspection, but must be checked at that time.

How to inspect. Is it better to inspect area by area, or item by item? For instance, is it better to inspect all copings, then all parapets, then all flashings, or do you inspect everything in one round of the roof walls?

It is a matter of choice and convenience. Certainly it seems sensible to complete one roof at a time. The important thing is not to miss any parts of any items.

Use a checklist. Best way to make sure you do not overlook an important detail in roof inspection is to arm yourself with a checklist. You can easily make up your own form, or you might get one from a leading contractor. Use a separate sheet for each roof.

A typical checklist shows all major roof items in the left column, such as copings, parapets, roof deck, roof covering, drains and gutters, skylights, and penthouses. Under each item is a subdivision of the point to be checked. *For example,* under roof covering you might list blisters, loose or torn seams, cracks, old patches, condition of mat. Across the top of the page are headings for vertical columns—condition OK, number of defects, repair at once, repair when convenient, check next inspection, special comments.

A good roof inspector will look at many things besides the roof mat for clues to actual leaks or those in the making. Obviously, the first thing to do is ask the building maintenance staff if there are any known leaks, or any complaints of leaks from employees. Such reports help pin point other symptoms later on.

We have grouped these symptoms into convenient parts of the roof structure.

1. *Exterior walls of building.* Look for settlement cracks or other evidences of building movement that might have strained the flashing or displaced drainage facilities. Efflorescence—that whitish, powdery excretion from mortar joints—may mean there are leaks in the coping or parapet up above.

Interior walls. Stains or seepage indicate leaking walls or roof. Damp walls, chipped or discolored paint are clues to roof leakage.

2. *Underside of roof deck.* Look for any signs of deterioration from leakage above. If the deck is of wood, list rotted or warped boards for replacement. Make a note to check roof above any watermarked boards. Sometimes a wooden roof deck is weakened by excessive heat and humidity from processes below it.

If the deck is of concrete or gypsum slab, look for cracks and stains. Spots of rust might come from wet reinforcing rods. In a gypsum deck, leaking water usually causes spalling. In metal decks, rust spots mean trouble with condensation or leaks.

Topside. Only a few defects are apparent in a topside inspection. A sharp indentation or break at right angles to the boards in a wood deck points to a sprung board. If the roof mat gives under you, the board may be rotted. But there are secondary clues. Cracks in roofing felt may be due to cracks in the roof deck. It is always a good idea to check the roof deck wherever you find leaks or holes in the roof mat.

3. *Drainage.* Check for any changes in the original slope of the roof. Has any part of the deck sagged, to produce hollows for standing water?

In a wood deck, you can try to correct or restore the proper level by timber shoring. When this is not feasible, and the hollow is less than four inches, a good remedy is to fill the low area with asphalt mastic either above the old mat or under a new one. Always add a water repellent surface over it.

Deeper hollows can be repaired by a "saddle" or false roof that bridges over the depression. This is covered by a new roof to match the built-up roof. Hollows in concrete roofs can be built up the same way. Sometimes you can clear the trouble by adding or relocating a drain.

Drainage system. Make sure no rain water accumulates on the roof during a rainfall. Slow acting drains and gutters may cause a backup of water above the parapet flashing. See that all drains are sound, flush to the roof, and clear of debris. If settlement or expansion has worked a drain spout above the roof level, re-install it.

4. *Copings.* Coping troubles are mostly of two kinds, either the coping material loses its water repellency and absorbs moisture; or the mortar in the coping joint cracks. In either case, water drains down into the parapet, and where it will finally come out is hard to tell.

Often you can see the effects on the outside facing as you approach the building. More than likely, however, the leak will drain out of the inside facing, because of poor masonry work. Once frost gets in, mortar and bricks may be pushed by ice pressure out of the wall.

Repairing the Roof

Cracked or crumbling coping joints. You can point them up with a mastic that adheres to the coping and adjusts itself to expansion and contraction. First chisel out the old material to a depth of at least one-half inch. If all the mortar is crumbling, remove it and pack all but the outer one-half inch of the joint with oakum. Then force the mastic in the outer groove with a caulking tool or gun, and finish it at surface level. If appearance is not a factor, you can use the less expensive black caulking materials. Otherwise you can get a mastic that will match in color and will not stain.

Porous copings. When copings absorb water, you need to treat the surface to seal them against moisture. There are several ways to do this by brush application of a sealer. Which sealer you use depends upon the need to preserve appearance and the degree of porosity. You can apply an "invisible sealer," but it does not weather as well as other sealers that do have a darkening effect on light copings.

Another method of keeping appearance is to use a pigmented mastic that actually simulates the original appearance. This mastic is available in a variety of colors to suit most conditions. It is especially useful where disintegration of the coping has reached only the early stages, before spalling has begun.

Broken or spalled copings. You can replace broken or spalled copings, but there is a less expensive way of repair. It involves restoration of the shape with suitable mortar and application of the protective coatings as just described. This method of face lifting will work as good as new.

Parapets. Disintegration of a parapet most often starts with a defective coping. But not always. The stormy gusts that sweep along a roof and hit the parapet are a severe test on the backup masonry. Or water may accumulate above the height of the flashing for several days. Thus it permeates the cracked or porous joint. The evidences are efflorescence, spalling, open joints and loose bricks, and leaks to the building interior. The repair of broken parapets is a masonry job.

Sometimes a maintenance superintendent will seek extra security for the inside of his parapet by applying a plaster coat of cement mortar containing a water resistant compound. Where units have been spalled, this procedure gives you a uniform surface. But remember, it does not eliminate water ingress from a defective coping.

There is a question about the advisability of sealing the interior or exterior wall surfaces. If walls are not allowed to breathe, according to some authorities, the moisture in building interiors can not migrate through the walls. This leads to excessive condensation of moisture entrapped in the walls themselves, and weakens them. Vapor barriers should not be applied without careful study of the principles and favorable applications.

Flashings. Flashing flaws are among the commonest causes of roof troubles. Too often flashing defects are overlooked when you inspect the roof for leaks. Look for loose flashings, or for torn or even missing sections.

Be sure to check all flashings for tightness of bond. A metal flashing may be in good condition, but may fail to do its job because of improper bond. This will allow water to seep between the edge of the mat and the base flashing, or between the counterflashing and the wall. Also, a flashing that is not turned up far enough may allow backup water to stand against the wall and leak down to the roof deck.

Once water gets behind a flashing at the parapet angle, frost action follows. The flashing is loosened from its fastenings, thus opening the way to worse damage.

Metal flashings, unless made of copper or other fairly noncorrosive metal, are subject to rust. It pays to give them a good protective coating. Once they get holes, they are poor protection.

You can replace defective metal flashings with so-called membrane flashings at lower cost. There are several types to satisfy various conditions. The "sliding and overlapping" type is most commonly used. Sometimes the "accordion pleat" type is necessary, or the "regleted" type. All are equally effective when properly employed.

Roof mat. Roof mat troubles are not usually traceable to a single cause. When you spot the following symptoms, check carefully for the cause, so you can make the right repairs.

Blisters. Three main causes for blisters are: (1) misapplication has entrapped air, (2) leaks have allowed moisture to form pockets between layers, or (3) volatile ingredients have given off gases that have formed pockets.

Small blisters do not need attention unless there are many of them. In such a case, you must cut them off before you give the roof a general membrane treatment. Cut all large blisters open with a criss-cross cut so you can lay back the roofing felt for examination. If any water is inside, mop it dry. Make sure the felt and deck are unharmed. Replace decayed timber. Recement the felts to the deck and apply a membrane covering over the slits.

Loose or torn seams. This occurs when the original bond of roof felts begins to weaken, putting all the strain on the seams. The seams loosen, lift, and are torn by the wind. When this happens, cement all loose edges back into place. Sometimes you need to reinforce the seams by cementing six-inch widths of membrane over their entire length and covering them with tar or asphalt.

Cracks. Cracks are caused by (1) contraction stains in the mat, and (2) drying out of original saturating oils which leave the mat hard and unelastic.

When an asphalt roof dries up it reveals a dry, powdery brittleness. On a tar and gravel roof you will find bare spots where the gravel has washed or blown away because the tar has lost its adhesiveness.

Contraction in a hardening roof mat often shows up most plainly at the seams. If seams are drawing or curling, it may mean the felts are losing their pliability. Improper application may cause the same effect. In the case of a nailed seam, contraction often withdraws the felt from the nails, so that the nail heads protrude. Unless repaired, this may lead to rusting, then holes and leaks.

Cracks at the ridges of sloping roofs are usually the result of contraction and a movement of the mat down the slope.

Sometimes hardening of the roof mat is abetted by poor results of previous maintenance efforts. Hot or cold applications that do not penetrate the felt, but merely seal the surface, are likely to stiffen and crack in time. Occasionally you will see a roof that has been treated many times this way cracked in an alligator pattern.

Fairly new roofs will also crack. This happens when the roof deck itself cracks. The real solution may be to install an expansion joint, or to make structural repairs.

Repair of local cracks and miscellaneous breaks follows a general pattern. All you need is roof cement and membrane. This membrane is made of cotton, jute, or glass fabrics saturated with asphaltic materials, or unsaturated. It comes in rolls of six, twelve, twenty-seven and thirty-six inches wide. The membrane itself is not waterproof. Its function is to reinforce the cement, which is the real water repellent. The membrane must be closely bonded to a supporting surface—do not use it to bridge over a depression.

To repair a break, first clean it thoroughly, cement any loose roofing felt back into place, and apply a bonding coat of cement. Then cover it with a patch of membrane, and over that apply a second coat.

Wearing spots. Check the causes of abrasions or erosions in the roof surface. Sometimes maintenance employees beat a path on a roof to make regular inspections of superstructures, or to raise the flag every day. For this condition we suggest a superimposed wood walkway. Other worn spots may be caused by water that spills at the same place. Here you need only lay down a splash board or tile to prevent further erosion.

Old patches. The fact that you have had trouble there before is a good reason why you should always check old patches. Make sure they are tight and standing up well.

Old roof. Let us assume that the roof you have inspected is an old built-up one, and that you find one or more of the conditions, just described, is widespread: bad cracks, dried up felt, large blisters, gravel surface gone, and open seams.

What are you to do about it? Here are six possibilities—consider which is best for your roof.

1. *Leave the roof alone.* Your roof may be guaranteed, and its condition the responsibility of those who laid it. So you decide to ignore the roof's deterioration, even at the risk of the well-being of the building.

2. *Rip it off.* But would you go to the expense of buying a new roof if the present roof has value in it that can be made to give trouble-free service?

3. *Cement a new covering to the old roof.* This practice of putting on a "cap sheet" seldom proves satisfactory. You are expecting one or two new plies to do the job of a multiple ply roof. You do not get a good bond—heavy winds may tear it. The moisture absorbed by the old dried up roof may cause serious blisters in the new roof.

4. *"Hot mop" the roof.* Such treatment builds up the coating, but it does not resaturate the dry felt, and it prolongs the roof life very little. Very heavy hot applications check and crack readily.

5. *Apply a resaturating agent.* This may preserve the roof, but it is no cure for leaks. It works only if the roof is watertight and you use an agent that insures continued flexibility and water resistance.

6. Cover the entire roof with a flexible membrane embedded into and coated with a roof preservative. Where there are still whole felts left on the old roof, but cracks and breaks occurring, this treatment may give the roof a new lease on life.

A good roof, properly maintained, will last the life of a building. The secret of trouble free, low cost maintenance lies in the regular resaturation of surface treatment of the roofing mat with a proper penetrant or coating while it is still sound and whole. And the early repair of cracks and breaks by the simple membrane treatment is economically sound and safe.

When breaking of felts is widespread, however, and deterioration is well advanced, we recommend you have the roof completely removed and a new roof built up from the base. Do not try to save such a roof by merely coating it with tar or asphalt. Unfortunately many plant maintenance executives have been educated to believe nothing can go wrong with a roof that a few barrels of asphalt or tar, and maybe a cap sheet, will not cure.

Roof Repair Hints

Planning. Know exactly what repairs are to be made and exactly what areas are to be treated. Mark them off with chalk and measure them. List every item. Write out the methods of treatment so that the job will proceed smoothly from beginning to end.

Now you are ready to order the needed materials, and arrange for the necessary equipment and crew. It is a good idea to plan where materials and equipment should be placed when they arrive.

You may need a hoist to lift material to the roof. Sometimes it is wise to store most of the materials on the ground to avoid cluttering up the roof.

You should also decide whether a roofing pump will be of any help. This is a portable power pump with hose attachment for piping cold materials from a container on the ground through a flexible hose to any place on the roof. Such a pump can be especially useful in saving time and labor.

First step. Cleaning all roof surfaces is the first step in major roof repairs. This includes parapets, copings, and flashings. Sometimes you can do this with a long-handled push broom. In the case of a tar and gravel roof, you have to cut the gravel off by hand or use a gravel removing machine.

Marking. Cleaning usually erases some of the original chalk marks. Go over the whole area again with roofer's chalk, indicating where work is to be done.

Local repairs first. It is well to make all minor and local repairs before you undertake roof area treatments. Complete the work on parapets and copings, *for example,* before starting work on the roof proper. By employing this sequence, you can remove the debris resulting from chiseling of mortar joints along with other roof dirt.

Parapet cleaning should include wire brushing of any efflorescence from the brickwork. Do not begin repair of flashings until completion of all pointing or resetting of parapet units and repair of coping joints.

Summary. No manual, however complete, will insure effective roof maintenance or repair. The skill, adaptability, and good judgment of the men on the job are important factors in doing a good job.

Technically there should not be any mystery about how to obtain proper roof maintenance. It really requires three simple procedures: (1) regular inspection to catch defects early, (2) determination of the best remedies, and (3) proper application of corrective measures.

21 / **ROOM CLEANING**

(*Source:* Buildings Management Division, General Services Administration, Washington, D. C.)

Job Description

The job of room cleaning consists of emptying wastepaper baskets and ash trays, sweeping or vacuum cleaning offices, vacuum cleaning rugs, sweeping adjacent corridors, dusting all parts of rooms and corridor spaces that can be reached while standing on the floor, damp wiping glass and other specified surfaces; also the following duties when they occur in an assigned work area, cleaning washbasins, private toilets, phone booths and drinking fountains; taking proper care of the room cleaning equipment; and performing other work assigned by the supervisor. Employees assigned to room cleaning should be instructed to turn out lights not in the immediate area being cleaned, and close any windows found open. They should also notice burned out lights and other defective items and report these to their supervisor.

Equipment, Materials and Supplies

A. *Equipment:*

For room cleaning:

a. Bags for collecting wastepaper and trash
b. Metal container for collecting cigarette butts and ashes
c. Radiator dust brush
d. Putty knife
e. Dustpan
f. Dustpan broom
g. Dust cloth (cheesecloth treated with polyethylene glycol)
h. Wiping cloths, waffleweave
i. Sponge
j. Bucket
k. Sweep mop (treated with polyethylene glycol)
l. Corn broom
m. Equipment carrier
*n. Toilet brush
†o. Vacuum equipment or vacuum cleaner with hose, bare floor tool and carpet tool

* To be used where needed.
† Alternate equipment.

B. *Materials:*

For room cleaning:

a. White soap cake
b. Sand soap
c. Detergent (soapless synthetic)
d. Liquid metal polish

C. *Supplies:*

For private toilets:

a. Hand soap (liquid, powdered or bar)
b. Towels
c. Toilet tissue

Job Methods

Operation Steps   *Explanation*

Step 1—Preparation for Work

1. Obtain necessary equipment, materials and supplies.

Obtain necessary equipment, materials and supplies as listed under "Equipment, Materials and Supplies."

Operation Steps	*Explanation*
2. Proceed to assigned work area.	All the equipment, materials and supplies should be taken to the starting point of the assigned work area, to be used as needed.

Step 2—Emptying

1. Empty wastepaper baskets.	Starting at one end of the work area empty each wastepaper basket into the bag for collecting wastepaper and trash. Replace empty basket in original location. When bag is filled place in the corridor for collection. Do not place wastepaper baskets on furniture.
2. Empty ash trays.	While in the area collecting wastepaper, empty each ash tray into the metal container provided for that purpose and replace the ash trays in their original location. Ash trays should not be stacked on furniture.

PRECAUTIONS

1. In order to prevent possible injury, empty wastepaper baskets directly into the bag without handling the contents.
2. Ash trays should not be emptied into wastepaper baskets or into bags for collection of wastepaper and trash.
3. Avoid spilling any paper or ashes on floor.

Step 3—Dusting, Wiping and Polishing

1. Dust rooms and corridor space.	Use a treated cheesecloth to dust horizontal surfaces daily and vertical surfaces as required. Start with highest surfaces that can be reached while standing on the floor and work downward. Surfaces such as radiators, desks, file cabinets, office door panels and louvers and elevator hoistway doors should be dusted.
2. Damp wipe certain surfaces.	Use damp wiping cloth to wipe mirrors, window sills, ash trays, bookcase glass, door glass, door sills, telephone booth glass and all other glass surfaces except windows and transoms.

Operation Steps	*Explanation*
3. Polish metal surfaces.	Use metal polish and dry cloth to polish metal surfaces as directed by supervisor.

PRECAUTIONS

1. Do not disturb papers, books or other material on desks, tables or files.
2. Do not damp wipe desks or steel cabinets.

Step 4—Sweeping

1. Sweep corridor floors.	a. Use the radiator dust brush to clean radiators as required.
	b. During the sweeping operation, use the putty knife to scrape any gum or other foreign material from the floor.
	c. Use the treated sweep mop to sweep all corridor space, including telephone booths, within the area of the zone.
	d. Use the dustpan and dustpan broom to pick up any loose sweepings.
2. Sweep office floors.	a. Use the radiator dust brush to clean radiators as required.
	b. During the sweeping operation, use the putty knife to scrape any gum or other foreign material from the floor.
	c. Use the treated sweep mop to sweep all office floors in the assigned work area. Start at the far side of the room and sweep toward the door.
	d. Shake or vacuum the sweep mop as required during the sweeping operation.
	e. Use the dustpan and the dustpan broom to pick up any loose sweepings.

NOTE

In some instances where corridor scrubbing or floor waxing is scheduled in the assigned room cleaning area it will be necessary to sweep these areas before proceeding with the routine operations.

Operation Steps   *Explanation*

Step 5—(When central vacuum cleaning equipment is available.)

1. Clean corridor floors.

    a. Use the radiator dust brush to clean radiators as required.

    b. During the vacuum cleaning operation, use the putty knife to scrape any gum or foreign material from the floors.

2. Clean with vacuum.

    Use central vacuum equipment with hose and bare floor tool to clean all corridor floor space, including telephone booths, within the assigned area.

3. Clean office floors.

    a. Use the radiator dust brush to clean radiators as required.

    b. During the vacuum cleaning operation, use the putty knife to scrape any gum or foreign material from the floor.

    c. Use central vacuum equipment with hose and bare floor tool to clean all office floor space in the assigned area.

NOTE

In some instances where corridor scrubbing or floor waxing is scheduled in the assigned room cleaning area it will be necessary to sweep these areas before proceeding with the routine operations.

Step 6

Replace furniture and equipment.

    Replace in their proper locations any furniture, equipment, wastepaper baskets, and ash trays which have become disarranged during the cleaning operation.

Operation Steps	*Explanation*

Step 7

1. Clean wash basins.	a. Use sponge, warm water, and white soap to clean all wash basins in the assigned work area. If the basin is unusually dirty, use a sand soap in place of the white soap.
	b. Use a damp cloth to wipe all chromium fixtures.
2. Clean private toilets.	a. Use a toilet brush to flush and brushwash the interior of all water closets. Work the brush as far into the trap as it will reach. Use the brush to wash thoroughly under rounded inside rim of bowl.
	b. Wash and rinse water closet seat with a clean wet wiping cloth and white soap as necessary.
	c. Use a wet wiping cloth with white soap to clean all exterior porcelain surfaces. If necessary, use sand soap in place of white soap.
	d. Use a damp wiping cloth to rinse and damp-dry all external porcelain surfaces.
	e. Flush toilet to rinse inside of bowl.
	f. Use a damp wiping cloth to wipe all chromium fixtures.
3. Replenish supplies.	Replenish soap, towels and toilet tissue.

PRECAUTIONS

1. *Do not* use sand soap on chromium finish.
2. Report leaky spigots to supervisor.
3. *Be sure* to keep wiping cloths used in private toilets separate from those used elsewhere.

Step 8

Clean rugs.	Use a vacuum cleaner or central vacuum system to clean all rugs on the assigned work area. Use corn broom to lay nap of rug after vacuuming.

Operation Steps	*Explanation*
	Corn broom may be used to clean rugs in buildings with only a few rugs where a vacuum machine is unavailable.

PRECAUTIONS

1. Empty vacuum machine dirt receptacle after each day's use.

2. Do not strike furniture or baseboards with vacuum equipment.

Step 9

Clean drinking fountains.	Use warm water, white soap and a sponge to clean the bowl of all drinking fountains. Wipe remainder of fountain with a clean wiping cloth. Wipe all chromium fixtures with a clean dry wiping cloth.

PRECAUTION

Do not use sand soap on chromium finish.

Step 10—Return equipment, unused materials and supplies to storage

1. Equipment and unused materials and supplies.	Gather all pieces of equipment and unused materials and supplies, put them in their places on the equipment carrier and return to the gear storage room.
2. Equipment.	Clean and store all articles of equipment. (For details of cleaning and storage see "Care of Equipment.")
3. Unused materials and supplies.	Return all unused materials and supplies to proper storage place.

PRECAUTIONS

1. *Be sure* that covers are replaced securely on the containers of all materials and supplies.

2. *Be sure* to hang wiping cloths so that cloths used on toilets will not be confused with those used elsewhere.

Care of Equipment

A. *Bag for Collecting Wastepaper and Trash:*

1. Do not empty ash trays into this bag.

2. Do not allow bag to be caught in door or on sharp objects as this might damage the bag.

B. *Metal Container for Collecting Cigarette Butts and Ashes:*

    1. Empty container daily.

    2. Use a damp wiping cloth to wipe the inside and outside of container to remove all remaining ashes and other material.

    3. Store container so that it will not be damaged.

C. *Radiator Dust Brush:*

    1. Comb tufts of brush out straight.

    2. Store brush on a flat surface so that tufts will be flat and straight.

    3. Do not wet the brush.

    4. Do not use a radiator brush for any purpose other than cleaning radiators.

D. *Putty Knife:*

    1. Use the putty knife to scrape gum and like substances from the floor.

    2. Do not use putty knife for a screw driver or other improper purposes.

    3. Store putty knife in a clean dry place.

E. *Dustpan:*

    1. Empty the dustpan into waste can and damp wipe it to remove all dirt and dust.

    2. Hang up dustpan so that it will not be bent or otherwise damaged.

F. *Dustpan Broom:*

    1. When broom becomes soiled, wash it in warm synthetic detergent solution and rinse it in clear water.

    2. Store broom so that its weight is not on the bristles. (This is especially necessary when bristles are wet.)

G. *Dust Cloth (cheesecloth treated with polyethylene glycol):*

    1. Keep the cloth clean and free from grime or oily material.

    2. Wash the cloth once a week or as required in a warm synthetic detergent solution, and rinse in clear warm water.

    3. Squeeze out the cloth and treat it with polyethylene glycol as directed.

    4. Hang the cloth to dry where there is a good circulation of air.

H. *Wiping Cloths (waffleweave):*

    1. Wash the cloths daily with white soap and warm water and rinse them in clear warm water.

    2. Wring the water out of the cloths and hang them up to dry where there is a good circulation of air.

I. *Sponge:*

    1. Rinse the sponge in clean water and squeeze out excess water after each day's use. Wash a very dirty sponge in a warm synthetic detergent solution, rinse in clean water and squeeze out excess water.

    2. Store in a clean dry place.

J. *Bucket (12 qt.):*

1. Rinse and dry the inside and outside of the bucket.
2. Avoid hitting anything with the bucket as this might cause leaks.
3. In storing do not place heavy objects on the bucket which would tend to damage it.

K. *Sweep Mop (treated):*

1. Treated sweep mops should be shaken or vacuum cleaned both during use and at the close of operations each day. They should be kept clean and free from grime or oily material.
2. Once every two weeks remove the mophead, shake out as much dust as possible and wash mop in a warm solution of synthetic detergent. Rinse in clear warm water.
3. Wring out as much water as possible and treat with polyethylene glycol as directed.
4. Replace the mophead on the handle and hang the mop so that a good air circulation will be obtained to assist in drying the mop.

L. *Corn Broom:*

1. Soak a new broom overnight before using it the first time.
2. Never stand a broom on the straws when storing.
3. So that the broom will always be dry, store it where there is free circulation of air.
4. Wash broom as required, using a warm synthetic detergent solution and rinse in clear water and hang broom to dry.
5. Never use the broom when it is wet.
6. Do not use the broom for scrubbing.
7. When using the broom rotate it so that it will wear evenly.

M. *Equipment Carrier:*

1. Do not allow carrier to strike walls, radiators, or other objects.
2. Do not take the carrier into offices; *always* leave it in the corridor.

N. *Toilet Brush:*

1. Wash the brush daily using a warm synthetic detergent solution.
2. Shake out excess water.
3. Hang up where air circulation is good so the brush will dry.

O. *Vacuum Cleaner and/or Equipment:*

1. Empty the dirt receptacle. Wipe machine after each day's use, with a dry wiping cloth. Wind cord loosely on the hooks provided.
2. Do not run machine over electric cord or pull against cord when it is plugged into receptacle.
3. Do not allow machine to strike walls, radiators or other objects.
4. Report needed servicing or repairs to the supervisor.
5. After use, return hose, carpet tools, and extension tubes to a clean dry storage room where they will not be damaged.

6. Do not allow doors to be closed on hose or electric cord.

7. Keep floor tool and carpet tool clean at all times.

P. *Instructions for Treating Mops (all kinds) and Dust Cloths:*

1. Treatment of mops and dust cloths with polyethylene glycol:

   a. *Instructions for Mixing solution:*

   Polyethylene glycol is not to be used as it is purchased but should be dissolved in water. Use three parts of water to one part of polyethylene glycol. After thorough mixing this solution can be applied to mops and dust cloths.

   b. *Instructions for Treating Mops and Cloths:*

   The mop or cloth should be hung up and the glycol solution sprayed on the cloth or on the head of the mop. Approximately one fluid ounce should be sprayed on a three-quarter pound mop, approximately one and one-half fluid ounces on a one pound mop, approximately two ounces on a one and one-quarter pound mop, and approximately one fluid ounce should be sprayed on a square yard of dust cloth. For mops of different weights the solution should be applied approximately at the rate specified above. The mop and/or cloth should be treated the day before they are to be used.

Performance Inspection Guide

A. *Trash Removal:*

1. All wastepaper baskets should be empty and in place, clean and ready for use.

2. All ash trays should be empty and in place, clean and ready for use.

3. Ashes and trash should not be left on floor.

4. The trash bags, when filled, should be conveniently and neatly placed for collection.

B. *Sweeping or Vacuum Cleaning:*

1. There should not be any dirt left in corners, behind radiators, under furniture or behind doors.

2. Baseboards, furniture and equipment should not be disfigured or damaged during the cleaning operation.

3. There should not be any dirt left where sweepings were picked up.

4. Furniture and equipment moved during sweeping should be replaced.

5. All radiators should be free of dirt.

6. There should be no trash or foreign matter under desks, tables or chairs.

C. *Dusting:*

1. There should not be any dust streaks on desks or other office equipment.

2. Woodwork, after being properly dusted, should appear bright.

3. Corners and crevices should be free from any dust.

4. There should not be any oily spots or smudges on walls, caused by touching them.

5. When inspected with a flashlight there should be few traces of dust on any surface.

6. Radiators, window sills, door ledges, door frames, door louvers, elevator hoistway doors, window frames, wainscoting, baseboards, columns, and partitions should be free of dust.

D. *Damp-wiping:*

Mirrors, window ventilators, ash trays, door glass, and all other glass that can be reached while standing on the floor, should be clean and free of dirt, dust, streaks and spots. (This job does not include window washing.)

E. *Clean Rugs:*

1. Rugs should be thoroughly clean and free from dust, dirt and other debris.

2. There should be no trash or foreign matter under desks, tables or chairs.

3. Any furniture moved during rug cleaning should be replaced.

F. *Clean Wash Basins:*

1. There should be no stains or spots on surfaces of wash basins.

2. Wash basins should be clean and bright.

3. Wall near wash basins should be free from spots or smears.

4. The floor should be free of water or soap solution.

5. All metal such as spigots and other hardware should be clean and bright.

G. *Clean Private Toilets:*

1. Toilet bowls and other porcelain surfaces should be clean and bright.

2. Towel, toilet paper and soap dispensers should be filled, clean and in good working order.

3. There should be no soil marks on the fixtures or walls.

4. The floor, wainscoting, and partitions should be clean.

H. *Clean Telephone Booths:*

1. Dust, dirt, and other foreign material shall have been cleaned from telephone booths.

2. Glass shall be clean and free of fingerprints, streaks and spots.

I. *Clean Drinking Fountains:*

1. The porcelain or white enamel surfaces of drinking fountains should be clean and free of stains.

2. The wall and floor around the drinking fountain should be free of spots and water marks.

3. All other surfaces of the fountain should be free of spots, stains and streaks.

Frequency and Production

A. *Frequency and Production Schedule:*

	Room Cleaning (Exclusive of rugs)
Frequency	Daily
Production Rate per Man-day	14,000 sq. ft., plus adjoining corridor area

B. *Qualifying Factor:*

Frequency rate may be modified as directed by supervisor.

Staffing

The man-day requirements of labor for office cleaning can be determined by use of the following formula:

$$\text{Man-days (of labor)} = \frac{\text{Quantity}}{\text{Production}} \times \frac{1}{\text{Frequency}}$$

where quantity equals the square feet of office area exclusive of corridors and exclusive of special areas, such as file rooms and laboratories which must be considered separately, and where frequency is the number of work days between operations.

If the frequency and/or production rate values as given in the Frequency and Production Schedule above have been modified to meet existing conditions at a particular location, then these modified values should be used in the above formula for the computation of the labor requirement.

For each rug twelve feet by fifteen feet in the assigned area, 175 square feet of office area should be subtracted from the production rate of 14,000 square feet.

SAMPLE CALCULATION

Consider a building that has 110,000 square feet of room area to clean daily which has no rugs, and which is occupied as normal office space so that the average cleaning values from the frequency and production schedules may be used.

$$\text{Man-days} = \frac{110,000}{14,000} \times \frac{1}{1} = 7.86 \text{ jobs}$$

To this figure must be added a factor to compensate for leave in order to arrive at the total number of positions needed to accomplish the work.

Conversion factor including compensation for leave = 1.15
Conversion factor × jobs = total positions required

Nine positions required to clean 110,000 square feet of office space daily, exclusive of rugs, plus adjoining corridor area.

• Where a room cleaning assignment does not require the full time of an employee, other duties should be assigned to secure 100 per cent utilization of his time.

Equipment and Materials Allocation and Replacement

Items	Allotment per Cleaner	Replacement or Reissue
Bags, wastepaper and trash	As required	As required
Broom, corn	1	1 per year
Broom, dustpan (hearth size corn broom)	1	1 per 2 years
Brush, radiator, dust	1	1 per year
Brush, toilet	1	1 per year
Bucket (12 qt.)	1	1 per 2 years
Cheesecloth	2 yards	52 yards per year
Cloth, wiping (waffleweave)	2	24 per year
Container (cigarette butts and ashes)	1	1 per 2 years
Detergent (soapless synthetic)	1 pound	50 pounds per year
Dustpan	1	1 per 2 years
Equipment carrier	1	1 per 10 years
Knife, putty (1¼")	1	1 per 2 years
Mop, sweep (complete)	1	1 per 3 years
Mop, sweep (refill only)	None	1 per year
Polish, metal (liquid)	1 pint	4 pints per year
Polyethylene glycol	1 pint solution	1 gallon glycol per year
Soap, sand	1 cake	
Soap, white (6 oz. cake)	1 cake	3 cakes per year
Sponge, scrap cellulose	1	25 cakes per year
Vacuum machine and attachments, (Domestic Type II, Class B, Size 2, Heavy Duty)	1	6 per year 1 per 10 years[*]

[*] Does not apply to replacement of vacuum cleaner attachments.

The allotment and replacement or reissue quantities are based on one room cleaner working regularly eight hours each working day on the job.

• Where other duties are assigned to a room cleaner to secure 100 per cent utilization of his time, consideration should be given to a reduction in the allotment and replacement quantities in relative proportion to the time spent per day on the other work.

22 / **STAIRWAY CLEANING**

(*Source:* Buildings Management Division, General Services Administration, Washington, D. C.)

Job Description

Stairway cleaning includes all cleaning work inside the confines of the stairwell that can be reached from the normal walking surface, such as sweeping stair landings and steps; removal of gum or other foreign substances; dusting stair railings, fire apparatus, doors, ledges, radiators and grilles; cleaning and polishing handrails, glass surfaces, metal doorknobs, and other metal and wooden surfaces; wall spotting; mopping or scrubbing stair landings and steps; thoroughly drying all water from such areas as a result of the mopping or scrubbing operation; and proper care and maintenance of the stair cleaning equipment. Employees assigned to this job should be instructed to notice lights out, loose railings and similar service defects, and to report them to their supervisors.

Equipment and Materials

A. *Equipment:*

1. For sweeping and dusting.
   a. Dustpan broom
   b. Dustpan
   c. Putty knife (1¼")
   d. Dust cloths (polyethylene glycol treated cheesecloth)
   e. Radiator dust brush

2. For polishing, wall spotting and mopping or scrubbing.
   a. Cotton mop (1¼ lb.)
   b. Deck scrubbing brush
   c. Bucket (with squeeze-type wringer)
   d. Wiping cloths (cheesecloth)
   e. Chamois

B. *Materials:*

1. For polishing, wall spotting and mopping.
   a. Warm water
   b. Liquid metal polish
   c. Lemon oil polish
   d. Detergent
   e. White soap (cake)

2. For scrubbing.
   a. Scouring powder
   b. White soap (cake)
   c. Warm water

Job Methods

Operation Steps	*Explanation*

A. *Sweeping and Dusting:*

Step 1

1. Obtain equipment needed. | Obtain equipment as needed for sweeping and dusting. (See list under "Equipment and Materials".)

Operation Steps	*Explanation*
2. Proceed to work zone.	Carry sweeping and dusting equipment to top landing where work is to start.

Step 2

1. Sweep landings and stairs.	Using the janitor set of broom and pan, start top landing and sweep all landings and stairs down to bottom landing, collecting the sweepings at each landing and each step into the dust pan.
2. Remove gum or foreign substances.	Use putty knife to remove any gum or other foreign substances from landings and steps during sweeping operation.
3. Dust radiators.	In the course of the sweeping operation use radiator brush to remove dirt and dust particles from radiators in stairway.

PRECAUTION

Make sure that all loose dirt is removed from the corners of the stair treads in the sweeping operation.

Step 3

1. Dust with treated dustcloths.	Start at bottom landing, and dust stair railings, fire apparatus, doors, ledges, radiator tops and grilles in the stairwell up to top landing. Use treated dustcloth to dust all surfaces that can be reached by standing on landings or steps.

PRECAUTION

Avoid using treated dustcloth on stairway walls.

B. *Polishing, Wall Spotting and Mopping or Scrubbing:*

Step 4

1. Obtain equipment and materials needed.	a. Obtain equipment and materials needed for this operation. (See list under "Equipment and Materials".)

Operation Steps	*Explanation*
	b. Place mopping or scrubbing equipment and materials at top landing clear of passageway until ready for use.
2. Secure clean bucket of warm water.	Obtain a bucket of warm water from the nearest service sink for use in cleaning glass surfaces and walls.

Step 5

1. Clean glass surfaces.	Use a clean, damp chamois to clean glass surfaces in doors and fire cabinets.
2. Clean and polish metal surfaces.	Use clean cloths, and metal polish as directed, to clean and polish metal handrails, metal door knobs and other metal surfaces.
3. Clean and polish wood surfaces.	Use clean cloths and lemon oil polish to clean and polish wooden handrails and other wood surfaces as directed.

PRECAUTION

Metal polish is not to be used on painted, lacquered, or other metal surfaces that have been specially treated.

Step 6

1. Normal wall spotting.	Use a clean, damp cloth to spot clean the wall up to a height that can be reached while standing on the stair landing or steps.
2. Removal of stubborn spots.	Use white soap on the damp cloth as an aid to removing any stubborn spots from the wall that cannot be cleaned off by normal wall spotting.

PRECAUTIONS

1. This step is for spot removal only and not to wash entire wall.
2. Wring cloths out after rinsing in bucket of clear water to avoid an excessive amount of water on the wall. Rinse cloths out often.
3. Be sure to wipe any soap particles from wall with a clean, damp cloth.

Operation Steps	*Explanation*

Step 7 (See Step 8.)

1. Mix warm water and detergent solution for mopping.	Mix one-half to three-quarters of an ounce of detergent per gallon of water.
2. Mop stairs and landings.	Wet mop with solution from bucket, start at top landing and mop stairs down to bottom landing. As may be necessary, grasp a few mop strands in your hand and rub the dirt from the stair tread corners during the mopping operation, and also remove any stubborn spots from the landings and stairs that are not cleaned off by normal mopping.
3. Dry stairs and landings.	Using mop, clean and well wrung out, thoroughly dry all water from the stair landings, steps, risers and baseboards.
4. Keep mop clean.	Rinse and wring out mop frequently in a clean bucket of water in order to properly clean and dry the stairs and landings.

NOTE

There should not be any water traces remaining after this step.

PRECAUTIONS

1. Be sure to rinse stairs and landings thoroughly after the scrubbing operation.

2. Avoid using an excessive amount of solution or water during the mopping, scrubbing or rinsing.

3. Take care not to splash or scar the walls, baseboards or stair risers with the equipment.

4. Do not allow the solution or water to run over the stair tread edges into the stairwell.

5. As may be appropriate, suitable warning should be given to the building occupants against the danger of slipping on the wet landings and stairs.

Operation Steps   *Explanation*

Step 8—When scrubbing is to be substituted for mopping
(See Step 7.)

1. Scrub landing.

Sprinkle scouring powder over landing. Use wet deck scrubbing brush, with handle, to thoroughly scrub landing.

2. Scrub stairs.

Remove handle from deck brush, sprinkle scouring agent on stairs and scrub thoroughly by hand.

C. *Returning Equipment and Materials to Storage:*

Step 9

1. Return all equipment and unused materials to storage location.

Gather all pieces of equipment and materials and proceed to proper storage location.

2. Mop and scrub brush.

Rinse out mop and scrub brush, wring or shake dry of excess water and place in proper storage position.

3. Cloths and chamois.

Rinse out all cloths and chamois in clean water and place for drying and storing.

4. Bucket and wringer.

Empty bucket, rinse and return bucket and wringer to proper storage position.

5. Brushes, dustpan and putty knife.

Clean all articles and return to proper storage position.

6. Unused materials.

Return all unused materials to proper storage place.

PRECAUTION

Make sure that lids are placed securely on the polish, detergent and scouring powder containers.

Care of Equipment

A. *Bucket and Mop Wringer:*
   1. Rinse and dry the bucket and wringer thoroughly after each use.
   2. Wipe the outside of the bucket free of any dirt.

3. Avoid striking the bucket and wringer against objects as such action tends to cause leaks in the bucket and shorten the life of the equipment.

4. Store in dry place so as to have no weight bearing on the bucket or wringer.

B. *Chamois:*

1. Rinse chamois in clean water and squeeze out excess water after each use.

2. Stretch chamois to original shape before placing to dry.

3. Avoid contaminating chamois with oils, polish or cleaning materials.

C. *Dust Cloths (polyethylene glycol treated):*

1. Thoroughly shake or vacuum dust cloths to remove loose dust.

2. When dirty, wash in warm detergent solution, (mix one ounce of detergent per gallon of warm water) rinse in clean water and wring or squeeze to remove excess water.

3. To treat new or washed cheesecloth, spray or sprinkle approximately one fluid ounce of polyethylene glycol solution (mixed in the proportion of three parts of water to one part of polyethylene glycol) to a square yard of cheesecloth. The cloth should be treated at least eight hours before using.

D. *Dustpan:*

1. Clean dustpan of loose dirt and dust before storing.

2. Hang by handle so as not to allow any damaging weight to be put on pan during storage.

3. Avoid getting the dustpan wet at any time.

4. In dumping the dustpan, avoid banging it with force against the waste container as such action tends to damage sides and edges of the pan.

E. *Dustpan Broom:*

1. Comb out broom bristles periodically.

2. Wash oily or dirty broom in warm water and detergent solution. Shake the broom and hang it up to dry. Allow to dry thoroughly before using.

3. When not in use, hang the broom in a clean, dry place so that the weight of the broom is not upon the bristles.

F. *Deck Scrubbing Brush:*

1. Rinse out in clean water after each use and shake dry of excess water.

2. Place for drying and storage in a position so that the bristles do not bear the weight of the brush.

3. Avoid knocking the brush against objects or walls as such action tends to split the brush block.

G. *Mop:*

1. After each use and before storage, rinse mop in clean water and wring or squeeze to remove excess water.

2. When dirty, wash in warm detergent solution, (mix one ounce detergent per gallon of warm water); rinse in clean water and wring or squeeze to remove excess water.

3. Fluff the mop strands by shaking.

4. Store mop with mophead up to allow better drying.

H. *Putty Knife:*

1. Use the putty knife only for removal of gum and other foreign substances during sweeping. Do not use a screw driver or hammer.

2. Keep the knife dry at all times.

3. Store ir a clean, dry place either by placing on a shelf or hanging on a nail.

I. *Radiator Dust Brush:*

1. Comb out brush bristles periodically.

2. Avoid wetting the dust brush at any time.

3. Store brush either by laying flat with bristles out straight or by hanging so bristles stand free of surrounding objects.

4. Do not use the radiator dust brush for any other purpose than for dusting radiators.

J. *Wiping Cloths:*

1. Rinse all cloths used, or when dirty wash them in warm detergent solution, and wring out.

2. Spread or hang cloths to dry in their proper storage places.

3. Avoid leaving wet, dirty cloths piled together in the storage cabinet.

Performance Inspection Guide

A. *Sweeping and Dusting:*

1. Stair landings, steps and all corners of stair treads should be free of loose dirt or dust streaks after sweeping.

2. Stair railings, fire apparatus, door mouldings, ledges, radiators and grilles should be dust free after dusting. The dust should have been removed rather than pushed around.

B. *Cleaning, Polishing and Wall Spotting:*

1. Glass surfaces should be clean and free of any smudges, finger marks, and dirt.

2. Handrails, door knobs and other surfaces should be clean and polished to an acceptable lustre.

3. Walls up to a standing height should be free of finger marks and other dirt spots of any kind.

C. *Mopping and Scrubbing:*

1. Stair landings and steps should be free of loose and/or caked dirt particles and should present an over-all appearance of cleanliness after mopping or scrubbing.

2. Walls, baseboards and stair risers should be free of water marks, scars

from the equipment striking the surfaces and splashing from the cleaning solution.

3. All surfaces should be dry and the corners and cracks clean after dry mopping.

D. *Equipment and Materials:*

1. All pieces of equipment should be clean and properly placed in their assigned storage locations.

2. All metal polish, furniture polish, soap and other similar materials left over from the stairway cleaning operation should be returned to their assigned storage locations.

Frequency and Production

A. *Frequency and Production Schedule:*

	Sweeping and Dusting	Polishing Fixtures and Wall Spotting	Mopping or Scrubbing
Frequency	Daily*	Weekly*	Weekly*
Production Rate (flights of stairs)	60	20	20

* Or as directed by supervisor.

B. *Qualifying Factors:*

1. *Frequency*

   a. The frequency of stairway cleaning is dependent upon weather conditions, type of building, type of occupancy, and amount of traffic. *For example,* a flight of stairs between the first and second floors that is in daily, constant use by the public as well as by the cleaning occupants would require a greater frequency of cleaning, especially in inclement weather, than would a flight of stairs between the sixth and seventh floors in the same building that mainly serves the building occupants or is used only in case of emergency.

   b. The frequencies given in the schedule are for a normal standard of cleaning under average conditions.

2. *Production Rate per Man-day*

   a. The term "flight of stairs" as used in the schedule is taken to mean an average stairway, approximately four feet in width and with its accompanying fixtures, such as railings, fire apparatus, and other items extending from one floor of a building to the next floor, and including the stair landing at one floor as well as any intermediate landings in between floors.

b. Due to the many and varied types and sizes of stairways in buildings, the production rate as established may be subject to modification at the various locations. It does, however, provide a standard from which such deviation should be figured.

Staffing

The man-day requirements of labor for stairway cleaning can be determined by use of the following formula:

$$\text{Man-days (of labor)} = \frac{\text{Quantity}}{\text{Production}} \times \frac{1}{\text{Frequency}}$$

where quantity is the actual total flights of stairs in the building; production is the number of flights of stairs cleaned per man-day; and frequency is the number of work days between operations.

If the frequency and/or production rate values as given in the Frequency and Production Schedule have been modified to meet the existing conditions at a particular location, then those modified values should be used in the above formula for the computation of the labor requirement.

SAMPLE CALCULATION

Consider a building that has fifteen flights of stairs and is of such construction and subject to such traffic conditions that the average cleaning values from the Frequency and Production Schedule may be used.

$$
\begin{array}{ll}
& \textit{For Sweeping} \qquad\qquad \textit{For Polishing} \\
& \textit{and Dusting} \qquad \textit{and Mopping or Scrubbing} \\[4pt]
\text{Man-days} = & \dfrac{\text{Quantity}}{\text{Production}} \times \dfrac{1}{\text{Frequency}} + \dfrac{\text{Quantity}}{\text{Production}} \times \dfrac{1}{\text{Frequency}} \\[10pt]
= & \dfrac{15}{60} \times \dfrac{1}{1} + \dfrac{15}{20} \times \dfrac{1}{5} \\[10pt]
= & .025 \qquad\qquad + \qquad 0.15 \\[4pt]
= & 0.40 \text{ man-days of labor required (jobs)}
\end{array}
$$

To this figure must be added a factor to compensate for leave in order to arrive at the total number of positions needed to accomplish the work.

Conversion factor including compensation for leave = 1.15
Conversion factor × jobs = total positions required
1.15 × 0.40 = 0.460 positions required

• Where the normal stairway cleaning duty does not require the full time of the employee, other related duties such as elevator cleaning, toilet cleaning or some similar job should be assigned to the employee to secure 100 per cent utilization of his time.

Equipment and Materials Allocation and Replacement

Items	Allotment per Cleaner	Replacement or Reissue
Bucket	1	1 per year
Chamois	1	1 per year
Cheesecloth	1 yard	18 yards per year
Deck scrubbing brush	1	1 per year
Deck scrubbing brush handle	1	1 per year
Detergent	1 pound	50 pounds per year
Dustpan	1	1 per 2 years
Dustpan broom (hearth size corn broom)	1	1 per year
Lemon oil polish	1 pint	4 pints per year
Metal polish (liquid)	1 pint	4 pints per year
Mop (1¼ lbs.)	1	2 per year
Mop handle	1	1 per year
Mop wringer (squeeze type)	1	1 per 2 years
Putty knife (1¼")	1	1 per 2 years
Radiator dust brush	1	1 per year
Scouring powder (for floors)	1 pound	20 pounds per year
White soap (6 oz. cake)	1 cake	25 cakes per year

The allotment per cleaner and replacement or reissue quantities in this standard are based on one stair cleaner having continuous stairway cleaning duty.

• Where the situation exists that other related duties are assigned to the stairway cleaner to secure 100 per cent utilization of his time, consideration should be given to a reduction in the replacement quantities in accordance with the actual amount of stairway cleaning assigned.

23 / STORAGE CLOSETS

One of the major causes of lost work time in the cleaning operation is the disregard of the fact that even the best supplies, unless easily available will not raise productivity to its maximum. When a worker must travel to the basement or some other out of the way storage area, an average of twenty minutes of work time can be lost. Multiply this figure by the number of employees who daily wander through the building searching for cleaning tools, and you will have a surprising number of valuable man–hours.

The best answer to this problem is a storage closet located on each floor, or strategically located in large areas, to keep travel time to a minimum. Each closet should be designed and laid out properly to include: buckets, wringers, mops, dustpan, counter brush, broom, rubber gloves, toilet brush, and dry mop. It should also include supplies such as: waxes, detergents, hand soap, toilet tissue, hand towels, deodorants, toilet bowl cleaners, cleanser, and polishes, or other products to maintain a station or area.

An ideal storage closet should be so arranged that every item has its own assigned space, and can accommodate such equipment as vacuum cleaners, floor machines, or other similar items if required. It should be designed to encourage neatness, and be provided with a drain and low utility sink with a stainless steel rim to protect porcelain finish. Lockers can also be provided for the employees to store their personal property.

Storage Closet Provisions

1. Low utility sink with stainless steel rim to protect porcelain finish.
2. Ample shelving.
3. Mopping outfit in storage position under shelving.
4. Floor machines and vacuums stored away from sink, and in a location easily removable.
5. Fitting and tools mounted on peg board.
6. Mop stored in assigned position.
7. Four-inch space between the mop and the wall to hold it out.
8. Aluminum or ceramic drip tray placed under mop.
9. Twenty-four-inch wide door lower.
10. Ceramic tile on concrete floor with drain.
11. Bibb (threaded) faucet, with brace.
12. Length of hose for washing equipment.
13. Minimum of 45 foot candles.
14. Small bulletin board.

24 / TOILET CLEANING AND SERVICING

(*Source:* Buildings Management Division, General Services
Administration, Washington, D. C.)

Job Description

The job of toilet cleaning and servicing includes all the cleaning work inside toilet rooms which can be reached while standing on the floor, including emptying the waste receptacles; servicing the soap dispensers, toilet paper holders, seat cover dispensers if provided, and paper towel dispensers; dusting window sills, ledges, grilles and similar items; cleaning the tile walls, mirrors, shelves, dispensers, receptacles; stall partitions and doors, wash basins, water closets and urinals; polishing metalwork as directed; sweeping and mopping or scrubbing the floors; and the proper care and maintenance of the toilet cleaning equipment. This work is easier if performed at night while the tenants are out of the building. Sufficient supply dispensers should be provided to reduce daytime servicing to a minimum. Each employee assigned to this job should be instructed to notice burned out lights, leaky fixtures, and other defective items and report them to his supervisor.

Equipment, Materials and Supplies

A. *Equipment:*

For toilet room.

    a. Bag for collecting wastepaper
    b. Bucket
    c. Cellulose sponges
    d. Chamois
    e. Cheesecloth
    f. Dustpan
    g. Dustpan broom
    h. Equipment carrier
    i. Floor sweep
    j. Mops, cotton
    k. Mop tank
    l. Polishing machine with scrubbing brushes
    m. Putty knife
    n. Radiator dust brush
    o. Rubber gloves
    p. Toilet brush or toilet bowl mop
    q. Wiping cloths, waffleweave

B. *Materials:*

For cleaning toilet room and fixtures:

    a. Grit soap
    b. Metal polish
    c. Multipurpose cleaner
    d. Paper bags (large and small)
    e. Scouring powder
    f. White soap
    g. Bowl cleaner

C. *Supplies:*

For servicing.

    a. Hand soap (liquid, powdered, or bar)
    b. Paper towels
    c. Seat covers *
    d. Toilet tissue

    * Optional

Job Methods

Operation Steps	*Explanation*

Step 1

1. Obtain necessary equipment, materials and supplies.	Obtain necessary equipment, materials and supplies. (See list under "Equipment, Materials and Supplies.")
2. Proceed to assigned work area.	All the equipment, materials, and supplies should be taken to the first toilet room where work is to begin.

NOTE

Items for cleaning toilet room fixtures must not be intermixed. The following tabulation shows the items this section prescribes for cleaning the various fixtures.

Fixtures	*To Clean (Item)*	*To Dry and/or Polish (Item)*
A. Mirrors and shelves	Green sponge	Chamois
Seat cover dispenser	Green sponge	Chamois
Soap dispenser	Green sponge	Chamois
Towel dispenser	Green sponge	Chamois
Wash basin	Green sponge	None
Wash basin chrome	Green sponge	Chamois
Waste towel receptacle	Green sponge	None
B. Urinal exterior porcelain	Yellow sponge	Waffleweave cloth
Water closet exterior porcelain	Yellow sponge	Waffleweave cloth
Water closet seat and hinges	Yellow sponge	None
C. Urinal interior	Toilet brush, straight head or mop	None
Water closet interior	Toilet brush, straight head or mop	None
D. Sanitary receptacle	Toilet brush, curved head or mop	Cheesecloth
E. Walls and stalls	Pink colored sponge	Damp dry with sponge

Step 2—Collect Used Towels and Other Trash

1. Empty waste towel containers.	Remove contents of waste towel receptacles.
2. Pick up wastepaper and trash.	Pick up all wastepaper and trash from floor and place in bag for collecting

Operation Steps	*Explanation*
	wastepaper. When the bag is full, tie securely and place it on the equipment carrier outside the toilet room.

PRECAUTIONS

1. Be careful of broken glass, razor blades, or other sharp articles that may be in the waste towel container.
2. Place glass and hard or sharp objects in a separate container, *not* in the bag for collecting wastepaper.
3. Wait for toilet room occupants to leave, and do not let others enter until your work is completed and you are ready to leave.

Step 3—Service Dispensers

Check and service dispensers of supplies.	a. Check soap dispensers and fill with soap of the type used (liquid, powder or bar).
	b. Check toilet tissue and seat cover dispensers and add supplies needed.
	c. Check the paper towel dispensers and put in towels needed to fill them.

PRECAUTION

Do not put supplies anywhere other than in the dispensers provided.

Step 4—Dust and Damp Wipe

1. Dust radiators, sills, and other items.	Use radiator dust brush and/or dust cloth to dust radiators, window sills, ledges, grilles, and other items located in the toilet room.
2. Damp wipe dispensers and waste towel receptacle.	a. Wipe towel, tissue, napkin and seat cover dispensers, and the waste towel receptacle, with a damp sponge (green colored) as required.
	b. Use a chamois if necessary to dry after damp wiping.

Step 5—Sweep Floor

Remove trash from floor.	a. Use floor sweep to sweep the floor.

Operation Steps   *Explanation*

b. Remove gum, tar or similar substances from floor areas with putty
knife during sweeping.

c. Use dustpan and dustpan broom
to pick up sweepings.

PRECAUTION

Do not sweep trash into the corridor or other adjoining area.

Step 6—Clean and Polish

1. Clean mirrors and shelves.

a. Use a damp sponge (green co-
ored) to wipe all mirrors.

b. Use sponge (green colored), white
soap and water to wash and rinse
shelves.

c. Dry and polish mirrors and shelves
with chamois.

2. Clean wash basins and soap dispensers.

a. Clean wash basins with a clean
sponge (green colored), white
soap and water. If basins are unusually dirty, use grit soap.

b. Use sponge (green colored) to
clean the outside of the soap dispensers.

c. Dry and polish soap dispensers
and chromium fixtures with a
chamois as necessary.

3. Polish metal.

As directed use metal polish and
cheesecloth to polish metalwork.

PRECAUTION

Grit soap should not be used on chromium finish.

Step 7—Clean Sanitary Receptacles

Empty and clean sanitary receptacles.

a. Remove paper bags, together with
the contents, from the sanitary receptacles daily. As each bag is
removed, close it by folding over
the top, and place it in a clean
paper bag, ready for disposal.
Fasten the collection bag securely
to prevent spillage.

Operation Steps · *Explanation*

b. Clean sanitary receptacle daily, both inside and out, with a curved toilet brush (or toilet bowl mop) and a solution of multipurpose cleaner.

c. Wipe receptacle with dry cheese-cloth.

d. Put in new paper bag.

NOTE

Prepare fresh cleaning solution for each toilet room. Mix cleaner and warm water in proportions recommended by manufacturer's instructions on container label.

PRECAUTIONS

1. Wear rubber gloves when cleaning sanitary receptacles.

2. The bags removed from sanitary receptacles, together with their contents, should be disposed of daily by burning or being hauled to the dump.

Step 8—Clean Water Closets and Urinals
(For cleaning with chemicals, see the discussion at the end of this section.)

1. Clean water closets.

a. Flush toilets before starting to clean. Then use a toilet brush (or toilet bowl mop) and multipurpose cleaner solution to brush wash interior of all water closets. Work the brush or mop as far into the trap as it will reach. Wash thoroughly under the rounded inside rim of the toilet bowl. Flush toilet to rinse inside of bowl.

b. Wash water closet seats and hinges with clean wet sponge (yellow colored) and multipurpose cleaner. Rinse thoroughly with clean water. Leave seats in raised position.

c. Use a wet sponge (yellow colored) with multipurpose cleaner to clean all exterior porcelain surfaces. If necessary, use grit soap. Use the damp sponge (yellow co-

Operation Steps	*Explanation*
	lored) to rinse and damp dry all external porcelain surfaces.
	d. Use the damp sponge (yellow colored) to wipe all the chromium fixtures. Polish with a dry cloth as necessary.
2. Clean urinals.	a. Flush urinals. Then use a toilet brush (or toilet bowl mop) and multipurpose cleaner to wash interior of all urinals. Wash thoroughly under the rounded rim of the urinal bowl. Flush urinal to rinse interior of bowl.
	b. Use a wet sponge (yellow colored) with multipurpose cleaner to clean all exterior porcelain surfaces. If necessary, use grit soap. Rinse as required.
	c. Pour approximately a cupful, or as otherwise directed, of multipurpose solution into the urinal. *Do not flush.*
	d. Use a wiping cloth to dry all external porcelain surfaces.
	e. Use the damp sponge (yellow colored) to wipe all chromium fixtures. Polish with a dry cloth as necessary.

PRECAUTIONS

1. Grit soap is not to be used on chromium finish.
2. Report leaky spigots and other defective equipment to the supervisor.
3. Keep sponges, cloths and brushes or mops that are used on water closets, urinals and sanitary receptacles separate from those used in other cleaning operations.
4. Wear rubber gloves when cleaning water closets and urinals.

Step 9—Damp Wipe Walls and Stalls

Clean tile walls, stall partitions and doors.	Use a damp sponge (pink colored) to damp wipe tile walls, stall partitions and doors. As necessary, wash them

Operation Steps   *Explanation*

with a solution of multipurpose cleaner. After washing tile walls, partitions, and doors, wipe them dry.

Step 10—Clean Floors (Mop)
(*For additional details see "Floor Mopping".*)

Mop floors.

a. In accordance with instructions on the container label, mix multipurpose cleaner and warm water in one bucket of the twin mop tank. Fill the second two-thirds full of clear water.

b. Use mop and the warm solution to thoroughly clean floor area. Dip mop into solution and wring out excess solution. Push mop around the edges of the floor, being careful to remove all dirt from the corners and around pipes. Then mop remainder of floor area. Avoid splashing walls and baseboards.

c. Wring mop and go back over mopped area to pick up excess cleaning solution.

d. Use a second mop and clean water to rinse and dry the mopped floor. Frequently rinse and wring mop during this operation.

Step 11—Clean Floors (Scrub) (See Step 10.)

Scrub floors.

a. Sprinkle floor with scouring powder, and wet with warm water.

b. Use a small polishing machine with scrubbing brushes to scrub floor.

c. Use a mop and clean water to rinse and dry scrubbed floor. Frequently rinse and wring mop during this operation.

PRECAUTIONS

1. Do not use so much water that it tends to splash or run beneath the floor covering.

2. Be careful that equipment does not bump against walls, doors, or stall partitions.

3. Change rinse water frequently.

4. Always start the mopping or scrubbing operation at the wall opposite the door and work toward the door.

5. Pay special attention to corners and other places where dirt accumulates.

Operation Steps   *Explanation*

Step 12—Return Equipment,
Materials and Supplies to Storage

Return equipment and unused materials and supplies.

a. Gather all pieces of equipment and unused materials and supplies and put them in their place on equipment carrier.

b. Return them to gear storage room.

c. Dispose of wastepaper and other waste.

d. Clean and store all items of equipment. (For details of cleaning and storage see "Equipment Care.")

e. Return all unused materials and supplies to proper storage place.

PRECAUTIONS

1. Be sure that covers are replaced securely on all containers of materials and supplies.

2. Be sure to hang wiping cloths so that cloths used on water closets and urinals will not be confused with cloths used elsewhere.

Care of Equipment

A. *Bag for Collecting Wastepaper:*

1. Do not put sharp objects or sweepings into the wastepaper collection bag. Place them in a separate container, such as a cardboard box.

2. Do not allow bag to be caught in door or on sharp objects as this might damage it.

B. *Broom, Dustpan:*

1. When broom becomes soiled, wash it in warm synthetic detergent solution and rinse in clear water.

2. Store broom by hanging in a clean dry place so weight of brush is not on the bristles.

C. *Brush, Radiator Dust:*
1. Comb bristles of brush periodically.
2. Avoid wetting dust brush.
3. Store brush on a flat surface so bristles will be flat and straight.

D. *Brush, Toilet or Toilet Bowl Mop:*
1. Wash brush or mop daily, using a warm multipurpose cleaner solution, and shake out excess water.
2. Hang to dry where air circulation is good.

E. *Bucket (12 qt.):*
1. Rinse and dry bucket, inside and out, after each use.
2. In storing do not place heavy objects on the bucket.

F. *Cloths, Wiping:*
1. Wash wiping cloths daily in a warm multipurpose cleaner solution and rinse them in clear warm water.
2. Wring water out of cloths and hang them up to dry where air circulation is good.

G. *Dustpan:*
1. Empty dustpan into waste can and damp wipe pan to remove all dirt and dust.
2. Hang up dustpan so it will not become bent or otherwise damaged.

H. *Equipment Carrier:*
1. Do not allow carrier to strike walls, radiators, or other objects.
2. Wipe free of moisture and dirt after each day's use.

I. *Floor Sweep (18"):*
1. Comb floor sweep bristles daily.
2. Wash an oily or dirty floor sweep in a warm solution of multipurpose cleaner and rinse in clean warm water. Shake excess water from bristles and hang to dry.
3. Store in a clean dry place so bristles do not bear weight of brush.
4. Once each week reverse brush block of floor sweep by placing handle in the other hole. (This increases the life of the floor sweep.)

J. *Gloves, Rubber:*
1. After each use, wash gloves in a warm multipurpose cleaner solution and rinse in clear warm water.
2. Always maintain gloves in first-class condition. Discard gloves when holes develop.
3. Be careful not to snag gloves on nails or other sharp objects.
4. Store gloves in a clean dry place.

K. *Knife, Putty (1¼"):*
1. Use putty knife to scrape gum and like substances from floor. Do not use it as a substitute screw driver or hammer.
2. Wipe free of dust and dirt after use and store in a clean, dry place.

L. *Mops, Cotton (2 lb.):*

1. After each use and before storage, rinse mops in clean water and wring or squeeze to remove excess water.

2. Wash dirty mops in warm solution of multipurpose cleaner. Rinse in clean water and wring or squeeze to remove excess water.

3. Pluff mop strands by shaking.

4. Store mops with mop heads up to allow better drying.

M. *Mop Tank (two 32-qt. buckets; chassis with casters, one wringer):*

1. Rinse and dry buckets and wringer thoroughly after use.

2. Wipe outside of buckets and the chassis free of any dirt.

3. Avoid striking mop tank outfit against objects, which tends to cause buckets to leak and to shorten life of the equipment.

4. Store in dry place so that no weight bears on any part of mop tank.

N. *Polishing Machine and Scrubbing Brushes:*

1. Remove brush (or brushes) from machine. Wash dirty brushes in multipurpose cleaner solution, rinse thoroughly, and shake free of excess water.

2. After each use, wipe machine and cord free of dirt and dust with a damp cloth. Use multipurpose clean solution to remove spots. Wipe machine and cord dry and rewind cord loosely on the hooks provided.

3. Wash and rinse wheels of machine and wipe with a dry cloth.

4. Use metal polish as directed to clean and polish machine. Store machine and brush, with brush removed, in assigned storage space.

5. Report needed repairs to supervisor.

O. *Sponges (cellulose):*

1. Rinse sponges in clean warm water after use. Wash very dirty sponges in a warm multipurpose cleaner solution, rinse in clear water and squeeze out excess water.

2. Store in a clean dry place.

Performance Inspection Guide

A. *Collection of Used Towels and Other Trash:*

1. All used towel receptacles should be empty.

2. All sanitary receptacles should be clean, both inside and outside, and contain a new paper bag liner.

3. No trash should be on the floor.

4. The large paper bags containing collected contents of sanitary receptacles should have been deposited in a large can pending burning or other approved disposal.

5. All unused towels should be at the designated disposal location.

B. *Replenishment of Supplies:*

All dispensers of supplies should be clean and filled with the proper supplies.

C. *Cleaning of Sanitary Receptacles:*

1. All sanitary receptacles should be empty except for a new paper bag "liner."

2. All sanitary receptacles should be free of spots, stains and finger marks.

3. All sanitary receptacles should be free of odors.

D. *Cleaning of Toilet Room Fixtures:*

1. All porcelain surfaces of wash basins, water closets and urinals should be free of dust, dirt, spots and stains.

2. The wall surfaces should be free of spots and smears.

3. All water closet seats should be left in raised position after cleaning. They should be free of spots and stains, and the seat hinges should be free of green mold.

4. The plumbing fixtures should be free of green mold and water stains.

CENTRAL SUPPLY BUILDING REPORT OF TOILET INSPECTION	Date of inspection
	Inspected by (Signature)

This form is part of Buildings Management's standard inspection procedure.

INSTRUCTIONS

1. Inspection of each toilet will cover all items on check list that apply to room being inspected.
2. Proper abbreviations for items requiring attention will be noted in the remark column.
3. Supervisor performing inspection will give one copy of this report to group foreman of laborers.
4. Foreman of laborers will notify superintendent or proper shop foreman of mechanical repairs required.
5. This report will be retained only as long as required for administrative purposes.

CHECK LIST AND ABBREVIATIONS

CLEANING		SUPPLIES		REPAIRS	
ITEM		ITEM		ITEM	
Floors	C1	Paper	S1	Water Closet	R1
Stall Partitions	C2	Soap	S2	Urinal	R2
Walls	C3	Towels	S3	Wash Basin	R3
Wash Basins	C4	Seat Covers	S4	Soap Containers	R4
Urinal	C5			Lights	R5
Water Closet	C6			Drinking Fountain	R6
General	C7				

Building	Room Number	Attendant	Inspection Time	Remarks and/or Items Requiring Attention
			Actual Size	
			8 x 10 1/2	

Figure 24-1

E. *Cleaning of Supply Dispensers, Tile Walls, Stall Partitions, Doors, Shelves, Mirrors and Floors:*

1. All supply dispensers should be clean and free of finger marks and water spots.

2. All shelves and shelf brackets should be free of gum, dust, fingerprints, water stains, smudges and other soil.

3. All mirrors should be free of streaks, smudges, water spots, dust and lipstick smudges, and should not be cloudy.

4. Walls, stall partitions and doors should be free of hand marks, dust, pencil marks, lipstick smudges, water streaks, mop marks, and green mold.

5. Floors (especially in corners), should be free of dirt and dust, gum, grease, black marks, loose paper, water, mop stains, and strings.

F. *Care of Equipment, Materials and Supplies:*

1. All pieces of equipment should be clean and properly placed in their assigned storage locations.

2. All materials and supplies left over from the toilet cleaning and servicing operation should be returned and stored neatly in their assigned storage locations.

NOTE

1. A mirror on an offset handle should be used for inspecting underside of rim on toilet fixtures.

2. "Report of Toilet Inspection" should be used as directed.

Frequency and Production

Frequency and Production Schedule:

	Toilet Cleaning	Toilet Servicing
Frequency	Daily	As required
Production Rate per Man-day	80 Fixtures (basins, water closets, urinals)	

The job of toilet cleaning and servicing includes the daily collecting of waste; cleaning dispensers and waste receptacles; cleaning wash basins, urinals, water closets, partitions, walls, shelves, mirrors, doors and floors; and servicing of the dispensers of supplies as required.

Staffing

The necessary staffing can be figured by dividing the number of public toilet room fixtures (wash basins, urinals, and water closets) in the building by the daily production shown in schedule. (Private toilets are cleaned by employees assigned to clean the offices in which the private toilets are located.)

Assume a building with toilet rooms (both men's and women's) containing a total of 76 fixtures (wash basins, water closets and urinals). From the production rate per man-day, each toilet cleaner in an eight-hour period should clean and service toilet rooms containing 80 fixtures (wash basins, water closets and urinals). By dividing the quantity of work to be done by the production rate, the required number of man-days to clean and service toilet rooms with this number of fixtures may be calculated.

$$\text{Quantity} = 76 \text{ fixtures} \qquad \text{Man-days} = \frac{76}{80} = .95 \text{ jobs}$$
$$\text{Production} = 80 \text{ fixtures}$$

To this figure must be added a factor to compensate for leave in order to arrive at the total number of positions needed to accomplish the work.

$$\text{Conversion factor including compensation for leave} = 1.15$$
$$\text{Conversion factor} \times \text{jobs} = \text{total positions required}$$
$$1.15 \times .95 = 1.09 \text{ positions required}$$

● Where the duty of cleaning and servicing toilets does not require the full time of an employee, other duties should be assigned to secure 100 per cent utilization of his time.

Equipment and Materials Allocation and Replacement

Items	Allotment per Cleaner	Replacement or Reissue
Bags for collecting waste towels	3	6 per year
Bags, paper (25 lb.)	24	6,000 per year
Broom, dustpan (hearth size corn broom)	1	1 per year
Brush, floor, sweep (18″)	1	1 per year
Brush, handle (for floor sweep)	1	1 per year
Brush, radiator, dust	1	1 per 3 years
Brush, scrubbing (for use on polishing machine)	1 set	2 sets per year
Brush, toilet (curved head)	1	2 per year
Brush, toilet (straight head)	1	2 per year
Bucket (12 qt.)	1	1 per 2 years
Chamois	1	2 per year
Cleaner (multipurpose)	1 pint	50 gallons per year
Cloth (cheesecloth)	1 yard	52 yards per year
Dustpan	1	1 per 2 years
Equipment carrier	1	1 per 10 years
Gloves, rubber	1	2 pairs per year
Mop, cotton (2 lb.)	1	4 per year
Mop handle	1	2 per year
Mop tank (two 32-quart buckets on twin chassis)	1 set	1 per 2 years

Items	Allotment per Cleaner	Replacement or Reissue
Mop toilet (optional)	1	2 per year
Mop wringer	1	1 per 2 years
Polish metal (liquid)	1 pint	2 pints per year
Polishing machine, scrubbing and (15″)	1	1 per 10 years
Putty knife (1¼″)	1	1 per 2 years
Scouring powder (for floors)	1 pound	25 pounds per year
Soap, grit	1 cake	25 cakes per year
Soap, white (6 oz. cake)	1 cake	25 cakes per year
Sponge, cellulose	2	12 per year
Wiping cloth (waffleweave)	2	12 per year

Supplies for Toilet Servicing *

Items	Unit of Issue
Soap, hand, (cake, V-type)	Case of 144 cakes
Soap, hand, liquid	Drum of 55 gallons
Soap, hand, powdered	Barrel of 175 pounds
Toilet seat covers	5,000 to a case
Toilet tissue (rolls)	Carton of 100 rolls
Toilet tissue (sheets)	Carton of 125 packages
Towels, paper (C-fold)	Carton of 25 packages
Towels, paper (single-fold)	Carton of 15 or 25 packages

* Use supplies required by dispensers.

The allotment of equipment and materials per cleaner and the replacement or reissue quantities in this section are based on one cleaner having continuous toilet cleaning and servicing duty.

• Where the situation exists that other duties are assigned to the cleaner to secure 100 per cent utilization of his time, consideration should be given to a reduction in the replacement quantities in accordance with the actual amount of toilet cleaning and servicing assigned.

Chemical Cleaning of Water Closets and Urinals

Porcelain surfaces of water closets and urinals with stains or incrustations should be cleaned with porcelain cleaner in accordance with the following procedure:

1. Wet hand mop in water to make it absorbent.
2. Pour porcelain cleaner in a nonmetallic container.
3. Saturate hand mop with bowl cleaner and apply to inside of fixture from top to bottom in a swabbing fashion.
4. Check with mirror to see that all incrustation has been removed from under flange at the top or front of the fixtures.
5. When the incrustation is heavy, it takes several minutes for the chemical action of the porcelain cleaner to remove all of the stain. Accordingly, in toilet rooms where heavy incrustations are found, the cleaner should first be applied liberally to the incrusted area of all fixtures, before completing the operation

described in procedure three and four. The removal of stubborn incrustations in traps will be facilitated by pouring hot water into the fixtures.

Although this bowl cleaner, which is an acid, contains an inhibitor that prevents damage to the toilet fixture parts, it is injurious to the skin. Rubber gauntlet gloves and face shields should be worn by personnel performing this job.

As an alternative to cleaning the fixtures as previously described, a sodium bisulfate toilet cleaner may be used every few days to keep stains and incrustation from forming in water closets and urinals. When using this cleaner, first flush the fixture, then sprinkle a small quantity of the cleaner above the water line. Use a toilet brush or mop wet with the solution to wash the area above the water line, and under the flange or rim at top or front of the fixture, and then flush.

Once the porcelain surfaces in water closets and urinals are free from stain and incrustation, the use of sodium bisulfate should keep them free from these deposits. When this is accomplished, subsequent cleaning with porcelain cleaner may not be necessary.

Instructions from the supervisor and/or the manufacturer should be closely followed in performing this job.

25 / URN AND JARDINIERE CLEANING (FLOOR AND WALL TYPE)

(*Source:* General Services Administration, Washington, D. C.)

Job Description

Jardiniere and urn cleaning, floor and wall type, includes the removal of refuse and debris from the jardinieres and/or urns, both floor and wall type, within the assigned area; cleaning all such units, and wiping them dry of moisture as necessary; refilling the units with fresh sand as may be necessary; replacing the units in their original positions; and proper care and maintenance of the jardiniere and urn cleaning equipment and materials. Employees assigned to this duty should be instructed to report to their supervisor any broken or defective jardinieres or urns noticed during the cleaning operation.

Keeping the jardinieres and urns neat and presentable during the day time is a part of the duties assigned to the corridor policing job.

Jardiniere and urn cleaning is assigned to individuals as a regular job, with the exception that cleaning of enclosed wall type urns is assigned as part of the room cleaner's job.

Equipment and Materials

A. *Equipment:*

For collecting refuse from the units.

a. Rubber gloves

b. Scoop or sieve
c. Device for collecting debris
d. Equipment truck (where necessary)

B. *Materials:*

For cleaning, polishing and refilling units.

a. Water
b. Detergent
c. Wiping cloths
d. Sand
e. Counter brush
f. Dustpan
g. Toilet brush (for use as necessary with liquid filled urns)

Job Methods

Operation Steps	*Explanation*

Step 1

1. Obtain necessary equipment and materials.	Obtain necessary equipment and materials as listed under "Equipment and Materials."
2. Proceed to assigned work area.	All equipment and materials should be taken to the starting point of the assigned work area, to be used as needed.

Step 2

A. *Enclosed Wall-Type Urns (no water or sand)*

Start at one end of the work area to clean and refill units.	a. Remove top of receptacle.
	b. Wipe underneath side of top with a damp cloth, using detergent, if necessary, to remove deposits that have formed there.
	c. Lift out bucket type container.
	d. Empty debris into metal collecting device.
	e. Wipe out bucket with a damp cloth, using detergent if necessary.
	f. Before replacing bucket wipe inside of urn with a damp cloth, as necessary, using detergent.

Operation Steps	*Explanation*
	g. Replace bucket.
	h. Wipe exterior with damp cloth, then wipe with a dry cloth.
	i. Use counter brush and dustpan to tidy up around urns as necessary.

NOTE

This type urn should be assigned to room cleaner for cleaning.

B. *Sand Urns, Floor-Type (Jardiniere) and Wall-Type*

Start at one end of the work to clean and refill units.	a. Screen sand with perforated scoop or sieve.
	b. Place refuse in metal collecting device.
	c. Remove metal pan containing sand, and clean interior of urn with a damp cloth, using detergent as necessary.
	d. Remove soiled sand and replace with fresh sand.
	e. Wipe off exterior of urn with damp cloth, using detergent. Polish with dry cloth.
	f. Use counter brush and dustpan to tidy up around urns as necessary.

Step 3

1. Return equipment for storage.	a. Return equipment to gear room.
	b. Clean and store in area designated by supervisor.

Care of Equipment and Material

A. *Brush:*
1. Wash brush daily, using a warm synthetic detergent solution.
2. Shake out excess water.
3. Hang up where air circulation is good so brush will dry.

B. *Device for Collecting Debris:*
1. Wash with detergent solution and dry.
2. Wipe outside free of dirt.

3. Store so it will not be damaged.

C. *Equipment Truck:*

1. Do not allow truck to strike walls, radiators or other objects.

2. Clean truck daily.

3. Report all defects and damage to the truck to your supervisor immediately. Make arrangements to have the truck wheels oiled regularly. Store truck near the source of sand.

D. *Rubber Gloves:*

1. Wash in soap and water.

2. Rinse.

3. Dry with wiping cloths.

4. Turn gloves inside out to keep them from sticking together.

E. *Scoop (Perforated) or Sieve:*

1. Wipe clean and store in a dry, clean place, either on a shelf or hanging on a nail.

2. Store so that no damaging weight is placed on the scoop or sieve.

F. *Wiping Cloths:*

1. Rinse all cloths after each use.

2. Wash dirty cloths in a warm detergent solution, (mix one ounce of detergent per gallon of water) and rinse in clean water.

3. Wring or squeeze to remove excess water and spread or hang the cloths to dry in their proper storage place.

Performance Inspection Guide

A. *Collecting Refuse From Units:*

Cigarette butts, burnt matches, and other discarded material should have been removed from the jardinieres and/or urns.

B. *Cleaning, Polishing and Refilling Units:*

All jardinieres and/or urns should have been emptied of refuse, and should be clean. Sand should be clean and neat appearing.

C. *Equipment and Materials:*

All pieces of equipment should have been cleaned and returned to their assigned storage locations.

NOTE

1. The use of the old umbrella stand type of jardiniere partly filled with water is not recommended. In cases where some of these still remain in the buildings, the methods used and the production rate should be approximately the same as given herein for the sand type.

2. In addition to nightly cleaning, policing of the jardinieres and/or urns should be done at least twice daily.

Frequency and Production

A. *Frequency and Production Schedule:*

	Urn and Jardiniere Cleaning
Frequency	Daily
Production Rate per Man-day	100

The job of urn and jardiniere cleaning includes the removal of refuse and debris from all types of urns and jardinieres, cleaning and polishing these units, and refilling with clean sand when necessary.

B. *Qualifying Factor:*

Production Rate

The production rate given is related to an average type office building with average density and type of occupancy, equipped with the usual type of jardinieres or urns. The rate as established may be subject to modification due to variations from the normal. It does, however, provide a standard from which such deviations (if any) should be calculated.

Staffing

The necessary staffing can be determined by dividing the number of jardinieres and urns in the building by the daily production shown in the Frequency and Production Schedule.

SAMPLE CALCULATION

Assume an office building containing seventy-five jardinieres. From the production standard, each employee in an eight-hour period should clean one hundred each. Using the formula

$$\frac{Quantity}{Production} = \text{Man-days per job performance}$$

calculate the number of employees required to clean the jardinieres in this area as follows:

$$\text{Quantity} = 75 \qquad \text{Man-days } \frac{75}{100} = .75 \text{ jobs}$$
$$\text{Production} = 100$$

To this figure must be added a factor to compensate for leave in order to arrive at the total number of positions needed to accomplish the work.

Conversion factor including compensation for leave = 1.15
Conversion factor × jobs = total positions required
$1.15 \times .75 = .863$ positions required

• Where the duty of jardiniere and urn cleaning does not require the full time of an employee, other duties should be assigned to secure 100 per cent utilization of his time.

Equipment and Materials Allocation and Replacement

Items	Allotment per cleaner	Replacement or Reissue
Brush, counter, dust	1	1 per 2 years
Brush, toilet	1	2 per year
Cheesecloth	2 yards	52 yards per year
Cloth, wiping (waffleweave)	2	24 per year
Container, metal (for collecting cigarette butts)	1	1 per 2 years
Detergent (soapless, synthetic)	1 pound	25 pounds per year
Dustpan	1	1 per 2 years
Equipment carrier	1 (where required)	1 per 10 years
Gloves, rubber	1 pair	2 pair per year
Sand, white (for sand urns)	100 pounds	5,000 pounds per year
Scoop or sieve (perforated)	1	1 per 2 years

The allotment per person and replacement or reissue quantities in this section are based on one employee cleaning jardinieres and/or urns full-time, in accordance with the standard.

• Where other duties are assigned to the employee to secure 100 per cent utilization of his time, a reduction in the replacement quantities should be made in accordance with the amount of time consumed at other work.

26 / UTILITY WORK

(*Source:* General Services Administration, Washington, D. C.)

Scope of Work

The job of utility work does not consist of the regular performance of a single well-defined duty. It includes, but is not limited to such activities as:

Servicing complaints; performing special cleaning necessitated by the building occupants vacating space, holding special conferences, meetings; performing special cleanup work made necessary by toilet room floods and similar occurrences; cleaning up results of accidents such as coffee and beverage spillages, dropped food items, broken glass, and many others.

Assisting truck drivers in loading, unloading and distribution of building supplies such as toilet room supplies and cleaning materials.

Assisting in laying down and picking up, at required times, mats in building entrances during periods of inclement weather; aiding in the removal of snow and ice from building areas and the placing and removal of sand, chemical compounds or other materials used in reducing slip hazards during such weather conditions.

Assisting in moving furniture as necessary during repainting of office and other types of space; moving light pieces of furniture within the building occupants' space; setting up and/or rearranging furniture items in auditorium and conference rooms to conform with requirements of activities scheduled therein.

Providing occasional help to building forces when necessary such as for digging and filling trenches for repair of sewers and plumbing; cleaning up debris resulting from alterations to the building; assisting the force as necessary in refilling fire extinguishers.

Performing other general duties as directed.

Special Jobs

In certain locations, some of the cleaning work not identifiable as a part of the other individual jobs as defined in pertinent sections of the handbook and/or cleaning standards may be of such nature and recurrence that it can be classified as a special job, rather than as a part of the utility work, and so programmed for in a way similar to that used for the regular cleaning jobs.

As a special job the work will have rates established for production and frequency. These rates could be the same as those for related cleaning jobs, such as policing work and room cleaning special areas. In the absence of established rates, observations and studies of the work procedures and needs should provide a basis for the determination of satisfactory values.

Examples of special jobs include: Cleaning escalators; emptying waste crocks located in experimental laboratory space; operation of incinerators; replenishing drinking water supply in individual water coolers, and others.

Job Methods, Equipment and Materials

The job methods, equipment and materials used in the accomplishment of any assigned duty should be in accordance with related work methods, equipment and materials prescribed in other related job descriptions.

Safety regulations and procedures prescribed for proper lifting and other manual effort exerted in the accomplishment of this work should be closely observed to avoid possible injuries to the worker and/or others.

Frequency and Production

Utility work. The frequency for the performance of utility work is generally described as daily.

The production rate, although not specifically defined in terms of individual work units for the varied work performed, is based upon building gross area and is set at 1,000,000 square feet gross per eight hour man-day.

Special jobs. The frequencies and production rates for special jobs should be, where possible, similar to those established for other related cleaning jobs. *For example*, special day time room cleaning work might be assigned on the standard basis of 14,000 square feet per man-day at whatever frequency local conditions require. Extra policing necessitated by tours, or other means, for instance, might be assigned on the standard basis of 300,000 square feet per man-day at the required frequency.

In those instances where established rates are not pertinent, the work requirements for the particular job should be studied in detail to determine appropriate values.

Staffing

The necessary staffing for the utility job can be figured by dividing the building area by the daily production rate of 1,000,000 square feet.

SAMPLE CALCULATION

Assume an office building with a gross area of 445,000 square feet. Using the formula given below, the required staffing is computed as follows:

$$\text{Man-days (of labor)} = \frac{\text{Quantity}}{\text{Production}} \times \frac{1}{\text{Frequency}}$$
$$= \frac{445,000}{1,000,000} \times \frac{1}{1}$$
$$= .445 \text{ jobs}$$

To this figure must be added a factor to compensate for leave in order to arrive at the total number of positions needed to accomplish this work.

Conversion factor including compensation for leave = 1.15
Conversion factor × jobs = total positions required
1.15 × .445 = .51 positions required

Staffing for special jobs, where established, may be determined by means of the same formula using the rate values as required for the particular work involved or through determination by other means of a satisfactory figure. The leave factor, also, has to be applied to the staffing developed for this duty in the manner shown in the formula to arrive at the total positions to accomplish this work.

• Where the utility work and/or special jobs do not require the full time of an employee, other duties should be assigned to secure 100 per cent utilization of his time.

27 / **VENETIAN BLIND CLEANING**

(*Source:* General Services Administration, Washington, D. C.)

Job Description

The job of venetian blind cleaning consists of washing the venetian blind slats and cleaning the tapes and cords by brushing with a stiff bristle brush or by washing.

Employees assigned to this job should be instructed to notice any defects in the blinds and report them to their supervisor.

Job Methods

Venetian blind washing, because of the many variables which affect it (such as the type of blind head, length, width and number of blinds, and availability of contract services), requires closer individual attention, as far as method is concerned, than many of the other cleaning jobs. The method used may vary from location to location to meet the problems in specific buildings. In deciding on the method to be used care must be taken to be sure that accurate costs are determined for each method considered and that similar results are obtained.

Washing in place. Where blinds with complex headers are installed, washing in place will eliminate the cost of labor to remove and replace the blinds, and to transport them to and from the windows, and therefore should be given serious consideration.

The method used when blinds are washed in place is as follows:

1. Before washing tilt all the slats in one direction and wipe down with a greased sweep mop. Then tilt slats in the other direction and repeat the process. If the blinds are extremely dusty, use a vacuum cleaner for this job to avoid spreading dust.

2. Adjust slats to the open position, and "dry-clean" tapes and cords with stiff, short-bristled brush.

3. With the slats in the open position, work from a "safety" stepladder and wash the blind, one slat at a time. Use a quarter section of waffleweave cloth and a bucket of detergent solution (mixed one ounce to one gallon of water). Rinse as necessary with a clean cloth and clear water. Then wipe the slat dry. Repeat this process for each slat, completing each one in turn.

4. When finished, wipe all dust and water spots from the window sill, and sweep the floor around the window.

When this method is used, particular care must be taken to avoid splashing or streaking the window glass.

Removal and washing by hand. When blinds can be removed easily from the windows for washing it is usually more productive to do this. Various types of tanks and other equipment are available to suit the various sizes and types of blinds to be washed and the space available for the washing equipment.

The method used when blinds are removed for washing by hand is as follows:

1. Remove blinds from windows and mark them for location identification before removing them from the individual rooms.

2. When the number of blinds that can be washed in one day have been accumulated on the hand truck, take them to the washing area.

3. Where necessary to soak the blinds before washing, place a few at a time in a tank of detergent solution (mix one ounce to one gallon of water). Limit the soaking time to the absolute minimum required to loosen the dirt film. Be especially careful with wooden slat blinds with worn or damaged finish, as long periods of soaking may result in further damage.

4. Remove the blinds from the soak tank one or more at a time and hang them on a suitable washing rack. Tilt the slats first in one direction and then the other, washing by agitation with a "pullman" brush or a scrub brush dipped in detergent solution. Additional water is supplied as needed, either through the hose connected to the pullman brush, or by a garden hose.

When soaking is not required before washing the blinds, hang the blinds directly on the wash racks and wash them.

5. Rinse blinds, as necessary, with the pullman brush or with the garden hose, and hang to dry.

6. Replace clean blinds in their original location the following day.

To reduce costs to a minimum commensurate with satisfactory results, the use of pullman brushes, drying racks and other labor saving devices should be considered.

Machine washing. In those areas where there are sufficient blinds to justify its purchase, commercially designed venetian blind laundry equipment may be used. The cost of such equipment ranges from approximately $500 upward. Some of the less expensive equipment is sufficiently portable to be moved from one group of buildings to another within a city, and possibly from city to city if desired.

The actual washing production of commercial laundries which use such equipment is reported to be in excess of one hundred blinds, four foot by eight foot, per eight man-hours. Production for the complete job, including removing and replacing the blinds, would of course be less.

The method followed when such equipment is used is as follows:

1. Remove blinds from windows and mark them for location identification before removing them from the individual rooms.

2. When a hand truck load of blinds is accumulated, take them to the venetian blind laundry location, and stack them in a rack to await washing.

3. Hang the blinds, one or two at a time, in the spray booth, and raise them to a sufficient height to permit them to be opened to their full length.

4. Spray blinds that are especially dusty with clear water to remove the

excess dust and dirt. (This rinse water is wasted to the drain.) This conserves the cleaning solution.

5. Adjust the valved connections so that when the cleaning solution is sprayed onto the blind it will run down into the drain through and back into the cleaning solution tank to be recirculated.

6. Spray the cleaning solution, under pressure, onto one side of the slats of the blind. Reverse the slats and spray the other side.

7. Spray the tapes and cords of the blind with the cleaning solution at the same time the slats are being sprayed.

8. Rinse both sides of the blind with clear water, under pressure. (First adjust the valved connections to allow this rinse water to be wasted to the drain.)

9. Remove blinds from the spray booth and hang to dry, in full extended position with the cords slack.

10. After drying, overnight or otherwise, take the blinds down, load them on the hand truck, and return them to the windows from which they were removed.

During the washing operation, inspect each blind, and if any are found in need of repair or repainting, separate them from the others and mark them for such action.

Exercise care to see that the length of time the blinds are removed from the window is kept to a minimum. A suggested procedure would be to remove the blinds one day, wash them the second day, and reinstall them by the third day. This procedure, of course, refers to those blinds not marked for repairs.

Frequency

The frequency for dusting venetian blinds should be once every six months. The frequency for washing is once per year. These frequencies generally will prove satisfactory.

Staffing

The man-day labor requirements for venetian blind cleaning can be determined by use of the following formula:

$$\text{Man-days (of labor)} = \frac{\text{Quantity}}{\text{Production}} \times \frac{1}{\text{Frequency}}$$

where quantity equals the number of venetian blinds to be cleaned; production is the rate of cleaning per man-day; and frequency is the number of work days between washings.

SAMPLE CALCULATION

Consider a building that has 1,500 venetian blinds for which the production rate has been determined to be thirty-five blinds per man-day, and for which the annual washing frequency is satisfactory.

$$\text{Man-days} = \frac{1500}{35} \times \frac{1}{252} = .17$$

To this figure must be added a factor to compensate for leave in order to arrive at the total number of positions needed to accomplish the work.

Conversion factor including compensation for leave = 1.15
Conversion factor × jobs = total positions required
1.15 × .17 = .196 positions required

• Where a venetian blind cleaning assignment does not require the full time of an employee, other duties should be assigned to secure 100 percent utilization of his time.

28 / WALL WASHING

(*Source:* General Services Administration, Washington, D. C.)

Job Description

The job of wall washing is the planned and scheduled periodic cleaning of wall surfaces either by hand or by machine.

The job consists of moving furniture away from the walls, removing pictures, drapes, and other removable articles from walls, covering floors and furniture with drop cloths, dusting walls before washing, as required, washing, rinsing and drying walls as described under "Job Methods", and the proper care and maintenance of equipment used.

Equipment and Materials

Equipment and Material:

For wall washing

a. Buckets (12 qt.)
b. Cloth, turkish toweling
c. Drop cloths (floor and furniture)
d. Gloves, rubber
e. Ladder, safety step (of proper height)
f. Scaffolding (where needed)
g. Sponges
h. Sweep mop
i. Steel wool No. 00
j. Truck, platform, push type
k. Wall washing machine with attachments
l. Detergent (may be prepackaged)

Job Methods

Operation Steps	*Explanation*

Step 1—Prepare for Work

Obtain equipment and materials.	a. Obtain equipment and materials needed for washing walls. (See "Equipment and Materials".)
	b. Take all equipment and materials to rooms where walls are to be washed.

Step 2

Prepare walls for washing.	a. Move furniture away from walls toward center of room, except heavy files.
	b. Remove pictures, drapes or other furnishings from walls and windows which will interfere with wall washing operation.
	c. Spread dropcloths over furniture and floors.
	d. Dust walls lightly with a sweep mop to remove loose soil.
	e. Remove cobwebs with an upward and outward lifting stroke to avoid smearing the walls.
	f. Set up ladder or scaffold and make sure it is firmly anchored.
	g. Prepare solution for washing. Concentration of detergent depends upon degree of soil on wall.

Step 3 (See Step 4.)

Wash walls (manually).	a. Dip sponge or turkish toweling into solution. Squeeze out excess solution so it will not drip.
	b. Apply cleaning solution to wall in corner next to floor from bottom up, covering an area of approximately ten to twelve square feet,

Operation Steps   *Explanation*

wetting the surface without rubbing to remove the dirt.

c. Repeat the washing operation, applying pressure, or rubbing, to remove the dirt.

d. A straight rubbing motion should be used, either side to side or up and down.

e. Immediately following the washing operation and before the wall becomes dry, rinse the section washed with clean sponges or terry cloth and wipe dry.

f. Lap over into the cleaned area when washing, far enough to prevent border marks.

g. Continue washing lower half of wall until entire lower half is completed.

h. Wash woodwork on windows and doors as reached.

i. Place ladder or scaffolding at starting point and commence washing upper half of wall.

j. Place pails on platform. Be sure ladder or scaffolding is in good condition and safe for this purpose.

k. Apply solution to wall in corner at point where washing of lower half of wall ended and wash as described in this step.

l. If solution spills on wall below, wipe off immediately with clean damp cloth.

m. Wash woodwork around ceiling (if any) as it is reached. (Ceilings washed as directed.)

n. Keep moving ladder or scaffolding as necessary and wash entire upper half of wall.

Operation Steps   *Explanation*

Step 4—Alternate Method (See Step 3.)

Wash walls (by machine).

a. Prepare solution for washing. Concentration of detergent depends upon soil on wall.

b. Pour solution into tank, fill rinse water compartment with clean water, replace pump unit and pump up to specified pressure.

c. Fold turkish toweling into the form of pads and fasten on the trowels.

d. Saturate towels on washing and rinsing trowels. *Be careful* not to flood wall or trowels.

e. Begin washing wall in lower corner, working up. Hold trowel flat against wall and move it with light pressure in long straight strokes, from side to side, where surface permits.

f. Wash walls twice rather than apply heavy pressure.

g. Overlap area just washed in order to avoid border marks.

h. Stubborn streaks or marks may be removed with the heel of the trowel.

i. Wash area of approximately five by six feet at a time.

j. Wipe area just washed with rinsing trowel to remove soiled cleaning solution.

k. Use drying trowel to pick up moisture still on surface.

l. Use cloths from trowel, folded, to wash trim, pipes, woodwork, and other places, if necessary.

PRECAUTIONS

1. Use fine steel wool with care on spots.

2. Be careful not to spill any cleaning solution on wall which has not

yet been washed as this will cause streaks which are very hard to remove.

3. Avoid getting sponge or cloth against ceiling as spots will result which cannot be removed unless entire ceiling is washed. (Ceilings washed as directed.)

4. Change towels when dirty.

5. When washing by hand change water and solution frequently to avoid redistribution of dirt over walls.

6. Do not damage walls and furniture with ladders.

7. Care should be taken to avoid snagging water hose over objects.

Operation Steps	*Explanation*

Step 5

1. Remove drop cloths.	Fold up and remove drop cloths from room.
2. Replace furnishings and furniture.	a. Replace pictures, drapes, or other furnishings removed from walls.
	b. Return furniture to proper locations.

Step 6

Return equipment and materials to storage.	a. Empty buckets and machine compartments and clean all equipment items before placing in their respective storage positions (See "Equipment Care".)
	b. Hang all wet cloths or towels, gloves, and mops to facilitate drying.
	c. Replace all unused materials in proper storage locations.

Care of Equipment

A. *Bucket:*
   1. Rinse and dry the inside and outside of bucket after each day's use.
   2. In storing, place the bucket so that it will not be damaged.

B. *Cloth Wiping:*
   1. Wash in warm detergent solution, rinse, squeeze out excess water and hang cloth to dry.

C. *Drop Cloth:*

1. Brush or shake cloth free of dust and dirt after each use.
2. If cloth becomes wet during use, hang to dry.
3. Avoid snagging or tearing.
4. Fold and store cloth in assigned storage location.

D. *Gloves, Rubber:*

1. After each day's use, wash gloves in warm detergent solution, rinse in clear water and shake free of excess water.
2. Store glove in a clean dry place.
3. Always maintain gloves in first-class condition. Discard when holes develop.
4. Be careful not to snag gloves on nails or other sharp-edged objects.

E. *Scaffolding:*

1. Damp wipe scaffolding to remove solution spillage, or any moisture.
2. Store the equipment in its assigned storage location. Avoid creating safety hazards in placing the scaffolding for storage.
3. Report defects or needed repairs to supervisor.

F. *Sponges:*

1. Rinse in clean water after each day's use.
2. When dirty, wash sponges in warm detergent solution, rinse thoroughly and squeeze out excess water.
3. Store in a clean dry location.

G. *Step Ladder:*

1. Damp wipe ladder to remove solution.
2. Store in assigned storage area.

H. *Sweep Mop:*

1. When soiled, wash mop in warm detergent solution, rinse thoroughly, shake free of excess water, hang to dry.

I. *Truck, Hand:*

1. Wipe truck free of dirt and debris after each day's use.
2. Report defects to supervisor.
3. The wheels of the trucks should be properly lubricated.

J. *Wall Washing Machine:*

1. Empty tanks and thoroughly rinse with clean warm water, and wipe machine dry.
2. Remove towels from all trowels and wash.
3. Discard any unused cleaning solution.
4. Force clean water through the hose and trowels to prevent clogging.
5. Drain hose and wind loosely on trowels.
6. Place trowels in proper storage location.
7. Store in clean dry place where it will not be damaged by heavy equipment.

Performance Inspection Guide

A. *Wall Washing:*

1. There should be no streaks or spots remaining on walls or signs of not overlapping.

2. There should be no smudge spots at point where cleaning of the lower and upper halves of the wall overlaps.

3. No water should have been spilled on floor or furnishings.

4. Wall should be uniformly clean all over.

5. Woodwork on doors, windows, and moldings should be clean.

B. *Furniture Replacement:*

1. All furniture, pictures, and other furnishings moved during the wall washing operation should be returned to their original positions.

C. *Equipment:*

1. All equipment used during the wall washing operation should be cleaned and properly placed in its assigned storage location.

2. Wall washing machine or mop tanks should be emptied, rinsed, wiped dry, and placed in proper storage location.

Frequency and Production

Frequency and Production Schedule:

	Wall Washing, Manual or Machine
Frequency	As required
Production Rate per Man-day	2,000 sq. ft. (wall area)

Staffing

The necessary staffing can be figured by use of the formula shown below. The labor supplies, and other items used in this work are chargeable against painting and decorating cost classification.

SAMPLE CALCULATION

Assume a building having a wall washing requirement of 100,000 square feet in an annual frequency. Then the man-day requirement is computed as follows:

$$\text{Man-days} = \frac{\text{Quantity}}{\text{Production}} \times \frac{1}{\text{Frequency (days)}}$$
$$= \frac{100,000}{2,000} \times \frac{1}{252}$$
$$= .199 \text{ labor required (jobs)}$$

To this requirement must be added a factor to compensate for leave in order to arrive at the total number of positions needed to accomplish this work.

Conversion factor including compensation for leave = 1.15
Conversion factor × jobs = total positions required
1.15 × .199 = .229 positions required

Equipment and Materials Allocation and Replacement

Items	Allotment per Cleaner	Replacement or Reissue
Bucket (12 qt.)	2	1 per year
Cloth, wiping (terry cloth toweling)	As required	As required
Detergent	As required	As required
Dropcloth	As required	As required
Gloves, rubber	1 pair	6 pair per year
Ladder (12 ft.)		
Scaffolding (optional equipment)	As required	As required
Sponges, cellulose or natural	As required	As required
Steel wool No. 00	As required	As required
Sweep mops (frame, handle and mophead)	1 or 2	1 or 2 per year
Truck (hand)	1	1 per 5 years
Wall washing machine (optional equipment)	As required	As required

29 / WASTE DISPOSAL

(*Source:* General Services Administration, Washington, D. C.)

29A / PAPER BALING

Job Description

The job of paper baling includes loading the paper into the baler, adjusting and tamping the paper, operating the baler to compress the paper into a bale, placing the baling wire around the bale, removing the bales to storage, stacking the bales and taking care of the baling equipment. Employees assigned to this job should be instructed to notice lights out, and any other similar service defects, or defects in the operation of equipment and report them to their supervisor.

Equipment and Materials

A. *Equipment:*

1. For baling paper.

    a. Floor sweep (24″)
    b. Gloves, gauntlet

      c. Shovel

      d. Goggles, dust

      e. Rake (heavy iron)

      f. Corn broom

      g. Basket (3 bushel, oak)

      h. Tamper

      i. Stevedore truck

      j. Respirator, dust

2. For equipment care.

    Wiping cloths

B. *Materials:*

1. For baling paper.

    Baling wire

2. For equipment care.
    Detergent

NOTE

The baling machine is considered to be included in the building equipment.

Job Methods

Operation Steps   *Explanation*

A. *Paper Baling:*

Step 1

Operation Steps	Explanation
1. Obtain equipment needed.	Equipment and materials needed for baling paper are listed under "Equipment and Materials."
2. Proceed to assigned work area.	Take equipment and materials not already stored there to the room containing the baling machine.

Step 2—Baling Machine in Pit (See Step 3.)

Bring paper to room where baling machine is kept.	a. Bring paper to baling machine.
	b. Cover the lower platen with cardboard.
	c. Lower the bottom platen to the lower limit.
	d. Remove carbon paper, glass, and

Operation Steps   *Explanation*

metal from the paper. Further segregate when required by contract.

e. Using a twenty-four inch floor sweep or metal rake, sweep or rake the paper into the filling chamber.

f. Using the tamper, tamp down the paper as it is swept into the chamber.

g. When the level of the paper in the filling chamber reaches the floor, close and lock the rear door.

h. From the front of the baler fill the remaining space up to the upper platen with cardboard, if available; otherwise fill with paper and place a piece of cardboard next to the upper platen large enough to cover the platen.

i. When the space up to the upper platen is filled and the cardboard has been placed next to the upper platen, close and lock the front door of the machine.

j. Push button to raise the lower platen and press bale.

k. Open both front and rear doors.

l. Feed in baling wire with the looped end going first from the back to the front, passing under the bale and through the slots in the platen, then up and from the front to the back, passing over the bale and through the slots in the platen. Tie each wire by passing the straight end through the looped end and drawing wire tight.

m. When the bale is securely tied lower the bottom platen to the desired level to permit easy removal of the bale.

n. Remove bale to a stevedore truck and store for disposal.

Operation Steps   *Explanation*

Step 3—Baling Machine on Floor (See Step 2.)

Bring paper to room where baling machine is kept.

a. Bring paper to baling machine.

b. With the upper platen at the highest position place a piece of cardboard large enough to cover the platen on the lower platen.

c. Close both front and rear doors and lock.

d. Swing down the top section of front door.

e. Remove carbon paper, glass, and metal from the paper. Further segregate where required by contract.

f. Using a scoop type shovel load paper into the filling chamber up to the opening.

g. Lower the upper platen and compress paper in filling chamber, then raise the upper platen to its original position.

h. Using the shovel, put in more paper; then lower upper platen and compress the paper again.

i. Raise the upper platen to its original position, load more paper and place a piece of cardboard the size of the platen on the top of the paper and compress again.

j. After the third loading and pressing operation leave the paper compressed and open both front and back doors.

k. Feed in baling wire with the looped end going first from the back to the front, passing under the bale and through the slots in the platen. Tie the wires by passing the straight end through the looped end and drawing wire tight.

Operation Steps	*Explanation*
	l. When the bale is securely tied raise the upper platen to the highest point.
	m. Remove the bale to a stevedore truck and store for disposal.

PRECAUTIONS

1. Be sure to cut the electric power off the machine after completion of the baling operations.

2. Do not smoke while in the trash room or while operating the baling machine.

3. Be careful of broken glass and materials with sharp edges. Always wear gloves.

4. Do not get into the filling chamber during the filling operations.

5. Stack bales at least two feet away from lights, sprinkler heads or steam pipes in the trash room.

6. Always wear dust goggles and dust respirator when loading trash and when tying baling wire around a bale.

B. *Cleaning Baling Machines:*

Step 4—Baling Machine in Pit (See Step 5.)

Clean baling machine.	a. Remove pit cover, *make certain* the light is on and the electric power to the baler is off, and then go down into the pit.
	b. Using corn broom, gather up all paper and trash in the pit.
	c. Place the paper and trash in the basket and haul the basket up to the floor level.
	d. After cleaning out the pit clean all paper and trash from around the machine on the floor level.
	e. Wipe off the entire baler with a damp wiping cloth.

Step 5—Baling Machine on Floor (See Step 4.)

Clean baling machine.	a. Clean all paper and trash from around the baling machine.

Operation Steps   *Explanation*

    b. Wipe off the entire baler with a damp wiping cloth.

PRECAUTIONS

1. *Be sure* to wear goggles and gloves when working on a baling machine.

2. *Do not* smoke while in the room with the baling machine.

C. *Returning Equipment and Materials to Storage:*

Step 6

Return equipment and materials to gear storage room.

    a. Gather all pieces of equipment and materials that are not normally kept in the baling room and proceed to the proper storage location.

    b. Clean the broom and floor sweep, and store them in their proper location.

    c. Clean and store the gauntlet gloves.

    d. Clean dust particles from shovel, rake, tamper and basket. Store in proper location.

    e. Clean off dust from goggles and respirator, and keep in first-class condition.

    f. Clean stevedore truck of dust particles and store.

    g. Return all unused baling wire to proper storage place.

Care of Equipment

A. *Floor Sweep (24"):*

    1. Clean floor sweep daily by combing.

    2. Wash oily or very dirty floor sweeps as necessary in a warm solution of synthetic detergent. Rinse in clear warm water. Shake out excess water and hang to dry.

    3. Store floor sweep in a clean dry place so that the bristles do not bear the weight of the brush.

    4. Once each week reverse the floor sweep by placing the handle

in the other hole of the brush block. This increases the life of the floor sweep.

B. *Gloves, Gauntlet:*

1. After each use, shake out all dust.
2. Always maintain gloves in a first-class condition. When holes develop the gloves should be repaired or discarded.
3. Be careful not to snag gloves on nails or other sharp objects.
4. Gloves should be stored in a clean dry place.

C. *Shovel:*

1. Using a dry wiping cloth, clean loose dirt and dust from shovel before storing.
2. Store shovel so it will not be damaged during storage.
3. Avoid banging the shovel against the baling machine or any other object as such action tends to damage the shovel.

D. *Goggles, Dust:*

1. Wipe goggles clean daily.
2. Care should be taken not to drop or strike goggles.
3. Goggles should be maintained in first-class condition. When they become chipped or otherwise damaged they should be replaced.

E. *Rake:*

1. Using a dry wiping cloth clean loose dirt and dust from rake.
2. Remove any paper that might still be clinging to it.
3. Store rake so the spikes will not be bent or otherwise damaged during storage.
4. Avoid hitting the rake against metal or concrete as such action tends to damage it.

F. *Corn Broom:*

1. Soak a new broom in water before using.
2. Never stand broom on straws when storing.
3. Store broom where there is free circulation of air, so that it will always be dry.
4. Use a synthetic detergent in warm water to wash the broom periodically, and rinse in clear warm water and hang to dry.
5. Never use broom when it is wet.

G. *Basket (3 bushels, oak):*

1. Always empty the basket after each use.
2. Wipe out any dust or dirt in the basket.
3. Store basket in such a manner that it will not be damaged.

H. *Tamper:*

1. Wipe tamper off with a damp cloth after each use.
2. Store the tamper so it cannot be damaged or damage other objects by falling.

I. *Stevedore Truck:*

1. Do not allow truck to strike walls, radiators, or other objects.

2. Clean thoroughly each week using a damp wiping cloth. Wipe off all dust or dirt.

3. All defects or damage to the truck should be reported immediately to the supervisor. Arrangements should be made to have the wheels of the truck oiled regularly.

4. Store truck out of the way of traffic to prevent anyone falling over it.

J. *Respirator, Dust:*

1. Wipe respirator clean daily.

2. Do not snag or strike respirator.

3. Respirator should be maintained in first-class condition. If it becomes damaged in any way it should be replaced.

K. *Wiping Cloths:*

1. Rinse out cloth used, or when dirty wash it in warm detergent solution, and wring out.

2. Spread or hang cloth to dry in the proper storage place.

3. Avoid leaving any wet, dirty cloths piled together in the storage place.

Performance Inspection Guide

A. *Paper Baling:*

1. The trash room should be in first-class condition. Any baled paper and trash should be stacked neatly so it will not fall. The floor should be swept clean.

2. The bales of paper should not contain any large quantities of carbon paper, metal, glass or similar material and should not have an excessive amount of paper protruding.

3. The baling wires should be tied properly and securely on the bales.

B. *Cleaning Baling Machines:*

1. The baling machine and the surrounding area should be free of paper and from dust and dirt.

2. The pit, if any, should be free of any paper, trash or other foreign material. The electric power to the baler should be off and the doors to the baler closed and locked.

C. *Equipment and Materials:*

1. All pieces of equipment should be clean and properly placed in their assigned storage locations.

2. All twine, detergent and similar materials left over from the job should be returned to their assigned storage locations.

Frequency and Production

A. *Frequency and Production Schedule:*

	Paper Baling
Frequency	Daily
Production Rate per Man-day	Bales—Total Weight
	10,000 lbs.

The job of paper baling consists of the daily baling of waste paper, including cardboard and cardboard boxes, and stacking those bales in the trash room for storage, pending disposal.

B. *Qualifying Factor:*

Production Rate

The production rate given relates to power operated balers capable of baling at least five hundred pound bales. The rate as established may be subject to modification due to the use of different types of balers or the degree of segregation of the paper. It does, however, provide a standard from which such deviations (if any) should be figured.

Staffing

Staffing can be figured by dividing the total paper to be baled by the daily production shown in the Frequency and Production Schedule.

SAMPLE CALCULATION

Assume there are 9,900 pounds of paper to be baled daily. From the standard, each baler operator should bale a total weight of 10,000 pounds in an eight hour period. Using the formula as follows, calculate the required number of man-days to bale the paper.

Quantity = 9,900 lbs.
Production = 10,000 lbs.

$$\text{Man-days} = \frac{9,900}{10,000} = .99 \text{ jobs}$$

To this figure must be added a factor to compensate for leave in order to arrive at the total number of positions needed to accomplish the work.

Conversion factor including compensation for leave = 1.15
$1.15 \times .99 = 1.14$ positions required

It is preferable to have two employees working together baling paper.

• Where the duty of baling paper does not require the full time of the employees assigned to this job, other duties should be assigned to them to secure 100 percent utilization of their time.

Equipment and Materials Allocation and Replacement

Items	Allotment per Cleaner	Replacement or Reissue
Baling wire	1 bundle	150 bundles per year
Basket (3 bushel, oak)	1	1 per 2 years
Broom, corn	1	1 per year
Brush, floor sweep (24")	1	1 per year
Brush handle	1	1 per year
Detergent (soapless synthetic, powdered)	1 pound	10 pounds per year
Gloves, gauntlet	1 pair	3 pairs per year
Goggles, dust	1 pair	1 pair per year
Rake (heavy iron)	1	1 per 2 years
Respirator, dust	1	1 per year
Shovel (scoop type)	1	1 per 2 years
Stevedore truck	1	1 per 10 years
Tamper	1	1 per 2 years
Wiping cloths (waffleweave)	1	6 per year

The allotment per cleaner and replacement or reissue quantities in this section are based on one paper baler having continuous duty baling paper.

• Where the situation exists that other related duties are assigned to the paper baler to secure 100 per cent utilization of his time, consideration should be given to a reduction in the replacement quantities in accordance with the actual amount of paper baling assigned.

29B / PAPER AND TRASH COLLECTION

Job Description

The job of paper and trash collection includes picking up this material, both combustible and noncombustible, and transporting it to the trash room for baling and/or storage until picked up by the disposal contractor. The paper and other trash is collected from predetermined locations (usually outside the offices) where the room cleaners have placed it. Employees assigned to this job should be instructed to notice lights out or any other similar service defects and report them to their supervisor.

Equipment and Materials

A. *Equipment:*

1. For collecting paper and trash:

   a. Four-wheeled push truck
   b. Dustpan

  c. Dustpan broom
  d. Gloves
  e. Container for non-combustible
   material

 2. For equipment care.

 Wiping cloths

B. *Materials:*

 1. For collecting paper and trash.

 Twine

 2. For equipment care.

 Detergent

Job Methods

<table>
<tr><td colspan="2">Operation Steps</td><td>Explanation</td></tr>
</table>

A. *Paper and Trash Collection:*

Step 1

1. Obtain equipment needed.	Equipment and materials needed for collecting paper and trash are listed under "Equipment and Materials."
2. Proceed to assigned work area.	Take equipment and materials to where the paper and trash have been placed by the room cleaners at conveniently accessible points for collection, starting usually at the top floor.

Step 2

1. Collect wastepaper and combustible trash.	Pick up all material that has been set out in bags, tie all bags securely and place them in a neat manner on the four-wheel push truck. Where baler is available in the building, paper may be collected loose in an open type truck.
2. Collect non-combustible trash.	Pick up all noncombustible trash and place it in the container (on truck) for that purpose.
3. Collect unused wastepaper bags.	Pick up all unused wastepaper bags

Operation Steps   *Explanation*

and place them in a suitable spot on the push truck.

PRECAUTIONS

1. Bags should be tied securely to avoid scattering paper and trash.

2. *Be careful* of broken glass and materials with sharp edges. *Always* wear gloves. *Do not* handle any trash with bare hands.

3. Use the dustpan and dustpan broom to pick up any small particles that fall on the floor during collection.

4. Do not take the push truck into offices.

B. *Removal and Disposal:*

Step 3

Removal and disposal of paper, trash, and unused bags.

a. Take all paper and trash from the areas of collection and deliver it directly to the trash room.

b. Stack the bags so they will not fall.

c. Empty the container for noncombusible material at the disposal point.

d. Keep all unmixed paper and cardboard separate. Tie and tag the cardboard.

e. Deposit all unused bags in the bag storage room.

PRECAUTIONS

1. Bags should be stacked at least two feet from lights, sprinkler heads, or steam pipes in the trash room.

2. *Do not* smoke while in the trash room.

3. *Be careful* of broken glass and materials with sharp edges. Always wear gloves. Do not handle any trash with bare hands.

C. *Returning Equipment and Materials to Storages*

Step 4

Return equipment and materials to gear storage room.

a. Gather all pieces of equipment and unused materials and proceed to the designated gear storage room.

Operation Steps   *Explanation*

b. Empty and sweep out with dustpan broom any trash remaining in the push truck.

c. Clean dustpan broom, dustpan, and container for collecting noncombustible material, and return to proper storage location.

d. Clean off all dust from gauntlet gloves and store.

e. Return the ball of unused twine to proper storage place.

PRECAUTION

Be sure the ball of twine is tied and placed so it will not fall or unwind.

Care of Equipment

A. *Four-Wheeled Push Truck:*

1. Do not allow truck to strike walls, radiators, or other objects.

2. Clean truck daily by sweeping it out with dustpan broom and wiping it off with a clean, dry wiping cloth.

3. All defects and damage to the truck should be reported immediately to the supervisor. Arrangements should be made to have the wheels of the truck oiled regularly.

B. *Dustpan:*

1. Empty the dustpan into the waste can provided in the vicinity of the trash room.

2. Wipe with a damp wiping cloth to remove all dirt and other matter.

3. Wipe with a dry wiping cloth to prevent rust.

4. Hang dustpan in storage closet so that it will not be bent or otherwise damaged.

C. *Dustpan Broom:*

1. Comb the broom bristles daily.

2. When the broom becomes soiled, wash it in a solution of synthetic detergent and rinse in clean water.

3. Store broom so that the bristles hang down, are free to straighten out, and do not support the weight of the broom. (This is especially necessary when bristles are wet.)

D. *Gloves, Gauntlet:*

1. After each use, shake out all dust.

2. Always maintain gloves in first-class condition. When holes develop the gloves should be repaired or discarded.

3. Be careful not to snag gloves on nails or other sharp objects.

4. Gloves should be stored in a clean dry place.

E. *Container for Collecting Noncombustible Material:*

1. Empty container after each use.

2. Using a damp wiping cloth, wipe interior and exterior of container to remove all remaining particles of dirt, dust, or other material.

3. Wipe with a dry wiping cloth.

4. Replace container on the push truck so it will not be damaged and will be ready for the next day.

F. *Wiping Cloths:*

1. Rinse all cloths used, or when dirty wash them in warm detergent solution, rinse and wring out.

2. Spread or hang cloths to dry in their proper storage places.

3. Avoid leaving wet, dirty cloths piled together in the storage place.

Performance Inspection Guide

A. *Paper and Trash Collection, Removal and Disposal:*

1. Bagged paper should be neatly stacked in the trash room two feet or more from lights, sprinkler heads and steam pipes.

2. All unused wastepaper collection bags should be in the proper storage location.

3. Cardboard boxes should be broken, tied together and stacked in the trash room.

4. All wastepaper, unmixed at the time of collection, should be separate from mixed wastepaper.

5. Any paper and trash spilled during the collection process shall have been cleared up.

B. *Equipment and Materials:*

1. All pieces of equipment should be clean and in their assigned storage location.

2. All detergent, twine and other similar materials left over from the job should be returned to their assigned storage location.

Frequency and Production

Frequency and Production Schedule:

	Paper and Trash Collection
Frequency	Daily
Production Rate per Man-day	600,000 sq. ft. gross area

The job of paper and trash collection includes collecting daily wastepaper and trash, including cardboard, cardboard boxes and noncombustible material and transporting this material to the trash room for storage pending disposal or baling.

Staffing

The necessary staffing can be figured by dividing the building by the daily production shown in the frequency and production schedule.

SAMPLE CALCULATION

Assume an office building with a gross area of 544,000 square feet. From the production standard shown in chart, each collector in an eight hour period should cover 600,000 square feet. Using the formula as follows, calculate the required number of man-days to collect the paper and trash in this area.

Quantity = 544,000 sq. ft.
Production = 600,000 sq. ft.

$$\text{Man-days} = \frac{544,000}{600,000} = .907 \text{ jobs}$$

To this figure must be added a factor to compensate for leave in order to arrive at the total number of positions needed to accomplish the work.

Conversion factor including compensation for leave = 1.15
Conversion factor × jobs = total positions required
1.15 × .907 = 1.04 positions required

• Where the duty of collecting paper and trash does not require full time of an employee, other duties should be assigned to secure 100 per cent utilization of his time.

Equipment and Materials Allocation and Replacement

Items	Allotment per Cleaner	Replacement or Reissue
Broom, dustpan (hearth size corn broom)	1	1 per year
Ash can container (10 gallon container for collecting non-combustible material)	1	1 per 3 years
Detergent (soapless, synthetic, powdered)	1 pound	6 pounds per year
Dustpan	1	1 per 2 years
Gloves, gauntlet	1 pair	3 pair per year
Push truck (four-wheeled)	1	1 per 5 years
Wiping cloths (waffleweave)	1 ball	40 balls per year
Twine, jute	1	6 per year

The allotment per cleaner and replacement or reissue quantities are based on one collector of paper and trash having continuous duty collecting paper and trash.

• Where other duties are assigned to the paper and trash collector to secure 100 per cent utilization of his time, consideration should be given to a reduction in the replacement quantities in accordance with the actual amount of trash collection assigned.

30 / **WINDOW WASHING**

(*Sources:* General Services Administration, Washington, D. C.; "Ladder Code," National Safety Council, Chicago.)

Job Description

The job of window washing consists of washing and drying both the inside and outside glass surfaces of windows; washing the draft deflectors; washing window sills and frames on the inside; dusting the outside frame and sill with a counter brush; checking safety anchors, glass and frames, and reporting any defects or stuck windows to the supervisor; careful observance of all prescribed safety practices; making daily reports of work accomplished and proper care and storage of equipment and materials.

This includes windows in buildings where the use of safety belts, ladders, scaffolding and/or boatswains' chairs are required to accomplish the work satisfactorily; and windows which present unusual problems in cleaning because of their construction, or other reasons.

Schedules for window washing should be planned so that windows are washed on the shady side of the building to slow up drying time and eliminate streaks.

Squeegees should be cut to fit the size of windows to be washed.

General Requirements

1. Window cleaners and other window maintenance personnel should observe the requirements of all pertinent standards.

2. No one under eighteen or over fifty years of age should be permitted to do window cleaning at heights, except in cases where specific approval is given by the personnel department and safety engineer after a special review of the circumstances and conditions of the case. The physical condition of persons engaged in this work should be thoroughly checked before employment, and rechecked twice yearly thereafter. Persons physically unfit should not be permitted to engage in this type of work.

3. No one should be allowed to work at window cleaning without first being properly trained.

4. No outside window maintenance work should be performed when weather

conditions (such as high wind or ice) are such that they add to the hazards of the operation.

5. Smoking is prohibited while cleaning windows.

6. Acids should not be used for cleaning windows.

7. All persons engaged in window cleaning or window maintenance should be provided with and instructed to use safety belts, ladders, scaffolds, or boatswains' chairs, as herein prescribed, *unless* such work can be safely performed from one of the following locations:

    a. From the ground or floor level.

    b. From a roof or similar area which has a slope of less than one inch to twelve inches, is at least six feet wide, and is capable of safely sustaining the weight of the worker and his equipment.

    c. From a balcony or fire escape with a railing at least three feet high.

    d. From some other safe walking surface which is similarly protected.

8. Where the window sill extends less than four inches out beyond the window frame, an approved portable auxiliary sill or other approved device should be used, together with the approved safety belt.

    a. If portable sills are used, they should provide a working platform at least ten inches wide and at least twenty-six inches long.

    b. Portable sills or other such devices should be so constructed that they can be readily put in position, will be safely held in place, and can be removed easily.

9. Windows should be cleaned by means of a safety belt only (1) safe foothold and a safe unobstructed passage through the window are obtainable, and (2) where it is possible to attach the belt terminal to the anchor by extending only one arm beyond the window sash opening.

10. The use of boxes or other makeshift arrangements for window cleaning should be prohibited.

11. Persons performing window cleaning or window maintenance from a sitting position, with their legs inside the room, should use an approved construction-type safety belt securely fastened to some substantial anchorage inside the room. Approval should be obtained from the safety engineer to do any such work without an approved safety belt.

12. Squeegees, brushes and other equipment used for cleaning windows should be attached to the window cleaner's person, either by a strong rope or a chain. This is to prevent the articles from falling and injuring someone, or damaging property. However, if there is no chance that such falling equipment could cause injury or damage, this requirement may be waived.

13. Pads for the protection of window sills should be of a nonskid or nonslip material to reduced the possibility of slipping and falling from a window. Sponge rubber or discarded carpeting with a nonslip backing are two of the materials which may be used.

14. Windows having frames or frame mullions that are not securely fastened in place, or that show evidence of decay, should not be cleaned from the outside

by means of a safety belt attached to anchors secured in such frames or millions. Anchors should be *removed* from such windows.

15. Broken or defective sash chains, cords, windows or frames should be repaired before allowing anyone to work on the windows by means of anchors and safety belts. The windows should be maintained in good repair, and should be arranged to swing or slide freely.

16. On horizontally pivoted (reversible) sash windows, provision should be made so that the outside can be cleaned without the window cleaner leaning outside or putting his weight on or against the sash.

17. Casement windows, the entire surface of which cannot be cleaned while standing safely inside, should either have anchor fittings (installed as specified for other windows) to permit cleaning by use of a safety belt, or should be cleaned by some other method approved herein.

18. On reversible (pivot) windows which cannot be opened properly because of their design, or because of obstructions, work should be undertaken only in the manner and with the equipment described herein.

Equipment and Materials

A. *Equipment:*

For washing windows.

a. Belt, Safety
b. Brush, Counter Dust
c. Bucket
d. Chamois
e. Cloth, Wiping
f. Ladder, Safety
g. Pad, Floor
h. Pad, Sill
i. Scraper
j. Sponge
k. Squeegee

B. *Materials:*

For washing windows.

a. Ammonia (or other prescribed cleaning material)
b. Water

REQUIREMENTS GOVERNING PURCHASE OF SAFETY BELTS

Specifications to Be Used

Requirements Governing Installation of Window Anchors:

1. Specifications covering safety should be used for the installation of window anchors.

2. No anchors should be installed or repaired by building service employees, except where such work is undertaken with the approval of the safety engineer.

3. The use of lag screws or expansion bolts as a means of fastening anchors is prohibited.

4. Anchors should not be installed on windows where safe access to the anchor is not provided, or where a secure attachment cannot be made.

5. Where it is necessary to pass through a window to clean the outside, and where the only access to the window from either side is by means of a ladder, anchors should be provided on both the inside and outside of the window.

6. Installations where it is necessary to wear a window cleaner's belt while repairing or cleaning wide fixed-sash windows, and the only access to the window is from adjacent smaller windows, and the windows are separated by a substantial mullion, two anchors should be installed at each mullion.

Ladders:

All ladders used in connection with window cleaning and maintenance operations should conform to the requirements of the National Safety Council.

Boatswains' Chairs:

Boatswains' chairs should be used only upon approval of the safety engineer *after* it has been determined that other means of window cleaning or window maintenance as herein specified cannot be safely applied.

The absence of a requirement covering specific equipment, operations or hazards will not relieve the supervisor or the employee of the responsibility of taking further action to provide maximum safety in the performance of window cleaning and window maintenance. Each supervisor is expected to report to the safety engineer any unsafe conditions or work practices not covered by this standard or by related standards.

Use of Safety Belts:

1. The use of belts made entirely of leather, or in which any of the component impact-carrying parts are of leather, is prohibited.

2. Before fastening a belt terminal, the anchor installation should be checked for visible defects, such as loose, cracked or badly rusted anchors. Supervisors should spot check anchor installations frequently for such defects. If any are found, use of the anchors shall be prohibited until the defects are corrected. If there is any question as to the safety of anchor installations, the matter should be referred to the safety engineer, who will determine whether their use is to be continued. If investigation indicates that the window hangers are becoming defective due to corrosion or cracking, the safety engineer should arrange for testing of the hangers.

3. When using a safety belt, the user should attach one belt terminal to the anchor *before* stepping out onto the sill. Immediately after stepping out, he should attach the other belt terminal to the anchor. During the window cleaning or repair operation both belt terminals should be attached to the anchors. Just before re-entering the building the user should detach one belt terminal, leaving the other terminal attached until he is entirely inside.

4. Belt terminals should always be attached to both heads of a double-headed anchor.

5. Window cleaners using safety belts should not move from window to window by shifting their belt terminals from anchor to anchor, but should repeat the process described in paragraph three for each window.

6. In cleaning wide fixed-sash windows using window cleaners' belts and where access to the window is from adjacent smaller windows, the belt terminals shall be attached to the two anchors on the left mullion of the large window to permit work on the left half of the large window from the smaller adjoining window. The belt terminals likewise should be attached to the two anchors at the right mullion while working on the right half of the large window.

7. Extra holes should not be punched in a belt, nor should a belt be tied up with wire, or altered in any way.

8. On a two rope type safety belt the safety and service ropes should never be tied or bound together. The service rope should always be shorter than the safety rope to prevent wear on the safety rope.

Job Methods

Using Safety Belts

Operation Steps	*Explanation*
	Step 1
1. Obtain equipment and materials.	a. Obtain the necessary equipment and materials as listed under "Equipment and Materials".
	b. Inspect and put on safety belt.
2. Proceed to assigned work area.	Take equipment and materials to first window scheduled for washing.

Step 2—Prepare to Wash Windows

1. Clear window area.	Raise blind or shade. Remove books, draft deflector glass, or any other items on window sill. Remove any furniture which is in the way.
2. Place sill pad.	Place nonslip pad on window sill inside room.
3. Place floor pad.	Place floor pad on floor and set bucket on pad, or where practical bucket may be set on sill pad.
4. Open window and place sponge.	Wet sponge and squeeze dry enough to prevent splashing and place on outside corner of window sill.

Operation Steps	*Explanation*
5. Hook safety belt.	Hook safety belt and test as stated for the type of belt used. Be sure squeegee and counter brush are attached.
6. Get positioned for outside washing.	If window washers belt is used attach belt as instructed, step outside and close window. If construction type belt is used sit on sill.

Step 3—Dust and Wash Windows

1. Dust outside window frames.	Dust frame and sill from top to bottom with counter brush.
2. Wash outside window.	Starting at the top, wash glass with sponge using straight overlapping strokes back and forth across the window.

NOTE

To remove spots, wet window thoroughly and starting at the top, use sharp scraper in up and down strokes. Never remove paint from other than glass surface as this breaks paint seal.

3. Dry outside window.	Wet the blade of the squeegee and pull across the window. Wipe the squeegee blade on the chamois after each pull.
4. Wipe corners.	Pick up water from the corners with the sponge braced with one finger. Wipe edges with chamois as necessary.
5. Unhook belt.	Unhook belt as stated for the particular type of belt used and close window.
6. Clean inside window.	Stand on sill pad and using same procedure as for outside of window, dust, wash and dry.
7. Clean sill.	Remove sill pad and wipe window sill with sponge and dry with cloth.
8. Clean draft deflector.	Replace draft deflector then dust, wash and dry it.

Operation Steps   *Explanation*

NOTE

Wash and rinse sponge frequently.

9. Replace items.   Replace all books, furniture, and other items that have been moved for access to the window.

Step 4—Proceed to Next Window

1. Inspect finished work.   Inspect window to make sure it has been washed properly. Be sure all moved items are replaced on the window sill.

2. Move to next window.   Move equipment and materials to next window location.

PRECAUTIONS

1. Make certain that safety equipment has been inspected.
2. Avoid any action which will break the glass.
3. Report all broken or loose glass and defective items to supervisor.
4. Avoid interference with activities carried on in the offices where windows are being cleaned.
5. Carefully observe all prescribed safety practices during performance of this work.

Step 5—Return Equipment and Material to Storage

1. Return to storeroom location.   Upon completion of day's assignment gather up equipment and unused materials and return to the storage area.

2. Clean equipment.   Clean all equipment items as directed.

3. Store equipment and materials.   Store equipment and unused materials in their assigned storage locations.

Alternate Methods

There are so many types of windows, it will be necessary to give careful study to each such job. For certain types of windows not equipped with safety hooks, such study may result in a safe, more productive way to perform the job.

The *six step method* is one which has proved satisfactory for washing double hung windows not equipped with safety hooks. This method is applicable to all two sash double hung windows with not more than four foot height per sash.

Step 1: Raise bottom sash, lower top sash, wash and squeegee inside of top sash.

Step 2: Lower bottom sash halfway, wash and squeegee outside top half of bottom sash.

Step 3: Lower bottom sash, wash and squeegee outside top half of top sash.

Step 4: Raise both top and bottom sash halfway, wash and squeegee outside of bottom half of top sash.

Step 5: Raise top sash to top, wash and squeegee outside of bottom half of bottom sash.

Step 6: Close bottom sash and wash and squeegee inside of bottom sash. Relocate blind.

Care of Equipment

A. *Safety Belt:*

Safety specifications should establish the safety requirements for window cleaning and other window maintenance and should be closely adhered to in the performance of such work. The following excerpt should be included in the standard as it pertains to:

Care of Safety Belts:

1. Each safety belt should be identified and a record of the date it was put in service should be kept in the office of the building (or facility) superintendent and checked at frequent intervals to insure that proper inspection is made of belts which have been in service for a considerable period. A record should also be kept of any repairs or replacements made to the belt.

2. Belts should be maintained in good condition at all times.

3. All safety belts should be examined by the supervisor at the beginning of each work shift. The person using this equipment should also examine the belt at the beginning of each work shift and at other times during the day to make certain that no defects have developed.

4. All belts should be stored, transported and handled so as to prevent corrosion or injury. Belts which have been damaged by mildew by the action of an acid, by contact with sharp tools or equipment, or by any corrosive or deteriorating agent, should not be used.

5. Impact carrying parts of safety belts should be repaired *only by the manufacturer or his designated representative,* unless the regional safety engineer especially authorizes another individual to do so.

6. Persons responsible for supervising the use and care of window cleaning or window maintenance equipment should make certain that all unsafe belts and other unsafe pieces of equipment are disposed of at once, and not left lying about where they can be picked up and used.

7. When a belt has been exposed to rain or snow, wipe it off with a clean rag and allow it to dry at room temperature.

8. Never expose belts to heat in excess of ordinary room temperature.

9. Belts should never be dropped or thrown from one elevation to another, or otherwise mishandled.

10. For standard anchors and terminals a %16-inch plug gauge can be used to check wear on the terminals. If the belt terminal slot is so wide at any point that it will accommodate a %16-inch plug gauge, the terminal should be replaced.

B. *Counter Dust Brush:*

1. When brush becomes soiled, wash it in warm detergent solution.
2. Rinse brush in clear water and shake out excess water.
3. Hang up where air circulation is good so brush will dry.

C. *Bucket:*

1. Rinse and dry the bucket inside and outside after each day's use.
2. In storing, place the bucket so that it will not be damaged.

D. *Chamois:*

1. Rinse chamois in clean water and squeeze out excess water after each day's use.
2. Stretch chamois to original shape before placing to dry.
3. Avoid contaminating chamois with oils and polish.

E. *Wiping Cloths:*

1. Rinse the wiping cloths in clean water after each day's use.
2. Wash dirty cloths as required in a warm detergent solution, rinse thoroughly and wring or squeeze out excess water before spreading them to dry.

F. *Safety Ladder:*

The National Safety Council or your own local safety regulations should establish requirements essential to the safe use and care of ladders and should be adhered to closely in performing work in which these items are required.

1. *Ladder Maintenance and Inspection*

   Ladder should be cleaned and inspected frequently and those which have developed defects should be withdrawn from service for proper repair or disposal. In either instance, such ladders should be tagged or marked "DANGEROUS! DO NOT USE!".

2. During routine inspections all ladders should be carefully checked for the following defects:

   a. Loose steps or rungs (consider step or rung loose if it can be moved at all with the hand).
   b. Loose nails, screws or bolts.
   c. Loose or missing shoes or antislip bases.
   d. Cracked, split or broken uprights, braces, steps or rungs.
   e. Slivers on uprights, rungs or steps.

G. *Floor and Sill Pads:*

1. Shake pad free of dust and dirt.
2. Keep pad clean and in usable condition at all times.
3. Replace pad as necessary to avoid dirtying window sill or floor surfaces.

H. *Scraper:*

1. Wipe scraper free of moisture and dirt particles.

2. Use only for scraping glass surfaces.

3. Store scraper in a safe manner.

I. *Sponge:*

1. Rinse sponge in clean water after each day's use.

2. When dirty, wash sponge in warm detergent solution, rinse thoroughly and squeeze out excess water.

3. Store sponge in a clean dry location.

J. *Squeegee:*

1. Rinse the squeegee blade in clean water after each day's use.

2. Wipe squeegee dry and store in a clean dry location.

Performance Inspection Guide

A. *Preparation for Work:*

1. The safety equipment should have been properly inspected before using.

2. The window area should have been cleaned of obstructions before washing the window.

B. *Dusting Window Frame and Sash, and Washing the Glass:*

1. The window frame and sash should be free of dust and loose dirt.

2. The washed glass should be clean and free of dirt, grime, and streaks, and should be clear of all excess moisture.

3. The window sash, sill and other surroundings should be free of drippings and other watermarks.

4. Items moved during the washing operation should have been replaced to original position.

C. *Use of Safety Equipment and Methods:*

1. The safety equipment should have been used in accordance with prescribed instructions.

2. Safety practices should have been followed throughout the window washing work.

D. *Care of Equipment and Materials:*

1. All items of equipment used in the window washing work should be in a clean and well cared for condition.

2. Equipment should be stored in assigned storage location.

3. Unused materials should be properly contained and stored.

Frequency and Production

Frequency and Production schedule:

	Production Rate per 8-Hour Man-days	Normal Frequency in Work Days
Double hung, 2 pane, 4′ × 7′	60	Every
Double hung, 4 pane, 4′ × 6′	55	22
Double hung, 8 pane, 3.5′ × 5.5′	45	Days

	Production Rate per 8-Hour Man-days	Normal Frequency in Work Days
Double hung, 12 pane, 2.5' × 5.7'	40	
Double hung, 16 pane, 4' × 6'	35	Every
Industrial, 20 pane, 4' × 7'	30	22
Austral casement, 6 pane 6' × 7'	35	Days

Staffing

The man-day labor requirements for window washing can be determined by use of the following formula:

$$\text{Man-days (of labor)} = \frac{\text{Quantity}}{\text{Production}} \times \frac{1}{\text{Frequency}}$$

where quantity represents the number of windows (by type) to be washed; production is the number of windows, according to type washed per man-day; and frequency is the number of work days between washings.

If the frequency and/or production rate values as established have been modified to meet existing conditions at a particular location, then these modified values should be used in the formula shown for the labor requirement computation.

SAMPLE CALCULATION

Assume a building having 430 double hung type windows of 4 pane, 4' x 6' size plus 120 industrial type of 20 pane, 4' x 7', with existing conditions such that the established frequency and production rate values may be used.

Then the man-day requirement is computed as follows:

$$\text{Man-days} = \frac{430}{55} \times \frac{1}{22} + \frac{120}{30} \times \frac{1}{22}$$

$$= 0.355 \quad\quad + 0.182$$

$$= 0.537$$

To this figure must be added a factor to compensate for leave in order to arrive at the total number of positions needed to accomplish the work.

Conversion factor including compensation for leave—1.15
Conversion factor × job = total positions required
1.15 × 0.537 = 0.62 positions required

• Where the window washing duty does not require the full time of the employee, other duties should be assigned to secure 100 per cent utilization of his time.

Equipment and Materials Allocation and Replacement

Items	Allotment per Cleaner	Replacement or Reissue
Ammonia, household *	As required	As required
Belt, safety	1	As required
Brush, counter dust	1	2 per year
Bucket (12 qt.)	2	2 per year
Chamois	1	4 per year
Cloth, wiping	2	24 per year
Ladder, safety	1	As required
Pad, floor Pad, sill Scraper	As required	As required
Sponge, cellulose	2	12 per year
Squeegee, window	As required	As required

* Or other prescribed cleaning material.

31 / **AIR COMPRESSORS**

(*Source:* Minneapolis-Honeywell Regulator Co., Minneapolis)

A definite schedule of maintenance should be provided for all compressors. Frequent inspections of the unit, along with cleaning and lubrication, will add considerably to the life of the compressor. While certain time intervals are indicated for maintenance procedures, in most instances they are considered minimum, and actual scheduling should depend upon usage.

A compressor inspection program should always include an examination of the air lines and thermostats near the compressor. Remove one or two thermostats and check for oil or water in the connections or in the controllers. Continued presence of oil is an indication that the compressor motor is worn. Moisture in the lines (assuming that the tank is drained regularly) is an indication that the source of air intake is improper or that moisture is condensing because piping runs through cold areas.

Frequently it is necessary to remove the air intake from the boiler room to the outside where the relative humidity will not be as great. Because of the prevailing high relative humidity in some sections, it may be necessary to install a moisture condenser downstream from the compressor.

Checklist for Servicing Compressor

Weekly

1. Check level of oil in crankcase.
2. Drain water from tank.
3. Drain combination filter-regulator.
4. Check regulator setting.

Every Three Months

1. Clean cooling fins on compressor.
2. Change crankcase oil.
3. Check oil in motor bearings.
4. Clean and reoil intake filter.
5. Clean filter element in combination filter regulator.
6. Check motor brushes and commutator.
7. Check pressure switch contacts.
8. Test belt tension.

Lubrication. Check the oil in the crankcase weekly. Drain the crankcase and change the oil after every 500 hours of operation or every three months, whichever comes first. Fill to level shown on sight gage. Do not overfill. A good grade of oil should be used, and temperature consideration should be given in choosing the correct oil.

Temperature above 50° SAE No. 30 High Detergent
Temperature below 50° SAE No. 10 High Detergent

Draining. Drain the tank periodically by opening the drain cock. Allow the compressed air to blow for a few seconds to insure a complete purging of oil and water from the storage tank. If increasing amounts of oil are present in the tank, the compressor pump should be checked for wear. The frequency of draining depends on climatic conditions. Weekly draining properly, is the minimum requirement, however in humid climates, daily draining may be necessary.

Drain the combination regulator, low pressure relief valve, and discharge air filter whenever the tank is drained. A drain cock is provided on the base of the assembly.

Filters. The air intake filter silencers have an oil wetted filter element. To maintain low resistance to air flow, this filter element must be thoroughly cleaned and reoiled whenever the compressor oil is changed. Unscrew the wing nut and remove the screen filter element. Wash it with trichlorethylene. *Do not* clean the filter element in gasoline. Gasoline fumes in the unit would be an explosion hazard. Allow the filter to dry, then dip it in SAE 30 to 50 weight engine oil. Drain off excess oil and reassemble the unit. The filter element may require periodic replacement.

The resin impregnated cellulose filter element of the discharge air filter should also be cleaned when the compressor oil is changed. Loosen the nut at the end of the regulator, remove the end plate, and slip the filter element off its shaft. Wash the filter element in trichlorethylene, allow to dry, and reassemble the unit.

Regulator setting. Check the setting of the combination regulator, low pressure relief valve, and discharge air filter weekly by reading the low pressure gage. If delivery pressure is incorrect, see that the tank pressure is adequate before changing the setting. To change the setting of the regulator, loosen the locknut on the adjusting screw, turn the screw clockwise to raise the outlet pressure, counterclockwise to lower the outlet pressure, and tighten the locknut.

V-belt adjustment. For maximum belt life, compressor efficiency and quiet operation, the V-belt must be kept at proper tension. Adjust the tension by sliding the motor in its slotted mounting holes. Correct tension will allow approximately one-half inch of belt depression.

Electric motor servicing. *Inspection.* The motor should bring its normal load up to speed within a few seconds. If it does not, check the connections between the motor and the power supply and the overload protector, if the motor is so equipped. Be sure the power supply is the correct voltage and frequency.

Cleaning. Clean the commutator when the copper is scored or blackened, by lightly touching No. 000 grade sandpaper against it while the motor is running. *Do not* use emery. If the motor has been exposed to dirt, grit, or moisture, clean and dry thoroughly. Remove dirt and oil from rotor and from stator windings.

Lubrication. Use only a light grade electric motor oil. Lubrication of bearings should be checked three or four times a year. When oiling be sure that the oil wells are completely filled. Wool yarn packing bearings, properly filled, will hold enough oil for a year's operation. As a safety precaution, be sure to disconnect the power supply before attempting to oil the motor.

Cleaning compressor. The cooling fins on the compressor cylinder should be cleaned periodically to prevent oil and dirt from collecting on them. When cleaning the compressor, check to see if any bolts have worked loose, or if the compressor, valves, gages, or connections have been loosened or damaged.

Low pressure relief valve. Every six months raise the outlet pressure of regulator (see "Regulator Setting"), watching the low pressure gage to be sure the pressure does not exceed the safe operating psi (pounds per square inch). Turn the adjusting screw of the regulator back to its original setting. The excess pressure should bleed off through the two orifices in the front of the regulator. This bleeding will clean the orifices and prevent clogging.

Tank relief valve. Manually open the tank relief valve and allow air to blow through for a few seconds once every six months to keep the valve from freezing in the closed position.

Trouble Shooting Chart

Trouble	*Possible Causes*	*Suggested Remedy*
Compressor inoperative— motor will not run.	Electrical:	
	blown fuse	Replace fuse.
	open switch	Close switch.
	overload protection cutout	Press reset button. (See "Motor Failure.")
	broken connection	Call electrician to repair connection.
	pressure switch—open	Release air in tank, inspect switch. (See "Repair Procedure, Pressure Switch.")
Compressor inoperative— but motor runs.	Check valve	Release all air in tank. (See "Compressor Failure and Repair Procedure.")
	Relief valve	See "Repair Procedure."
	Broken compressor	Rotate fly wheel by hand. (See "Compressor Failure.")
Compressor runs all the time or takes too long to build up.	Faulty devices or leaks in system	Check system.
	Undersized compressor	Replace, or add additional compressor.
	Carbon on compressor valves	Remove carbon. (See "Repair Procedure.")

Trouble	Possible Causes	Suggested Remedy
	Combination regulator set wrong or not working	Reset. (See "Ineffective Operation.")
	Plugged intake filter or line	Clean filter and/or line.
	Pressure switch set for wrong cut-in and cut-out pressure	Reset. (See "Ineffective Operation.")
	Compressor needs repair	See "Repair Procedure."
Noisy compressor	Carbon buildup	Remove carbon. (See "Repair Procedure.")
	Worn bearings or rods	Replace or repair. (See "Repair Procedure.")
	Lubricating failure	See "Lubrication Failure."
Compressor uses too much oil.	Worn parts or overfilling	See "Excessive Oil Consumption."

NOTE

See additional trouble shooting information following.

Treatment of Malfunctions

Compressor does not operate. *Motor failure.* If the compressor does not function, disconnect the belt and see if the motor will run. If the motor does not run, if it is possible that it is not receiving power. Check for blown fuse, faulty manual or magnetic starter (if installed), corroded contacts on pressure switch, or a short circuit in the wiring.

If the power supply checks out, the motor is probably burned out and will require replacement.

The cause of the motor burnout should be determined.

Examine relief valve and check valve. Check for a faulty pressure switch.

If proper maintenance has been ignored, the tank may be full of water, resulting in reduced tank capacity and placing unusual demands on the equipment. Water in the tank may also damage or corrode other equipment in the system.

Compressor failure. If the motor runs when the belt is disconnected, the compressor may be seized or "frozen." Rotate the flywheel by hand for evidence of binding which is proof of serious damage to the compressor pump.

Other points of inspection are the check valve, the relief valve, and the pressure switch. The failure of any of these may prevent the motor from starting the compressor.

Compressor operates but ineffectively. If the compressor operates, but the system does not function effectively, check out the system for bad connections, faulty devices, leaks, plugged intake or intake filter, or other difficulty. If the system is in good condition, check the operating time of the compressor and the rapidity of the pressure build-up in the tank.

Make a check with intake line and filter off. If the compressor is running most of the time, or if the compressor does not build up tank pressure from 50 to 65 psi within three minutes with the system disconnected or not calling for air, the compressor, or its auxiliary equipment is not operating correctly.

This may result from the installation of an undersized compressor, or from incorrect V-belt tension, leaky air lines and connections, carbon on the valves, or incorrect setting or action of the pressure reducing valve.

The combination regulator may be defective. Check performance with the following procedures:

1. Stop air flow through the regulator. Use the shutoff valve if one is provided or disconnect the line from the regulator and install a pipe plug in the regulator outlet. If the compressor is running, wait until it stops before performing the next step.

2. Manually open the tank relief valve and allow air to bleed off until the compressor starts. Close the relief valve and note the reading on the low pressure gage.

3. Take a second reading when the compressor shuts off. A difference in psi between the two readings may indicate that the regulator needs repair.

Cut-in and cutout pressures should be checked to determine the performance of the pressure switch.

There are two springs in the pressure switch. The larger one determines the cut-in pressure. Cut-in pressure is factory set for psi, but may be raised by compressing the spring. The amount which you are allowed to raise is generally described in the maintenance and repair bulletin accompanying the compressor when purchased.

The smaller spring determines the differential between cut-in and cutout pressure. This is factory set for psi.

If no other cause for inefficient operation can be located, the trouble probably lies in the compressor itself. Carbon build-up or dirt and foreign matter lodged under the compressor valves will cause the compressor to operate below normal efficiency.

Valve difficulty is particularly likely whenever the compressor loses efficiency although it continues to operate at normal speed and although the system has been checked and is in good condition. (See "Repair Procedure.")

Noisy compressor. Noise may be caused by carbon on the piston head and on the valves. Carbon on the piston head will cause rapping as the piston hits the valve plate. Valves must be inspected for carbon build-up which may limit port or lift area. (See "Repair Procedure.") Remove carbon carefully with putty knife. Carbon build-up may be decreased by improving ventilation for compressor room and by providing cooler intake air.

A noisy compressor may also be caused by worn main or connecting rod bearings, excessive end play, or excessive wear of other parts. (See "Repair Procedure.")

Lubrication failure. If the source of difficulty has been located in the compressor itself, or if it appears that the motor has had an insufficient power supply, or the motor or the sheaves have been replaced at any time, a lubrication failure may have damaged the compressor. The size of the sheaves, speed of the motor, and required power supply to the motor are indicated on the installation sheet. Actual speed of the compressor can be checked with a tachometer or by calculating rpm (revolutions per minute) as follows:

$$\text{Motor rpm (see motor nameplate)} \times \frac{\text{Dia., motor sheave}}{\text{Dia., comp. sheave}} = \text{Compressor rpm (approx.)}$$

Excessive oil consumption. A piston type air compressor must pass some oil for proper lubrication of the upper cylinder. It is difficult to determine just how much oil constitutes excessive oil consumption, because the rate of consumption is influenced by several types of operating conditions:

1. High ambient temperature increases oil consumption.
2. A high percentage of running time will cause greater oil consumption than a small percentage of running time.
3. Light weight oil will be consumed faster than heavy weight oil.

Consideration must be given to the preceding influences before a decision can be made that the rate of oil consumption is excessive.

Certain compressor conditions will cause oil consumption:

1. A plugged or dirty intake air line filter.
2. Worn cylinder walls, piston rings, etc. cause increased oil consumption.
3. Loose or worn gaskets or seals will cause oil loss.

Corrective action should be taken to eliminate the cause of oil consumption or loss when these conditions exist.

In general it is recommended that the crank case be drained and oil replaced once each year. If it is necessary to add oil (because the oil level in the sight gage has dropped from the full line to the add oil line) more than twice between changes it can be assumed that the compressor is using excessive oil and the above conditions should be checked to determine the cause, and the cause eliminated.

The discharge air filter should be checked and cleaned every three months.

32 / **AIR CONDITIONING SYSTEMS**

(*Source:* The Trane Company, La Crosse, Wisconsin)

Failure to maintain proper conditions of cleanliness in air duct systems and carelessness in connection with repair operations have been important contributing causes of several fires which have involved air-conditioning systems. Systems operated only part of the year should be given a thorough general check up before starting operation and again after shutting down.

The following recommendations apply, in general, to the period of operation of the system:

General Recommendations

Fresh air intakes. Conditions outside the fresh air intake should be examined at the time of inspection of the ducts. Items to be noted are: accumulations of combustible material near the intake; presence of buildings or structures which may present an exposure to the intake allowing smoke and fire to be drawn in; operating condition of any automatic damper designed to protect the opening against exposure fire.

If accumulations of combustible materials are noted, they should immediately be removed, and arrangements made to avoid such accumulations.

Inspection and cleaning of ducts. Inspections to determine the amount of dust and waste material in the ducts (both discharge and return) should be made semiannually, except that if after several inspections such frequent inspection is found unnecessary. The interval between inspections may be adjusted to suit the conditions.

Cleaning should be undertaken whenever inspection indicates the need.

Cooling and heating coils should be cleaned, if necessary, at the time of cleaning the ducts. Thorough cleaning of ducts may require scraping, brushing, or other positive means. Vacuum cleaning may not remove dust of an oily or sticky nature, or heavy accumulations in the elbows or seams. The amount and kind of dust and dirt will depend greatly on the occupancy and the arrangement of the duct system.

Inspection and cleaning of plenum chambers. Plenum chambers should be inspected quarterly, except that if after several inspections such frequent inspection is found unnecessary. The interval between inspections may be adjusted to suit conditions.

Cleaning should be undertaken whenever inspection indicates the need. Where plenum chambers are found used for storage, arrangements should be made to prevent this, such as keeping the doors locked.

Filters. All air filters shall be kept free of excess dust and combustible material. Unit filters shall be renewed or cleaned where the resistance to air flow has increased to five times the original resistance, or when it has reached a maximum of 0.5 inch water gage, whichever is higher. A suitable draft gage should be provided for this purpose. Draft gages, of a type, which will operate a warning light or produce an audible signal when excessive dust loads have accumulated, are recommended. If the filters are of the automatic liquid adhesive type, sludge shall be regularly removed from the liquid adhesive reservoir.

Disposable filters should never be cleaned and reused.

Care should be exercised in the use of liquid adhesives, use of an adhesive of a low flash point would create a serious hazard.

Electrical equipment of automatic filters should be inspected monthly, observing the operation cycle to see that the motor, relays and other controls function as intended. Drive motors and gear reductions should be inspected at least semiannually, and lubricated when necessary.

Fans, fan motors, and controls. Fans and fan motors should be inspected at least quarterly, and cleaned and lubricated when necessary. Care should be exercised in lubricating fans to avoid allowing oil to run onto the fan blades. Fans should also be checked for alignment, and to see that they are in operable condition.

Fire doors and fire dampers. Each fire door and fire damper should be examined once a year, giving attention to hinges and other moving parts, to see that it is in good operable condition.

Repair work. Great caution should be exercised in the use of open flames or spark emitting devices, inside of ducts or plenum chambers, or near air intakes.

Air Conditioning Equipment

Today's air conditioning plant deserves good periodic care the year round, not just the customary spring and fall checkups at the time the system is started up or shut down. If some sort of regular year-round maintenance program is followed, any air conditioning system will pay off with years of good dependable service, to the advantage both of the user and the contractor who installed it.

Certainly there are a great many items within an air conditioning system which require attention at the beginning of each cooling season. In far too many cases, however, inspection and maintenance are performed only when a breakdown occurs and perhaps at the time the system is started up at the beginning of each hot weather period.

There are no shortcuts to adequate year-round servicing of air conditioning equipment. By following recommendations, it is possible to increase the life and efficiency of any air conditioning installation.

Before considering the frequency of maintenance or inspection periods, let us first establish that there are two times in the year when a complete changeover must be made within the system. These changeovers occur in the spring and fall, when changing from heating to cooling and from cooling back to heating.

These two periods are important ones. A major portion of the maintenance work on the system can be accomplished at these times. The amount of work can be greatly reduced if good periodic attention is given throughout the year. In this connection there are three important points to be considered.

First, it is important that a program of periodic inspection be initiated. The work can be done either by the owner's maintenance personnel or by a reliable air conditioning service contractor.

Second, it is important to see that once such a program is started, it is kept up and each inspection made carefully and completely. After all, there would be no point in conducting such a program if the inspector did not carry out his work faithfully and consistently.

Third, it is important that records be kept of each inspection, indicating the work performed and the parts or material required. From these records the maintenance man and the owner will always know the frequency of replacements, and have a good running account of the cost required to maintain the air conditioning system.

To assist in the program, a complete check sheet should be made up to cover the system. The check sheet should be printed in such a way as to provide a record as well as a checkoff list for inspection points. This could be done on a single sheet to cover a one year period, or on a form that would be complete after each inspection.

A suggested form is shown in Figure 32-1 together with some notation on the work involved. You will note that in our check sheet we have divided the inspection periods into four columns: spring start-up, summer, winter and fall shutdown. In each column are dots indicating those points to be checked during the different inspection periods. Where no dot is shown, that particular point of inspection may be skipped during that period of the year. (See Figure 32-1.)

Figure 32-1

AIR CONDITIONING CHECK SHEET

CONTROLS	Start-up	Monthly S	W	Shutdown
Clean commutators D.C. motors.		•	•	•
Check thermostat setting and clean points.	•	•	•	•
Check contact points in starters. (Clean if necessary.)		•	•	•
Check steam valves and traps, dirt, leakage, etc.			•	•
Check damper motor.	•	•	•	•
Observe operation of system.	•	•	•	•
Check controls on water cooler.	•	•		
Air controls—drain water.		•	•	
Clean air compressor intake.		•	•	

CONTROLS	Start-up	Monthly S W	Shutdown
Check air compressor oil.		• •	
Oil air compressor motor.		• •	

As mentioned previously, it is important that each spring and fall the entire air conditioning system be gone over carefully and checked for signs of wear and deterioration. Through the winter months, when cooling is not required, the maintenance man will have a good opportunity to make repairs of a preventive nature.

The Refrigeration System

There are three important things to protect in the refrigeration system: the compressor, the motor driving the compressor, and the refrigerant.

Cooling required in the colder months can usually be accomplished with outside air. It is not necessary for the refrigeration equipment to operate. In the fall, the refrigeration system should be pumped down and the refrigerant valved off in the condenser or receiver. By confining the refrigerant in the part of the system with the smallest number of joints, changes for loss will be minimized. Preventing loss of refrigerant is most important in shutting down a system.

After pumping down the refrigerant, the piping and vessels in which it is stored should be checked for leaks with a halide torch. If leaks are found in the condenser or receiver, the refrigerant should be removed from the system and leaks repaired. The system should be pressure tested after repairing. When pressure testing is completed, the system should be evacuated with an auxiliary vacuum pump. The refrigerant should then be charged back into the system and the system pumped down.

In the spring when the valves in the system are opened, the system should again be checked for refrigerant leaks. If, when opening the valves, only a small amount of refrigerant is allowed to pass from the condenser into the rest of the system and the system checked for leaks, a large amount of refrigerant can be saved should a leak exist.

The Compressor Unit

When the refrigeration system is pumped down, the compressor should be valved off thus preventing any loss of refrigerant through the compressor. If the compressor unit is belt driven, the motor should be shifted toward the compressor to lessen the tension on the belts. This prevents the drive belts from taking a "set". In the spring when the compressor unit is being readied for the summer months, the belt drive should be adjusted so as to give the proper belt tension. This is a good time to check the condition of the belts themselves and to order replacements if necessary.

If the compressor and motor are connected by a drive coupling, the coupling should be examined for tightness and wear.

The drive motor should undergo an annual cleaning. If the motor has ball bearings, the existing grease in them should be removed and replaced.

Once a year, the compressor should be checked thoroughly to determine if parts need repair or replacement. Overhaul services are best performed in the colder months when the unit is out of operation. If the crankcase oil is dirty or contains sludge, it should be drained from the compressor, the crankcase cleaned, and new oil put in.

Water Cooled Condensers

In the fall, water cooled condensers should be drained and checked for scale and mud. If the condenser tubes are fouled, they should be cleaned to deliver maximum efficiency. If the condenser is located in an area where subfreezing conditions are experienced, water should not be allowed to remain in the condenser, in the supply lines, or in the fittings.

Towers and Evaporative Condensers

Due to location and methods of evaporative condenser and cooling tower operation, complete and careful maintenance is required to preserve and prolong their operating efficiency. The fact that they are continuously handling warm moist air promotes fouling and deterioration. If not attended to periodically, their operating efficiency will be lost rapidly.

The unit should be drained at regular intervals and all sediment flushed from the sump. In the fall and spring, all metal surfaces should be examined for signs of rust. Where corrosion is taking place, the surface should be scraped or cleaned with a wire brush. The bare metal should then be covered with a protective coating of good chlorinated rubber base paint.

The following four suggestions have to do with care for working parts of the evaporative condenser:

1. Check the condition of the condensing coil. If scale has formed, it should be removed.

2. Spray nozzles should be checked and cleaned if necessary.

3. Pump strainer, water strainer, and air intake screen should be flushed and cleaned.

4. Float controls should be inspected and repaired as necessary.

In the fall, the entire unit should be prepared for winter inactivity. The fan motor and drive and the water pump and drive should be removed and taken indoors, or at least protected from the elements. If this is done each year, the work of placing the system into operation in the spring will be greatly reduced.

When shutting down the tower or the evaporative condenser in the fall, all points should be examined for low spots where water might collect and freeze, thus causing breakage. If such a condition should be discovered, it is suggested that the piping be disconnected at certain points to permit venting and complete drainage.

When water is drained from the pump, the pump should be protected against corrosion while it is allowed to remain idle. In many installations it may be possible to fill the pump with a light oil. When placing the pump in operation in the spring, the major portion of oil can be poured out of the pump and the remaining oil flushed from the pump by the water passing through it.

Wherever drives include belts, the belts should be removed and stored indoors during the winter months. Gear boxes should be cleaned, serviced and protected against cold weather conditions. All shafting should be inspected for rust, cleaned and protected. In the spring before placing the equipment in operation all of the belts should be inspected for wear and replaced as necessary. Gear boxes should be cleaned and filled with fresh lubricant.

In the spring, all bearings should be checked for wear, tightness, alignment and proper lubrication. Worn bearings should be serviced or replaced. Grease type motor bearings should be examined, flushed and regreased.

Air Units

At the beginning of the heating season and again at the beginning of the cooling season, the air handling units of the air conditioning system should be gone over completely as follows:

1. All motor, fan shaft and pump bearings should be inspected, serviced and lubricated.

2. All set screws and drives should be checked and tightened. If they have worked loose, the shafting should be checked for damage.

3. Drive belts should be checked for drive alignment and wear.

4. Air filters should be cleaned or replaced. Outside air intakes should also be examined and cleaned.

5. Other important components to be checked and cleaned are pumps, line strainers and spray nozzles.

6. In the fall, water cooling coils should be drained. The surfaces of direct expansion coils, water cooling coils and steam coils should be inspected for lint or dirt collection. Where necessary the coil surfaces should be cleared and cleaned. Since most of the foreign material deposited on coils is grease, a good detergent should be used to clean the surface.

Controls and Accessories

Last, but certainly not least, are the following check points on controls and accessories:

1. Clean thermostat points.
2. Clean or replace contact points of starters as necessary.
3. Check steam valves and traps for dirt or leakage.
4. Check damper motor and action of dampers.
5. Check the condition of dampers and damper linkage.
6. Check the seal around dampers and replace felting or other material as required.
7. Observe operation of the system.
8. Periodically, water should be drained from the pneumatic controls. The settings should be checked, adjusted or calibrated as required.
9. Clean intake on air compressor.
10. Check air compressor crankcase oil level.
11. Oil the air compressor motor.

It is important that this plan for systematically starting up, checking, and shutting down cooling systems be followed as closely as possible if they are to be expected to operate with maximum efficiency and minimum emergency service. Compared with the investment represented by the original cost of such systems, the small amount of time, effort or money which must be expended for periodic checkups is more than compensated for by the longtime trouble-free operation which will result. (See Figure 32-2.)

Figure 32-2

CHECKLIST FOR YEAR-ROUND AIR CONDITIONING SERVICE

COMPRESSORS	Start-up	Monthly S	W	Shutdown
Lubricate motor bearings.	•	•		•
Check drive.		•		
Check oil level.	•	•		
Check head pressure.	•	•		
Check suction pressure.	•	•		
Check pressure at settings.	•			

Figure 32-2 (*Continued*)

CHECKLIST FOR YEAR-ROUND AIR CONDITIONING SERVICE (*Continued*)

COMPRESSORS	Start-up	Monthly S	W	Shutdown
Check rotation.	•			
Slack off belts.				•
Align and adjust belts.	•			
Check head bolts.	•	•		•
Check cylinder bypass pressure at setting.	•			
Check oil pressure.	•	•		
WATER COOLED CONDENSERS				
Check water regulating valve for best economy.	•	•		
Drain condenser.				•
Reconnect condenser piping.	•			
EVAPORATIVE CONDENSERS				
Lubricate motor bearings.	•	•		•
Grease fan bearings.	•	•		•
Grease pump bearings.	•	•		•

Figure 32-2 (*Continued*)

CHECKLIST FOR YEAR-ROUND AIR CONDITIONING SERVICE (*Continued*)

EVAPORATIVE CONDENSERS	Start-up	Monthly S	W	Shutdown
Check drive belts.		•		
Slack off belts.				•
Check rotation of fans.	•			
Check condition of coils (scale).		•		•
Check spray nozzles. (Clean if necessary.)	•	•		•
Clean drip pan and drain.		•		•
Clean water strainer.		•		•
Clean pump strainer.		•		•
Clean air intake screen.		•		•
Check float control.	•	•		•
Drain water piping and drip pan.				•
Reconnect water piping.	•			
Align and adjust belts.	•			
Check fans for alignment.	•			

Figure 32-2 *(Continued)*

CHECKLIST FOR YEAR-ROUND AIR CONDITIONING SERVICE *(Continued)*

AIR UNIT	Start-up	Monthly		Shutdown
		S	W	
Lubricate motor bearings.		•	•	
Grease fan bearings.		•	•	
Grease pump bearings.		•	•	
Check drive belts.				
Check fans for alignment.	•			
Check filters.		•	•	
Clean expansion valve, drip pan and drain.				•
Clean drip pan and drain.				•
Clean oil air intake screen.		•	•	
Check expansion valve adjustments.	•	•		
Clean pump strainer.		•	•	
Check spray nozzles. (Clean if necessary.)		•	•	
Drain water coils. (Water cooling.)				•
Reconnect lines to water coils.	•			

(*Source:* "Pneumatic Temperature Controls," *National Engineer,* March 1961, illustrations—Johnson Service Co., Milwaukee)

Types of Systems

Automatic control systems may be classified into four general types, depending upon the basic operating principles. *Self-contained* control systems have their own motive power, while *pneumatic, electric* and *electronic* types are dependent upon an external source of energy. In addition to heating, ventilating and air conditioning, other building, mechanical and electrical systems may be supervised by central control.

Self-contained devices have many applications. They are not generally used where sequence operation is required. They cannot be interlocked to provide integrated control of valves, or motors and dampers. Installation is difficult where the thermostat must be remote from its controlled valve, and the self contained system is difficult to repair. However, the construction is rugged and simple and there is little in the mechanism to cause failure.

Pneumatic temperature controls. Pneumatic temperature control systems have been in existence nearly as long as the temperature control industry itself. "Pneumatic" simply means air and a pneumatic control system is operated by air. All of the control equipment in a system is interconnected by small concealed copper or plastic tubing into which compressed air is released.

The thermostat controls the pressure of the air. This air pressure furnishes the power for the system. "Thermo" comes from the Greek word meaning heat, and "stat" is derived from the Greek word meaning apparatus to render something stationary. Put them together and you have an instrument that will keep the temperature always the same.

The thermostat automatically allows just the right amount of compressed air to pass to the dampers or valves which respond by opening or closing to let more or less heat into a room. Inside the thermostat is a small paper thin bimetal strip or element composed of two different strips of metal bonded together. One is a metal that expands when it gets warm, while the other remains constant. Because of this, the strip bends as the surrounding temperature changes.

The bimetal element in the thermostat is mounted in front of a small hole or control port. Through the control port, varying amounts of compressed air is allowed to escape, regulating the output pressure of the thermostat. By its movement, the bimetal element determines how much or how little air escapes. As more air escapes, the output pressure is decreased and the valve gradually opens. As less air escapes, the output pressure increases, gradually closing the valve. All controllers and controlled devices in an air conditioning, heating, or ventilating control system generally operate on the same principle.

Electric and electronic controls. All electric controls, which may be interlocked and easily extended, are generally the choice for smaller simple mechanical systems. When the number of control points needed and the amount of synchronization and correction increases, pneumatic controls become more economical. When a system becomes larger and more complicated, it is far less costly to link the control elements with pneumatic tubing and pneumatic operators than with electric wire conduit and motors. Electric controls are known to offer economy, when packaged air conditioning does not exceed fifty tons. Pneumatic equipment is most effective for central systems of thirty tons or over, where there are several zones to be controlled.

It has become common practice to integrate electric and electronic devices with pneumatic control systems. The difference between electric and electronic systems lies in what is known as esoteric refinement in equipment. In an electric control system, the thermostat transmits its signal directly to the component which must be regulated (valve, motor, or dampers, etc.). In an electronic control system, the thermostat sends its signal to an electronic relay which measures and amplifies it. These command pulses are transmitted to the receiving relays by means of carrier current pulses superimposed on the light and power mains of a building or a group of buildings, and are produced by two basic types of equipment: tube transmitters and rotary generators. After receiving the pulsed signal and decoding it, special relays activate various types of motor starters, motorized valves, magnetic switches, etc. Electronic control equipment may be used to energize any type of electric or pneumatic device in a number of ways, or operation cycles.

A thorough semiannual inspection should be made of all operating equipment—relays, breakers, motors, valves, thermostats, and associated equipment. They should be cleaned and calibrated, oiled and greased if necessary, packing should be checked, and they should be tested for correct operation monthly. Compressors should be blown down weekly, motors and other operating parts should be checked monthly.

This work can be done by *trained* men from the maintenance department. It is imperative that they thoroughly understand the complete function of the system. The disconnecting of a relay-shutting of a valve may prove costly, and may be the cause of much discomfort. Maintenance agreements are generally available to cover periodic maintenance, emergency service, parts and replacements.

33A / FUNDAMENTALS OF AUTOMATIC COMBUSTION CONTROL

(*Source:* "Fundamentals of Automatic Combustion Control," by Crayton H. Schwestka, Hays Corporation, Michigan City, Indiana)

As a prerequisite to solving any control problem, whether it is the servicing of an existing control system or the working out of a new application, an understanding of basic control theory is helpful. This, at first glance would seem to be a bewildering undertaking.

Especially with automatic combustion control, much confusion lies in the fact that there are numerous mechanisms used in such control systems, different in application and design yet quite similar in operation. It is with the purpose of explaining and illustrating some of this basic theory that these articles are presented.

Controller Actions

Automatic controllers may be broadly divided into two groups: discontinuous and continuous controllers.

Typical of the discontinuous type are the on-off, two position, multiple position, and average position controllers. A good example of this type controller is a room thermostat which simply turns the heating equipment on and off to hold room temperature close to its set point.

Although the discontinuous controller is inexpensive and easy to adjust, it is useless in most process control because there is insufficient capacitance in most of the processes to allow its use.

Continuous-type controller action is subdivided into three classifications: proportional position, integral, and derivative action.

As an introduction to the formal discussion, refer to Figure 33-1. This is a representation of a control system involving a human being, a tank of water with variable demand, a water supply, and a control valve. All three controller actions are involved as follows:

Proportional position. The lower the water level, the wider will the valve be opened and vice versa.

Integral. As the level stabilizes at a new control point, valve is readjusted to return the level to its correct set point.

Derivative. If level changes suddenly, valve will be opened or closed beyond that position required for normal control in order to bring the level back to set point more quickly.

Each of the above controller actions will be discussed individually in this section.

Proportional Position Action

Proportional position action is that action in which a continuous linear relation exists between the value of the controlled variable and the position of the final control element.

This is illustrated by Figure 33-2. Here, water level is to be controlled at a predetermined point. There is an exit pipe through which a demand flow of water leaves the tank. Inlet water is varied by means of the gate valve so as to maintain desired water level in the tank. In this diagram, the automatic controller consists of the float, balance beam with its pivot or fulcrum, and the gate valve. The float controls one end of the beam and the opposite end of

Figure 33-1 / Three basic controller actions are involved when human operator controls water level in tank. Automatic controllers can do the same job—better, if properly applied.

the beam determines position of the valve in the inlet water line. The float is the primary element of the measuring means. It obtains information as to the value of the controlled variable, the water level. The end of the beam "Y" is the operator. The gate valve is the final control element which varies water flow, the manipulated variable.

Assume that the inlet water line is 10 inches in diameter and that the amount of water flow is directly proportional to the position of the gate valve. For example, if the gate valve is fully open, water flow is 100 gallons per minute; if it is 50 per cent open, the flow is 50 gpm. Assume that the fulcrum is at the exact center of this beam balance so that the arm X equals the arm Y and that, when the outlet valve is completely closed, the water level is 40 inches in the tank. It can be seen that when there is a 50-gpm demand for water in the outlet pipe, water level in the tank will drop and position of the valve will be directly proportional to that water level until the water level has dropped to the 35-inch level.

Assume the demand for water at a 50-gpm rate and level of water in the tank to be maintained at 35 inches when the inlet flow equals the demand. The 35-inch level is termed the "set point," in this case at 50 per cent of the range of the controlled variable. As the demand for water increases or decreases, the level will deviate from this set point and actuate the automatic controller in order to allow more or less water to flow through the inlet pipe.

Departure of the controlled variable from the set point is termed deviation. Sustained deviation, which always occurs when the demand exceeds or falls below the 50-gpm rate, is termed offset. The new value at which the controlled variable is maintained for this new demand is termed the control point.

Proportional band. Proportional band is the range of values of the controlled variable which corresponds to the full operating range of the final control element. If the position of the final control element (or operator) is represented by V and the deviation from the set point of the controlled variable is represented by θ, it follows that:

$$\frac{\theta}{V} = -k$$

where k is the proportional band factor. The value of k is negative to show that the corrective action is opposite to the deviation.

As shown in Figure 33-2, full operating range of the final control element is 100, and the range of values of the controlled variable is 100, then:

$$-k = \frac{\theta}{V} = \frac{100}{100} = 1.0$$

or, as is more common, expressed in percent of controller scale:

$$\% \text{ proportional band} = 100 \, \frac{\theta}{V}$$

In Figure 33-2 proportional band is adjusted by changing the ratio of the beam lengths x and y. With the fulcrum as shown, arm x equals arm y, so that in this case:

$$\% \text{ k} = \frac{x}{y} \, 100 = 100\%$$

This may also be represented by the graph (Figure 33-3).

Suppose the fulcrum is moved to the left, so that the beam length y is 10 times that of the length of arm x. In this case:

$$\frac{x}{y} = \frac{1}{10} \, 100 = 10\% \text{ proportional band factor.}$$

By further analysis, it will be seen with this ratio if the 50 per cent open position of the valve corresponds to a 35-inch level of water in the tank; then, as the demand for water increases to the maximum flow capabilities of the inlet pipe, or 100 gpm, deviation of the level will be only ½ inch below the set point. Conversely, if the demand decreases to zero, upward deviation of the controlled variable will also be only ½ inch to enable full closing of the valve.

Thus, in an automatic controller having proportional position action, as the proportional band factor is decreased the offset is also proportionally decreased. The reverse is also true. In addition, the set point can be located at any point in the normal operating range of the controlled variable. In Figure 33-2, the set point can be changed by adjusting the position of the float sus-

Figure 33-2 / Simple proportional position controller will do adequate job on applications such as this. The automatic controller consists merely of the horizontal beam.

Figure 33-3 / **Dotted line indicates proportional band can be shifted in set point without affecting its slope.**

pension rod in the x end of the beam to the desired level for equal inlet to outlet flow conditions:

Stability. Referring to Figure 33-2, if the proportional band were made extremely narrow, for example, by moving the fulcrum so that the ratio $\frac{x}{y} = 1\%$, deviations of the level will be only 5 per cent above or below the set point for full motion of the gate valve. This action closely parallels action of the two-position or on-off control. Here, any disturbance will cause oscillation or hunting of the automatic controller. It has been shown, conversely, when the proportional band is high, the sustained deviation or offset will be proportionally high. Thus it can be seen that in an automatic controller having proportional position action, a compromise must be made between decreasing the proportional band to decrease offset and keeping it large enough to prevent instability. In a process in which large load changes are apt to occur, proportional position type action is apt to be inadequate unless a narrow proportional band can be used. Danger of oscillation or hunting then becomes a major factor. The above problems are expressed graphically in Figure 33-4, which shows the response and tendency toward hunting or the lack of it for various proportional bands.

Combustion control. The application of a proportional position master controller in a combustion control system to fairly high capacity, low-pressure boilers is quite acceptable. Steam pressure, as the controlled variable, reflects boiler load almost exactly. On such installations some variation in the con-

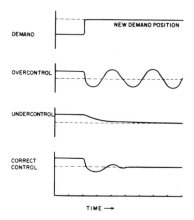

Figure 33-4 / **Characteristic of proportional position action allows stabilization by increasing the proportional band.**

trolled pressure is generally permissible and the proportional position action is sufficient for control purposes. The master controller sets up a loading impulse for the remaining controllers, proportional to steam pressure (boiler demand), in order to maintain a uniform steam pressure.

In the Electric Master Controller, illustrated in Figure 33-5, steam header

Figure 33-5 / **Hays Electric Master Controller for Combustion Control uses mercury switch pilot device to operate master motor. Approximate 1% pressure variation results from 25% load swing.**

pressure is applied to the metallic bellows on the right and is balanced by effect of the calibrating spring on the left. A drop in load (increase in pressure) is shown. Through linkage and the pilot device, the loading motor, located in the rear of the Master Controller, resets center horizontal lever to return pilot device operating magnet to its neutral position. In so doing, however, the loading motor travels through an angular distance in direct proportion to the increase in boiler pressure. Since the fuel and air controllers are loaded by the motor, firing rate is also reduced proportionally.

Integral Action

Most common forms of integral action are usually expressed in terms of floating action or as reset. Reset, however, is a term applied only to a particular form of floating action when used with proportional position action. This will be discussed later.

Floating action may be subdivided into two common types: (1) single speed floating, and (2) proportional speed floating.

To conveniently illustrate single speed floating action, the mechanical level controller previously described is converted to an electrical controller. Initially, its proportional position action is retained.

This is shown in Figure 33-6. Assume that the transmitting slidewire position is exactly balanced by the rebalancing slidewire position. When the condition holds, there is electrical balance. If water level in the tank drops, the transmitting slidewire moves downward.

Figure 33-6 / Proportional position controller, using electric components, has advantage of permitting remote operation of valve from float. Removal of link between valve and wiper provides single speed floating action.

This puts the transmitting slidewire at a potential more negative than that of the rebalancing slidewire. Current flows from negative to positive through the coil of the polarized relay. When current flows in this direction, the armature is moved to the right to make contact with the counterclockwise terminal of the motor operator or power unit.

The motor shaft revolves in a counterclockwise direction, and the wiper of the rebalancing slidewire is moved upward to a more negative position. At the time it reaches the equivalent negative position to which the transmitting slidewire has moved, no current flows in the polarized relay and its armature returns to the neutral position. Thus, rebalancing has occurred and, in so doing, the motor operator has also lifted the gate valve or final control element to allow more water to enter the tank. The converse is also true.

Proportional band control is added to this circuit by controlling voltage to either or both of the slidewires. The dotted lines in Figure 33-6 show a proportional band adjustment potentiometer added to adjust voltage across the rebalancing slidewire.

Suppose that the proportional band adjustment potentiometer wipers are moved closer together as shown so that the potential e_1 is 50 per cent of the potential e_0 applied to the transmitting slidewire. When this is done, it can be seen that full range movement of the rebalancing slidewire wiper must be obtained for a movement of the transmitting slidewire wiper equal to the voltage range shown by e_1. Since the full operating range of the final control element is 100 per cent and the range of values of the controlled variable is only 50 per cent, the proportional band can be expressed as:

$$100 \ \frac{e}{V} = 100 \ \frac{0.5e_0}{e_0} = 50\%$$

Single speed floating action. To illustrate this action, the link between the final control element and the wiper of the rebalancing slidewire shown in Figure 33-6 is removed. The wiper is then moved manually to a position representing the desired set point, termed the set point adjustment.

Assume that equilibrium conditions are obtained, i.e., the position of the float or transmitting slidewire wiper is electrically equal to the set point. When demand increases, tank level decreases, thus dropping the float and its slidewire to a more negative position. This unbalances the circuit, and the gate valve is opened wider. It continues to be opened more and more until the level of water in the tank increases and the float and its wiper are again raised to an electrical position equal to the set point. At this time, the electrical circuit again becomes balanced and the motor operator is deenergized.

However, the gate valve may have been raised or opened to a position greater than that needed to maintain the level at the set point. If this is true, the level will continue to rise and the circuit will again become unbalanced but in the opposite direction. This will allow the gate valve to drop and decrease the flow of inlet water. However this can become a cyclic recurrence known as "hunting" or "oscillation." Tendency of the single speed floating action controller toward hunting or continuous oscillation is one of its great disadvantages. One of its great advantages, however, is that of not suffering from any offset plus the fact that it is adapted to control of nonlinear final control elements.

Proportional speed floating action. It can be seen in the following example that, when a small increase in demand flow occurs, the rate of change of tank level will be small. Motor speed is required proportional to the deviation. This type of action can be obtained and is known as proportional speed floating. (See Figure 33-6A.)

Figure 33-6A / **Proportional speed floating action controller has great advantage of no offset control. This is extremely important in control of furnace draft, for example.**

Here the polarized relay is replaced directly by the armature winding of a DC motor having a separately excited field. Rotation speed of this motor is directly proportional to the voltage across the armature circuit. Direction of rotation is determined by direction of the current through the armature winding. With this arrangement, if the change in demand flow is small, the level change is small, and vice versa.

Therefore, if a large sudden drop in level occurs, the motor speed will at first be great and raise the valve at a fast rate. As the inlet flow rapidly increases and raises the level of the float in the tank, the voltage difference is reduced, producing a gradual reduction in motor rpm proportional to the increase in level until the set point is reached. The proportional band potentiometer in this example controls the voltage appearing across the controlled variable slidewire which affects, in turn, the amount of voltage appearing across the motor for a given deviation from set point. This determines the motor speed for that deviation.

Combustion control. Proportional speed floating controllers are the "work horses" in most phases of boiler control. Typical of these applications are boiler feedwater control, superheat and reheat controls, and fuel air ratio controls.

Proportional speed floating action is obtained in the majority of diaphragm unit controllers by adding a piston type pneumatic pump, driven by the motor operator or power unit. This pump is referred to as the feedback or stabilizer piston. Its output is connected into the diaphragm unit impulse line to partially oppose any change.

Electric control. A typical controller of this type is illustrated in Figure 33-7, which shows a Constant Suction Controller (CSE) used to operate an induced draft fan damper. Furnace draft applied to the diaphragm is balanced by the calibrating spring. Unbalance produced by an increase or decrease (deviation) of furnace draft from the set point moves the magnet arm to close either the decrease or increase mercury switch, respectively, causing the power unit to so move.

Figure 33-7 / **Hays Type CSE Constant Suction Controller as applied to furnace draft control.**

Initial motion of the power unit is at a constant speed. This motion, while changing the damper position in a direction to correct the draft deviation also operates the feedback piston, which develops air pressure in the diaphragm in a direction opposing the change in furnace draft. This causes the mercury switch to open and the power unit to stop.

Within a short period, pressure developed by the piston is absorbed in the furnace draft line. If a deviation from the set point still exists, the mercury switch is again closed and the above action is repeated. Thus, power unit motion is a series of on-off steps which, when integrated with respect to time, exhibit speeds proportional to the deviation. This is illustrated graphically in Figure 33-8.

Figure 33-8a / **On-off motion of motor operator (power unit) plotted versus two steady state values of deviation. Integrated motion with time (speed) is proportional to deviation.**

Figure 33-8b / **Typical proportional speed floating action showing deviation, corresponding motor operator motion, and deviation reduction occurring during a load change.**

Electronic control. The Electronic Ratio Controller is applied whenever greater threshold and resolution sensitivity that can be obtained with the mercury switch controller are desired. Its dead band and hysteresis characteristics are correspondingly less. Action of the EARE can be either proportional position or proportional speed floating. Figure 33-9 shows its application as a fuel-air ratio controller, for instance. An electronic amplifier raises the deviation signal level, detects it, and controls a pair of relays, for controlling the increase and decrease windings of the power unit or motor operator.

While the rotational speed of the power unit is at a fixed rpm when energized, action of the electronic amplifier is to energize the power unit intermittently. The on-time to off-time ratio of applied motor energy is proportional, within limits, to the deviation and can be adjusted by means of the dwell control of the EARE. This, as in the CSE, provides a series of on-off steps of the power unit shaft rotation which when integrated with respect to time effectively provides proportional speed floating action.

Desirable Features of Proportional Position Action Combined in a Single Unit

As previously mentioned, proportional position control action will always exhibit offset or droop when load changes occur. On the other hand, integral control action will not immediately compensate for sudden load changes and can exhibit considerable oscillation when measuring lags are high.

To overcome these limitations the two actions are combined to provide proportional plus integral control action. Either single speed floating action or proportional speed floating action in the classification of integral action is used, the latter being more common. When proportional position action is combined

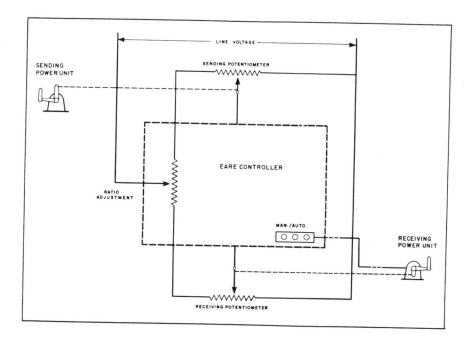

Figure 33-9 / Hays EARE electronic proportional position controller provides extreme sensitivity through use of thyratron relay tubes. Ratio between sending and receiving potentiometer position is adjustable.

with proportional speed floating action, the result is given the term "proportional plus reset action."

Proportional position action has been defined as that in which a continuous linear relation exists between the value of the controlled variable and the position of the final control element.

Proportional speed floating action has been defined as that in which the final control element is moved at a speed proportional to the deviation.

Proportional plus reset action is the result of combining proportional position action and proportional speed floating action. The reset action which then results is defined as that in which the final control element is moved at a speed proportional to the extent of proportional position action.

Figure 33-10 again shows the proportional position action controller applied to regulate water level. For example, with a 50 per cent valve position, tank level is maintained at 50 inches. If water demand increases so that the tank level drops and a stablized condition is reached at 40 inches, the 10-inch difference in level from the 50 inches set point is a sustained deviation or offset.

How can this offset or droop be corrected? One method might be for the operator to loosen the set screw holding the float to the transmitting slidewire wiper of the controller, and readjust the float upward to the desired set point. When the float and wiper assembly is released, the proportional action of the controller will open the valve allowing more water to enter until the level in

Figure 33-10 / **Proportional position controller illustrated suffers from offset whenever control point is different from set point.**

the tank again reaches the set point. At this point equilibrium conditions are again obtained. The same effect could also be accomplished by the operator loosening the set screw attaching the gate valve to the output of the automatic controller and adjusting the gate valve to a more open position. Again, the water level would rise to the desired level or set point. This action of the operator to "reset" the automatic controller to the set point describes "reset action" in proportional plus reset.

Either of these methods would be time consuming and would be required for each load change. The automatic controller with proportional plus reset action does this resetting action automatically.

Proportional plus Reset Action

Proportional position action. Figure 33-11 illustrates one way in which this can be accomplished. To the right of the dotted line is the familiar proportional position section. For simplicity, float motion is shown transmitted by a cable passing over a pulley actuating the transmitting slidewire wiper. Unbalance, due to water level fluctuation between it and the rebalancing slidewire wiper connected to the valve actuates the motor operator until balance is effected.

Proportional speed floating action. To the left of the dotted line is the proportional speed floating section of the controller. The float level here also determines the position of the transmitting slidewire wiper of this section. At equilibrium, this is electrically equivalent to the position of the set point

Figure 33-11 / **Proportional plus reset controller includes means for overcoming offset. For simplicity, method for setting proportional band and reset rate is deleted.**

potentiometer wiper. However, when a deviation exists between the float wiper and the set point, the error voltage causes the reset motor to rotate at a speed proportional to the deviation. The pulley over which the cable to the proportional band transmitting wiper travels is thus moved to reduce the proportional speed floating section error voltage.

Assume the control is in equilibrium at a water level set point of 50 inches. The proportional position section wiper is at 50 per cent and the valve is also at 50 per cent position. The proportional band is 100 per cent. A step change disturbance lowers the water level to 40 inches, a drop equal to 10 per cent of range. Since the transmitting wiper is then moved to the 60 per cent position, the proportional position section will immediately (neglecting operating time) open the valve to the 60 per cent position. Equilibrium would then be attained for this section, if used alone.

However, the error voltage, existing in the proportional speed floating section between the level slidewire wiper and the set point slidewire wiper, acts to rotate the reset motor clockwise. This raises the pulley to attempt to decrease the error voltage. Initially, however, the level has not changed, resulting in the wiper of the proportional position transmitting slidewire being raised. The proportional position section is thus again unbalanced and the motor operator is actuated to raise the valve. The resulting increased water flow eventually raises water level to the set point. Thus the proportional position section is stabilized, and a re-setting action has occurred to overcome offset.

Reset rate. The amount of integral action in a controller with proportional plus reset action is usually expressed in "repeats per minute" i.e., the number of times per minute that the integral action repeats the motion of the propor-tional position action after a step deviation from the set point. In the example given, if one minute is required for the reset motor to raise the wiper of the proportional position transmitting slidewire an additional 10 per cent the reset rate is 1.0 repeats per minute. This action is plotted graphically in Figure 33-12 for a condition (not normally encountered) where the deviation remains constant.

Figure 33-12 / **Proportional plus reset ac-tion for a step deviation which then remains constant. If $v_2 = v_1$ and $t_2 - t_1 =$ one minute, the reset rate is 1.0 repeats per minute. Reset rate is usually adjustable and may be calibrated in steps from 0.1 to 10 repeats per minute.**

Figure 33-13 / **A typical pro-portional plus reset action restoring set point to overcome offset.**

Reset rate is, therefore:

$$\frac{V_2}{(t_2 - t_1)\ v_1}$$

A typical plot is shown in Figure 33-13 of the action obtained when the deviation is corrected by proportional plus reset controller.

Combustion and process control. The type LPME master steam pressure controller was shown to have proportional position action. When its inherent offset characteristics are intolerable, a similar master controller may be used in which integral action is combined with the proportional position action. This is known as the type HPMEC Master Controller.

As we mentioned previously describing integral action, the majority of mercury switch controllers equipped with feedback pistons normally provide proportional speed floating action. However, when the combustion or other process to be controlled exhibits considerable lag or sudden load changes, proportional position action is added to provide greater speed of response. This action is then proportional plus reset.

Typical of the diaphram-actuated controllers utilizing proportional plus reset action is the Adjustable Differential Pressure controller type ADE-A, illustrated in Figure 33-14. This shows its use to control the speed of a forced draft fan turbine. By comparison with Figure 33-7 the similarity is apparent. However, a diaphragm unit with three chambers, termed a trifferential unit, is employed together with a "proportional band tank" and a bleed valve or floating rate adjuster. The top diaphragm of the trifferential unit is simply a sealing diaphragm. The large center diaphragm is the differential pressure measuring diaphragm while the small bottom diaphragm measures the feed back pressure.

Figure 33-14 / ADE-A, Adjustable, Low Differential Pressure Controller, applied to air flow control. This is a typical Hays design diaphragm actuated controller including feedback or stabilizer piston and proportional band chamber.

Differential air pressure equivalent to air flow is balanced by the calibration spring, or external loading force. When an increase in differential air pressure occurs, the magnet is moved by the diaphragm to close the decrease mercury switch to operate the power unit. While the power unit is rotating to decrease steam to the turbine, the feedback piston acts to build up air pressure in the proportional band tank and the small "stabilizing" section of the trifferential diaphragm unit. Since the capacity of the proportional band tank is large compared to the stabilizing section of the trifferential unit, considerable time is initially required to build up pressure in the system. When sufficient pressure is built up in the tank and differential unit to balance the change in draft, the magnet is returned to center position and the power unit stops.

Meanwhile, the open bleed or floating rate adjusting valve allows air to slowly escape from the proportional band tank. If the deviation persists, pressure loss causes the mercury switch again to operate the power unit. Now, however, the proportional band tank is almost at full air pressure so that a relatively smaller power unit motion is required to balance the diaphragm and stop the power unit motion. This action is repeated with successively smaller steps until equilibrium is obtained.

This action, then, is the same illustrated graphically in Figure 33-12 with true proportional plus reset action resulting.

Derivative Action

Derivative action is that in which there is a predetermined relation between a time derivative of the controlled variable and the position of the final control element. The first derivative, or rate action, is most commonly used. Nonstandard terms such as anticipatory action, preact, damping, or stabilizing action are used occasionally, and may refer to some type of rate action. Rate action is similar to the action applied by a manual operator when he "anticipates" the amount of corrective action required by observing the rate at which a deviation from the set point is occurring. Hence the term "anticipatory control."

Rate action. Rate action is that in which there is a continuous linear relationship between the rate of change of the controlled variable and the position of the final control element, or motor operator acting upon the final control element. Because rate action is not affected by the error signal itself, but only by the rate of change of the error signal, it is not used as a single control mode.

Rate action may be added in limited amounts to a controller having proportional position action. When so used, it will decrease or narrow the effective proportional band. Otherwise, decreasing the proportional band of a proportional position controller usually increases its instability. Hence the term "stabilizing action" which is sometimes used. Some processes have inherently excessive lag. Rate action is added to automatic controllers to overcome this lag in such processes.

Figure 33-15 illustrates one means of adding rate action to an automatic controller having proportional position action. The proportional position section shown has 100 per cent proportional band and will open or close the valve in proportion to a respective decrease or increase in water level. Here the motor operator is equipped with a direct armature winding so that its motion is proportional to the voltage across that winding.

Action of the proportional position section is conventional. If a difference in voltage between the float wiper and the motor operator or valve wiper is created due to a change in water level, the motor operator will be energized. Its movement will position the valve and change water flow until the rebalancing wiper is moved to a position at which no potential difference exists. However, the rate action bridge, here shown connected to a separate source of direct current, will also have a difference of potential existing between its float wiper and the valve wiper. This voltage is impressed across the differentiating network, consisting of resistor R_1 and condenser C_1. If the voltage was to remain constant, in a short time the condenser would be charged up to full value of this voltage, and no current would flow through R_1. However, when the float wiper is moved with respect to the valve or rebalancing wiper position, a changing voltage is produced

Figure 33-15 / **Proportional position plus rate action controller will help overcome inherent process lags. Reset may be added to eliminate offset.**

which is impressed across R_1C_1. When this occurs, there will be a current, I_1, flowing through R_1C_1 which is proportional to the rate at which this voltage is changing.

The product of this current times resistance (I_1R_1) is a voltage proportional to the rate of change of the error between water level and valve position. This voltage is added algebraically (and vectorially) to the proportional position section error voltage. This increases or decreases the normal motor speed as a function of the rate at which the error is increasing or decreasing.

For example, from a stabilized position, if the water level and therefore the float start to drop at a constant rate with respect to the valve position, a voltage will be produced across R_1. If, by the addition of this voltage, the voltage appearing across the proportional position bridge alone is doubled, the motor will tend to rotate at twice its previous speed. The resulting action is graphically illustrated in Figure 33-16. The solid line indicates the speed with which the valve position would be changed with proportional position action alone. Dotted line indicates the faster response time when rate action is added.

At this point, it may appear that considerable overshoot might result from this combination. However, in practical application, the rebalancing action will reduce the rate of change and the resulting rate action signal. Also, after a sudden discreet change in level, the motor operator is still rebalancing that portion of the bridge, and a signal will be produced proportional to the rate of change of motor operator position. This signal will have a polarity opposite that due to a change in float level and will therefore add to the stabilizing action.

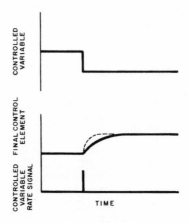

Figure 33-16 / Response time
of final control element due to proportional position action alone
(solid line) is made faster (dotted
line) by addition of rate signal.

Note that this controller does not have reset action and therefore suffers
from offset. When desired, reset action can be added to a controller having
proportional plus rate action.

In practice, the amount of rate action added to proportional position action
is made variable to meet varying application requirements. This may be done by
changing the voltage applied to the rate action bridge circuit, or by changing the
value of R_1 or C_1. Various combinations of these three also may be used.

Rate time. Rate time is the interval by which rate action increases the motor
operator motion due to proportional position action alone. It is determined for a
constant given rate of change of controlled variable. The time required for a
given motion of the motor operator due to proportional plus rate action is subtracted from the time required for the same motion due to proportional position
action alone. The difference is rate time and is usually expressed in minutes. It is
desirable to have the rate time adjustable with respect to the proportional
band adjustment in order to meet varying process characteristics. Representative
rate times vary from .01 minute to 10 minutes. Rate narrows proportional band.

As we stated earlier, the proportional band is the range of values of the
controlled variable which corresponds to the full operating range of the motor
operator. In Figure 33-17, if 100 volts are applied across both the float slidewire
and the value or rebalancing slidewire, the proportional band would be 100 per
cent. If, however, the float slidewire has a voltage across it of twice the value of
that across the rebalancing slidewire, the proportional band is only 50 per cent.
This is because the float slidewire need move only through 50 per cent of its
range to equal the voltage difference appearing across 100 per cent of the value
or rebalancing slidewire.

Figure 33-17 / Increase of voltage across transmitting (float) slidewire with respect to receiving (valve) slidewire narrows proportional band. Rate action accomplishes this automatically during change of float position.

We have shown that the voltage produced across R_1 of the rate action section during a change in float level is added to that developed by the proportional position action section. This, in effect, momentarily increases the voltage at the float slidewire with respect to the rebalancing slidewire. Thus the effective proportional band is decreased, or narrowed, during this change. The magnitude of this decrease is proportional to the rate of change of the error and the relative setting of the proportional band and rate adjustments on the controller.

Combustion control. The electronic totalizer Model EART is an extremely versatile controller. It is frequently used whenever it is desired to totalize varying amounts and types of fuels in multiple burner installations for the purpose of proportioning and controlling the necessary air input. This controller, by suitable arrangement and connection of input auxiliary devices, can be applied to exhibit proportional position action and proportional speed floating action. By using other suitable auxiliary equipment, reset action can be added.

Ability of this controller to function similarly to the proportional plus rate action controller is illustrated in Figure 33-18. This shows a Model EART applied to control gas flow as a function of boiler steam pressure. The resulting gas flow is metered, and is connected into the totalizer circuit in such a way as to provide 'stabilizing action."

Three equal independent voltages are supplied from separate windings of the power transformer. Each voltage is individually variable by means of its respective slidewire winding as shown. The instantaneous polarity shown by the

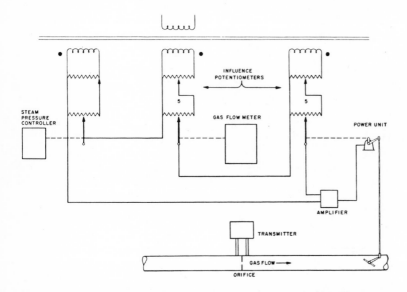

Figure 33-18 / **Hays Model EART controller applied to control gas valve to maintain steam pressure. Gas flow influence as used here permits narrowing proportional band during steam pressure changes, a distinguishing feature of rate action.**

Figure 33-19 / **Rate action narrows proportional band during a disturbance. Dotted line typified initial narrow proportional band obtained at start of upset and shift to wider band at completion of corrective action.**

dots adjacent to the secondary windings indicates that the steam pressure signal may be balanced by either the gas flow or gas valve slidewires, or both.

For example, assume the steam pressure influence potentiometer at 100 per cent, the gas flow influence potentiometer at 0 per cent, and the gas valve influence potentiometer at 100 per cent. With this arrangement, the gas flow slidewire is effectively out of the circuit. Thus a 100 per cent proportional band exists between the steam pressure and the gas valve position. This is illustrated in Figure 33-19. If the gas valve influence potentiometer now is set to 50 per cent, the 50 per cent proportional band characteristic plotted in this graph results. Now if the gas flow influence potentiometer is brought from 0 per cent to 50 per cent, a proportional band of 100 per cent can be seen to exist, providing the gas valve and gas flow slidewires move in unison.

However, if initially there is no motion of the gas flow slidewire due to lag, while the gas valve slidewire does move, a proportional band of 50 per cent will be obtained. As the gas flow slidewire then eventually moves to a position equivalent to the gas valve slidewire, the 100 per cent proportional band is again

ACTION	APPLICATIONS TO SYSTEMS HAVING:	ADVANTAGES	DISADVANTAGES
Proportional Position	Need for direct proportionality Good self regulation Little or no lag Little or no dead time Slow response time Tolerance at offset	Precise proportionality Fast response time No overshoot No phase shift	Set point error or offset oscillation at narrow proportional bands
Single Speed Floating	Good self regulation Little or no lag Little or no dead time Fast response time	No offset	Overshoot Oscillation Requires dead band Negative phase shift Slow response time
Proportional Speed Floating	Good self regulation Little or no lag Little or no dead time Low disturbance rate Fast response time	No offset Requires no dead band Can be applied to nonlinear system	Tendency to overshoot Tendency to oscillate Negative phase shift Slow response time Floating rate must be matched to system response
Proportional + Single Speed Floating	Little self regulation Some lag Little or no dead time Fixed response time Medium disturbance rates	No offset Fast response time Can be applied to nonlinear system	Oscillation on systems having dead time Some negative phase shift Single speed Reset not applicable to wide load changes
Proportional + Reset	Little self regulation Some lag Little or no dead time Variable disturbance rates Variable response time	No offset Fast response time Compensates for wide load variations Good stability Can be applied to nonlinear systems	Oscillation on Systems having dead time Some negative phase shift
Proportional + Rate	Need for proportionality Good self regulation Large lags Large dead time Variable response time Variable disturbance rate Tolerance of offset	Positive phase shift Compensates for systems lags	Offset Rate increases gain Rage amount limited
Proportional + Reset + Rate	Poor self regulation Large lags Large dead time Variable response time Variable disturbance rates	Ultimate in controller action Rate phase shift compensates for reset phase shift	Some degree of complexity in adjustment of made controls for system condition

Figure 33-20 / **Three basic control modes (proportional, reset, and rate) and their combinations are listed in the left-hand column. Note that rate action can never be used by itself in control work.**

obtained. The resultant dynamic variation in proportional band characteristic is illustrated by the dotted line in Figure 33-19. This is equivalent to the dynamic proportional band characteristic for the controller illustrated in Figure 33-15.

This describes only one possible application of the Model EART controller. This unit and the Electronic Feedwater Controller (Model EFW) are typical examples of the flexibility of controllers in combining various modes of automatic controller action to meet a wide range of practical applications.

Proportional position action and integral action modes may be used singly; however the derivative mode can only be used in combination with one or more of the other two. There are advantages and disadvantages peculiar to each mode. Combinations of these modes are made in a single controller to gain the advantages of each.

These basic modes as used in practical control applications and the majority of their combinations possible are listed in Figure 33-20. This chart shows, in general, the process or system characteristics to which each is applicable, and in brief, the respective advantages and disadvantages.

Automatic controllers or their combinations are available to meet the application requirements of each of the seven modes and combinations listed. A typical installation of automatic controllers applied to a multiple-fuel-fired boiler is illustrated in Figure 33-21. This system of control is designed for boilers equipped with gas burners, oil burners, pulverizers, and constant speed fans.

Figure 33-21 / **System schematic of 3-fuel-fired boiler illustrates use of automatic controllers to do the work of the human operator.**

All of the advantages of electrical transmission, direct-connected power units, fuel pressure control, convenient load distribution and fuel-air ratio adjustments, boiler base loading control and simple remote manual control are provided. Three fuels can be controlled automatically at substantially equal ratings, one fuel may be controlled automatically with the others base loaded, or a single fuel may be controlled.

Master controller. This is a model with proportional plus floating action. It measures steam pressure and electrically loads the Fuel Feed Controllers to maintain the correct firing rate to maintain set point steam pressure.

Fuel feed controllers. An Adjustable Pressure Controller with its power unit controls the gas valve. A High Pressure Controller controls the oil valve. Where control of atomizing steam is required, a constant differential valve is installed in the steam line or a lever-operated valve is controlled in parallel with the oil valve. Each controller measures fuel pressure at the burner and balances that value against Master Controller loading. Burner fuel pressures are, therefore, independent of valve position, supply pressure, number of burners in service, and the condition of the burners. Exact minimum pressures are established to safeguard ignition at low loads.

The Model EARE Controller and its electric power unit control the exhauster fan damper to regulate the flow of pulverized coal to the burner. The transmitting potentiometer for the EARE Controller is mounted on the Master Controller. The receiving potentiometer is adjusted by the exhauster fan damper power unit. A manually adjusted biasing potentiometer in the EARE Controller changes the ratio of coal flow to Master Controller loading, thereby changing load distribution.

A Model EARE Controller adjusts the lever on the pulverizer feeder to proportion coal input to primary air. The transmitting potentiometer is adjusted by the exhauster damper power unit and the receiving potentiometer is operated by the fuel feed power unit. A biasing potentiometer in the EARE Controller permits changing the ratio of coal feed to primary air flow.

The system is designed for automatic firing of the three fuels in equal amounts, or with one at a higher value than others. It is also possible to fire only one fuel or to fire them in any combination of automatic and manual control.

Fuel-air ratio controller. A Model EART Totalizing Controller with its power unit controls the forced draft damper, fan turbine valve, hydraulic coupling lever, or magnetic coupling rheostat. The EART Controller has three transmitting potentiometers. One of them is adjusted by the gas flow meter, one by the oil flow meter, and one by the pulverizer feeder. The voltages established on these potentiometers are added and balanced against a single voltage on a receiving potentiometer adjusted by the air flow meter. The EART Controller proportions air flow to the total fuel input, regardless of whether the fuels are controlled automatically or manually. The biasing potentiometer in the EART Controller makes it possible, either manually or automatically, to vary the air flow with respect to total fuel input.

Furnace draft controller. A Model CSE Constant Suction Controller measures furnace draft and, with its electric power unit, controls either the boiler outlet or induced draft fan damper. If control of induced draft fan speed, instead of the damper, is desired, a Model CSE-A Proportional Plus Controller is used. Both types of controllers have calibrated manual adjustments for draft set point.

Safety and interlocking controllers. In addition to the basic controllers shown, additional equipment can be provided to limit fuel and air input to the available draft, to limit fuel input to the available air, and to shut off the fuel if the limiting action is ineffective after a definite time interval.

Although this example concerns itself with combustion control, all principles used are applicable to any control problem.

34 / **BOILER MAINTENANCE**

(*Source:* International Correspondence Schools, Scranton, Pa.)

When performing any type of repairs, it is wise to make an estimate of the length of time, the number of people required, the kind of tools to be used, and the probable cost. This is especially true when undertaking *boiler repairs*, because the work must frequently be done rapidly and on an overtime basis to prevent more than a minimum of outage or down time (the period of inactivity of the boiler during normal working hours). Every item necessary for repair should be available prior to starting the work. A stock of main repair parts should be maintained. The tools needed to make various kinds of repairs should be available to enable the repair work to be made promptly. In determining the outage or down time of a boiler, sufficient leeway should be allowed, depending on the work to be done, to insure a measure of protection, because the work does not always progress as rapidly as planned, especially if workmen are required to be on the job for many successive hours. No repairs of any kind should be attempted on a boiler while it is under pressure. Repairs attempted under these circumstances are not only exceedingly dangerous to the workmen, but also endangers the continuity of operation of the equipment. This should be taken into account in requesting a scheduled outage, for it will take some time for the pressure to be worked off the boiler after it has been taken off line, and additional time will be required for it to cool sufficiently for repair work to proceed.

Repair of Cracks in Steam Boilers

Fusion welding. Progress in the art of fusion welding, particularly electric arc welding, has progressed.to the point where repairs made by welding do not affect the strength of the original metal for all practical purposes. Fusion welding is a well recognized and effective method of making many types of repairs to steam boilers, provided the work is done carefully and proper procedures, materials and qualified welders are employed.

The American Society of Mechanical Engineers' Boiler Code Committee has issued detailed regulations covering all aspects of permissible fusion welding, including materials, procedures and qualifications of welding operators. The Code is continually revised as progress is made in the art of fusion welding, and as various questions arise. Most regulations by state or municipal authorities recognize the A.S.M.E. Code and do not permit fusion welding on pressure vessels unless the work is done in accordance with the Code requirements.

Repairing cracks in boiler plates. The repair of cracks in boiler plates can be accomplished most effectively by the fusion welding process. This work is generally subject to inspection by a certified inspector. He will require that all traces of the cracked metal be chipped, ground, or otherwise machined out so that only solid parent metal exists over the area to be repaired. The edges of the groove are to be properly beveled; the welding rod to be suitable for use with the parent metal; each layer of weld metal to be properly cleaned and possibly peened before the next layer is placed; preheating to be done; and the completion of work be followed by stress relieving by heating the area around the weld to at least 1100° F. or higher if this can be done without distorting the plate. If the crack extends entirely through the boiler plate, a backing up plate is generally required under the narrow portion of the V-groove.

Repairing cracks in tubes. Cracks in tubes with the presence of small blisters accompanied by a rupture at the surface of the blister frequently can be repaired by heating the tube to a red hot temperature and driving the metal back into position. This is followed by cleaning and lace welding over the surface to restore the tube strength.

Calking cracks. When welding tools are not available, small cracks may be temporarily repaired by calking. It must be remembered that this method merely closes up the crack, but does not restore the original strength of the parent metal. The crack should be repaired by welding.

Plugging cracks. Plate cracks less than 1¾″ long are sometimes repaired by plugging. The plate is center punched on the crack midway of its length, and a hole drilled through the plate of sufficient size to remove all cracked metal and to permit the hole to be threaded with a standard pipe tap. The hole is carefully tapped and a steel or wrought iron pipe plug is screwed in tightly. After a plug is installed as tightly as possible, it is cut off flush with the fire side of the plate and the head is peened over to further expand the plug in the hole. When the repaired plate is not directly exposed to the fire, the plug need not be cut off flush.

Stop rivet. When a crack extends inward from the edge of a plate on an outer seam, it will generally go farther unless stopped. Repair with a stop rivet can be made when the crack does not go beyond the seam. A hole of suitable size is drilled at the end of the crack and a properly heated and tightly fitted rivet is driven in the hole. The crack should then be closed by calking.

Rivets. All loose rivets should be replaced as soon as possible because they cannot be made permanently steam tight. However, they may be tightened up temporarily by calking. The effectiveness can be tested by the use of a hammer determining the sound of the rivet.

Removing rivets. The heads of rivets ordinarily used in boilers can be cut off by using a cold chisel and hammer. After the rivet is cut off flush, the rivet can usually be backed out of the hole by using a driftpin and hammer.

Replacing rivets. When loose or defective rivets have been removed from a boiler plate, the rivet holes are usually found to be in bad condition and it is advisable to ream the holes for rivets one size larger than the old ones.

Seal welding rivet heads. When rivet heads have been improperly calked so they still leak, and when they cannot be replaced, seal welding may be employed under the supervision of an authorized inspector. Care must be taken to use the proper welding material. The welding should be done preferably from the pressure side of the plate to prevent entrance of chemicals which could cause embrittlement of the metal. It must be remembered that seal welding merely stops off a leak. It will not strengthen the holding power of the rivet.

Soft patches. When a patch plate is applied to a damaged boiler sheet that is not exposed to the fire, the patch may be installed without removing the damaged portion of the sheet. This type of patch plate is called a soft patch to distinguish it from other types of patches. The patch plate should be of the same material as the boiler plate and of equal thickness. It should never be applied to a boiler sheet exposed to incandescent gases. The double thickness would restrict heat transfer, causing the patch plate to be damaged by overheating.

Hard patches. A hard patch differs from a soft patch in that the damaged metal is cut out of the boiler plate before the patch is applied. It is riveted in place and then securely calked. A hard patch constitutes a permanent repair when authorized by the inspector having jurisdiction. A hard patch is usually applied on the water side of the damaged plate so that internal pressure on the boiler will press the plate into position and so that the rivets will not be put under tensile stress. Furthermore, placing the hard patch on the water side of the shell plate prevents the formation of recessed pockets into which sludge or loose scale flakes might settle, thus leading to overheating owing to the insulating qualities of such foreign materials.

Fusion welding of patches. The common practice today is to weld a patch into a boiler to take the place of riveting. Such fusion welded patches can be depended on to develop almost the full strength of the original boiler drum plate, provided the work is done properly and in accordance with A.S.M.E. Code requirements. It must of course, be done with the permission of, and under the jurisdiction of a qualified inspector.

Repair of Furnaces

Replacement of corrugated furnaces. A corrugated furnace in an internally fired boiler may collapse because of overheating, as shown in Figure 34-1, in which case it will probably have to be entirely replaced.

The replacement procedure depends on the make of boiler and the type of furnace lining used. In some cases it may be necessary to remove the boiler tubes and take out the front head before the furnace can be replaced. In other boiler units, the furnace is of the removable type as shown in Figure 34-2.

Repair of corrugated furnaces. When the furnace is bulged inward to such a small extent that it does not require entire replacement, it can be repaired by heating the metal to a cherry-red temperature and then forcing the bulged part back to its original position.

The preparatory work consists of removing all fittings from the interior

Figure 34-2 / Inserting new furnace in scotch boiler.

Figure 34-1 / Collapsed scotch boiler furnace.

a. furnace   *b.* furnace flange
c. flanged furnace opening

of the furnace, and providing the necessary tools and a source of heat, generally gas torches. Care must be taken to have all water drained from the boiler and all vents open. In sledging the heated metal, care must be taken not to dent the plate or nick it with sharp edges of a hammer. It is much better to drive with a maul or against hardwood blocks, if there is enough space to use such equipment. It is still better to use blocks corresponding to the corrugations and to employ a hydraulic jack to force the heated plate back into position. The opposite end of the jack is supported against the cold shell with suitable planking, to distribute the force over a large area.

Repair of cracks in corrugated furnaces. Cracks sometimes occur in corrugated furnaces as shown in Figure 34-3.

Figure 34-3 / **Crack in corrugated furnace.**

A crack like the one shown in the illustration presents a sizable repair problem, because considerable stress exists at a point *a*, and the crack may run in a ragged line as shown by *b*. The shell plate expands and contracts; hence, there is considerable bending force and nothing but fusion welding under the direct supervision of an authorized inspector and in accordance with the A.S.M.E. Code can be considered a satisfactory repair.

Refractory Repairs

Refractories are used in furnaces largely as a convenient means for containing the fire and forcing the hot gases to travel over boiler heating surfaces without damaging other portions of the structure or the setting. It is evident, therefore, that the refractories must be kept in good repair; otherwise the equipment may be extensively damaged, or the efficiency may be reduced. The frequency or type of refractory repairs needed depends largely on the severity of the service, the type of materials originally used, their design and construction. When refractories must be replaced, it is usually advisable to use the same or better grade, because a large portion of the expense involved is in the labor required for repair, not in the cost of the material. Repair work must be done carefully by skilled workmen, otherwise the repair cannot be expected to stand up to the severe requirements of boiler service.

Plastic refractories. Plastic refractories consist largely of materials normally used for making a good grade of firebrick. Plastic refractory should be rammed down solidly by repeated blows from a pneumatic rammer or wood mallet. The ramming should be done in a downward direction, for gravity assists in keeping the fill solid. Proper ramming closes out all voids in the material and works the mass together, thus avoiding cracks in the finished job.

Castable refractories. Castable refractories ordinarily do not have as good temperature resisting characteristics as plastic refractories, because various materials such as water glass or lumnite cement are used in order to give them air setting properties. Castable refractories will develop considerable strength without the application of heat. They are valuable for installation as furnace linings in close contact with water cooled surfaces, because the water cooled surfaces prevent the lining from reaching a temperature at which the refractory would develop strength by vitrifying.

Chrome-ore plastic refractories. Chrome-ore plastic refractory is used extensively where temperature and slagging conditions are severe. It is a dense, hard material, having good heat-conducting properties and considerable resistance to slag penetration. The spaces between water wall tubes are frequently filled with this type of refractory to make a practically indestructible furnace lining.

Super refractories. A furnace wall will generally last longer if super refractories are used in the fuel bed area. An 85 per cent silicon carbide brick is known to have good resistance, very dense and not subject to corrosion by coal ash, and resists clinker adhesion and erosion far better than fire clay. Silicon carbide works best when placed to fuel bed depth because it resists abuse and wear. Hand fired furnace walls last longer when side and back walls have three rows of silicon carbide bricks at fuel bed area. For the hotter area above, use four rows of mullite bricks on side walls, five rows on back wall. Generally the front wall will not need any. This refractory is ideal because it forms inert crystals of mullite that prevent fluxing to ash. Bonded mullite and bonded silicon carbide brick both stand temperatures above 3000° F. For single retort stoker jobs, silicon carbide bricks need only be laid to protect the side and bridge walls. Follow the fuel bed pattern with only the trouble spots being laid. For multiple retort stoker furnace walls, silicon carbide refractory should be placed on all four walls. For spreader stoker walls, silicon carbide should be installed at grate line, and higher on the back wall to resist abrasion of coal chucks during heavy feeding rates. Mullite can be used above fuel bed. They should be laid in cements of their own composition with thin joints, and bonded to the fire brick backing. Use standard brick laying methods. When chosen and installed correctly, their life is generally several times that of common refractories.

Mortars used with firebrick. Air setting mortar has the property of bonding with brick to produce a solid structure before the application of heat. It is usually supplied in a prepared state, requiring only a thorough mixing with the liquid in the container to make it ready for use. The joint should not exceed approximately $\frac{1}{16}$ inch in thickness. When walls are laid with air setting mortar, they will air dry and afford a good bond between adjacent bricks.

Heat setting mortar is usually premixed, requiring only the addition of fresh water to make it ready for use. No other substance should be added, because the fusion point of the mortar is likely to be decreased, causing the formation of a weak wall structure.

Laying firebrick. There are a number of ways of laying firebrick to produce a satisfactory wall, but the following method is one most generally used. One end and one side of the brick are dipped into the mortar. It is good practice to use a sliding, edgewise motion to eliminate air pockets or bubbles and completely cover the desired surfaces of the brick with mortar. The brick is then lifted and any excess mortar is allowed to drip off before the brick is placed in position. No additional mortar should be used, the coating adhering to the drip brick is sufficient. The brick is then placed in position and tapped into place with a wooden mallet to work the mortar out of the joints and produce a mortar joint thickness of approximately 1/16 inch. The bricks should be carefully placed. Any excess mortar should be removed from the wall. The completed wall must be true, without projecting edges of brickwork or bulges.

Drying out refractory lining. Much damage can be done to a new refractory lining in a furnace, or to one that has been extensively repaired, by warming it up too rapidly. The brickwork should be allowed to air dry for at least twelve hours before a fire is placed in the furnace. Circulation of air should be provided during this time for the purpose of removing as much moisture as possible. The actual drying out period under fire will depend on such factors as the extent of the furnace repair job and the size of the setting. If there is any doubt about time, it is better to prolong the drying out period and keep the firing rate low, then to try to hurry the job by firing too rapidly.

Tube Repairs

Tube repairs are required when blistering, rupturing, cracking, corrosion, leaky joints or other types of failure occur. Repairs may also become necessary when inspection reveals progressive deterioration and possibility of tube failure before the next outage can be scheduled. The method of repair to be used depends on the type of weakness found. It may vary from the rerolling of a tube end to the complete replacement of the tube.

Fusion welding. Small ruptured blisters and certain types of cracks in tubes may be temporarily repaired by fusion welding, using a qualified welder to do the work in accordance with A.S.M.E. Code. This type of repair should never be undertaken without a qualified inspector's permission and supervision. To do so may mean cancellation of insurance or infraction of legal, local or state regulations.

Rerolling tubes to stop end leaks. Boilers that are fired up too rapidly or cooled down too rapidly may develop leaks at the rolled joints. The reason for this is that the tubes are affected by the temperature changes more rapidly than the thick drum plates into which they are rolled; hence, the compression stress in the original rolled joint is released. The same effect may occur when a boiler is overheated by being operated with low water and when other damage has not resulted. A similar condition may be found in new boilers when the tubes have been underrolled at the time of installation. Rerolling by use of suitable expanders may constitute a thoroughly satisfactory and permanent repair in such cases.

Caution: The tube expander is a powerful tool and it is readily possible to overexpand a tube to such an extent that the plate is distorted or the end of the tube thinned out or crystallized, making more extensive repairs immediately necessary.

Temporary fire-tube repair. When a fire-tube boiler cannot be taken out of service for any great length of time to enable permanent tube repairs to be made, boiler inspectors may permit plugging of damaged tubes by the use of a tube stopper. Figure 34-4 shows a steel ferrule used for stopping leaks at the ends of tubes in Scotch marine and other types of fire tube boilers.

Boiler Maintenance / 355

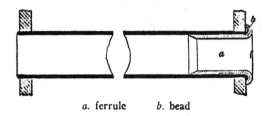

a. ferrule   *b.* bead

Figure 34-4   /   **Steel ferrule for stopping tube leak.**

Figure 34-5 shows the use of plugs and a tie rod for the purpose of closing off the ends of a tube having a crack or other type of failure that cannot be covered with a ferrule as shown in Figure 34-4.

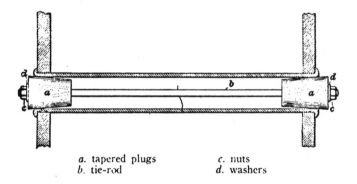

a. tapered plugs   *c.* nuts
b. tie-rod   *d.* washers

Figure 34-5   /   **Tube stopper for interior tube leaks.**

There are a number of forms of the tapered plug arrangement. A fault common to all of them is that the plugs are subjected to boiler pressure tending to force them out of the tubes, also they are vulnerable to temperature because they are exposed at the tube sheets. Their use should be of a most temporary nature only.

Temporary water tube repair. Water tubes are subjected to internal pressure and also to exterior application of heat from hot gases. When they are plugged off, water and steam cannot circulate through them, hence, they will quickly overheat to a dangerous degree. Boiler inspectors occasionally may permit leaving a ruptured tube in place to permit temporary plugging at tube sheets, if the tube is located in a cool zone where the metal is not apt to be destroyed by high temperature and when there is no possibility of building up internal pressure. It is considered good practice to remove the tube by cutting it off at the tube sheets, removing the expanded portions from the tube sheets and rolling in key caps or stub ends. The tube may be left in the boiler setting if there is not sufficient repair time available to effect its removal, for it can do little damage when it is cut loose from the tube sheets and when the holes through the sheets are plugged off properly.

Removing tubes. When the portion of a tube on the side of the sheet opposite the flared end can be reached externally, an oxyacetylene blowpipe or torch can be employed to cut the tube off at a distance of about ¼ inch from the tube sheet. A blunt chisel is then applied on one side of the cut tube end remaining in the sheet and is driven in forcibly to collapse and loosen this end. Once it has been forced inward, and rolled joint is loosened, hence a hammer can be used to drive the tube end out of the hole.

a. shaft
b. cutter

c. collar
d. tube-sheet

Figure 34-6 / **Tube cutter for fire tubes.**

Various types of tube cutters, such as those shown in Figures 34-6 and 34-7 are available for cutting off tubes that cannot be reached readily to allow the use of a torch. After the tube has been cut off by use of these or similar tools, a cape or ripping chisel may be used to make one or more longitudinal grooves in the circumference of the tube end. Care must be taken not to make this groove so deep as to damage the tube sheet.

Installing new boiler tubes. The basic principles are employed for installing tubes in both fire tube and water tube boilers. The ends of fire tubes are usually beaded to prevent overheating owing to the intense heat of the gasses of combustion at the hot side of the tube sheet, however the ends of the water tubes are usually belled because they are cooled by contact with the boiler water.

Before installing new tubes, the tube holes must be thoroughly cleaned and freed of burrs or irregularities. If the hole has been damaged by the cutting action of escaping steam or water, the hole should be repaired by welding in a suitable bead of metal. This should be followed by filing and grinding to make a smooth surface. In case the seat has been grooved to insure tightness of rolled tubes in high pressure boilers, the grooves should be cleaned out and formed properly

a. cutter-head   d. ratchet   g. handhole
b. cutter   e. trigger   h. tube header
c. handle   f. guide

Figure 34-7 / **Tube cutter for water tubes.**

in a circumferential direction. The tube ends are prepared by removing any paint or grease and by polishing with a wire brush, emery paper, or other effective means.

Some codes require tubes be belled or beaded under existing codes, but some boiler manufacturers recommended that the belling operation be dispensed with in case of water tube boilers.

Tube expander. The general form of a tube expander used for rolling and belling a tube is shown in Figure 34-8.

1. mandrel   5. jig   9. thrust-collar nut   13. hand nut
2. expanding rolls 6. collar   10. collar   14. body
3. flaring roll   7. thrust collar   11. stem   15. thrust bearing
4. cage   8. thrust bearing 12. thumbscrew   16. cap
                                                                17. thrust plate

Figure 34-8 / **Tube expander.**

By use of this tool, the boiler tube is expanded by the pressure exerted when a tapered mandrel is rotated inside the rolls. The mandrel, when turned by hand or by motor, feeds into the rolls because they are set at a small incline in the cage. When the direction of rotation of the mandrel is reversed, it feeds outward because of these inclined rolls.

The expander shown has two sets of rolls, one set of expanding rolls and one set of flaring rolls. Both the expanding and flaring rolls are contained in the same cage.

Method of expanding tubes. The improper use of a tube expander can severely damage both the tubes and the tube holes. Underrolling will result in leaky joints that may cut the metal before being discovered. Excessive rolling may crystallize and crack the tubes and may also enlarge the tube holes. Overrolling has been known to stress the tube sheet so greatly as to loosen otherwise perfect joints in adjacent tubes.

An experienced tube roller developes a "feel" of the expander which tells him the precise point at which to stop rolling. The success in rolling operation, regardless of the method used, or of the size, gage, or composition of the tubes, is tightness of the joint and freedom from overrolling as evidenced by a damaged tube sheet. The completion of the rolling process is always followed by a hydrostatic test one and one-half times the operating pressure of the boiler.

General reminders. Water tube boilers generally have $\frac{1}{32}$ inch clearance between the tube and tube sheet hole at both ends. Due to the fact that firetube boiler tubes become scaled, their clearance is generally $\frac{1}{32}$ inch at the fire end and $\frac{1}{16}$ inch at the opposite end, which aids in their removal. The A.S.M.E. Code requires end tubes in water tube boilers, extended $\frac{1}{4}$ to $\frac{1}{2}$ inch and to be flared $\frac{1}{8}$ inch in diameter larger than the tube. Never overroll tubes. It is good practice to roll slowly and to stop when tiny flakes start leaving the tube sheet around the tube. Overrolling will enlarge and deform the tube sheet, thins the tube and weakens the tube sheet, hardens the inside of the tube and tube sheet causing early failure and can cause surface tears.

Casing Repairs

There are various types of boiler casings which serve the general purpose of providing airtightness with structural support, improvement in appearance, aid to cleanliness, and reduced cost of maintenance. The type of casing used, the severity of service, and the will to maintain a generating unit in first-class operating condition at all times, will largely determine the kind of repairs, and frequency.

Various types of casings:

Steel Clad. This casing is entirely enclosed by steel plates fastened together.

Plaster Covered Insulation. Insulated blocks or blanket insulation wired to structure, covered with metal or chicken wire to form a base for plastering.

Canvas Covered Insulation. Hard block insulation covered with canvas.

Plastic Air Seal Coatings. Several types are available. Check with the manufacturer to ascertain the maximum temperature they will withstand.

Casings of all types must be kept tight if the generating unit is to operate efficiently. All leaks, cracks, and voids must be closed immediately. Their appearance is the signal for investigation and sometimes repair.

Figure 34-9 / Methods of rolling tubes.

Dampers

The boiler damper is of great importance in the successful operation of a steam generator or hot water boiler. When the damper is in the open position, it should provide as little obstruction in the damper frame as possible, and when it is in the closed position, it must seat as tightly as possible to prevent leakage. At intermediate positions, it must work freely, so that its effectiveness as a control means will not be impaired.

Lost motion should be taken out of the actuating mechanism as lost motion in automatically controlled damper installation cannot develop all the sensitivity of which it is capable. Damper bearings should be maintained in first-class repair to prevent sagging of the damper shafts, binding and sticking, and excessive air infiltration. Damper shafts and blades are subject to high temperatures and considerable stress which sometimes causes deformation which may prevent them from opening widely or seating tightly. The shafts and damper blades should be straightened or replaced if they are damaged beyond repair. When the boiler is out of service, a complete inspection of the damper assembly should be made and all repairs and replacements made at this time.

Cooling Down and Emptying Boilers

When taking a boiler out of service, it is desirable to reduce the load gradually and to maintain a low load for a time before actually killing the fires. This procedure will insure that any suspended sludges and scale flakes have a maximum opportunity to settle out of circulation in proximity to the blow off line so that they can be readily removed. When fires are being killed, the water level of the boiler should be raised to a high point, because this can be done safely under a low load condition and there will be ample water reserve to blow down the water under pressure after the fires have been killed. When the boiler is at full pressure, the blow off valves should be given a quick blow (drain) to remove sludges and loose scale flakes as far as possible. This will reduce the water level, but should not be continued to a point where low water level is obtained, or to the point where feed water has to be admitted to restore the water level. Cold feed water should not be put into a hot boiler as it may contribute to loosening of rolled tube joints. After being blown down under pressure, the boiler should be cooled slowly, at a recommended rate of approximately 100°F. per hour. A slower rate of cooling will do no harm, but a more rapid rate may be harmful by causing unequal contraction strains. The water level will settle as the boiler cools down, so long as it remains in sight at the bottom of the gage glass, feed water should not be admitted to the cooling boiler.

When the furnace has cooled to a temperature at which a person can enter and remain in the furnace, the boiler may be entirely emptied without danger. It should be emptied at a rapid rate as possible by opening the main blow off valves wide because this will assist in removing sludges that settle out in the vicinity of the internal blow off lines. The steam drum vents or safety valves should be wide open, thus permitting the entrance of air to the drum, otherwise, the water will not drain from the boiler entirely.

Boilers containing superheaters of a nondrainable type should be cooled down in such a manner as to prevent admission of air to the superheater tubes. The superheater tubes will condense full of pure water, having a greater affinity for oxygen, hence oxygen corrosion on the interior of the superheater tubes will occur if air is permitted to enter. The recommended procedure is to open the superheater vent valves while cooling down the boiler to make sure that the steam flows through the superheater while pressure is being worked off. These vent valves should then be closed when there is still a steam pressure of 10 psi on the boiler so that the superheaters will condense full of water. They should remain closed as the boiler is emptied to make sure that air cannot enter the superheater to cause corrosion during the outage period.

Parts, Tools, and Equipment

Boilers and their auxiliaries are used to produce steam, or hot water as it is needed by an office building, plant, or factory, failure of some minor part can often cause a forced outage with a resultant loss of time and production. It is important that all equipment be kept in first-class condition at all times. Items which might cause plant or building shutdown are:

1. Parts that move and are consequently subject to wear.
2. Parts subject to extreme temperature.
3. Parts damaged by foreign material.
4. Equipment damaged by improper handling.

Inspection, adjustment and repair are the general rules for successful boiler room operation. These operations require the use of certain tools and replacement parts. A card filing system is generally used containing such information as, manufacturer's name and address, style, serial number, speed of operation, and purchase date. Space for inspection dates, conditions found, and adjustments and repairs should be provided for.

An inventory of boiler tools, and spare parts should be maintained to insure immediate information when required. Overhaul schedule should be established during low load periods and can also be noted on the card.

Inspection, Preparation, and Operation

Inspection schedules. Inspection of boilers and pressure vessels is required at periodic intervals by the state or municipal inspectors having jurisdiction, or by your insurance company. A convenient date for both the chief engineer and the inspector should be arranged. This is generally scheduled during the low load periods, to reduce the number of outages. The chief engineer will overhaul all his equipment prior to inspection, and discuss the results of the inspection with the inspector to insure that any discrepancies and recommendations are thoroughly understood. Supplemental inspections should also be scheduled to insure proper operation.

Blowing tubes. Prior to taking a boiler out of service, the soot should be cleaned from the fireside of the boiler. This is generally done by blowing air or steam against the tubes, with automatic soot blowers or a hand lance. Tubes should not be blown with wet steam as moisture cakes the soot, and can plug the area between tubes. Gas passages are stopped and the tube heat absorption surface reduced, and sulphuric acid formed, which will corrode the tubes.

This can be avoided if superheated steam is used, or in any case all condensate should be drained by a drain valve in the header prior to using the soot blower.

Boiler cleaning. After the boiler has been drained, the manhole covers on any upper drum should be removed and the drum and tubes entering it should be washed down with a hose, using warm water, just as soon as the drum is cool enough to enter. Other covers on lower drums or water wall headers may be removed to provide air circulation to accelerate the cooling process. A heavy stream of water should be used to wash down the drums and tubes before the sludge has had time to dry out. The access doors to the furnace and setting should be opened next and all refuse removed as thoroughly as possible by working through these openings with available cleaning tools. Opening the boiler damper will create a draft into the openings, pulling any dust up the chimney, and reduce to a considerable extent, the physical hardship of removing refuse. It is good practice to clean from the furnace front toward the rear of the unit so that any dislodge dust will float out ahead of the workmen.

Certain precautions should be observed by workmen engaged in the cleaning operation:

1. No workman should be permitted to enter any drum until it has been thoroughly ventilated, to insure sufficient air is available.

2. Some person should stand outside the drum to offer assistance if needed.

3. All drum openings such as blowoff lines, control valves, feed pumps, fans, fuel valves, and others should be shut off and tagged to be kept inoperative.

4. Extension cords and electric lamps used for illumination *must be* rugged construction, and kept in good repair. A breakdown in insulation, or breakage of an unguarded bulb can result in electrocution if space is damp.

Fusible plug. The cross tee plugs in the water column should be removed so the piping can be examined, and a brush run through every time the boiler is cleaned internally. The fusible plugs in the steam drum should be renewed each year.

Stack. The breeching should be examined for indications of structural weakness in the plates or supports. Air leaks into joints and connections, through corroded places or through leaking dampers on idle units will seriously interfere with the stack capacity and reduce the available capacity of steaming units. Soot and fly ash accumulations inside the breeching will reduce the area, overload the supports and cause corrosion in the presence of dampness. All dampers and damper operating mechanisms should be operated and inspected to insure that they are in a serviceable condition.

Valves. Valves should be kept packed and in operating condition because steam leaks are costly, as an inoperative valve may constitute a hazard.

Piping. Water piping, pressure connections to gages, automatic control lines and all other piping should be inspected to insure that they are in good condition. Safety valve vent piping should be inspected to insure that there are no obstructions at the discharge end, and that it is securely anchored to withstand the force of the steam released by the valve, and that the piping is self-supporting and does not put any strain on the safety valve body. The piping between the drum and the water column should be checked for tightness to insure that the correct water level will be shown in the gage glass. Column connections should be checked to insure that they are unobstructed. If there are any valves in the water column lines, they should be left open. The water piping between the drum and the bottom of the column should be level, or pitched toward the drum. The water column supports should be checked to make sure that the column is being maintained at the proper height in relation to the drum. The high and low water alarms should also be checked for proper functioning.

Feedwater regulating equipment, check valves, control valves, and all piping and supports should be inspected, because a failure at any point in the feed system will create a low water hazard. Blowoff valves and their piping should be thoroughly inspected, as the failure of any part of the equipment may have serious consequences. The soot blower piping and the soot blower heads should be thoroughly examined to ascertain whether the soot blowing system can operate efficiently. No water pockets should be allowed in the piping because slugs of water driven into the soot blower heads or elements may cause serious trouble.

Corrosion. Rusting, or corrosion, on the fire side of boilers is not likely to be caused by oxidation, unless it occurs in a natural way. *For example,* when the boiler is washed down and then allowed to stand in a humid condition. Fireside corrosion more generally results from acid attack on the metal caused by moist accumulations of soot or fly ash within the boiler or setting. Acid accumulations of this nature will readily absorb moisture from even a moderately dry atmosphere and will rapidly destroy the boiler metal. This destructive action can be detected by removing the soot deposit and then scraping the metal surface. The black, pockmarked surface and the thin layer of corroded iron that flakes away with the soot are typical indications of destructive corrosion.

Abrasion. The wearing away of the metal by rubbing or sandblasting action is called abrasion. It may occur whenever there is relative movement between parts in contact; where fly ash particles concentrate and impinge on the metal; where fuel rubs against headers or water wall tubes by stoker action, or where cleaning tools are used frequently. The detection of abraded metal and the general appearance of the defect usually enable you to determine its cause and remedy.

Leakage at joints. Leakage at rolled joints inside boilers may be revealed by the appearance of moisture or a flowing stream of water when the boiler is subject to a hydrostatic test; by accumulations of chemicals or cemented soot deposits when the boiler is dry, or by a hissing sound when the boiler is under steam pressure. Leaks may develop when boiler tubes are not rolled hard enough to create the required stress in the tube seat; when the tubes do not enter the tube hole squarely; when the tube is belled without being supported or rerolled in the straight portion of the seat; or when the tube and seat have not been properly cleaned. Leaks at rolled joints may also result from overrolling to the point where the ductibility of the metal is lost; from overheating caused by scale or sludge accumulations; by some types of foaming action; and by low water. Rapid temperature changes such as those that occur when cold water is fed to a hot boiler, or when a boiler is fired up too rapidly or cooled down too fast, can loosen tubes that have been rolled perfectly.

The inspector. The inspector must bear in mind all the various types of metal deterioration, and should carefully examine all portions of the pressure parts of the boiler for indications of such deterioration. A thorough inspection should also be made of the refractories, supports, baffles, soot blower supports, tube clamps, and all other items which may fail and lead to damage of the boiler metal.

Brickwork, refractories and insulation should be closely examined to determine if there is any dangerous cracking, loosening or deformation that might lead to failure. Air spaces provided for cooling support members should be checked to insure that they are not obstructed and especially that they are not filled with combustible refuse. Mud drums should be externally inspected for any indications of overheating or corrosion. All connections to drums should be examined for indications of leakage, as indicated by damp spots on the refractory or insulation cover, damp soot accumulation, and scouring of the tube wall, or deposit of chemicals from escaping boiler water.

Plates exposed to the fire or to the hot gases, such as the lower shells of horizontal return tubular boilers, upper drums of some types of water tube boilers, crown sheets, water legs, and other parts must be given attention to reveal any evidences of overheating or cracking metal. Moderate overheating will produce discoloration accompanied by slight bulging, whereas severe overheating will produce pronounced bulging and scaling. Repeated heating and cooling will eventually produce cracks. Any such evidence must be explored fully to determine the cause. Immediate action should be taken on the cause. Feed water entrance nipples should be given special attention because cold water entering the hot boiler creates severe localized stress in the plate at the point of entrance.

Boiler tube inspection. Straight tubes in either fire-tube or water tube boiler should be examined for straightness because any sagging or warping is usually an indication of overheating, even when blistering or bulging is not present. Upper tubes in water tube boilers are particularly subject to such deformation as a result of alternate heating and cooling. Temperature variations of great magnitude can occur rapidly when the boiler is operated at high rating with the boiler water in a foaming condition. Foam bubbles move sluggishly through the tubes and slugs of water follow them. The tube metal heats rapidly when the tube is filled with foam and chills quickly when the foam is displaced by the boiler water. Tubes may be inspected by using any of the following methods, flashlight mirror, cupping of the hand, or measuring the correct diameter against area of suspected bulging.

In boilers of bent tube type, remove the insulation from the outside surfaces of both the mud drum heads and between the brick setting and the heads. They should be checked for overheating and cracking, particularly if they are subjected to high temperature gases or to repeated bending stresses by boiled drum or header movements.

Soot blowers. Soot blower elements are subjected to extreme and rapid temperature changes, especially when they are close to the furnace. Their failure may result in damage to boiler metal or baffles. They should be examined for straightness, length, and fire cracks. Their supports should be checked for soundness and for distance from adjacent boiler tubes, to prevent rubbing. Nozzle spacing in tube lanes should be checked. When doing so it should be remembered that nozzles are often set closest to tubes nearest the soot blower head so that the nozzles will be in mid position of lanes when operating temperature is reached. Nozzles should never be closest to tubes farthest away from the blower head because expansion of the element would then probably produce tube impingement.

Baffles. Boiler baffles should also be examined for indications of overheating, misplacement, or shifting of supports. As a general rule, gas leakage through damaged baffles will increase flue gas temperature and reduce efficiency. Leakage of high temperature gases may be harmful to the circulation characteristics of some types of boilers, and leakage of gases carrying abrasive particles may lead to erosion of tubes. Steel baffles are often attached to boiler tubes by hook bolts or they may rest on tube clamps. The baffle plates may vibrate or the tubes may move relative to the supports. All such action may possibly cause rubbing and erosion of boiler metal.

Internal inspection of boiler heating surfaces. The principal items to be looked for when checking the interior of the boiler heating surfaces are scale deposits, sludge accumulations, corrosion and pitting, the mechanical condition of internal fittings, and evidence of improper circulation.

Scale deposits are formed on boiler heating surfaces when impurities in the boiler water are deposited on the boiler metal as the water is heated or as steam is generated. Scale of any thickness whatsoever, acts as an insulator and reduces the rate of heat transfer through the boiler metal. As a result, the boiler metal becomes hotter for any given steaming rate and the flue gases reach a correspondingly higher temperature. Hotter boiler metal implies the possibility of metal damage and hotter flue gases reduce the boiler efficiency.

Sludges are also the result of impurities in the boiler water. They consist of small particles of matter which do not readily attach themselves to the boiler metal but generally remain suspended in the water while it is moving at a high velocity through the boiler tubes. These sludges may settle out in the drums or headers in which water movement is slowed down. Blowoff valves have been provided for their removal. The general purpose of the chemical treatment of boiler water is to produce such sludges from unavoidable feed water impurities and thereby prevent the impurities from depositing as scale. Settled out sludges may block circulation through drums, headers, or supply tubes, and may pile up in drums to cause overheating. If such sludge deposits are found, the adequacy and operating frequency of the blowoff equipment should be questioned.

Corrosion and *pitting* are both destructive to boiler metal, although the physical appearance of their destructive action differs materially. General corrosion will likely produce a black magnetic iron oxide powder on the surface of a dried boiler metal and a typically rough etched surface when this coating is wire brushed. This type of metal deterioration is not likely to be present when the surface is protected by scale deposit. The best preventative measure against corrosion consists of proper feed water treatment of boiler water conditioning. Pitting is a form of localized attack, usually by oxygen, that corrodes the metal in small areas at first but which continues rapidly if not checked. The pits will be filled with hard, crusted iron oxide and will have pimples or small bumps of iron oxide all over them. Upon finding such pimples or bumps on the surface of boiler metal, it should be determined what lies under them. If pits are found, a number of them should be thoroughly cleaned out to their full depth so that the amount of damage can be appraised and appropriate repairs or preventive action taken.

Improper circulation is seldom found in well-designed standard boilers. Failure of tubes is often attributed to faulty circulation or to flame impingement when no reason other than scale deposit or a foaming condition of the boiler water exists. If scale has flaked off or if sludges have settled out in sufficient quantity to fill lower headers or supply tubes, there will naturally be inadequate circulation until the obstruction is removed. If improper water treatment deposits sticky sludges on supply tubes, their effective areas are reduced. This also causes inadequate circulation. If oils find its way into the boiler water, or if other foam producing elements are present, some of the tubes may be filled alternately with foam and water. Overheating followed by sudden quenching, then occurs. The tubes will warp and bulge. Fatigue cracks may be expected at points where hot gases come in contact with the tubes. Clean tubes that have adequate water supply and an adequate steam releasing area, will take very large absorbing rates for years without any signs of distress.

Water level. The boiler manufacturer or builder determines the correct normal working water level for the boiler unit and specifies this in his construction drawings that the center of the gage glass must correspond to this level.

As the steam flow increases, more water must be fed. The object is to maintain the water level in the boiler at a point as close to the design level as is consistent with other operating features. The boiler operator should become thoroughly familiar with the feed water system, as he may be required to take quick action in case of improper performance of any equipment. Auxiliary feed pumps are normally installed for use in the event of failure of the main feed pumps. Auxiliary feed lines are often installed to permit delivery of water to the boiler.

Boilers are generally equipped with a stop valve in the feed line system immediately adjacent to the boiler. The valve is usually mounted on a nipple extending from the boiler drum. Next to the stop valve is a check valve so positioned as to prevent the discharge of water from the boiler in the event of failure of any part of the feed system. Both valves should be kept in first-class condition. Regulation of feed water is generally accomplished by valves exterior to the check valve, and may be of the automatic or hand type. This principle is applicable in both a steam or hot water boiler. However, in low pressure hot water systems, normal main water pressure is sufficient.

In most installations, the center tri-cock of the gage column corresponds to this mid-point on the gage glass. Water columns and gage glasses should be blown down at least once each watch to prevent sludges from settling in the connections and interfering with the correct registering of the water level. The column should normally be blown first because it is larger and will accumulate a greater quantity of sludges. Blowing the column first will also insure removal of cooler water and return of hotter water to the column and gage assembly, so that when the gage is later blown there will be less temperature change on the gage glass. The blowoff of water and steam through the lines will rapidly remove any sediment that may have collected. If the lines are entirely clear, the water will return when the valves are closed. If the water does not return promptly or the action seems sluggish, it should be reported to the chief engineer for slowness may be an indication of clogged lines, representing a dangerous condition.

Gage glasses. Gage glasses are subjected to very quick temperature changes, and difficulty is sometimes experienced in maintaining them. Leakage at gage glass connections will accelerate deterioration and breakage and will cause a false water level to be indicated, therefore, it is doubly important that leakage at these connections or at any other valves or fittings in the gage or water column assembly be avoided at all times.

Tubular gage glass is generally used up to 300 psi. The glass should be handled carefully prior to installation. A scratch or chip may cause failure. A tubular gage glass may be cut to the proper length by glass tube cutter.

When a gage glass breaks proceed as follows:

1. Shut off top and bottom cocks.
2. Open drain valve that is used for blowing down gage glass and/or bottom pet cock.
3. Remove broken glass, then open top and bottom cocks to blow out any broken pieces.
4. Place nuts then washers on new gage glass, add a small amount of graphite to the washer so the nut does not twist the glass, close pet cock.
5. Install, open top cock slowly to heat glass gradually, open bottom cock slowly, close drain.

If valves are used instead of cocks, they should be closed and opened daily, so that cleaner extension or stem can remove any possible scale.

Flat gage glass. High pressure boilers are normally equipped with flat gage glasses of which there are a number of designs. Instead of glass, strips of transparent mica are used in some high pressure gages. When flat glasses are used, they are normally protected by mica gaskets to prevent etching of the glass and to provide a certain amount of resiliency in order to prevent breakage of the glass when it is tightened up in assembly. The flat type gage glass usually must be disassembled from time to time for cleaning purposes. Particular attention must be given to the mica gaskets because mica has a laminated structure and therefore may cause difficulty by flaking or by wearing through.

When a gage glass breaks proceed as follows:

1. Close upper and lower gage cocks. Remove the clamps, glass gaskets, mica, graphite, the threads, and run them down.
2. Remove the old gasket.
3. Polish surface, perfectly smooth.
4. Clean both ends of gage.
5. Clean surface thoroughly and oil with molybdenum disulfide.
6. Install new gasket, mica, new glass, another new gasket and clamps. Let glass heat by conduction.

7. The bolts should be pulled up hand tight, then those at the center should be pulled up lightly, then the remaining bolts should be tightened lightly.

8. All bolts should be again tightened progressively until the pressure is uniform. Crack top cock first to heat glass gradually.

9. Open both gage cocks slowly. If additional tightening is required close gage cocks so they are not being tightened under pressure.

10. Keep safe distance away the first time the gage glass is blown down.

Discoloration of gage glasses can occur from a variety of causes. Glasses should be discarded if they are etched or scratched in any way. Glasses can sometimes be cleaned by using a solution containing six ounces of fresh water, one ounce of common salt, one ounce of acetic acid to which a small amount of baking soda is added.

Causes of Low Water Level in Boilers:
1. Failure of the feed pump.
2. Leaks in the discharge relief line of the feed pumps.
3. Improper regulation or defective valves.
4. Low water in feed tank.
5. Water at pump inlet too hot.
6. Leak in feedwater heater.
7. Leak in boiler.
8. Priming.

The first two causes are the result of faulty feed pump operation and may be overcome by using the auxiliary feed pumps until the main pump has been repaired. Improper operation of feed water regulators or defective valves can be compensated for by using the auxiliary feed line or auxiliary feed line valves. Low water in the feed tank is the result of lack of make up or supply water. If the water temperature is too high, vapor will form, causing the pump to become vapor bound. This trouble results when the reduced pressure in the feed suction pipe caused the hot water supply to flash into steam. It may be corrected only by increasing the pressure at the pump inlet, or by using cooler water. When leaks occur in the feed water heater system or in the boiler, the equipment must normally be taken out of service immediately, pending repairs or adjustments. Priming of the boiler can have serious consequence, hence, the load on the boiler should be reduced or the boiler water concentration should be lowered until the cause of the priming is ascertained and corrective measures can be applied.

Low water level. When the water level drops in a boiler so that it is out of sight in the gage glass, its exact location is unknown. Blowing down the glass for a couple of seconds and then closing the valve may cause the water to momentarily reappear in the glass and give some indication of just how low it may be. It is not safe to continue operation of a boiler for any period of time after the water has dropped so low as to become invisible in the glass. The fires should be put out immediately when this condition develops.

The fire should be secured, and removed from the fire box as soon as possible. Every effort should be made to prevent doing anything which would increase the furnace temperature and cause overheating of the boiler. The boiler should be allowed to cool slowly. Make up water should not be added under any circumstances while the dangerous overheated condition prevails. No attempt should be made to reduce the pressure by venting the safety valves, as a sudden rush of water lifting in the boiler may cause an explosion. It is considered good practice to just let the boiler cool gradually, preventing further danger or damage.

The unit should then be entered for inspection to determine the extent of the damage. If no damage is found, a hydrostatic test should be placed on the unit. If tube failure resulted from low water, the water level should be maintained with additional water until the pressure is worked off. The boiler dampers should be left open to carry any escaping steam up the stack. The fires should be killed immediately.

Filling the boiler with water. It is customary to open the drum vents to provide a means for the air to escape as it is displaced by the water. It is normally proper to fill a boiler to the level of the lower tri-cock, remembering that the water will expand when heated. In some cases of boilers equipped with water walls, some engineers prefer to fill the boiler to a high level and to drain off excess water through water blowoff valves as steam pressure is raised on the unit. This will assist in starting circulation and avoid sudden temperature changes in the water wall system.

Foaming. When steam boiler water containing chemicals that will produce a foaming condition is heated, it will produce a foaming condition of the water of foam bubbles that will pass out of the boiler with the steam and will carry considerable quantities of water and chemicals with them. Foaming can sometimes be detected through abnormal agitation of the water level and the condition will be shown in the gage glass. When a boiler is foaming badly, a sudden increase of load will cause a larger than usual use in water level and enormous quantities of foam to be carried into the steam liner. A sudden reduction of load will cause the water level to drop rapidly, and possibly disappear from the glass entirely. The remedy for a foaming condition is to remove the impurity by blowing down the boiler. This may be accomplished by blowing down through the lower blowoff valve and replacing the water by increased flow of feed water, or by increasing the quantity of surface or continuous blowdown when the boilers are equipped with surface blowoff system.

Priming. Priming in a boiler is the entrainment or carry-over of water with the steam in the absence of a foaming condition of the boiler water. Priming in a boiler may be caused by forcing the boiler beyond its rated capacity or increasing the load too quickly; carrying the water level too high; sudden opening of nonreturn valves when the boiler is cut into the line with excess pressure, lifting of the safety valve when the boiler water level is carried too high, and faulty design of the boiler or faulty adjustment of steam purifying and steam washing apparatus in the boiler drum.

The most effective remedy is to reduce the load on the boiler, or reduce the water level by blowdown. If the load cannot be reduced, the only remedy is to carry the water at a low point. When cutting a boiler on line, the water level should be reduced.

Blowing down boilers. The primary reason for blowing a boiler down is to reduce concentration, remove scale and sludges as much as possible. Blowdown to reduce concentration can be either from the lower main blowoff valves or by use of a continuous blowdown system. Blowdown to remove sludges and scale flakes is always from the lower main blow off valves. Another reason for blowing a boiler down is to reduce the water level to prevent carry over. The frequency of blowing down a boiler is determined by the type of treatment, make up feed water and type of boiler. Blowdown valves must work freely, be kept properly packed, and all external piping and fittings should be thoroughly inspected for corrosion or other damage when the boiler is out of service.

Safety valves. If the pressure in a boiler were allowed to increase without restriction, it would become so great that with even the strongest boilers, an explosion would occur. To prevent this from happening, safety valves are set to open at a pressure far below the bursting pressure of the boiler. There are three types of high pressure steam drum safety valves which are generally used: (1) jet flow, (2) huddling chamber, and (3) nozzle reaction. The type of safety valves on your boiler should be determined along with the name of the manufacturer. Written adjusting instructions and overhaul procedures should be secured from manufacturer. If it is set by the inspector, it should not be tampered with, as it is the only insurance against excess boiler pressure.

Internal cleaning. After a boiler drum has been taken out of service for cleaning, the interior of the drum will normally be found to contain various types of deposits. The nature of the deposits determines the cleaning process to be used. Mud and sludges are easiest to remove when they are still damp, therefore the boiler drums should be entered for cleaning purposes just as quickly as their temperature permits. The temperature should be brought down to 150° or less before sluicing with cold water. A fire hose will loosen much of the mud and sludge, and will be an aid in saving on labor. Sludges remaining on the shell plates after the sluicing operation can sometimes be removed by scrubbing the plates with brushes. Wire brushes curved to the drum radius, and of a thickness that will permit them to slide between adjacent tube ends will be found helpful. Wire brushes mounted on a hand drill or pneumatic tool will save much manual labor.

When mud and sludges have been allowed to dry out, they can often be removed by flaking off the larger particles with a putty knife or a thin chisel. After the large flakes are removed, smaller flakes and areas not accessible with the scraper or other tools can be cleaned by using wire brushes and in some cases may be mounted to portable drills or other pneumatic tools. When adherent scale is present, it can sometimes be removed by tapping the surface with a light hammer. Some types of scale will separate readily from the drum metal and can be removed in rather large flakes by this method. Other types of scale adhere so tightly that they must be removed by the chiseling action of a hammer and a cold chisel or similar tool. In the latter event, much labor can be saved by providing the workmen with pneumatic or electric tools equipped with chisel points of shape and size to meet the requirements best. In using chisels, care must be taken not to nick the shell plate or to drive against the expanded tube ends.

After all sludges or scale have been cleaned down to the bare metal, the surface of the shell plates should be examined for pits that might have been caused by corrosion. These pits can normally be detected by the presence of pimples or by irregular spotted appearance of the surface before cleaning. A knife blade or chisel may be used to remove the pimples and thus expose a black core with an underlying depression corroded into the boiler metal. All of these pits in the metal should be cleaned out thoroughly to expose bare boiler metal. To retain the corrosion will invite further attack at the same point when the boiler is returned to service. Progressive corrosion of the drum shell will eventually destroy it and require its replacement, or necessitate a reduction of the operating pressure on the boiler. The surest preventive measure is to treat or condition the boiler feed water to remove or inhibit the causes of corrosion. Repair of the pitted surfaces may consist of painting them with a protective coating to prevent further attack, or to weld them up under the supervision of a qualified inspector, grind down the weld to bring the metal flush with the general surface of the shell, and follow that by the application of a protective coating.

Cleaning fire side of tubes. Before taking a boiler out of service, the soot blowers should be operated thoroughly to remove as much dust and soot accumulations as can be removed by these means. When the unit is cool enough to permit the access doors to be opened, further cleaning can be done by blowing accessible areas, using steam or air lances. When the gas passages can be entered, air lances can be used for further cleaning. This procedure can be followed by brushing with any available cleaning equipment. Care must be taken to remove thoroughly all refuse, especially refuse lodging in constricted spaces, for this material will absorb moisture and corrode the boiler metal if the boiler is laid up for any length of time.

Cleaning water side of tubes. Mud, sludges, and loose scale particles can usually be removed in large quantities from boiler tubes by washing them with a fire hose before they have dried. In the case of a water tube boiler, the drum must be sufficiently cooled to allow entrance in order to proceed with the washing operation. In the case of a horizontal return tubular boiler, or similar type of boiler, considerable areas of tubes can be reached by using a fire hose through the manhole opening, while further cleaning can be done after the boiler is sufficiently cooled to allow entry.

Tube scrapers and brushes. The fire side of fire-tube boiler flues sometimes acquire a tenacious, hard coating of soot requiring more than usual effort for removal.

The flexible steel blades (a) are of a spiral form to give a slicing action when they are pushed through the tube, and they are springy to give them good contact with the tube wall. They are firmly attached to the heads (b) and (c) and a pipe handle of proper length is screwed into one of the heads so that the scraper can be readily pushed through the entire length of the tubes. When the deposits are too tenacious to be removed readily with the scraper shown in Figure 34-10, a combination scraper and brush as shown in Figure 34-11, will be found more effective.

The cutting blades (a) are formed in a steep spiral so that they will have a powerful scraping action when the tool is pushed through the tubes. They

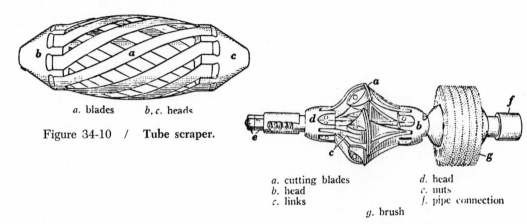

a. blades   b, c. heads

Figure 34-10   /   **Tube scraper.**

a. cutting blades   d. head
b. head   c. nuts
c. links   f. pipe connection
              g. brush

Figure 34-11   /   **Combination scraper and brush.**

are mounted on the cleaner by being flexibly connected to the head (b), and to the head (d) through the links (c). The head (d) is mounted loosely on the shaft so that it may be forced toward the head (b) by applying spring tension when the nuts (e) are tightened. This action forces the cutting blades outward, hence the cleaner may be adjusted to fit tubes of different diameters and to apply internal pressures. The brush (g) is normally made of stiff wire to facilitate brushing the loosened material from the tubes. A pipe handle of suitable length is screwed onto the cleaner at (f) for convenience in handling.

Power driven cleaner for fire-tube boilers. A tube cleaning motor driven by compressed air or water can be equipped with a variety of attachments for specific purposes. One such attachment is a rotary brush arrangement for cleaning the interior surfaces of fire-tube boilers or air heaters. Another attachment for a power motor is illustrated in Figure 34-12.

a. body   b. knocker   c. locknuts   d. boiler scale

Figure 34-12   /   **Turbine cleaner for fire-tube boilers.**

This tool is essentially a vibrator consisting of a body (a) on which the knocker (b) is eccentrically mounted and secured by the locknuts (c). The construction of this attachment is such that when the head is rotated rapidly, the three lobes of the knocker deliver repeated light blows to the inside of the tube, causing scale to be loosened from the exterior of the tube as shown. Power driven cleaners of this kind are known as turbine cleaners.

Power driven cleaner for water tube boiler. Power driven cleaners are manufactured in a variety of sizes and degrees of flexibility to fit tubes of various diameters and to allow working around bent tubes of normal curvature. One form of turbine cleaner used for removing scale from the inside of water tubes is shown in Figure 34-13 (a).

a. cutter-head	*f.* coupling
b. roughing cutters	*g.* nozzle chamber
c. finishing cutters	*h.* nozzle
d. drive shaft	*i.* paddles
e. shell	*j.* impeller
	k. universal joint

Figure 34-13 / Turbine cleaners for water tube boilers.

Figure 34-14 / **Drill-type tube cleaner.**

It consists of a cutterhead containing three sets of roughing cutters and three finishing cutters. The head is keyed to a shaft which is, in turn, attached to the motor. The motor or turbine may be driven by compressed air or water admitted by a flexible hose which is also used for moving the cleaner through the length of the tube. The operating pressures required are from 80 to 100 psi. The exhaust from the turbine is forward toward the cutter head, hence loosened material is driven out the far end of the tube and is not blown back to inconvenience the operators. View (b) shows the cutterhead connected to the motor by a flexible joint to enable the cleaner to be moved readily around the curvature of bent boiler tubes.

Scale on the interior of boiler tubes sometimes may close a tube almost entirely or be very hard and difficult to remove. In this event, the type of cutter-head illustrated in Figure 34-14 is used.

This type of drill will enlarge the opening through the tube sufficiently to permit the use of the larger diameter, flexible cutterheads. The action of the turbine cleaner is quite fast and the cutters used are hardened so that they will not wear rapidly in breaking up and cutting the various types of hard scales. The cutterheads must therefore be used with judgement to prevent damaging tubes. If the cutter should strike hard material which may impede the forward movement of the tool, the operator should back the cutter up and immediately try again, thereby saving the tube wall from damage.

Laying up a boiler. Moisture is one of the primary causes of boiler deterioration. This is likely to occur during the nonheating season. The external surfaces, and the fireside should be kept dry. If gas and oil fired boilers are not used in the summer, it is recommended that the boiler be kept warm (approximately 100°F.). The boiler should be filled and the temperature raised to 200°F. to drive off gases. If feed water is normally treated, add the compound at this time. Leave the boiler filled until the beginning of the next heating season.

The following precautions should be taken if firing is to be discontinued:

1. All heating surfaces should be cleaned of soot, ash, or other residue.

2. The heating surfaces should be given a coating of oil or grease.

3. Stack connections should be cleaned.

4. The water side should be cleaned thoroughly with a high pressure hose.

5. The boiler should then be dried out with a small kerosene burner or small wood fire. Care should be taken to see that the boiler is not overheated.

6. The grates and ash pits should be thoroughly cleaned.

7. Remove any rust or other foreign matter from external surfaces, and apply a coat of preservative paint where required, if the parts are generally painted.

8. All firing equipment, operating and safety controls should be checked. If repairs are required, they should be made immediately.

Alkalinity of Feed Water

Hydrogen-ion concentration. The corrosion-forming characteristics of boiler feed water depend to a large extent on the degree of acidity of the water. Whether the water will be acid or alkaline is determined largely by the manner of ionization of the water molecules. Although water is a very weak electrolyte, it does dissociate to a very slight extent into positive hydrogen (H^+ ions) and negative hydroxyl (OH^-) ions, as indicated by the equation:

$$H_2O = H^+ + OH^-$$

Equal numbers of both H^+ and OH^- ions are formed in the dissociation of pure distilled water. Since neither H^+ nor OH^- predominates, the solution is termed neutral. A solution that contains an amount of H^+ ions in excess of the OH^- ions is spoken of as an acidic because it has an acid reaction. Conversely, an excess of OH^- ions over H^+ ions will produce a basic or alkaline condition. The H^+ ions liberated by the dissociation of the solution, attack the metal of the boiler, causing it to dissolve. The greater the hydrogen-ion concentration, the more rapid will be this attack and vice versa.

It has been established that the product of the hydrogen-ion concentration and the hydroxyl-ion concentration in water is a constant. By electrical measurements, this constant has been found to be .00000000000001 or 10^{-14}, at 21°C. Therefore since, in pure water the H^+ ions exactly equal the OH^- ions, each must have a concentration of .0000001 or 10^{-7}. It also follows that any increase in the concentration of one group of ions must result in a decrease in the concentration of the other group. Hence, a measure of the hydrogen-ion concentration is actually also a measure of the hydroxyl-ion concentration. By measuring the hydrogen-ion concentration in a sample of the feed water, it can be determined what corrective measures should be taken to counteract the corrosive characteristics of the water.

*p*H scale of H-ion concentration. The hydrogen-ion concentration in water is very small. Pure water contains only 0.0000001 grams of hydrogen ions per liter. When such water contains more hydrogen ions, it has an acid reaction, and with fewer hydrogen ions, it has an alkaline reaction. Because of the extremely small hydrogen concentration, it is inconvenient to express the percentages of such concentrations in decimal form. Instead a scale has been evolved based on numbers from 0 to 14 and known as the hydrogen ion, or *p*H scale. Each number represents a definite hydrogen ion concentration.

Figure 34-15 / pH·scale.

The *p*H number of water of any solution indicates whether the liquid has an acid or an alkaline reaction. A neutral liquid, such as pure water, is neither acid nor alkaline and has a *p*H value of 7. Liquids having *p*H values between 0 and 7 indicate acidity, the degree of acidity being less for a high *p*H value than for a lower value. Thus, a *p*H of 4.5 indicates a greater degree of acidity than a value of 7.2. Liquids having *p*H numbers between 7 and 14 have an alkaline reaction, the degree of alkalinity increasing as the *p*H value of the liquid increases.

The *p*H scale is illustrated in Figure 34-15. Each successive number on the scale represents 1/10 the concentration of the preceeding number. For example, a *p*H reading of 5 indicates a hydrogen-ion concentration 1/10 as great as that for a *p*H reading of 4, and 10 times the concentration for a *p*H reading of 6.

Boiler Tube Failures and Water Treatment

Boiler generating tubes fail for one of three reasons: (1) overheating, (2) attacked chemically on water side or fire side, and (3) thinned down from the fire side.

Overheating may be caused by deposits on the water side which prevent adequate cooling of the tube metal, or by unusually hot zones in the furnace. Two of the common deposits found in boiler tubes are hard scale, and sludge.

Hard scale treatment: Lime and soda ash or zeolite ahead of the boiler, and phosphate internally.

Sludge treatment: Concentrates of phosphate silica and alkali. Frequent wash outs and blow downs.

Chemical attack is in some cases related to overheating, as high temperatures greatly speed up certain chemical reactions involving iron. Most chemical attacks can be prevented by proper boiler water treatment.

Chemical Attacks	Treatment
Steam	Increase circulation, change baffles.
Caustic	Use sodium nitrate.
Acid	Frequent alkalinity checks.
Concentrated boiler water	Amine treatment to reduce deposits of corrosion products.
Stress corrosion	Baffle repair, and other repairs, if necessary.
Oxygen	Aeratoring with sodium sulphite.

External thinning may be caused by the improper placement of soot blowers and, in rare cases, by abrasive particles in the fuel. Many of the difficulties arising on the water side of the tube are the result of overheating. This condition may be the result of difficulties on the fire side, such as defective baffling or poor furnace design. Sometimes the arch is not properly designed in forced draft chain grates, and also in underfeed stokers there is a blow pipe effect near the lower ends of the tube, due to the constriction of gases in this region, extreme temperatures are obtained. Corrosion on the fire side of tubes is sometimes a problem in coal fired boilers equipped with an economizer section. Most bituminous coal contains some sulfur which decomposes to acid gases on burning. In some economizers, temperatures are sufficiently low to allow moisture containing these gases to condense on the outside of the tubes, thus producing sulfuric acid which is extremely aggressive to the tube metal. Tubes may also fail from the fire side by the abrasive action of fly ash and dirt particles in the fuel.

On closed hot water systems, chromate is generally used, the amount dependent on the characteristics of the raw water and cycles of concentration.

A complete analysis of your boiler water should be made to determine the proper chemicals to be used. This should be done by an expert, and personnel should be trained in making the required analysis and the frequency established by the need.

35 / DATA PROCESSING ROOMS

Basic elements are required for *data processing rooms*. Some of these are ceiling height, floor strength, lighting levels, electrical power, temperature and humidity controls, sound levels, air flow, space for movement between auxiliary equipment, and future expansion requirements.

Acoustical ceilings, and sometimes walls acoustically built down to shoulder height are recommended. Noise levels for this room and also that of adjacent areas must be considered, along with the problem of noise traveling through ducts from this room. Proper insulation and use of acoustical materials will correct these conditions.

A *ground floor* site for the computer will reduce the problem of vibration. Floor and wall construction should be capable of preventing transmission of vibrations to other areas of the building. The weight point load of the equipment should be secured from the manufacturer, and the floor designed accordingly, including possible future increases. A raised or "floating" floor is an accepted type floor for computed installations. This is a secondary floor over the original floor of the building. This type of construction allows power cables, receptacles, temperature controls, air-conditioning ducts and other facilities to be concealed yet readily accessible. Access to the underfloor area is achieved by lifting any of the panels. This type of floor is equipped with leveling devices. With a raised floor, a ramp rather than steps leading into the data processing room will make it much easier to get equipment in and out of the area. When new floors are poured in a new building which will contain a data processing room, raceways are generally provided in the floor, or large segments of floor duct installed. Sometimes channel raceways are provided in side walls approximately six inches off the floor.

The equipment manufacturers generally agree that a 40-foot candle, measured thirty inches above the floor is sufficient. Direct sunlight is not desirable, as easy observation of the console and the signal lights requires a *low level* of *illumination*. It is recommended that lighting be zoned, so that sections can be turned on or off as desired.

Electrical power requirements are critical, as the computer requires a constant rate of power in order to perform accurately. Separate feeders should be considered and separate transformers or installation of a motor alternator may be required. Separate breakers should be installed in the data processing room, and should be turned off when the equipment is used for only one or two shifts per day. When considering the power requirements, air conditioning and lighting must also be provided for.

Careful *temperature* and *humidity control* must be maintained. The temperature must generally be maintained between 65 to 90 degrees, and the humidity between 20 and 80 per cent. A midpoint between the two figures is considered good for operating, and the temperature and humidity should be kept constant with as little variation as possible. Independent air conditioning units are recommended for data processing rooms. Heat dissipation is an important part of any computer installation, and must be figured when sizing the air-conditioning unit along with walls (inside or out), glass, windows, insulation, lights and outside temperatures. In some cases, exhaust hoods may be desirable, with a canvas flap between the hood and the machine, making a tight seal. If windows are provided, special glass is recommended to prevent condensation during low outside temperatures, and transmission of heat during high temperatures. It is also recommended that the glass be tinted slightly to prevent excessive sunlight which can effect signal lights on the computer.

Physical maintenance is of utmost importance. Changing of filters in the air handling units should be done periodically upon the basis of inspection needs. Computers also maintain filters and should be changed by the customer service engineer when required. If the data processing room has carpeting, it should be vacuumed nightly. If it is equipped with tile, it should be dry mopped nightly with a treated mop. Dusting of equipment should be done nightly with a treated duster or wool duster. Doors should be equipped with automatic door closers to keep dust to a minimum.

Supplies or other items should be dusted and cleaned thoroughly before being brought into the room. Dust is inclined to gather under raised floors and must be removed periodically, before it can circulate into the machine area. Perforated acoustical tile or perforated walls should be vacuumed periodically to prevent dust accumulations. Walls should be washed a minimum of twice a year. Tile floors should be scrubbed, waxed, and buffed periodically as required. Ventilation should be sufficient along with temperature control to keep windows closed at all times. Windows should be calked thoroughly to prevent the entrance of dust and dirt. If drapes have been installed, they should be vacuumed twice per year.

The best way to insure savings in time, cost, and future maintenance, is to consider all areas mentioned and to provide for them in the original design or conversion.

35A / PROTECTION OF ELECTRONIC COMPUTER SYSTEMS

Reproduced, with editing, from "Standard for the Protection of Electronic Computer Systems" (NFPA No. 75), 1962 edition, copyrighted by the National Fire Protection Association. Copies of the complete Standard in its current edition ($.50) are available from the Association, 60 Batterymarch St., Boston, Mass.

Purpose. The purpose of this standard is to set forth the minimum requirements for the protection of electronic computer systems from damage by fire or its associated effects.

Scope. This standard covers the fire protection requirements for installations of electronic computer systems where special building construction, rooms, areas, or operating environment are required for protection of the system.

This standard presently does not cover systems which can be installed without this special construction.

This standard, however, may be used as a management guide for the protection of electromechanical processing equipment, small table top or desk type units and electronic computer systems that do not require specifically constructed rooms or areas.

Building construction. The computer area shall be housed in a fire-resistive, noncombustible or sprinklered building, or when the portion of a nonfire-resistive structure housing a computer area is a separate fire division, only that portion of the structure housing the computer area is required housed in construction as noted above.

Location of computer area. The electronic computer area shall be located to minimize fire, water, and smoke exposure from adjoining areas and activities. The computer room shall not be located above, below or adjacent to areas or other structures where hazardous processes are located unless adequate protective features are provided.

Computer room construction. The computer system shall be housed in a room of noncombustible construction. All materials including walls, floors, partitions, finish, acoustical treatment, raised floors, raised floor supports, suspended ceilings, and other construction involved in the computer room, shall have a flame-spread rating of 25 or less. (See NFPA Standard Method of Test of Surface Burning Characteristics of Building Materials, No. 255.)

1. Floor covering materials, such as asphalt, rubber or vinyl floor tiles, linoleum or carpeting may be used to cover any exposed floors.

2. All metal floors should be grounded.

In multistoried buildings, the floor above the computer shall be made reasonable watertight to prevent unnecessary water damage to equipment. Any openings at beams, pipes, etc. shall be sealed to watertightness.

Computer room fire cutoffs. Where exposure to the building housing the computer is unfavorable, good protection against exposure shall be provided. This protection should consist of blank masonry walls, or other suitable exposure protection, depending upon local conditions. (See NFPA Suggested Practice for Protection Against Fire Exposure of Openings in Fire Resistive Walls, No. 80A.)

The computer room shall be cut off from other occupancies within the building by noncombustible, fire-resistance-rated walls, floor and ceiling. The fire-resistance rating shall be commensurate with the exposure, but not less than one hour.

The fire-resistant walls or partitions enclosing the computer room shall extend from the structural floor to the structural floor above, or the roof.

Raised floors (where required). Raised floors including the structural supporting members shall be made of concrete, steel, aluminum or other noncombustible material. Pressure impregnated, fire-retardant treated lumber having a flame-spread rating of 25 or less may be used. (See NFPA Method of Test of Surface Burning Characteristics of Building Materials, No. 255.) Other types of wood construction shall not be used for raised floors. Existing combustible, structural floors shall be covered with an insulating noncombustible material before installing a raised floor. Access sections or panels shall be provided in raised floors so that all the space beneath is readily accessible. Openings in raised floors for electric cables or other uses shall be protected to minimize the entrance of debris or other combustibles beneath the floor. This may be accomplished by covers, grilles, screens, or by locating equipment directly over the openings.

Cable openings. Electric cable openings in floors shall be made smooth or shall be otherwise protected to preclude the possibility of damage to the cables.

General Computer Room Requirements

Materials and equipment permitted in the computer room. Except as noted below, only the actual electronic computer equipment and such input-output or other auxiliary electronic equipment electronically interconnected with the computer, or which must be located in close proximity to the electronic computer equipment, shall be permitted within the computer room itself.

All office furniture in the computer room shall be metal.

Small supervisory offices and similar light hazard occupancies directly related to the electronic equipment operations may be located within the computer room if all furnishings are metal and adequate facilities are provided for containing the necessary combustible material. Supplies of paper or other combustible material shall be strictly limited to a minimum needed for efficient operations.

Limited records may be kept in the computer room.

The following shall not be permitted within the computer room:

1. Any activity or occupancy not directly associated with the electronic computer system(s) involved.

2. Supplies of paper or other combustible material in excess of that necessary for efficient operation.

3. Service and repair shops and operations except for that servicing and repairing performed directly on machines which are impractical to remove from the computer room.

4. Bulk storage of records.

5. Any other combustible material, equipment or operation which constitutes a hazard and which can be removed.

Combination of systems. Separate electronic computer systems should not be combined in a single computer room unless the systems are interconnected electronically, use the same input-output equipment or must be located in the same room for other operational reasons. Computers may be located in adjacent rooms with properly protected communicating openings in separating walls.

General storage. The operation of an electronic computer system frequently requires considerable quantities of stationery supplies and other combustible support materials. This material can present a serious fire exposure within the computer room capable of causing serious damage to vital equipment or records.

Paper stock, unused recording media, and other combustibles within the computer room shall be restricted to the absolute minimum necessary for efficient operation. Any such materials in the computer room shall be kept in totally enclosed metal file cases or cabinets.

One or more storage rooms outside of the computer room shall be provided for reserve stocks of paper, unused recording media and other combustibles.

Construction of Computer Equipment

Types of computer equipment:

Type I. So designed that, when any component or part is ignited, the fire will be confined to the immediate area where the source of ignition is located, to the extent that the affected parts can be readily replaced; or so designed, by the use of special construction and material, to be inherently free from the possibility of ignition of any component or material. The equipment shall include automatic means to de-energize the circuits before components or units are caused to operate at, or to be subjected to, hazardous temperature conditions.

Type II. So designed that when de-energized fire is not likely to spread beyond the external housing of the unit in which the source of ignition is located.

Type III. Includes all equipment not defined in Types I and II above.

Classification of all equipment into the three types described above is being developed by the testing laboratories. Until this information is available, Underwriters' Laboratories listed equipment may be considered as meeting at least the Type II rating.

Use of approved or listed equipment. Wherever possible, each installed electronic computer system or individual computer unit shall be a recognized Type I or Type II construction.

"Recognized" equipment is that equipment which has been accepted by the authority having jurisdiction as meeting the requirements for Type I and Type II. Approval or listing as Type I and Type II by Underwriters' Laboratories, Inc., Factory Mutual Engineering Division or other nationally recognized independent fire testing laboratories shall be considered as proof that the equipment has met such standards.

Any equipment not of a recognized construction shall be considered to be of a Type III construction in determining the applicable installation requirements pertaining to that particular equipment.

Design features. Approved flexible cord and plug assemblies, not to exceed 15 feet in length, may be used for connecting the computer to building wiring to facilitate interchange.

Interconnecting cables and wiring between units should be of a type approved for the purpose by a nationally recognized testing laboratory. Such cables shall be considered as a part of the computer system and suitable for installation on the floor or under a raised floor. If cables or other interconnecting wiring is of any other type, the equipment shall be so designed that the cables or wiring can be installed in accordance with the NFPA National Electrical Code (No. 70).

Individual units of a system should be housed in metal or noncombustible enclosures with suitable subdivisions to minimize the likelihood of fire spreading from one section to another within a single unit structure. Enclosures shall be designed to permit easy access to all interior sections in the event of an emergency.

Air filters for use in individual units of a computer system shall be of approved types that will not burn freely or emit a large volume of smoke or other objectionable products of combustion when attacked by flames, so arranged that they can be readily removed, inspected, cleaned or replaced when necessary.

Each electronic computer system shall be so designed that, in the event of an emergency, the system can be de-energized by the operation of a suitably marked control at one location.

Except as noted below, oil shall not be used as a component of a unit of an electronic computer system. If the design of the unit is such that oil or equivalent fluid is required for cooling or other purposes, it shall have a flash point of 300°F. or higher, and the container shall be of a sealed construction, incorporating automatic pressure relief devices.

All sound-deadening material used inside of computer equipment shall be noncombustible.

Protection of Computer Rooms and Equipment

Protection of computer rooms. If the construction of the computer room contains any combustible material other than that permitted, or if the computer housing or structure is built all or in part of combustible material, then the computer room shall be protected by an automatic sprinkler system.

If the operation in the computer room involves a significant quantity of combustible materials, the computer room shall be protected by an automatic sprinkler system.

Automatic sprinkler systems protecting computer rooms or computer areas shall conform to NFPA Standard for the Installation of Sprinkler Systems (No. 13). Sprinkler systems protecting computer rooms should preferably be valved separately from other sprinkler systems.

To minimize water damage to the electronic computer equipment located in sprinkler protected areas, it is important that power be off prior to the application of water on the fire. In facilities which are under the supervision of an operator or other person familiar with the equipment (during all periods that equipment is energized), the normal delay between the initial outbreak of a fire and the operation of a sprinkler system will provide adequate time for operators to shut down the power by use of the emergency shutdown switches. In other instances where a fire may operate sprinkler heads before discovery by personnel, a method of automatic detection should be provided to automatically de-energize the electronic equipment as quickly as possible.

Smoke or fire detectors shall be provided in the air space below existing combustible raised floors to sound an audible as well as visual alarm and to shut down all electric power passing through the air space.

Air spaces below existing combustible raised floors shall be subdivided by tight, noncombustible bulkheads into areas not exceeding that required for one system or, in any case, not more than 10,000 square feet.

The air space below a raised floor or above a suspended ceiling may be used as a plenum chamber for air conditioning if construction is noncombustible and all wiring is of an approved type. Interconnecting cables and wiring between units should be of a type approved for the purpose by a nationally recognized testing laboratory. Such cables shall be considered as a part of the computer system. If cables or other interconnecting wiring is of any other type, the equipment shall be so designed that the cables or wiring can be installed in accordance with the NFPA National Electrical Code (No. 70).

Portable fire extinguishers. Approved portable carbon dioxide extinguishers shall be provided and maintained for electrical fires. See NFPA Standard for the Installation, Maintenance and Use of Portable Fire Extinguishers (No. 10).

Approved Class A type extinguishers shall be provided and maintained for ordinary combustible materials such as paper.

If it is desired to provide other types of extinguishers, advice should be obtained from the computer equipment manufacturer and the authority having jurisdiction as to their acceptability.

In installations where conditions may require the provision of inside hose, it shall be 1½-inch rubber lined with shutoff combination solid stream, water-spray nozzles.

Training. Designated persons working in the computer area shall be thoroughly trained in how to use each of the available types of manually operated fire fighting equipment. This training should show the capabilities and the limitations of the extinguishing equipment.

All hand-type extinguishing equipment shall be plainly marked to indicate the type of fire for which it is intended, and installed and maintained in accordance with NFPA Standard for Portable Fire Extinguishers (No. 10).

Protection requirements for equipment. In addition to the protection required elsewhere in this standard, each unit of an electronic computer system shall be provided with the following special protection:

Type I Equipment. Type I equipment requires no special protection.

Type II Equipment. There shall be available to each unit of Type II equipment an adequate means of extinguishing the maximum fire which may occur as follows:

1. Carbon dioxide fire extinguishers or carbon dioxide hand hose systems installed in accordance with NFPA Standard for Carbon Dioxide Extinguishing Systems (No. 12), shall be considered as providing adequate extinguishing protection provided all of the following conditions are met:

a. The equipment, during all periods that it is energized, is under supervision of an operator or other person familiar with the equipment and trained in the operation of the types of extinguishers or hand hose systems involved.

b. Adequate controls are readily accessible to shut down power and air conditioning to the involved equipment.

c. All interior sections are readily accessible to manual application of the extinguishing agents.

d. There is located within the computer room and not more than 50 feet from the equipment under consideration either a carbon dioxide fire extinguisher or carbon dioxide hand hose system having a capacity of at least one pound of carbon dioxide for each cubic foot of volume of the unit under consideration if the equipment is on open racks; one-half pound for each cubic foot of volume if the unit under consideration is enclosed in a cabinet.

2. Type II equipment not meeting the requirements of (1) above shall be protected by a fixed carbon dioxide extinguishing system conforming to the requirements of NFPA Standard for Carbon Dioxide Extinguishing Systems (No. 12).

Type III Equipment. Because of the hazard presented by the possibility of communication of fire to other equipment outside of Type III units, hand applied extinguishing agents shall be considered inadequate except in the case of small (table top or desk size) units. Except for the previously mentioned small units, all Type III equipment shall be, protected with a fixed carbon dioxide extinguishing system.

Fixed carbon dioxide extinguishing systems installed may be manually actuated when the equipment is, during all periods when it is energized, under the supervision of an operator or other persons familiar with the equipment. In all other instances, the extinguishing systems shall be provided with both manual and automatic actuation means. The automatic actuation should be by an approved method of detection meeting the requirements of NFPA Standard for Proprietary Protective Signaling Systems (No. 72). Particular attention shall be given in the choice of actuation means, to insure detection, considering the air flows usually involved in such systems, and the small heat released under fire conditions.

When called upon to operate, each fixed carbon dioxide extinguishing or carbon dioxide hand hose installation shall be arranged to automatically sound an alarm, and shut down power and air conditioning supplied to the equipment involved.

Protection of Records

General. The operation of most electronic computer systems involves obtaining, using, creating and storing large amounts of records. In many operations these records are as important to the continuity of the operation and its mission as the computer itself.

Record media. Records may be commonly encountered paper records, punch cards, plastic or metal base electronic tapes (on metal or plastic reels and in metal, plastic or cardboard containers), paper, control panels, magnetic discs, memory drums, memory cores or various other means of maintaining for future use information in plain or machine language, inside or outside of electronic equipment. Some of these records such as magnetic discs, memory drums and memory cores are usually found as an integral portion of electronic equipment and as such the protection of these records is covered in a previous section.

It is extremely important to note that the degree of resistance of magnetic tape to fire exposure is not completely known. It is known, however, that fire exposures (heat and/or steam) that would not damage records on paper media may damage records on magnetic tape. The protection of records or magnetic tape by storage methods presently available must be considered limited.

Types of records. Records involved in computer operations fall into five basic types which must be safeguarded according to their importance and the difficulty involved in their replacement as follows:

Input data. Raw or partially refined information to be entered into the computer system, either as memory for later use or for immediate use in the solution of a problem, development of a statistic or production of some other product.

Memory. Information previously converted to language or symbols immediately recognizable to the computer equipment and held for future use. Memory may be on any media which can be directly read by the computer system.

Program. Data, which may be on paper, punch cards, photographic, magnetic or electronic media, used to direct the computer as to which input or memory data to use, how to use it and the type of results to obtain. Also to be considered are any diagrams or other records which can be used to reproduce programs.

Output data. The final product of the computer system. This may consist of printed material or electronic data.

Engineering records. Those plans, specifications, and other records which provide the engineering record of the construction, wiring, and arrangement of the computer system and its housing area. Of particular importance are records of modification made following the original installation.

Value of records. The evaluation of records should be a joint effort of all parties concerned with the safeguarding of computer operations. The amount of protection provided for records shall be directly related to the importance of the records as measured by evaluation of what the loss of a particular record would mean in terms of the mission of the computer system and the re-establishment of operations after a fire. In order to maintain a reasonable sense of consistency, it is assumed that computer equipment capable of properly using the records will be available. The following classifications of records are based on the recommendations of NFPA Standard on the Protection of Records (No. 232). All records shall be evaluated and assigned to one of these categories to ensure that adequate protection is provided where necessary and that unimportant records are not overprotected.

Class I (Vital) Records. Records that are essential to the mission of the equipment, are irreplaceable, or would be needed immediately after the fire and could not be quickly reproduced. Examples might include key programs, master records, equipment wiring diagrams, and certain input-output and memory data.

Class II (Important) Records. Records that are essential or important but which, with difficulty or extra expense, could be reproduced without a critical delay of any essential missions. Some programs, wiring diagrams, memory and input-output data have this level of importance.

Class III (Useful) Records. Records whose loss might occasion much inconvenience but which could readily be replaced and which would not be an insurmountable obstacle to prompt restoration of operations. Programs and procedures saved as examples of special problems are typical of records in this category.

Class IV (Nonessential) Records. Those records which on examination are found to be no longer necessary.

Protection required. *Records kept within the computer room.* 1. The amount of records kept within the computer room shall be kept to the absolute minimum required for efficient operation. Nonessential records shall not be kept in the computer room.

2. Any records regularly kept or stored in the computer room shall be provided with the following protection:

a. Class I (Vital) or Class II (Important) records shall be stored in Class C or better records protection equipment.

b. Class III (Useful) records on paper based or plastic materials shall be stored in metal files or cabinets.

c. Class III (Useful) records on metal based material require no special protection.

Records stored outside of the computer room. 1. To the maximum extent consistent with efficient operation, all record storage shall be outside of the computer room.

2. Record storage room.

a. Class I (Vital) and Class II (Important) records shall be stored in fire-resistive rooms. The degree of fire resistance shall be commensurate with the fire exposure to the records, but not less than two hours.

b. Unless the records are contained in metal files, cabinets or other non-combustible containers, records storage rooms shall also be provided with an automatic sprinkler system.

c. Class III (Useful) and Class IV (Nonessential) records do not require any special fire protection unless these records are stored with vital or important records. In such case the requirements for the most valuable records apply to all records.

d. The records storage room shall be used only for the storage of records. Spare tapes, however, may be stored in this room if they are unpacked and stored in the same manner as the tapes containing records. All other operations including splicing, repairing, reproducing, etc. shall be prohibited in this room.

When records are kept in cases, boxes or other containers, protection shall be that required for the highest level of damageable media in the total assembly of records and containers.

It is recommended that the following be considered as limitations in the design of record storage rooms:

1. Rooms containing only paper records shall not exceed 50,000 cubic feet.

2. Rooms containing plastic based records in noncombustible containers shall not exceed 10,000 cubic feet.

3. Rooms containing plastic based records in combustible containers shall not exceed 5,000 cubic feet.

Duplication of records. The best protection for records consists of storing duplicate records in separate areas not subject to the same fire. In some electronic computer operations the duplication of records on the same or different media is a common practice. The keeping of duplicate records is particularly important when records on magnetic tape are involved.

1. All Class I (Vital) records shall be duplicated on the same or different

media and the duplicates stored in an area which is not subject to a fire that may involve the originals, preferably in a separate building.

2. Whenever practical, Class II (Important) records shall be similarly duplicated and stored.

3. Class I (Vital) records not duplicated shall be protected in accordance with NFPA Standard on the Protection of Records (No. 232).

Protection against building collapse. In any building where a fire may result in a building collapse which could either drop the records storage equipment or drop structural members on the records storage equipment, the records storage equipment shall be of types designed to protect the records against damage from the impact involved.

Utilities

Air conditioning systems. Air conditioning equipment shall conform to the requirements of NFPA Standard for the Installation of Air Conditioning and Ventilating Systems of other than Residence Type (No. 90A), and to the additional requirements set forth below.

A separate air conditioning system should be provided for the computer area.

Air ducts serving other areas should not pass through the electronic equipment area. When it is impractical to reroute such ducts, they shall be encased in a fire-resistive duct, equivalent to the fire resistance of the enclosure for the electronic equipment area.

Air ducts serving other areas shall not pass through any computer records storage room.

All duct insulation and linings shall be noncombustible, including vapor barriers and coatings.

Air filters for use in air conditioning systems shall be of approved types that will not burn freely or emit a large volume of smoke or other objectionable products of combustion when attacked by flames and shall be so arranged that they can be readily inspected, cleaned and/or replaced when necessary.

If the computer area is within an area which is air conditioned and additional air conditioning capacity is not required, the ducts serving the computer area should have suitable fire dampers.

Electrical service. The requirements in this section apply to all power and service wiring supplying the electronic computer equipment. They do not apply to wiring and components within the actual equipment or to wiring connecting various units of equipment.

Service equipment supplying the main power requirements of the computer room area should be of a type arranged for remote control or located to fulfill the requirements as covered previously.

All wiring shall conform to the NFPA National Electrical Code (No. 70).

Service transformers should not be permitted in the electronic computer area. However, if such a transformer must be installed in this area, it shall be of the dry type or the type filled with a nonflammable dielectric medium. Such transformers shall be installed in accordance with the requirements of the NFPA National Electrical Code (No. 70).

Protection against lightning surges shall be provided where needed in accordance with the requirements of the NFPA National Electrical Code (No. 70).

The number of junction boxes in underfloor areas should be kept to a minimum. If they must be used, they shall be metal, completely enclosed, readily accessible, properly grounded and in compliance with the NFPA National Electrical Code (No. 70) requirements as to construction. They shall be securely fastened to the floor. No splices or connections shall be made in the underfloor area except within junction boxes or approved type receptacles or connectors.

Emergency power controls. In addition to any emergency shut-down switches for individual components or other units of equipment, controls for the disconnecting means provided as a part of the main service wiring supplying the electronic computer equipment shall be located near the operator's console and next to the main exit door to readily disconnect power to all electronic equipment in the electronic computer area and to the air conditioning system.

Provision should be made for emergency lighting.

Fire Emergency Procedures

Preplanning for continued operation in a fire emergency. The continued operation of an electronic computer system is dependent on information stored on cards, tape, discs, drums, etc. Therefore, the preplanning for continued operation should include:

1. A program to protect records in accordance with their importance as set forth by the section on protection of records.

2. Arrangements for emergency use of other installed computer equipment to cover:

a. Plans for transportation of personnel, data and supplies to emergency computer locations.

b. Agreements and procedures for the emergency use of the computer equipment.

3. Programs designed with adequate number of checkpoints and restarts to ensure rapid recovery to normal operations.

Personnel should receive continuing instructions in:

1. Method required for turning off all electrical power to the computer.
2. Turning off the air conditioning to the area.
3. Alerting the fire department or company fire brigade.
4. Evacuation of personnel.
5. The location of and proper operation and application of all available fire extinguishing and damage control equipment. Because of the noise and of the need for skillful operation of carbon dioxide extinguishing equipment, computer room personnel should be fully trained in carbon dioxide usage through actual operating of the equipment on a practice fire.
6. The importance of records and their storage requirements.

Emergency fire procedure. A written emergency fire plan should be prepared for each installation which assigns specific responsibilities to designated personnel. The following major items are suggested as minimum features of this plan:

1. *Remove all power to the computer system.*
   a. MEANS
   Main line circuit breaker or equivalent for turning off all power.
   b. LOCATION OF CONTROL FOR DISCONNECTING MEANS
   Remote controls for operating the disconnect located near the operator's console and next to the main exit door.

2. *Shut down air conditioning system.*
   a. IN CASES OF COMPLETELY SEPARATE SYSTEMS ONLY
   Emergency means as previously described provided to turn off the computer room air conditioning. They should also be located near the emergency power shutoff device.
   b. IN CASES OF REGULAR BUILDING SYSTEMS ONLY
   Emergency means as previously described provided to close off all duct dampers leading to and from the computer room. They should be located near the emergency power shut-off device.
   c. IN CASES OF COMBINING THE REGULAR BUILDING SYSTEM WITH A SUPPLEMENTARY SYSTEM
   Emergency means provided to simultaneously accomplish the similar action as described in the preceding (a) and (b) items.

3. *Notification of proper authority.*
   a. BUILDING FIRE BRIGADE
   Fire brigades shall be called immediately.
   b. OUTSIDE FIRE-FIGHTING COMPANY
   Outside fire departments shall be called in accordance with the emergency fire plan.

Damage control. Means should be provided to prevent water damage to electronic equipment. The proper method of doing this will vary according to individual equipment design. Consideration should be given to the provision of waterproof covers.

Whenever electronic equipment or any type of record is wet down, smoked up or otherwise affected by the results of a fire or other emergency, it is vital that immediate action be taken to clean and dry the electronic equipment. If the water, smoke or other contaminations are permitted to remain in the equipment longer than absolutely necessary, the damage may be grossly increased.

Glossary

Associated effects. Smoke, wind, heat, water.

Business interruption. Loss of use of the equipment and restoration to the former level of operation.

Check point (restarts). A predetermined point in the programming of information where the operator can return to continue that portion which was accidentally interrupted. These points are spaced to minimize lengthy reruns.

Console. Unit containing main operative controls of the system.

Control panel (plug board). A removable wiring panel for manually changing the operation of a component of an electronic computer system.

Electro-mechanical processing equipment. Individual units which are not electronic in nature and do not constitute a system or complete a total function.

Electronic computer system. Any electronic digital or analog computer, along with all peripheral, support, memory, programming or other directly associated equipment, records, storage and activities. The most common types of electronic computer systems are of the digital computer type and are usually classed as Electronic Data Processing Machines (EDPM), Automatic Data Processing Machines (ADPM), and/or Integrated Data Processing systems.

Electronically interconnected. Units that must be connected by a signal wire to complete a system or perform an operation.

Input-output (I-0). That equipment electronically associated with the computer which feeds information into the computer for computation or receives information which has been computed and displayed in a form familiar to the operator.

Interconnecting cables. Signal and power cables for operation and control of system (usually supplied by computer manufacturer).

Master record. A record of information on a medium which can be referred to whenever there is a need to rebuild a program.

Program. Instructions to direct systems operation.

Raised floor. Platform on which machines are installed for housing interconnecting cables, and at times as a means of supplying conditioned air to various units. Sometimes referred to as a false floor or secondary floor.

Readily accessible. When the covers, panels, doors or other enclosure for the electronic components within the equipment or the flooring can be removed by quick, simple operations to expose any area which might be involved in fire and permit the application of an extinguishing media. Preferably no special tool or other removable device should be required to perform this operation. Where safety from electrical shock requires the extra security for electronic components, a simple tool may be required provided the tool is kept in a convenient tamperproof location on or near the machine. Quick removal of the machine enclosure means that any component can be exposed by the average male employee in not over one minute. Where a special tool or device is required to assist in facilitating accessibility to underfloor areas, the number and arrangements of the devices shall be such that any space beneath the floor can be exposed to application of the extinguishing media by the average male employee in not over one and one-half minutes.

Separate fire division. A portion of a building cut off from all other portions of the building by fire walls, fire doors and other approved means adequate to prevent damage from any fire which may occur in the building from involving more than one such separate fire area. In nonfire-resistive buildings, this includes protection against building collapse as a result of a fire outside the separate fire area.

The battery compartment must be ventilated in a manner to keep out water, oil, dirt, and other foreign matter. It is essential that the battery be properly blocked in the compartment to prevent excessive movement or shifting.

Any surfaces which are to be bolted together should first be made clean and then coated with a film of "NO-OX-ID" grease or pure vaseline which also should be applied to the bolt studs before making the connection. A soft wire brush should be used for cleaning the lead plate connections. After all connections have been securely tightened, they should be gone over a second time. All connections should then be wiped off with a clean cloth to remove the surplus grease. Do not leave excess grease on any surface. Only a thin film is needed to accomplish the desired purpose.

Adding Water

Approved or distilled water should be added to all cells of the battery at sufficiently frequent intervals to keep the electrolyte level above the top of the splash cover. Do not fill above the level recommended by the manufacturer, which is generally indicated on the battery or in literature accompanying the battery when purchased. The battery manufacturer will generally test the local water for you, determining if it is usable in the battery.

During freezing weather, water should be added just before the battery is placed on charge, so that the water will be thoroughly mixed with the electrolyte during the charge and thus avoid any danger of the water freezing. All cells of the battery should require the same amount of water. If one cell takes more water than the others, examine it for leakage. A written record should be kept of the date water is added and the amount.

Cleanliness

Keep the battery, its connections and surrounding parts clean and dry, but do not remove the grease from the seal nuts. The vent plugs should be kept in place and tight, including when the battery is on charge.

If any electrolyte is accidentally spilled or if any parts are damp with acid, apply a solution of bicarbonate of soda (baking soda), using one pound to one gallon of water, then rinse with water, and dry. An old paint brush is effective for getting the soda solution under the connectors. Do not allow solution to get into the cells. If this treatment is given three times a year and the battery kept clean between times by regular washings with water or blowing off with an air jet, the life and service of the battery in general and the trays in particular will be increased considerably. Before washing a battery without removing it from the compartment, the equipment manufacturer should be consulted for advisability.

If the terminals or connections show any tendency to corrode, clean the corroded surface with a soft wire brush, wash it with a soda solution, rinse with water, wipe dry, and coat it thinly with vaseline or "NO-OX-ID" grease. No corrosion will be experienced unless electrolyte is spilled and allowed to remain. Soda solution or ammonia applied promptly, will neutralize the effect of acid on clothing, cement, or other material.

Battery Storage

If the use of a battery is to be temporarily discontinued, give it an equalizing charge, and add water to the cells during this charge so that the gasing will insure thorough mixing and prevent its freezing in cold weather. Add enough water to meet the level specified by the manufacturer. After the charge is complete, remove all fuses to prevent the use of the battery during the idle period. *Make sure* all vent plugs are in place. The battery should be reconnected, water added and charged every two months in climates averaging 70° to 80°F., and every six months in climates averaging 40°F.

Placing Batteries in Service Again

Add water if needed, and give a charge until the gravity of the electrolyte has ceased rising over a period of three hours.

37 / ELECTRIC MOTORS

(*Sources: Plant* magazine; F. C. Osterland, Allis-Chalmers Mfg. Co.)

Each building and plant has its own special operating conditions due to geographic location and plant or building environmental conditions.

General Recommendations

General recommendations to aid in the understanding of motor care are as follows:

Dust. Dust is probably the most natural enemy of a motor. Dust is contantly settling on motors, housings, windings, slip rings, and commutators, trying to work its way into the bearings. This danger is naturally at a minimum when totally enclosed, fan cooled motors are used. On windings, dust acts as a layer of insulation, confining heat until it may reach dangerous temperatures. Dust also plugs ventilation spaces which further interferes with proper cooling. It will act as an abrasive, and insulator, on slip rings and commutators, multiplying the wear and blocking full passage of current. Once inside bearings, dust can be harmful as sandpaper to the highly polished surfaces. If it is allowed to fill the open spaces in a winding, it turns the entire wound section into a sponge for soaking up harmful oil, moisture, and acid fumes.

Methods of cleaning. The time to catch dust in motors is before it has a chance to unite with water or oil to form a gummy mass. This means wiping off the motors on regular inspections, their housings, slip rings, commutators, and occasionally blowing dust out of the wound section with fairly low pressure (not over 40 psi) compressed air. The compressed air must not contain grit, metal, or moisture. If there is any danger that blowing may shoot abrasive or conductive material into the air gap or windings, suction may be the preferable method of cleaning. Oil filter caps must be kept closed at all times, and dust seals and gaskets must be kept in good condition. Worn or rotted seals should be replaced, their replacement is much easier than a burned out bearing.

Oil. Inside bearings, oil can be the "lifeblood" of motors; but outside the bearings, oil is strictly poison to them. As mentioned, dust can soak up stray oil. This trouble-making teamwork operates the other way, too. Sticky oil catches dust. When both oil and dirt cover a commutator, good commutation is impossible. The faces of the brushes become glazed and packed with dirt. Harmful sparking is the result. Oil also harms commutators by deteriorating the mica insulating segments between bars. Oil is even more harmful to taped and varnished insulation on windings. Once a winding is thoroughly oil soaked, the motor is in immediate danger of a burn-out or breakdown. Oil is most dangerous to a motor when it has had a chance to unite with dust in the windings to produce a greasy gum. Then ventilation is smothered, windings are under continuous attack from oil, and metallic dust present is caught and held in this "gum," a constant threat of shorting or grounding.

Build-ups of oil and dust on varnished windings should be removed with the aid of a solvent, preferably a non-inflammable one. If brushes or scrapers are used, care must be taken not to scrape the insulation.

Solvents must be handled with caution. Insulation should not be soaked as the solvent is apt to have a softening effect. When all the oil and dirt have been removed, windings should be dried and insulating varnish applied.

If a motor is insulated with silicone, rubber, or epoxy resin, time can be saved in cleanups by washing off oily deposits with detergent and warm water. The dry out period can be eliminated since these materials are highly resistant to moisture. In addition such insulation need not be revarnished as a part of maintenance procedure.

Sometimes a certain amount of cutting oil and other oils reach a motor in the form of a mist. That which lands on the outside should be wiped off before it can travel inside. Much can be accomplished in fighting stray oil by keeping a motor's own lubricating oil where it belongs. For example, sleeve bearings equipped with oil rings should never be lubricated when the motor is running. The oil level then does not indicate full supply. A certain amount of oil is riding the ring above the level. Overfilling and escape of oil can result.

Moisture. Motors are available for high humidity applications with sealed insulations being employed to keep out moisture. Conventional insulations however, are actually hygroscopic and really absorb moisture. One general aim of effective maintenance is to keep conventionally insulated motors completely dry.

If your motor does acquire moisture, it should be disposed of as quickly as possible for two reasons. First, it takes time for moisture to soak and soften insulation. Often, it is possible to get it out before the damage is done. Also evaporated moisture is pure water when it first condenses in a motor. It is then at its least dangerous stage. But every extra hour water stays in a motor, it gives it just that much more time, to absorb harmful compounds. Water in liquid form should be prevented from dripping on, splashing or flooding a motor. When resistance has dropped to a dangerous point, the motor should be dried by one of the following methods:

1. Heating in an oven, as this is the best method of drying.
2. Circulating current through the windings to produce heat inside the insulation to drive moisture outward. The armatures should be locked to prevent rotation and a rheostat employed to apply low voltage current.
3. Forcing air through hot elements (resistors, steam pipes, and other elements) and into the windings with a fan.
4. Enclosing the motor with nonflammable materials and conveying heat to it through ducts.
5. Covering the motor with a tarpaulin, leaving openings at top and bottom for air circulation, and providing heat with one or more electric light bulbs.

Care should be taken that the drying is accomplished without damage to the insulation. It is better to interrupt the baking for a resistance test than to bake insulation to the point of brittleness or burning. (The baking temperature should not greatly exceed the boiling point of water.) When dry, the motor's resistance to moisture can be renewed by applying a good grade of insulating varnish.

Lubrication. No wear can take place within a bearing if the surfaces are smooth and properly lubricated. A film of oil keeps them apart and prevents metal to metal contact. But in actual practice, bearings often receive an insufficient supply of oil, or the wrong type of oil. Sometimes grit gets into the oil and causes scraping, or so much load is put on the bearing, that the film of oil breaks down. Manufacturer's lubrication instructions should be followed closely. Oil is the lowest item of operating costs, yet no one thing is more certain to cause trouble and expense than incorrect lubrication. Only best quality oil and correct grade suited to the requirements of each individual motor should be used. In case of doubt, the manufacturer will be pleased to send you proper lubrication instructions.

Sleeve bearings require the oil ring be free and turning with the shaft. The oil reservoir should be flushed out, refilled, and the dust seals checked at regular intervals.

With the antifriction type of bearings (ball or roller) it is well to keep in mind that the main purpose of the grease is to guard the steel rolling elements and races from corrosion, not friction. Too much grease promotes friction and heat. In any type of bearing, the effective film lubricant is often microscopically thin. Excess load can break it down and cause metal to metal scraping and bearing failure all in a matter of seconds.

Misalignment. Examples of motor damage commonly caused by misalignment are: sprung or broken shafts, burned out bearings, and overload failure. The damage can occur in drive or driven machinery too. When these elements are lined up incorrectly, bending, breaking, or excessive wear must result.

Misalignment is not always the result of improper installation, settlement of foundation, heavy floor loading, excessive bearing wear are other factors to be considered. Mounting motor and machine on a common, rigid base is not proof against misalignment. The base itself may have been mounted off level.

Often spur gears, when employed in the drive, tend to push apart and in time disturb alignment. Sometimes misalignment gives warning. Excessive temperature may warn that misalignment is causing bearing overload. Increased vibration may be the warning signal, or a rapid knocking, a sign that a shoulder of a shaft is being driven against the end of a bearing.

It may be possible, if the installation is not too heavy, to loosen the mounting bolts of the motor or machine and experiment with the variations in position while the set is in operation. Changes in degree of noise or vibration will guide workers making the adjustments until the set is in line and the symptom disappears. If a motor is found to be off level, shims can be placed under the motor legs until the units are in line.

Vibration. One important cause of motor vibration is misalignment, but other causes should be considered. Vibration in the driven machinery may be transmitted to the motor. Also careless servicing can put rotors out of balance, motor mounting bolts can work loose, bearings can wear to the point where shaft oscillation of considerable amplitude is permitted. Because the vibration resulting from such conditions can shake loose motor parts and electrical connections, crystallize meals, and multiply friction wear, excessive vibration must be located by a process of elimination; a suggested order of checking points is as follows:

1. Tighten all mounting bolts and check motor for loose parts.

2. For solidity, compare foundation with that of non-vibrating motors. Further improvement of conditions leading to vibration may be unnecessary.

3. Check bearings for looseness. Generally, allow two thousandths of an inch clearance plus one thousandths of an inch for each inch or fraction of an inch of journal diameter.

4. Disengage vibrating motor from driven machine. If motor operates far more smoothly when disconnected (proper alignment is assumed), then the machine should be examined for sources of vibration.

5. If vibration trouble seems to date back to its repair, check rotor for balance (dynamic balance), if possible, otherwise static. Cap screw the needed weight to the point of unbalance—hooking weight around part of motor to relieve pull on screw.

Uneven wear. Wear of slip rings and commutators of electric motors is accepted as inevitable, because none of these rotating parts exposed to constant friction can be lubricated with petroleum products. However, the wear can be minimized by preventing conditions leading to "grooving" (concentration of wear in narrow rings or ruts). Dust is an abrasive agent and should be wiped off the surfaces of slip rings and commutators at regular intervals. Be sure that a thin film of oil does not collect on their surfaces, as oil catches dust and also prevents proper contact with the brushes. When the surfaces of rings or commutators are rough or otherwise uneven, the first opportunity before grooving, pitting, sparking, and increasingly accelerated wear can occur. Running the rotor, or slip rings do not need to be removed when a commstone in a suitable holder is employed. After commutators are turned down, the mica separating bars should be relieved to a depth of about one thirty-second of an inch. Mica should always be undercut when high, or even level, to forestall excessive brush wear and sparking. Brushes themselves, can contribute to excessive wear. When worn unevenly, they should be true or replaced with a new set before they can damage slip rings or commutator. To assure maximum, smooth contact, new brushes should be "sanded in" to the proper arc. Should a motor with sleeve bearings and belt drive not oscillate (the shaft floats back and forth axially), a change in alignment may permit this movement. The advantage is that wear is spread over a wider area.

Overload. Overloads will cause motors to heat up and eventually break down or burn out. To prevent this, manufacturers commonly rate the capacity of their motors below their particular breaking point. The margin of safety thus provided should never be narrowed by deliberately making a motor carry too great a mechanical load. Overloading is not always intentional. It can be produced by error in application, obstruction in the drive, or driven machine, excessive friction within the motor itself, or by efforts to obtain greater output from the driven machine than the motor is capable of carrying. If any of these conditions cause the current in a motor to exceed its nameplate current rating, heating may increase as much as the square of the current increase. The danger is that insulation will be "fried", soldered connections melted, and bearings burned out.

High temperature insulation should not be depended upon as a guarantee of motor capacity. Nameplate ratings should never be exceeded, except in emergency, regardless of the "class" of insulation used on the motor windings. The insulation might be able to take temperatures that will cause trouble with mechanical fits or bearing life.

Motors are given various forms of "overload protection". In most cases, a thermal element is connected in the power circuit to the motor. Heat from the element operates an overload relay which opens the circuit to the motor. But whether the protective unit be thermal element or a fuse, it should be of the proper capacity as listed in the national code. A unit of more than this recommended value should never be employed. Continuous production should be protected by guarding against the conditions that trip or blow the overload protection devices. Fuses and heater coils are cheaper than motors.

Underload. Underload penalties are less severe, but underloading an induction motor is just as clearly improper as overloading it. When induction motors are working only partly loaded, "power factor" (ration of power to total power) is lowered. A low power factor, produced by induction motors working underloaded, results in the following disadvantages:

1. Higher line losses, higher voltage drop and motors lose torque.
2. Increased load on a utility line and equipment. In many cases this causes breakdowns and interrupted service which slow down production.

3. Frequently a higher energy cost to the user.

4. Motors are apt to overheat as a result of excessive currents set up by the high proportion of wattless current.

5. To correct a condition of underload causing low power factor, the rated capacity of each induction motor and its actual load should be determined and the data listed on a large sheet. Data may indicate that some motors, except the largest, can be advanced to heavier jobs. Small motors may be replaced with even smaller capacity. Such handling of equipment almost suggests itself, once the facts are gathered and organized.

Minimizing underload is the preventive way of improving power factor. Corrective measures include use of synchronous condensers, synchronous motors, and capacitors.

Check List of Symptoms, Causes and Cures of Electric Motor Troubles

The trouble shooting chart is divided into symptoms that can be seen at a glance, those that can be heard in passing, those that can be felt, and some that are worth searching for. The type of machine covered by each notation is coded as follows:

Critical equipment. Critical equipment should be so identified on the card. It is generally considered vital if failure directly or indirectly interrupts or delays production. Preventive maintenance on this type of equipment is a must.

Planning. Downtime can be minimized in two ways:

1. Carry a stock of critical renewal parts.
2. Schedule preventive maintenance and overhaul well in advance.

Close coordination is required to insure that men and materials are available for such programs, to prevent delays, and overstaffing. Normal maintenance and overhauls should be scheduled during normal downtime, weekends, or during scheduled vacations, whenever possible.

Pillow tanks (electric). Many man-hours in the maintenance of oil bearing substation transformers and circuit breakers can be saved by using rubberized fabric pillow tanks for storing oil during periods of routine overhaul or repair. The pillow tank is placed near the transformer or circuit breaker with the oil being pumped into it, then returned after the repairs or maintenance have been performed. This eliminates the time consuming job of stting up a system using 50-gallon drums. This type of equipment is especially valuable during times of emergency.

Trouble Shooting Chart

KEY FOR CODE

M	Motor
G	Generator
DC	Direct Current
AC	Alternating Current

Key for Code (*Continued*)

C	Cage (motor)
WR	Wound Rotor (motor)
S	Synchronous (motor or generator)

Symptoms That Can Be Seen

Symptom	Cause	Code	Cure
1. Motor will not start (with or without humming sound).	No power. Faulty control.	M	Check power supply and connections to control and motor.
	Wrong rotation.	M	Replace fuses and check clip contacts, or allow overload trip to cool. Investigate cause.
	Low voltage.	M	Check control rating and connections.
		M	Reverse any two main leads.
		M	Check nameplate against power supply.
		M	Use adequate wire size. Check for excessive voltage drop during starting.
	Short or open-circuited or grounded winding.	M	Starting tap too low.
		M.	Check stator and rotor windings (including cage or damper bars) and repair.
	Single-phasing.	AC M	Replace fuse. Check for external or internal open circuits.
	Field excited.	S M	Check operation of control.
	Wrong field connections.	DC M	Check for reversed field connections or opposing shunt and series field.
	Blocked or locked rotor.	M	Remove foreign matter from between stator and rotor. Make sure rotor is not touching stator.
		M	Free or replace frozen bearings. Check pressure lubrication system. Use special lubricant if conditions are unusual.
	Excessive load.	M	Check unloading device.
		M	Start pressure lubricating system.
		M	Reduce belt tension.
		M	Reduce load or change motor.

SYMPTOMS THAT CAN BE SEEN (*Continued*)

Symptom	Cause	Code	Cure
2. Motor starts but: Stops.	Power stoppage.	M	See Item 1, this section.
		DC M	Check rheostat and setting; starting with weak field may actuate overload relays.
Runs too slow.	Excessive load.	M	See Item 1, this section.
	Low voltage.	M	See Item 1, this section.
	Brushes ahead of neutral.	DC M	Correct brush setting.
	Short circuit in armature or commutator.	DC M	Locate and repair.
	Open circuit in rotor.	WR M	Locate and repair.
	Field excited too soon.	S M	Check control.
	Abnormal bearing friction.	M	Check bearings and lubrication.
Runs too fast.	Weak field.	DC M	Check for poor field connection or ground.
	High voltage.	DC M	Correct voltage.
	Brushes back of neutral.	DC M	Correct brush setting.
Fails to "pull in."	Excitation troubles.	S M	Make sure field-applying contactor is operating, but not too soon.
		S M	Make sure exciter and rheostat setting provide sufficient excitation.
		S M	If starting voltage drop is large, greater discharge resistor may be helpful. Consult motor manufacturer.
	Excessive load flywheel effect.	S M	Consult motor manufacturer about reducing discharge resistor.
Pulls out of step.	Excitation troubles.	S M	Check exciter output and circuits for reversed field coil.
	Low voltage.	S M	Correct, or raise excitation if safe.
	Excessive torque peaks.	S M	Check driven machine adjustment.
3. Excessive sparking, or flashing of brushes and rigging and/or blackened commutator.	Overload.	M G	Reduce load or change motor.

SYMPTOMS THAT CAN BE SEEN (*Continued*)

Symptom	Cause	Code	Cure
	Dirty, rough or eccentric commutator or rings.	M G	Sand, grind or turn commutator or rings.
		DC	Undercut mica.
	Brush troubles.	M G	Adjust springs for sufficient, equal brush pressure.
		M G	Clean, sand or replace sticking, incorrectly fitted, burned, wornout, or unsuitable brushes.
		M G	Check connections between brushes and holders.
		DC	Check brush position and holder and bracket alignment.
	Shorted or open armature winding.	DC	Check and repair.
4. Smoke, charred insulation. Solder "whiskers" on armature.	Overload.	M G	(See Item 2, "Symptoms That Can Be Felt.")
5. Commutator grooving.	Brushes not correctly staggered.	DC	Adjust staggering.
6. Fine dust under coupling with rubber buffers or pins.	Misalignment.	M G	Realign unit and repair coupling.
7. Excessive brush wear.	See Item 3, this section.	M G	See Item 3, this section.
8. Generator fails to develop normal voltage.	Short-circuited or partially reversed shut field.	DC G	Check and correct.
	Loss of residual magnetism (self-excited machine).	DC G	Separately excite fields for few minutes.
	Incorrect brush position.	DC G	Check and correct.
	Poor fit or riding of brushes or commutator.	DC G	Clean and sand brushes. Check commutator surface.
	Excessive resistance in field circuit.	G	Check and correct.

Symptoms That Can Be Seen (*Continued*)

Symptom	Cause	Code	Cure
	Below normal speed.	G	Check prime mover.
	Faulty instruments.	G	Check and repair or replace.
9. Generator requires excessive overhauling.	Partially short-circuited field coils.	G	Check and correct.
10. Motor draws excessive current at normal speed.	Overload.	M	Reduce load. See Item 1, this section.
	Wrong brush setting.	DC M	Check and correct.
	Armatture short circuit.	DC M	Check and repair.
	Abnormal bearing friction.	M	(See Item 3, "Symptoms That Can Be Felt.")

Symptoms That Can Be Heard

Symptom	Cause	Code	Cure
1. Excessive hum.	Uneven air gap.	M G	Check air gap. Center rotor. Replace bearings if necessary.
	Unbalanced rotor.	M G	Rebalance, especially after repairs.
	Loose punchings.	M G	Tighten holding bolts.
	Single-phasing.	AC M	Stop motor and try to restart. If it will not start, check power supply, fuses, and for internal or external open circuits.
2. Regular clicking, scraping or grinding sound.	Foreign matter in air gap or between other rotating and stationary parts.	M G	Remove and check for damage.
	Rotor rubbing stator.	M G	Replace worn (sleeve) bearings, check air gap and alignment.
	Noisy ball bearings.	M G	Check lubrication, and replace bearings if necessary.
3. Rapid knocking.	Shaft shoulder hitting bearing.	M G	Realign unit.
4. Brush chatter or hissing.	Extreme vibration.	M G	(See Item 1, "Symptoms That Can Be Felt.")
	Brush troubles.	M G	Check brushes for correct fit in holders.

SYMPTOMS THAT CAN BE HEARD (*Continued*)

Symptom	Cause	Code	Cure
		M G	Check holders for excessive clearance or incorrect angle.
		M G	Use brushes suited to service.
		M G	Check brush spring pressure.
	High mica.	DC	Undercut.
5. Miscellaneous noises.	Loose coupling, foundation bolts, and other items.	M G	Tighten bolts, recheck alignment.

SYMPTOMS THAT CAN BE FELT

Symptom	Cause	Code	Cure
1. Vibration.	Misalignment.	M G	Realign unit.
	Vibration in drive or driven machine.	M G	Eliminate source if possible. Consider belt drive, and other parts.
	Unbalanced rotor.	M G	Rebalance.
	Loose bearing.	M G	Correct or replace.
	Loose parts or mounting bolts.	M G	Tighten and recheck alignment.
2. Overheating.	Overload.	M	Check for excessive friction in motor, drive, driven machine.
		M G	Reduce load or starting requirements, or replace unit.
	Dirt.	M G	Clean windings, vents, air filter, or wherever dirt may be seen. Remove external obstructions.
	Incorrect voltage and/ or frequency.	M	Check and correct.
With vibration, noise and low starting torque.	Defective rotor bars or joints.	AC M	Install new bars or rods. Clean and rebraze or resolder joints.
Part of winding hot, and part cool. Field coils hot.	Uneven air gap, with or without rotor rubbing stator.	M G	Replace bearings, check shaft.
	Shorted or grounded winding. Single-phasing.	M G	Check fuses. Locate and repair breaks, loose connections or grounds.
	Excessive excitation.	M G	Reduce excitation. (Avoid operating dc motor below normal speed.)

SYMPTOMS THAT CAN BE FELT (*Continued*)

Symptom	Cause	Code	Cure
3. Bearing overheated. (*Warning:* Keep shaft turning until bearing cools—to prevent "freezing.")	Misalignment.	M G	Realign unit. Check anti-friction bearing fit, end-shield or pedestal alignment, and other parts.
	Faulty lubrication.	M G	Use correct amount of clean, high-grade, suitable oil or grease.
		M G	Check oil ring operation, oil flow, and other functions.
	Excessive chain or belt tension.	M G	Reduce tension.
	Excessive end thrust.	M G	Reduce thrust. See that unit is level, not tilted.
	Improper radial clearance.	M G	Check bearings and seals for excessive wear or misadjustment.
	Damaged bearing parts or shaft journal.	M G	Check and correct or replace.
4. Commutator or rings overheated.	Excessive load.	M G	Reduce load.
	Brush troubles.	M G	Check particularly for correct grade of brush and absence of excessive brush pressure. (See Item 3, "Symptoms That Can Be Seen.")
	Rough commutator or rings.	M G	Sand, grind or turn.

SYMPTOMS IN HIDING

Symptom	Cause	Code	Cure
1. Dropping insulation resistance.	Usually moisture and dirt, sometimes damage.	M G	Check and record at least once a year. Clean, dry and repair before trouble develops.
2. Faltering air gap.	Sleeve bearing wear.	M G	Periodic checking with feeler gages, at least once a year, can prevent work stoppages.
3. Production process change.	Increased load peaks, higher ambient temperature, and other causes.	M G	Check motor frequently to make sure it is suitable for revised application.

SYMPTOMS IN HIDING (*Continued*)

Symptom	Cause	Code	Cure
4. Aging or vanishing lubricant.	Mostly just the nature of things.	M G	Periodic inspection and appropriate action.

Electric Shock

The amount of current does not always determine the severity of the injury, which may be a shock, a burn, or death. However the higher the voltage, the greater the danger. Lower voltages are also known to be dangerous. The path which the current takes in passing through the body generally determines the extent of damage. The heart is the most vulnerable organ, however in the average heart beat, there is a time when it is less susceptible to shock. For this reason the instant of the shock can determine the amount of injury.

The majority of electrical shocks in industry are in the low voltage range. Low voltage current is extremely hazardous when the body is wet, which can be caused from perspiration, rain, damp floors, and other moisture. The body would have to be in contact with the ground and the live conductor.

High voltages across the body will cause a non-breathing shock condition. Generally over half of the cases of this type of accident can be revived if artificial respiration is promptly applied. Artificial respiration should be started immediately, in some cases, you may not be able to hear the heart beat, however it should be continued for several hours (at least two) or until a physician arrives.

Electric shock does not always show immediately. The victim's temperature will generally rise fast, then he may become nauseous, then unconscious. Persons that have received severe shock should be kept under observation for several hours, as the shock sometimes causes damage to organs, tissues, or muscular system which becomes uncontrollable, causing a fall. Persons that survive electric shock completely recover in a short time without any ill effects or permanent disability.

38 / **LUBRICATION**

(*Source:* "How to Select Grease for Bearings," *Power Transmission Design,* June 1960)

Lubrication greases are solid to semifluid products composed of oil and thickening agents. The amount of thickening agent determines, to a great extent, consistency of the mixture. The type of agent also affects consistency, but gives other qualities too. Consistency is the most important difference between grease and oil. Grease is semifluid or plastic, it does not run like oil and, therefore, tends to remain where it is put. It does, however, flow in the direction of motion in a bearing and lubricates in the same way oil does. Grease has much higher adhesive properties than oil. This means that more pressure is needed to squeeze a grease film into and out of two bearing surfaces.

Grease is good on applications not readily accessible to lubricant replenishment. The sealed for life bearing is probably the best example of this. An automobile wheel bearing is another example where grease needs replenishing only at long intervals, of many thousand miles. Grease works well in oscillating bearings where there is no continuous rotary motion of the journal in the bearing. Under these conditions, hydrodynamic lubrication cannot exist and grease will do a better job than oil because of its thicker film and higher adhesion.

Grease forms an effective seal that prevents entrance of dirt into a bearing. It does not necessarily have to be sealed in the bearing to stay in. Under normal operation, it stays put and only the simplest seals are needed.

How Grease Lubricates

Grease becomes fluid when sheared, or worked in a bearing. Therefore, the bearing is actually lubricated by an oily film at points of contact. But, where the grease is not being sheared, as at the edges of the bearing, it remains a semisolid, and therefore, continues to do its sealing job. In some bearings it is believed that lubrication is performed by oil which bleeds from the main body of the grease to the moving surfaces. There are also indications that the grease itself may flow to the bearing due to heating, vibration and temperature.

Dropping point. Temperature at which grease melts or changes to liquid from semisolid state is the dropping point. This point is important because it is a measure of the highest temperature at which the grease is expected to perform satisfactorily. Some oil will separate or bleed from some greases before the whole mass melts.

Penetration. Consistency of grease is important because it is a measure of how easily grease may be squeezed out from between the parts being lubricated. Also, it is a measure of the resistance to motion the grease offers in an antifriction bearing. Grease with too high consistency in an antifriction bearing may offer more resistance to the motion of the bearing than the friction it is supposed to reduce.

The National Lubricating Grease Institute (N.L.G.I.) has set up a system of numbers for expressing grease consistencies. Each number corresponds to a particular range of penetration numbers.

N.L.G.I. Number	Worked Penetration Number
0	385-355
1	340-310
2	295-265
3	250-220
4	205-175
5	160-130
6	115-85

Thickening agents. Thickening agents used to make grease from oils largely determine the characteristics and applications. Most thickening agents are metallic soaps, such as: calcium, sodium, aluminum, barium, and lithium soaps. Some

Figure 38-1

TABLE OF THICKENING AGENTS

Property	Thickener							
	Calcium Soap	Calcium-Resinate Soap	High-Melting Point Calcium Soap	Sodium Soap	Sodium-Calcium Soap	Aluminum Soap	Lithium Soap	Solid Thickener
Texture	Buttery	Buttery	Buttery	Fibrous or smooth	Buttery to fibrous	Buttery to stringy	Buttery to stringy	Buttery to stringy
Highest continuous usable temperature	175°F.	200°F.	225°F.	300° to 400°F.	250°F.	150°F.	300°F.	Depends on oil
Dropping point	200° to 225°F.	275°F.	280°F.	300° to 450°F.	315°F.	200°F.	360°F.	500°F.

Reaction when heated above melting point and then cooled	Separates unless chemically stabilized	Separates	Separates	None if worked	None if worked	Texture changes, does not separate	None if worked	Retains texture, but may harden
Water resistance	Good	Good	Good	Poor to fair	Poor to fair	Good	Good	Good
Resistance to work softening	Poor to fair	Poor to fair	Excellent	Poor to excellent	Poor to excellent	Poor to fair	Poor to excellent	Poor to excellent
Application	Plain bearings	Heavy bearings at low speeds	Ball, roller and plain bearings automotive and industrial	Ball and roller bearings at low to medium speeds, vehicle bearings and chassis	All types of ball and roller bearings at high temperatures, depends on Ca-Na percentages	Special applications where high adhesion, resistance to centrifugal throwout are needed	Aircraft, 100° to 300°F., also automotive and industrial	For high temperatures

greases use solids such as silica, carbon black, finely divided clay and clay derivatives. Figure 38-1 shows how the characteristics of greases vary with thickener, and the applications or uses for the different types.

Maintenance

HOT BEARINGS

Causes	Remedies
No oil.	Check lubricators and bearings on scheduled periods to insure safe operation.
Dirty oil (causes undue friction).	Keep oil supply clean and stored properly.
Out of line (load on small area).	Bearings should be lined up properly.
Wrong grade oil (will not support shaft).	Use correct grade of oil, as specified by the manufacturer.
Uneven bearing.	Reduced bearing area cause heating, replace the bearing.
Tightly keyed (no space for oil between bearing and shaft).	Loosen bearing bolts until shutdown.

STEPS TO COOLING

1. *Flood with oil,* remove cup and pour oil into the bearing.
2. *Remove wicks,* pour oil into box to flood bearing.
3. *Feel shaft near bearing,* if temperature goes up after flooding, investigate further.
4. *Examine oil,* if gritly and dirty keep flooding bearing to wash out grit.
5. *Increase water flow,* if water cooled bearing, check feed and discharge line to insure water is flowing.
6. *Pour oil on shaft,* if temperature continues to increase.

EMERGENCY MEASURES

1. Remove the load. (Do not stop engine.)
2. Throttle engine to slow speed, but do not stop engine, as the bearing may seize to the shaft or pin.
3. Remove oils and flood with oil while engine is turning slow.
4. Slacken setscrews on bearing cap nuts and flood bearing with heavy oil, as it stands the heat much better.
5. When bearing cools, increase load or speed slowly keeping constant check on the temperature.

39 / LUBRICATION GUIDE
FOR PACKINGS AND SEALS

(*Source:* "Lubrication Guide for Packings and Seals," *Plant Engineering*)

The prevention of fluid leakage between relatively moving surfaces calls for a close conforming device described as a packing or seal which may be defined as follows:

1. A *dynamic packing* is a nonautomatic or adjustable item installed in a stuffing box and adjusted by a gland to the desired shaft fit. Such items are often called jamb packings.

2. A *dynamic seal* is an automatic or nonadjustable item installed in a predetermined space.

Packings, whether adjustable or nonadjustable, usually function under fluid pressure. This fact demands close conformity with the moving surfaces and the ability to carry this pressure which is the equivalent of a bearing load.

Therefore, packings are in a sense, bearings—because every effort is made to eliminate an oil wedge between the surfaces, and to maintain so-called "contact" with the shaft around its entire periphery.

Figure 39-1 / **An efficient packing seal.**

No true contact is established, of course, since a lubricating film is necessary for the operation of any dynamic packing.

Without the film, excessive heat would be produced, and the result would be wear, scoring, and destruction of both the packing and its journal, the shaft. On the other hand, the film must be exceedingly thin to prevent it from flowing through the clearance to produce excessive leakage.

The first consideration of packings discussed is limited to dynamic applications of the broad range of nonautomatic devices—that is, to jamb packings as they are employed between two relatively moving surfaces. Included among these packings are braids, duck and rubber coils and rings, jacketed packings, and certain of the plastics—bulk mixtures of various fibers; solid lubricants such as graphite, mica, or molysulfide; and bits of soft metals commonly bonded together with grease or an elastomeric binder.

In *braided packings,* the type of lubricant employed varies with the specific function of the braid. For cold water service, a waterpoof grease must be supplied; for work against solvents, castor oil, soap or hydrogenated fish oil may be used.

Figure 39-2 / **Oil seal sections show how springs maintain lip contact with shaft.**

Duck and rubber rings are normally impregnated with a mineral oil, but occasionally must depend upon water which they attract in service. For plastic packings the oil or grease in the binder usually provides the initial lubrication, and there is also a high percentage of graphite or similar material which functions as a dry lubricant. Some of the plastic packings contain bits of soft metal, such as babbitt, resiliently supported in the mix. The metals are in themselves excellent bearings; combined with the plastic, they provide superior service.

In *automatic packings,* such as molded V-packings, U and O-rings, flanges, and cups, the fluids being handled act as lubricants. Since these packings are automatic, they squeeze the shaft more tightly as the pressure increases. The film is thus thinned and the probability of leakage is decreased.

The lubricant is drawn by the shaft under the packing by the reciprocating action of the rod or piston. (While automatic packings are not generally used with rotating shafts, partly because there is no feasible method of drawing the fluid under, they are sometimes employed on slow speed, low pressure jobs.)

Because of this condition, lubrication engineers have attempted to determine the ideal shaft surface. Under normal conditions, a surface finish of between

16 rms (root-mean-square) and 32 rms has been found most practical. This degree of roughness produces excellent pockets to carry the lubricating liquid under the packing with a minimum cutting or wear.

With high pressures, a finer finish (approximately nine rms) is considered necessary, and in extreme conditions a finish of four rms is used. These recommended surface finishes may vary slightly with the lubricity of the liquid, its ability to wet the shaft and the type of packing.

Metal packings, in the form of floating segmental rings held in initial sealing relationship with the rod or cylinder by a spring, are also in this category. They require that the lubricant be drawn under the rings by the reciprocating rod. Where such lubricant is not present in the gas being handled (this packing is normally for high pressure gases or steam) lubrication must be provided from external sources.

"Dry" Bearing Materials

Some good results have been achieved on dry gases, where the temperatures are low without external lubrication, by using "dry" bearing materials such as special mixtures of "Teflon". Such mixtures are usually referred to as "filled" and consist of minute glass fibers or carbon graphite filling in a matrix of "Teflon".

The oil seal, a lip type packing, is designed for nonpressure service; however it does respond to act automatically under pressure. Since it operates on a very narrow wear band, any fluid loading must be kept very low to avoid excessive unit loading on the wear band which would burn up the seal. (See Figure 39-2.)

Under seal design conditions of no pressure, it cannot be automatic. However, such action is achieved by building in a spring loading device. A finger or coil spring is provided around the lip thus forcing it inwardly against the shaft. The loads used are low, normally ranging from one-quarter pound to three-quarter pound per linear inch of circumference. High pressure velocity ratios are not satisfactory in oil seals.

Another method of introducing the lubricant employs the oil cup, and depends upon the lantern, an annular ring having a spool or H-shaped cross section. The lantern ring which is associated with a lubrication connection through the stuffing box wall, may be machined from a short metal cylinder with clearances adequate to fit within the stuffing box and around the shaft.

The mid-section of the cylinder is provided with annular grooves—one each on the i.d. (inside diameter) and o.d. (outside diameter)—which are interconnected by a series of holes through the remaining web. A lubricant, introduced through the side wall of the stuffing box, fills the voids in the lantern, thus reaching the shaft and packing.

The stuffing box lantern ring serves not only as a means of introducing the lubricant, but also as a reservoir for it, and may be fed by a grease cup, by a drip oiler, or by oil under pressure. A positive means, such as the latter, is much preferred to the grease cup or grease gun fitting, which supplies only intermittent servicing.

An oil bottle may also be used to good effect in keeping the oil under pressure. The bottle is energized by pressure from the discharge side of the pump; and since the shaft is on the inlet side, the discharge pressure creates an adequate differential.

Another applicable device is the differential cylinder, used chiefly when it is desirable to maintain the pressure in the lantern at a slightly higher level than in the medium being packed. The differential pressures involved are not great, generally ranging from five to ten pounds.

Finally, it is possible to employ a completely independent lubricating system, which may operate either continuously or intermittently.

Lantern Rings

Besides serving as a means of introducing the lubricant and as a reservoir for it, the lantern ring also performs another function—cooling. By locating an outlet equipped with a bypass valve on the opposite side of the stuffing box, it is possible to adjust a constant flow of the lubricating agent to the packing and around the journal, thereby removing a high percentage of the heat generated inside.

The thin film which lubricates a packing is also used as a sealing agent. Since it is generally introduced at a pressure several pounds higher than the fluid being handled, co-mingling is expected. For this reason the two substances must be compatible.

In packing mayonnaise, *for example*, pure food regulations must be observed: vegetable or cotton seed oil is often used as the lubricating agent. Other examples are more obvious: one would not use glycerine in the lantern ring or seal ring of a pump that was pumping nitric acid—nitroglycerine would be formed. The object, in all cases, is to assure compatibility while maintaining the greatest possible lubricity. (See Figure 39-3.)

Figure 39-3 / **In plastic packings, oil or grease in the binder provides initial lubrication.**

Adjusting a set of soft (nonautomatic) packings, should be accomplished by tightening the gland stud by not more than one flat of a hex nut at a time, after which the packing should be allowed to run uninterrupted for ten or fifteen minutes. Any attempt to eliminate leakage completely is almost certain to result in a burned-up set of packing, often in a few minutes' time.

In cases where the set is in good condition and still contains adequate lubricant, the lubricant acts as a safety valve. However, if the packing is over-tightened, friction becomes excessive, heat is produced and the set tries to expand, as a result the lubricant becomes thinner and more mobile and is squeezed out, thus the volume of the set decreases and equilibrium is reached. However, should there be insufficient lubricant remaining, the result may be a cloud of smoke, destroyed packing and a scored journal.

Automatic packings should not require adjustment. Cups, U's, O-rings, V-packings and flanges, have a predetermined depth of the stuffing box or axial space between the retaining surfaces.

In replacing a packing, cleanliness is the major factor to be considered. Rings should be carefully slipped into place with joints of soft packings staggered. They should be positioned true and square and free of all foreign matter. A split wooden block or cylinder that one can slide into the box can be used to tamp the packing in place uniformly. After the stuffing box has been filled, it should be tightened up snugly, then backed off to allow the packing to expand.

In this manner, provision is made for a certain "looseness", so that the pump can be started up without danger of overheating or damaging the packing or journal in any way. The shaft and especially the piston and the rings supporting it must also be checked to insure that it is true and properly supported.

High-Pressure Work

In high-pressure work, precautions concerning clearance must be observed, since failures in the operation of automatic packings, cups, O-rings, and V's are most often caused by extrusion into the clearances. Elastomeric materials, whether used alone or as a binder in a fibrous packing, are deformable. Even with recommended fine clearances, the O-ring requires special back-up or anti-extrusion rings above 1500 psi.

Under several thousand pounds of pressure, very fine clearances, on the order of one or two thousandths, are required. If such close tolerances are not practicable (as is usually the case), a strong backup ring is considered necessary. These rings range from the familiar adapter rings used with V-rings to metal-backed cups.

The choice of a packing is not an easy one to make, since thousands are available. A brief guide, however, might be useful:

Braided packings are manufactured from a variety of fibers, including cotton, flax, jute, ramie, asbestos (both blue and white), "Teflon", rayon, nylon, and dacron. Some of these packings are equipped with metal jackets.

Metal makes a good bearing. When used around a core to make a foil jacket, shaft movement beyond that which a solid piece of metal can handle is normally expected. The core provides the resilient springback to the metal surface. Most such packings are used in rotary service or mild reciprocating work.

Coil and *ring packings* are fabricated from duck and rubber, and are

Figure 39-4B / **Sections show various packing shapes to fit machine contours.**

Figure 39-4A / **Metal packing rings are used almost exclusively for high-pressure reciprocating work involving gases.**

generally used in reciprocating work. Occasionally, however, they come into service as end rings for rotary service as well.

Molded and *automatic* types of *packings*, some of which are reinforced with certain of the fibers mentioned above or they may be a homogenous rubber compound, are generally recommended for use in reciprocating work.

Floating metal packings are segmental rings of packing generally held in initial contact with the shaft by means of a garter spring circling the surface of the ring, and are manufactured of cast iron, bronze, phenolic, carbon, and "Teflon". This type of packing is used almost exclusively for high-pressure reciprocating work involving gases.

The standard oil seal employs a nitrile rubber element, although other elastomers and leathers are sometimes used. It is used more often for rotating service than for reciprocating service and is designed for "nonpressure" applications.

Mechanical seals, though expensive, are probably the most efficient packings. They are used exclusively for rotary service, and are manufactured from many materials and combinations such as metals, ceramics, plastic, elastomers, carbon, and many others.

Figure 39-5A / Braided packing. Lattice weave of the material increases its durability.

Figure 39-5B / Spiral packings are generally recommended for reciprocating service.

Figure 39-5C / Asbestos core with metal foil is used in rotary or mild reciprocating work.

Regardless of how colorful plumbing fixtures are, they can perform their function only if the piping behind the walls and in the basement is made of quality materials, correctly designed and installed, and periodically inspected.

Periodic inspections of piping should be made where conditions are particularly severe, such as in elevator shafts and boiler rooms, and where stresses of high temperatures prevail. In some types of buildings, the life of piping is shortened by vibration chemicals, condensation, electrolysis, and by alternation of temperatures over short periods.

Insulation of piping will minimize piping hazards resulting from condensation and excessive heat or cold. It will add life to piping and effect economies in heating and cooling. It will also keep the water at a higher temperature.

Water heavily laden with oxygen is particularly destructive to hot water lines and boiler tubing. The installation of deaerators or deactivators will lengthen the life of the pipe. Water softening equipment is sometimes required due to the hardness of the water, and aids in keeping the pipe free of scale.

Leaky pipes may be the result of chemical decomposition of the pipe caused by electric current. Inspection should be made periodically to determine if anyone is using the pipes for ground wires. If so this practice should be discontinued.

A good quality valve or fitting should always be used. Valves should be turned open and closed at least once every three months. Valves which stick should be replaced.

The use of an adequate number of valves both on industrial lines and on individual fixtures will prevent inconvenience to tenants should it become necessary to shut down certain areas of the building for repair. A union should always be placed in the line just ahead of the valve to aid in its replacement.

Identification

Valve identification. Valves should be identified so that their function can be easily identified. This can be accomplished by the use of a tag on the valve explaining its function, or with a number or letter system that corresponds to a keyed chart.

Pipe identification. Pipes or their covering can be painted for identification. Color codes generally used are:

Cold Water	Blue	Waste Lines	Yellow
Hot Water	Red	Vent Pipes	Black

Water faucets should be inspected for leaks once every three months. Filter screens should be cleaned every other month. Toilet bowls and urinals should be inspected for leaks, cracks, and correct seating, once a year.

Washrooms

Important factors in washroom planning are the layout and the equipment and materials to be used which will effect the overall maintenance costs. Non-porous materials are best for washrooms because they keep maintenance to a minimum. Floor materials in this category are concrete, terrazzo, and ceramic tile. Wall surfaces should be impervious to moisture. Non-porous surfaces are the easiest to be kept clean.

Wall hung fixtures provide an unobstructed washroom floor for rapid hosing or mopping. It pays to buy good quality faucets and fittings made for durability. Combination faucets are preferred to separate hot and cold water faucets for lavatories. This permits the user to temper the water to suit his wishes. Do not economize in buying a toilet. The better toilets have a larger water seal which will reduce stoppages. Better toilets are equipped with quieter and more positive flushing action. Elongated bowls are recommended, and are sometimes required by the plumbing code.

The best way to provide for ease in servicing is to have an access chamber in back of each washroom. If men's and women's washrooms are back to back, one chamber will do for both. All supply, waste piping, and the flush valve mechanism will be easily accessible, and it will be rarely that a maintenance man will have to enter the women's rest room for the purpose of making adjustments.

Washroom facilities per person. State or local laws normally will specify minimum washroom facilities to be provided in industrial buildings. Office occupants should have facilities above this minimum. A desirable standard to cover these facilities provides for:

WOMEN

No. of Employees	Toilet Booths	Washbasins
1-5	1	1
6-15	2	2
16-25	3	2
26-40	4	2
41-70	5	3
71-100	6	4
101-140	7	5

Note: One toilet booth is allowed for every 45 employees over 140, and three basins are allowed for every four toilet booths.

MEN

No. of Employees	Toilet Booths	Urinals	Washbasins
1-5	1	—	1
6-25	2	1	2
26-50	3	2	2
51-80	4	2	3
81-125	5	3	4

Note: One toilet booth is allowed for every 45 employees over 125, one urinal for every 60 persons and three basins are allowed for every toilet booth.

Stoppages of toilets. Fill the fixture approximately two-thirds with water. Then use a rubber suction and force type plunger to try to dislodge the stoppage. The overflow pipe should be covered to help concentrate the pressure produced on the drain. If this does not clear the stoppage, a flexible spiral wire (plumber's snake) should be inserted into the clogged pipe either through toilet bowl or a cleanout. If a pipe is only partially blocked and water will still flow, drain pipe solvents can sometimes be effective. Caution should be noted in using lye or other strong alkali, as soap may be formed with grease, thus increasing the problem of removing the stoppage.

Elements of Maintenance

Cleanout covers. These should be removed at least twice per year to determine the condition of the pipe, and to prevent the covers from sticking. If a cover cannot be turned with an ordinary pull on a wrench, sometimes tapping the cover at the same time force is applied to the wrench will aid in loosening the cover. A cleanout cover can also be loosened by applying heat to the outside of the pipe. *Be sure* to keep the cover cool.

Traps. A plumbing trap is a fitting placed in a drain pipe for the purpose of holding water or other fluid to form a seal that will prevent the passage of gases and odors from the drain pipes into the immediate area. The seal may be destroyed when water is blown or sucked out of the trap as a result of variations in pressure in drain pipes, when the water discharging through a trap at a high rate of velocity does not fall sufficiently to maintain or restore the seal, or when water evaporates from the trap. Proper venting will control these difficulties, *except* evaporation.

Grease traps. Grease traps are required in waste pipes from sinks and fixtures in which greasy foods are prepared, and where dishes are washed which contained greasy foods. Traps of this type are generally installed in restaurants, hotels, schools, laboratories, hospitals, and all institutional type buildings.

These are installed in the waste pipe for the purpose of separating grease from the liquid retaining the grease. The construction of the trap permits cooling of the liquid sufficiently to precipitate some grease from solution and to permit suspended grease to rise to the top of the trap where the grease is held.

Leaks in water closet flush valves. When water runs continuously from a water closet flush tank, either one of two conditions may exist.

1. The float on the float valve is submerged more than it should be, and water is running through the overflow. The float should be inspected to see if it is water-logged and needs to be replaced. If the inlet valve is leaking, a new seat or repacking may be required. If both the float and valve are in satisfactory condition, the bar holding the float should be bent so that the float will rise sooner and close the valve tightly.

2. The flush valve is not seated and water runs into the toilet bowl. The rubber ball, the guide, or the flush valve seat may need adjustment or replacement.

Care of Water Pipes

Cleaning. Pipes can be cleaned by pushing or pulling through them, a cutting tool attached to a flexible wire twisted by hand or power. Pneumatic tools are also available which delivers a slug of compressed air hydraulically.

Thawing frozen water pipes. Pipes burst due to force of the expansion of water as it turns into ice. If ice is allowed to expand as it forms, the pipe will not burst. The moment the movement is obstructed, such as at a valve, a bend, or a rough spot, it will burst at that obstruction.

A frozen pipe may be thawed by:

1. Applying cloths soaked in hot water.
2. Playing steam on the pipe.
3. Injecting steam into the pipe.
4. Pouring hot water into the pipe.
5. Unslacked lime wrapped in a waterproof material—water poured over the lime.
6. Or other methods of applying heat to the pipe that *are not considered dangerous.*

Air in water pipes. Air may enter pipes from draining them, or from a period when the pressure was low enough to siphon air in through an open faucet or flush tank valve. To correct this condition:

1. Put an aerating attachment on the faucet from which air is escaping.
2. Insert an air relief valve at the high point of the piping system.
3. Place a frequently used faucet near the point of supply concentrating the trouble there.

Water hammer. Water hammer may be caused by the sudden closing of valves or faucets, or any other method of quickly stopping the flow of water in a pipe. Other causes are:

1. Displacing air from a closed tank or pipe from the top.
2. Condensation of steam in water in a closed pipe.
3. By pumps, sudden stopping, damaged or worn gaskets.

Water hammer can be prevented by:

1. When filling a closed tank or pipe, it should be filled from the bottom up to allow the air to escape at the top.
2. Steam and water should not be allowed to come into contact in a closed pipe.
3. Downward dips in steam pipes should be avoided or drains should be provided.
4. Installation of air chambers may control water hammer. Air chambers should be installed near the valve that is causing the water hammer in a vertical position over the top of a riser pipe.
5. Use of pressure reducing valves.

Combating Destructive Return-Line Corrosion

(*Source:* "7 Ways to Combat Destructive Return-Line Corrosion," by J. G. Roussos, *Power*, February 1963)

Corrosion of return lines and steam lines mean expensive piping and valve replacement, curtailed production because of forced shutdowns and inefficient operation of heat-transfer equipment. Virtually all corrosion in steam and condensate lines is caused by oxygen or carbon dioxide in the presence of moisture. And when both gases are present the rate of corrosion is appreciably greater than either could produce alone.

Oxygen corrosion is characterized by deep pit marks that ultimately penetrate the pipe wall. CO_2 attack grooves the pipe proper and produces marked thinning at threaded joints.

A classic example of return-line corrosion induced by CO_2 is shown in Figure 40-1. Note deep grooving of piping on the bottom surface and actual metal failure at the threaded end. Corrosion has removed about 50 per cent of the pipe-wall thickness. This specimen was taken from the condensate system in a large industrial plant where steam produced at 600 psi generates electricity and meets both process and general heating needs.

Fouling with corrosion products is marked in Figure 40-2. Deposits of this type are frequently found in traps, valves and other areas where flow is restricted. Section of piping removed from a large textile mill (Figure 40-3) is also fouled by corrosion products in its upper section and the lower pipe wall is deeply gouged.

Seven proven methods. Many factors contribute to steam and return-line corrosion. One plant's solution to the problem is not necessarily the best answer for another. But here are seven proven ways plant engineers can combat corrosion:

1. *Good insulation practice is a must.* Well-insulated, dry steam lines show very little corrosion, if any, but poorly insulated mains increase amount of steam condensation and permit absorption of oxygen and CO_2. Carbonic acid forms as moisture combines with the CO_2 ($H_2O + CO_2 = H_2CO$). *Result:* accelerated oxygen and acid corrosion attack. When repairing or replacing steam or return-line piping make sure insulation is replaced.

2. *Provide enough return-line pitch.* Improperly pitched return lines decrease flow rate of the condensate, giving it more time to cool. And as temperature drops, solubility of oxygen and carbon dioxide increases. So if flow is low or stagnant in a line, condensate can absorb more oxygen and CO_2. *Result:* low pH and severe corrosion. Vertical lines where condensate velocity is high almost always show much less corrosion.

3. *Reduce steam and condensate losses.* Keeping required flow of makeup water at a minimum means less dissolved gas enters the feedwater system. Dividends include lower cost of makeup, fuel and water treatment.

In many cases, steam losses can be drastically reduced by switching from direct to indirect steam heating and recovering condensate for boiler feed. Cost of installing necessary heat-exchange equipment is then charged against saving in operating cost.

Figure 40-1

Figure 40-2

Figure 40-3

Leaks in steam and condensate lines are obvious losses that cannot be tolerated. Compare chlorides in the feedwater with chlorides in the makeup to obtain actual percentage of makeup and condensate returns. These figures should check closely with separate estimates of condensate-return flow. If not, chances are good that steam and condensate leaks account for the difference. Some plants bury their return lines underground, making leak detection very difficult. But even then it pays to locate and repair system leaks.

Process condensate is frequently discarded because of possible contamination that could harm the boiler and steam system. But how much high-quality condensate is wasted to avoid this contamination? As a more economical arrangement, return condensate to the boiler but set up automatic controls to detect contamination. Then discard condensate only if quality is unacceptable.

4. *Minimize air leakage.* Temperature drop in condensate-storage tanks can produce a partial vacuum which sucks outside air in through vents or the overflow connection. One way to minimize this fairly common trouble is the addition of a heating coil in the tank to keep temperature at 180°F. or higher at all times. Another calls for installing a vertical unloaded check valve in the vent or overflow pipe.

5. *Proper system lay-up is vital.* It's good practice to drain all idle lines in steam and condensate systems completely. If condensate is left in return lines when the system isn't operating, it picks up CO_2, which corrodes the piping in the presence of air. This type of attack is often called sectional return-line corrosion. It takes place in parts of the system not in continuous use, such as circuits used only during the heating season.

6. *Provide efficient deaeration.* Most economical approach is to remove oxygen from the feedwater as completely as possible. This can be done by mechanical deaerating, by chemical oxygen scavengers such as catalyzed sulfite, or a combination of both methods. In any case feed enough chemical to maintain an adequate sulfite reserve in the boiler water. Any oxygen not removed will go over with steam from the boiler and corrode return-line piping. That's why it's extremely important to continuously check deaerator performance.

Temperature of water in the deaerating section should correspond with temperature of saturated steam at heater's temperature above 216°F. (corresponding 1.3 psi). When heater is working properly, temperature of water in the deaerating section is normally one or two degrees higher than water in the deaerated storage compartment.

Watch sulfite dosage as a possible clue to faulty operation. When heater is not removing oxygen, sulfite requirement goes up—often to many times its normal level.

7. *Use the proper feedwater treatment.* Even though oxygen and CO_2 are removed from the feedwater by deaeration, CO_2 enters the steam cycle and reaches condensate-return lines in another way. Bicarbonate and carbonate alkalinity in the feedwater makeup decompose to liberate free CO_2 at boiler operating pressure and temperature. This CO_2 leaves the boiler as a gas and is absorbed by condensate to form carbonic acid. The higher the bicarbonate or carbonate alkalinity of the makeup the more CO_2 is liberated in the steam.

Basic aim of feedwater treatment is to prevent damage from scale or corrosion. This is generally handled by external treatment followed by application of internal-treatment chemicals or, in many cases, internal treatment may be all that is actually required.

Many factors have to be considered and carefully weighed before you know which type treatment will be best for a particular plant. Chemical analysis of raw-water makeup required for the boiler are paramount. Boiler pressure, type of boiler, amount of makeup, space available, initial investment required, operating cost are all part of this picture.

Treatment. External treatment, from a return-line corrosion point of view, should provide for reducing alkalinity of the makeup before it enters the feed-water cycle. Common treatment systems include: (1) hot and cold process softening (2) sodium-zeolite softening followed by acid treatment and degasification (3) split-stream zeolite (4) dealkalization by anion exchange (5) demineralization and (6) evaporation. The split-stream technique involves blending hydrogen-zeolite-softened water with sodium-zeolite-softened water, then passing the water through a degasifier.

Internal treatment for corrosion prevention involves feeding some chemical as a corrosion inhibitor. Ammonia was one of the first. Added to the boiler, this alkaline chemical evaporated with the steam, redissolved in the condensate and raised its pH. But ammonia is not in common use today because it dissolves copper in the presence of oxygen, attacks brass or bronze fittings and valves.

A class of chemical compounds known as amines is now employed. There are two basic types: a volatile neutralizing amine and a high-molecular film-forming type.

Selecting an amine for an individual plant depends on: (1) steam pressure (2) amount of steam and condensate piping in the system (3) distance to farthest point in the system (4) per cent of blowdown (5) temperature of feedwater and (6) makeup-water analysis.

Neutralizing amines in common use have low boiling points. They are alkaline in nature and very soluble in water. They behave much like ammonia, raising pH of the condensate, with one vital difference—they will not attack copper. Special feeding equipment is not required and dosage is easily controlled by making simple checks of pH on samples of condensate.

In many plants, operating conditions vary greatly at different points in the same system. Conditions like this are best handled by a mixture of these amines with different boiling and condensing characteristics.

High-molecular film-forming amines, unlike the neutralizing type, depend on the film to protect internal surfaces of steam and condensate piping. In theory this film acts as a barrier to keep acid condensate or oxygen from touching iron piping. Satisfactory results require film formation on all metal surfaces—a thin, uniform film that will not affect heat-transfer efficiency.

Because of their adhering and insoluble characteristics, film-forming treatments have been known to produce deposits in steam traps and boilers. Plants with steam turbines should add these amines to the steam after it leaves the unit. Filming amines call for their own tank and pump setup; dosage is determined by daily evaporation.

(*Source:* The material on pump maintenance is taken largely from an article entitled "Preventive Maintenance of Pumping Units by Otto M. Kristy, published in the February 1959 issue of *Journal American Water Works Association.*)

Preventive Maintenance

Preventive maintenance of a pump begins the day the pump is selected. Important considerations in choosing a pump in order to keep maintenance to a minimum are:

1. The materials selected should be capable of handling the fluid to be pumped. The materials of which the pump is made is an important factor in the initial cost of the equipment. A high initial cost for better materials to withstand corrosion, abrasions, temperature, dust, and dirt, may be much cheaper in the long run than continuous overhaul and repair of a pump made of less expensive but inferior materials. When costs of labor, materials, and production time lost are added up, it frequently is found that better materials actually begin to save dollars after a few years of operation.

2. The bearings and lubrication should be adequate with respect to ambient temperature, dust, and moisture conditions.

3. In order to handle the fluid in a correct manner, a decision should be made whether to use a mechanical seal or packing in a stuffing box. Consideration should be given as to the use of mechanical seals if no leakage from the pump is desired, if the fluid being pumped is not abrasive, and if the temperature and pressure are not excessive.

If a packing stuffing box is used, a shaft-sleeve material should be chosen that will give maximum service and will not be attacked chemically. The packing should be chosen with the sleeve material in mind, and should be capable of withstanding the chemical attack of the fluid as well as the effects of temperature and pressure.

One of the important factors in pump maintenance is the coupling alignment. Coupling misalignment can damage couplings, bearings, shaft sleeves, packing or mechanical seals, wearing rings or shafts. The vibration and noise level of the machinery will also be affected. Periodic checks should be made to determine that the alignment is being maintained.

The bearings should be carefully checked for signs of overheating. It is wise to inspect, drain, flush, and relubricate bearings during the first few months of operation in order to establish an individual timetable for bearing lubrication. The ambient temperature, the dust and dirt condition, and the humidity will make the timetable for one installation differ greatly from that of another. There may even be considerable differences in timetables between one pump and another pump in the same plant. The pump manufacturer generally furnishes recommendations covering grease or lubricating oil. Lubrication suppliers, or supply houses, can normally give advice as to what type of lubricant should be used. It may be possible to use the same lubricant for several applications, thus requiring the storage of fewer types of lubricants.

Each plant or building should set its own lubrication timetable, oil-lubricated bearings usually requiring at least daily attention and grease lubricated bearings usually requiring attention at infrequent intervals—usually every two to three months. Care should be taken with oil lubricated bearings to prevent the various fittings from leaking and allowing the oil to drop below the safety level or fill above the full line, causing too high an oil level, which will make the bearing overheat. Grease lubricated bearings must not be too full or under pressure. Excessive fullness or pressure will pack the grease in and around the balls and will prevent them from rolling. This will result in the balls sliding, which in turn will cause scoring, galling of the bearing races, and rapid failure of the bearing.

The stuffing box should be checked daily to determine that the proper amount of leakage is taking place. If a mechanical seal is being used many units will require either flushing or cooling and lubrication flows to the sealing faces. This pressure and capacity must be regulated and maintained during operation. When a stuffing box is repacked, it should be checked to make certain that the box is clean down to the base metal, and that the shaft sleeve is not cut worn. The packing should be cut to an exact length so that the ends just butt firmly. Each ring should be pushed firmly to the bottom of the box with a packing tamping tool. The joints of each ring should be staggered 90 degrees. Special attention should be paid to the water seal ring, if one is used, to make sure it is in position directly under the flushing line connection to the stuffing box. This requires the correct number of rings placed both in front of and behind the seal ring. When the packing is all installed and there is no pressure in the pump, the gland should be securely tightened to squeeze the packing out against the stuffing box wall and around the sleeve. Then the gland should be loosened to permit the packing to expand. Gland bolt nuts should be retightened only finger tight. The packing should then be ready for service.

If further adjustment is required, it is preferable to stop the pumps, drain the casing and repeat the entire process. Often, however, this cannot be done. If adjustment must be made on a running pump, the gland should be tightened only one flat of the gland bolt nut, no oftener, then once every twenty minutes. This will enable the packing to expand slowly so that it will not score the sleeve or burn the packing.

The shutdown procedure for the pump is also important in preventive maintenance. It is recommended that a gate valve be located in the discharge line. Prior to complete stopping of the pump, this valve should be closed to keep the casing filled with fluid and to prevent metal to metal contact of the wearing surfaces. A centrifugal pump should never be throttled on the suction side, nor should it be stopped by closing the valve on the suction side. These actions will prevent the fluid being pumped from entering the casing and lubricating the close rotating clearances.

If the pump is to be shut down for a long period of time, the fluid should be drained from the casing to prevent corrosion products from filling the close run clearances. Additional protective steps should be taken to prevent corrosion of bearings, stuffing box parts, and couplings. The shut down pump should be turned over slowly by hand at least once per week.

Wearing rings should be replaced when the clearance has increased to a point at which either the driving motor is overloaded or the pump is no longer capable of producing rated capacity. In general, when the clearance has increased from two to three times its original size, the rings should be replaced.

In most cases it is preferable to use factory replacement parts for a pump because this will make it possible to keep the pump equipped with parts of correct dimension, size, and material. The factory supplying replacements may also be able to recommend a change of materials or design which will make possible longer and better service.

Annual Inspection

If it is possible without jeopardizing operations, the pump and drive should be subjected to a thorough annual inspection. The inspection should cover the following points:

1. The bearings should be removed, cleaned, inspected, and replaced, if necessary.

2. The entire casing and the bearing body should be cleaned.

3. The old packing should be removed and the shaft sleeve should be inspected. Both should be replaced if worn.

4. All of the rotor parts should be inspected and replaced if necessary.

5. If a new rotor is required, it should be checked for straightness and assembled in the pump, using new gaskets where necessary.

6. The casing should be checked for pipe strain and realigned and doweled if necessary.

7. The drain, vent, recirculation, and lubrication lines should be disconnected and cleaned and flushed.

8. All gages and instruments should be tested and recalibrated.

If the service requirements will not allow taking the equipment down for an annual inspection, then the preventive maintenance program increases in importance. This program should be designed to periodically check the various items that prevent a major breakdown of the pump.

42 / ROOF COOLING

A large part of the heat load in a building is produced by the sunshine on the roof. Surface temperatures of walls are approximately equal to those of the air. If the wall temperature were 100° and the inside temperature 75°, there would be 25° F. pushing inside. Since roof temperatures sometimes are around 150° F., this would result in three times as much heat pushed in per square foot of roof area. This multiplied by the length and by the width of the plant, can often be more than half the load.

Roof cooling can make your plant or building more comfortable in which to work. Roof cooling is also recommended to cut down on air-conditioning requirements. The rate of heat flow through each square foot of roof is obtained by multiplying the overall heat transmission coefficient by the equivalent temperature differential across the roof. Values of equivalent temperature differential for sprinkled roofs are known to be only one-third the maximum of that for roofs exposed to the sun.

Keeping the roof temperature down preserves the life of the roof. If a pond is used, the roof must be drained in order to make repairs, or for painting equipment. Ponds are sometimes breeding places for mosquitoes, algae, fungus and bad odors. The pond has a heat storage effect also. An even spray is considered a much better method of cooling a roof.

Water is the most efficient refrigerant, as one pint (pound) will handle over 1000 units of heat. Melting ice handles 144 units, and Freon 12, 72 units. Therefore less than 0.04 gallons of water are needed per hour for a square foot of roof surface. Effectiveness of any system of roof spraying depends upon the quality of the installation to wet the roof. Controls should be installed for turning the water on automatically for short intervals at a time. A heavy spray or thick drops avoid loss of water into the air.

43 / WATER TREATMENT FOR COOLING TOWERS

(*Source:* Bulletin No. 47A, Allis-Chalmers Mfg. Co., Milwaukee)

As a result of receding water tables and general water shortage, industry is faced with the increasing necessity for adopting conservation measures.

Water used for cooling constitutes a large portion of industrial demands. One effective means of reducing this requirement is the use of a cooling tower. The following covers one aspect of this general field—water treatment for cooling towers.

Types of Cooling Systems

In general, there are three types of cooling systems: the *once-through* system, the *closed* system, and *recirculating* or *recycling* system.

The *once-through cooling system* is not common and finds application only where there is an abundant, inexpensive source of cool water. This system employs no cooling tower, hence no evaporation takes place, the water merely being increased in temperature and discharged to waste. It offers relatively no scale or corrosion problems and treatment, except for chlorination, is rarely used.

The *closed system* is illustrated by the "inner-cooler" or "jacket cooler" in a diesel engine installation. Water circulates through the engine jacket, absorbs heat and enters the shell and tube heat exchanger where it is cooled by the water from the recycling system, and then the cycle is repeated. In a closed system no evaporation occurs and therefore there is no concentration. Neither is the water subjected to aeration. Makeup requirements are very low and are due primarily to leakage. Little difficulty is encountered with scale unless extremely hard water is used for makeup. Since the makeup requirements are so low, zeolite softened water is economically justified. In a system of this sort, corrosion is controlled by using inhibitors which render the metal surfaces passive.

The recycling system utilizes a cooling tower to lower the temperature of the water which is then recirculated. Evaporation of the water in the tower concentrates its impurities and obviously presents a wide range of problems.

In general, difficulties arising from the use of cooling water are those resulting from the reactions promoted during the transfer of heat from a metallic surface to water in contact with this surface.

Cooling Systems Problems

Cooling system problems usually encountered are: (1) corrosion of metal surfaces; (2) inorganic scaling; (3) organic growths such as algae and bacterial slime; and (4) delignification of the wood in the tower.

Corrosion of a surface condenser to the point of leakage leads to condensate contamination with its attending difficulties. A similar situation in a diesel plant results in contamination of the water in the closed system and damage to the unit because of insufficient cooling. Failure of heat exchangers through corrosion results in forced outages and production loss.

In the case of *scaling*, a deposit of water origin adheres to metal surfaces and, because of its insulating qualities, greatly reduces the efficiency of heat exchange. In a turbine condenser, the obvious result is loss of vacuum and drop in turbine efficiency. Scaling of heat exchange surfaces in diesel engine operation causes overheating. Under these conditions, maintenance costs increase.

In addition to forming insulating layers in themselves and aggravating fouling by combination with silt or calcium carbonate, *organic slimes* may promote corrosion by forming membranes for concentration cells and furnishing a source of corrosive gases as ammonia, hydrogen sulfide and sulfur dioxide during the process of bacterial metabolism.

The action generally termed *delignification* results in a weakening of the wooden sections of the cooling tower. If allowed to progress to the point where the wood fibers separate, extensive replacement of the wood is required.

Corrosion

The large volume of water used in cooling systems magnifies the problem of completely controlling corrosion by chemical treatment.

Aqueous corrosion of iron and steel is an oxidation reaction involving the formation of iron oxides; hence, the problem is accentuated in recirculating systems which permit the cooling water to become saturated with oxygen. Further the rate of attack is greater with waters of low pH. If cooling towers are located in highly industrialized areas, the water may become even more aggressive due to the absorption of corrosive gases.

Effective protection by chemical treatment requires care in selection of chemicals and a rigid control procedure. Further, the chemical balance to be maintained should be determined not only from the limitations presented by the water supply but also by the type of metals in the cycle.

In general, corrosion may be minimized by using chemical inhibitors such as polyphosphates, silicates or chromates which form protective films on the metal surfaces.

Inorganic Scaling

Calcium Carbonate. Calcium carbonate is by far the most troublesome deposit in heat exchange systems. It normally constitutes some 90 per cent of the total deposit.

The factors controlling the deposition or solution of calcium carbonate are very complex, but depend mainly upon (1) the total calcium hardness, (2) the total alkalinity, and (3) the pH value.

The curves in Figure 43-1 represent equilibrium conditions for calcium carbonate and indicate the interdependence of these three relations at a temperature of 25 C (77°F.). In the use of the figure the two conditions of calcium hardness and alkalinity locate the point either to the right of the proper pH curve (scale forming area) or to the left of the curve (scale dissolving area). *For example,* suppose a condition indicated by point A in which the total alkalinity of the water is 100, the calcium hardness is 700 and the pH value is 7.0. In this instance it occupies a point exactly on the curve for pH 7.0. Calcium carbonate will not be precipitated from solution under those conditions.

Consider the case of another water in which the pH and the calcium hardness are the same as the first, namely 7.0 and 700, but the alkalinity is 130 as at point B. Point B is above and to the right of the curve and, therefore, calcium carbonate would be expected to precipitate. This water could be brought back to equilibrium in two different ways, either by reducing the hardness or by reducing the alkalinity. This is the reasoning used in correcting a scale forming circulating water to one which is not scale forming.

Figure 43-1 must be used with considerable reservation, however, as it represents equilibrium conditions for a temperature of 25 C (77°F.) only. At higher temperatures lower values of calcium hardness, alkalinity, and pH are necessary to avoid calcium carbonate deposits.

Calcium sulphate. Calcium sulphate deposits are formed when the calcium sulphate concentration of the cooling water has been allowed to reach too high a value. Solubility as calcium sulphate is close to 1500 ppm (parts per million), and this is usually set as a maximum permissible concentration in cooling systems. It is considerably more difficult to remove chemically than calcium carbonate for it is only slightly soluble in acid.

Magnesium compounds. Magnesium deposits are rarely found since the

Figure 43-1 / Equilibrium conditions for calcium carbonate at pH values (77°F.).

Figure 43-2 / Softening of water by lime treatment.

Figure 43-3 / Makeup compared to cycles of concentration.

necessary factors of time, temperature and concentration seldom exist in a cooling cycle.

Iron oxides. Iron oxide is occasionally found as a major constituent of a deposit. Its presence in quantity in a scale indicates deficiencies in corrosion control measures.

Scale Prevention

Scale preventive procedures fall into the following classes: (1) softening; (2) alkalinity reduction; (3) surface active treatment; and (4) deconcentration.

Softening. Softening by lime is an effective way of removing calcium bicarbonate from water. The calcium in the water and that added as lime are both precipitated by lime but it is not necessary to remove the magnesium because it does not ordinarily form exchanger deposits. As lime is added to water, the pH value increases and the removal of carbon dioxide, calcium bicarbonate and magnesium bicarbonate takes place in the order mentioned. Up to pH 8.4, carbon dioxide is neutralized and precipitated. As more lime is added, the pH value rises between 8.4 and 9.8, during which time calcium bicarbonate precipitates to the limit of its solubility. As more lime is added, magnesium begins to precipitate until a value of 10.8 is reached. After this, any further addition in lime increases the hardness due to excess calcium hydroxide remaining in solution. The water from the lime softener is supersaturated, and since the temperature will be increased in passing through the system, the supersaturation is broken by adding acid. Sufficient acid is usually added to bring the pH value below 8.2. (See Figure 43-2.)

Zeolite softening reduces calcium hardness to zero eliminating the danger of calcium carbonate deposits. The resulting high alkalinity, however, may cause delignification of the cooling tower.

Alkalinity reduction. Frequently a heat exchanger scaling problem can be overcome by the use of acid alone without any softening. The use of acid accomplishes a reduction in total alkalinity, by neutralizing part of the bicarbonate as well as reducing the pH value. This provides a more stable condition by increasing the solubility of calcium bicarbonate. In passing through the tower, CO_2 is released and the pH value increases, requiring additional acid. In practice, a continuous acid feed is employed.

Surface active treatment. One of the most effective methods of preventing precipitation of calcium carbonate is the use of surface active agents. These include certain phosphorous compounds such as metaphosphate and pyrophosphate. Several of the organic dispersives have also proved to be effective. Application can be as simple as dripping a solution into the suction of the circulating pump as continuously as possible. The hardness, alkalinity and pH values are not affected by the small amounts of treatment which are required. The usual control is to feed that amount required to maintain an effective concentration of the treatment in the circulating water.

Deconcentration. Salts will not precipitate from solution unless their solubility is exceeded. Therefore, another method of scale prevention is control of the concentration of the critical salts. This is accomplished by blowdown from the cooling tower basin.

The interdependence of calcium hardness, alkalinity, pH and temperature is shown in Figure 43-1. For any particular cooling system, if some of these values are unknown, they must be estimated. This method can be used to estimate the concentration of calcium hardness permitted before its maximum solubility is reached.

The maximum solubility limits of 600 ppm calcium hardness and 1000 ppm sulfates with a pH value of about 6.3, have been found to be applicable over a great percentage of the cooling systems observed. However, if the makeup water is zeolite softened, the sulfates can be allowed to increase above 1000 ppm since there will be very little calcium to precipitate the sulfate as calcium sulfate.

The number of cycles of concentration to be maintained in the system will be limited by either the calcium hardness or the sulfates. If the calcium hardness of the makeup water allows only three concentrations before reaching 600 ppm, but the sulfates could be concentrated four times before reaching 1000 ppm, the limit of the system will be three cycles.

The curve shown in Figure 43-3 illustrates the savings in makeup water that are gained from recycling water in cooling systems.

The greatest amount of water is saved in the first few cycles. Thereafter, increased cycling results in a smaller percentage of water saving, but greater economy in the use of treatment chemicals.

44 / CHARTS AND GRAPHS

Statistics enable a building superintendent, plant engineer, or owner of a business to secure information by which he can plan better, compare costs, number of personnel, and other operating statistics by the month, year, or any particular period. Statistics is concerned with the collection, presentation, and analysis of numerical data. Techniques have been developed which help the reader understand the significance of large groups of figures by reducing them to smaller amounts or by portraying them on charts or diagrams.

Charts

As a means of simplifying the interpretation of figure facts, graphic presentation is often used. Figure 44-1 shows a comparison of five columns representing the shareholders' equity from 1953 to 1957.

Column charts are frequently used because they are easy to construct and understand. They show magnitudes by means of upright bars or columns, sometimes expressed in terms of money, physical units, percentages, or absolute amounts.

Figure 44-1

Figure 44-2

Figure 44-3

Bar charts differ from column charts only in the fact that the bars are laid off on a horizontal scale from left to right, rather than on a vertical scale from bottom to top. (See Figure 44-3.)

Pie charts are most logically used to indicate totals and the groups into which they are divided. A protractor is used to divide the circle. Pie charts are seldom used when results for more than one year are to be shown. (See Figure 44-4.)

HOW THE PHILANTHROPIC DOLLAR IS DIVIDED

Data: U.S. Department of Health, Education and Welfare, Giving USA, The Chase Manhattan Bank

Figure 44-4   Figure 44-5

Graphs

The most popular method of displaying magnitudes over a period of years, however, is by means of graphs in which trends are shown by curves. A graph is a diagram that shows in graphic form the relation between two quantities. It may be a straight line, a smooth curve, a broken line, or an irregular curved line. Graphs are useful in engineering work, as data can be recorded in the form of diagrams. (See Figure 44-5.)

If two variable quantities are related so that a change in the value of one produces a change of the same proportion in the value of the other, the graph showing this relation will be a straight line. (See Figure 44-6.)

The graph below contains three curves showing the relation of speed, efficiency, and current to horsepower for an electric motor. (See Figure 44-7.)

1. As the horsepower increases, the speed steadily decreases.
2. The efficiency rises rapidly at first, then falls off.
3. The current increases at a rate that gradually grows more rapid.

Geographical charts can be used to show population densities, sales areas, or spot specific locations. (See Figure 44-8.)

Figure 44-6

Figure 44-7

Figure 44-8

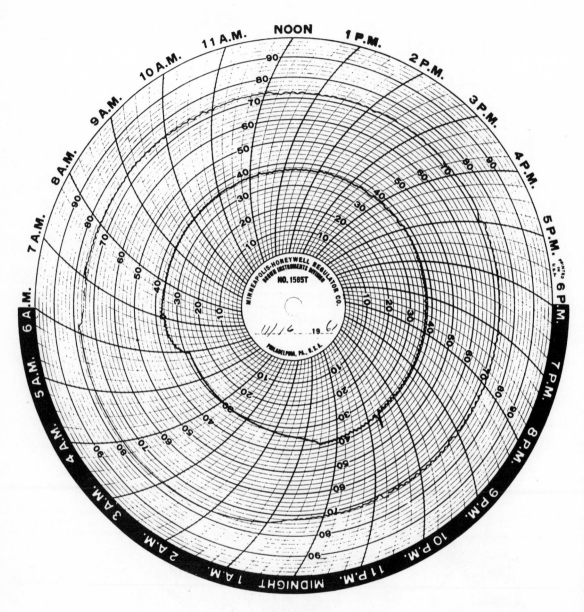

Figure 44-9

Temperature and humidity charts can be of great assistance in recording the temperature and humidity from a recording unit for all hours of the day (Figure 44-9) or week (Figure 44-10).

Many types of graph papers are available in standard stock or they can be printed to specifications.

Some useful charts and graphs to the building superintendent or plant engineer are:

Income

Expenses

Rent

Fuel

Electric

Wages

Number of employees

Truck costs

Production records

Repair costs

Attendance records

Safety records

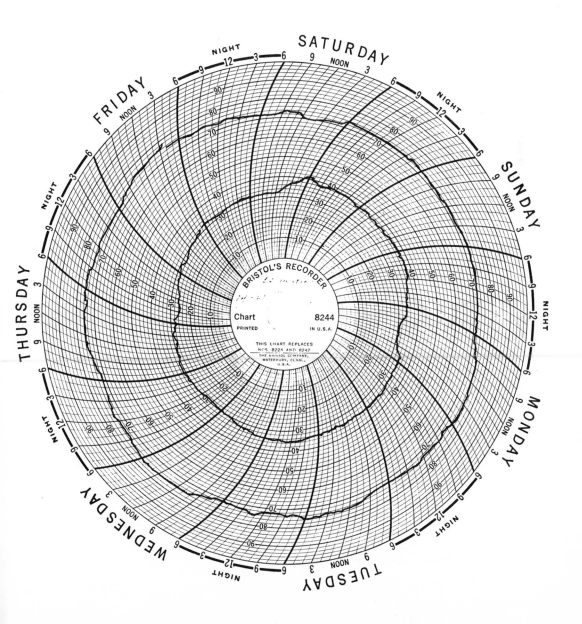

Figure 44-10

45 / EMERGENCIES AND DISASTERS

(*Sources:* Office of Civil and Defense Mobilization, Washington, D. C.; "Pre-Planning for Industrial Emergencies and Disasters" by John E. Lockhart and James A. Davis, *Plant Engineering*)

Pre-planning for emergencies and disasters is a necessity. In planning to be prepared for such occurrences, you should:

1. Insure the safety of employees.
2. Protect shareholders' investment.
3. Have direction to insure continued operation in the shortest expenditure of time.

Such occurrences may be caused by fire, power failure, explosions, collapse, flood, hurricane, tornado, freezeup, earthquake, contamination, or enemy attack. In planning for your particular situation, you should first list the emergencies which strike your building. This list may be influenced by your type of construction and geographic location. A review of such emergencies will reveal if your own or local resources are fully available and reliable. A review should be made annually. Persons responsible for drafting the plans should be made by top management, and a permanent committee formed. A good emergency plan will:

1. Anticipate probably hazardous situations.
2. Provide for speedy restoration of operation.
3. Insure protection for the employees.

An inspection of facilities should be made by the Emergency and Disaster committee to determine if personnel are obeying all underwriters' recommendations, if prevention methods are being adhered to, if personnel understand how to evacuate the building, isolate and secure equipment, and know their function in time of an emergency. When an emergency occurs with gas, electric, or water, all employees should know what to do immediately. Who should be notified, and how. Someone should be designated to assume immediate responsibility of setting the program in motion.

A thorough investigation should be made of insurance coverage, to determine if it is adequate, and that top management understands exactly what is covered. Recommendations should be made in writing if coverage is inadequate.

Committee Planning Considerations

1. Proper assessment of damage.
2. Resources on hand:
    a. personnel
    b. tools
    c. parts and materials

3. Outside Resources:

    a. utilities
    b. municipal
    c. contractors
    d. hospitals
    e. civil defense
    f. military

4. Plant security during emergency.

5. Information. A central source of information should handle all releases and interviews.

6. Welfare. A person should be designated to be responsible for coordinating food, shelter, first aid, and for securing aid from civic and governmental organizations, if required.

7. A financial advisor should be available for consultation of the emergency chief, or others.

8. Legal advisor.

9. A mutual aid organization can be formed with local companies, or local governments. An inventory of resources and facilities should be made.

10. Planning by top management for extreme situations—desirability of rebuilding, expanding, abandoning, financing.

11. Training of employees.

12. After the plan has been completed, have it typed for future reference and revision.

Emergency Lighting

Emergency lighting should be provided in key areas in order to permit orderly continued operation, or shutdown, if the main source of light power is put out of service. Such emergency lighting should be provided in control rooms, turbine rooms, boiler rooms, exit stairs, and passageways. This power supply should be completely independent of the normal source. This can be done through standby generators or batteries. The emergency luminaires themselves are the normal light units transferred to the new source of electricity as the occasion demands. The luminaires can be of low wattage, which will aid in giving greater area coverage (at low brightness level) with minimum power.

Boiler and Air Conditioning Emergencies

Consideration should be given to restoring a boiler plant or central air conditioning plant in emergencies. Plans should be made to determine if:

1. Any coverage can be secured from neighboring plants, or buildings, and the time required to adapt the system.

2. There are any units available locally, which can be used temporarily.

3. The system must be supplied with the same unit, and if it must come from the manufacturer, what is the availability of the equipment, and shipping time.

The use of mobile steam generating equipment in emergencies has proved very successful. Boilers are mounted on trucks, and can be quickly adapted to meeting an emergency. The mobile steam units are complete steam plants. It is generally only necessary to connect power and water lines to start producing steam. They carry their own water softening equipment, and usually a full day's supply of fuel oil. Sizes of the steam generating units vary from 15 to 100 hp mounted on trucks. Some trucks also carry motor generator sets. Investigation should be made to determine the nearest mobile unit location, to service your plant or building in times of emergency.

Fallout Shelter

Fallout shelter is needed everywhere. One thing is certain, if this country is attacked with nuclear weapons, our air and missile bases will be primary targets. The enemy would try to knock out our retaliatory power. He may try to destroy our cities. No one is sure how far he would go. However, it must be emphasized, that even if an enemy confines his attack to our retaliatory bases, the radioactive fallout from his nuclear bombs would threaten life in the entire country. An atomic burst on the ground sends up a mushroom cloud from which radioactive dust will fall hundreds of miles away. Fallout from one test explosion spread over 7,000 square miles of the Pacific Ocean.

Five Steps to Safety

Learn

1. Warning signals and what they mean.
2. Your community plan for emergency action.
3. Protection from radioactive fallout.
4. First aid and emergency preparedness.
5. Use of CONELRAD—640 or 1240 for official directions.

The safety of employees should be planned, in the event of an emergency attack. If safe below ground shelter can be provided, the route of evacuation should be properly posted

Shelters. You can protect yourself from fallout radiation. Any mass of material between you and the fallout will cut down the amount of radiation that reaches you. Sufficient mass will make you safe. Concrete or bricks, earth or sand, are some of the materials heavy enough to afford protection by absorbing radiation. There is about the same amount of shielding in eight inches of concrete for instance, as in twelve inches of earth, sixteen inches of books, or thirty inches of wood. In most of the country, except in areas hit by exceptionally heavy fallout, these thicknesses would give ample protection.

Buildings (plants, offices, schools, apartments) of masonry or concrete, provide better natural shelter than the usual family dwellings. In general, such buildings afford more protection than smaller buildings because their walls are thick and there is more space. The central area of the ground floor of a heavily constructed apartment building, with concrete floors, should provide more fallout protection than the ordinary basement of a family dwelling. The basement of such a building may provide as much natural protection as a specially constructed concrete block shelter recommended for the basement of a family dwelling.

The Federal Government will aid local governments to survey residential, commercial, and industrial buildings, to determine what fallout protection they would provide, and for how many people.

The problem for multi-story plants, office, or apartment buildings, is primarily to plan the use of existing space. Such planning will require the cooperation of other occupants and of the plant engineer, building superintendent, or apartment manager. The space available should be identified and assigned to those who are to use it. The plan will work more smoothly if it is rehearsed. The owner of the building may find it necessary to modify the basement ventilation, water supply, and sanitation system. Basic supplies should be stored in the basement to insure ample preparedness.

Basement shelters are one of the most common, least expensive, and most substantial. The best protection is an underground shelter with at least three feet of earth or sand above it. Two feet of concrete will give the same protection. If the shelter has an adequate door and air filter, it will give almost complete protection. Large buildings offer good protection, as their masonry or concrete construction generally makes it harder for radiation to get through. Basements, inside rooms, or corridors are safest.

The radioactivity of fallout decays rapidly at first. Forty-nine hours after an atomic burst, the radiation intensity is only about one per cent of what it was an hour after the explosion. However, the radiation may be so intense at the start, that one per cent may be extremely dangerous.

Radio reception is cut down by the shielding necessary to keep out radiation. A radio check should be made from the shelter. It probably will be necessary to install an outside antenna, particularly to receive CONELRAD broadcasts.

Lighting is an important consideration. Continuous low level lighting may be provided in the shelter by means of a four cell hot shot battery to which is wired a 150-millampere flashlight type bulb. Tests have shown that such a device, with a fresh battery, will furnish light continually for at least ten days. With a spare battery, a source of light for two weeks or more would be assured. A flashlight or electric lantern should also be available for those periods, when a brighter light is needed. There should be a regular electrical outlet in the shelter, as power may continue in some areas.

Windows. If there are outside windows, they should be shielded or blocked during an emergency.

Sanitation supplies:
   Cans for garbage.
   Covered pail for toilet purposes.
   Can for human waste.
   Toilet tissue, paper towels, sanitary napkins, ordinary and waterless soap.

If there are children in the building, disposable diapers may be necessary.

Grocery bags, newspapers, and plastic bags.

Household chlorine and DDT—five per cent solution.

Waterproof gloves.

Water and Food:

You should know:

Where to find safe water.

How to turn off water service valve.

How to purify water.

What foods to store and how to prepare them.

How to dispose of garbage.

How to dispose of human waste.

You should have:

Stored water or other liquid.

Supply of canned food.

Cooking and eating utensils.

Special foods for babies.

Wrench, screw driver, shovel, tool kit, radiation meter, fire fighting equipment.

First aid kit, and other medical supplies.

A complete analysis of supplying temporary water supply should be made. This should include a check with the local water company of other mains available, neighboring plants aiding in supply, or other sources of supply which may be located on your property or neighboring properties. (See Figure 45-1.)

Figure 45-1 ·

Supplies for Shelters

Assemble supplies, wrap them in a moisture-proof covering, and place in an easily carried box. Paste this sheet to the box cover and place the box in your shelter area.

For These Purposes	Use These	Or These	Suggested Quantity
For open wounds, scratches, and cuts. Not for burns.	1. Antiseptic solution: Benzalkonium Chloride Solution, U.S. P., 1 to 1,000 parts of water.	Quaternary ammonium compounds in water. Sold under trade names as Zephiran, Phemerol, Ceepryn, and Bactine.	3–6 oz. bottles.
For faintness, adult dose ½ teaspoon in cup of water; children 5 to 10 drops in ½ glass of water. As smelling salts, remove stopper, hold bottle under nose.	2. Aromatic spirits of ammonia.		4–2-oz. bottles.
For shock—dissolve 1 teaspoonful salt and ½ teaspoonful baking soda in 1 quart water. Have patient drink as much as he will. Don't give to unconscious person or semiconscious person. If using substitutes dissolve six 10-gr. sodium chloride tablets and six 5-gr. so-	3. Table salt.	Sodium chloride tablets, 10 gr., 50 tablets in bottle.	1 box.
	4. Baking soda.	Sodium bicarbonate or sodium citrate tablets, 5 gr., 50 tablets in bottle.	3–10 oz. boxes.

SUPPLIES FOR SHELTERS (*Continued*)

For These Purposes	Use These	Or These	Suggested Quantity
dium bicarbonate (or sodium citrate) tablets in 1 qt. water.			
For a sling; as a cover; for a dressing.	5. Triangular bandage, folded 37 by 37 by 52 in., with 8 safety pins.	Muslin or other strong material. Cut to exact dimensions. Fold and wrap each bandage and 2 safety pins separately in paper.	16 Bandages.
For open wounds or for dry dressings for burns. These are packaged sterile.	6. Eight medium first aid dressings, folded sterile with gauze enclosed cotton pads, 8 in. by 7½ in. Packaged with muslin bandage and 4 safety pins.	a) Eight emergency dressings 8 in. by 7½ in. in glassine bags, sterilized. One roller bandage, 2 in. by 10 yds. b) Four large sanitary napkins, wrapped separately and sterilized. One roller bandage, 2 in. by 10 yds.	As indicated.
For open wounds or for dry dressings for burns. These are packaged sterile.	7. Eight small first aid dressings folded, sterile with gauze enclosed cotton pads and gauze bandage, 4 in. by 7 in.	2 doz. sterile gauze pads in individual packages, 3 in. by 3 in. One roller bandage, 1 in. by 10 yds.	As indicated.
For eyes irritated by dust, smoke, or fumes. Use 2 drops in each eye. Apply cold compresses every 20 minutes if possible.	8. Eye drops.	Bland eye drops sold by druggists under various trade names.	4–10 oz. bottles with dropper.
For splinting broken fingers or other small bones and for stirring solutions.	9. 2 doz. tongue blades, wooden.	Shingles, pieces of orange crate, or other light wood, cut to approximately 1½ in. by 6 in.	As indicated.
For purifying water when it cannot be boiled. (Radioactive contamination cannot be neutralized or removed by boiling or by disinfectants.)	10. Water purification tablets, Iodine (trade names— Globaline, Bursoline, Potable Aqua) Chlorine (trade name—Halazone).	Tincture of iodine or iodine solution (3 drops per quart of water) Household bleach (approx. 5% available chlorine) 3 drops per quart of water.	Tablets— Bottle of 200 or 500. Liquid— Three small bottles.
For bandages or dressings: Old soft towels and sheets are best. Cut in sizes necessary to cover wounds. Towels are burn dressings. Place over burns and fasten with triangular bandage or strips of sheet.	11. Large bath towels.		8
	12. Small bath towels.		8
	13. Bed sheet.		4

Supplies for Shelters (*Continued*)

For These Purposes	Use These	Or These	Suggested Quantity
Towels and sheets should be laundered, ironed, and packaged in heavy paper. Relaunder every 3 months.			
For administering stimulants and liquids.	14. Paper drinking cups.		100-200
Electric lights may go out. Wrap batteries separately in moisture-proof covering. Don't keep in flashlight.	15. Flashlight.		4
	16. Flashlight batteries.		12
For holding bandages in place.	17. Safety pins, 1½ in. long.		4 Doz.
For cutting bandages and dressings, or for removing clothing from injured body surface.	18. Razor blades, single edge.	Sharp knife or scissors.	12
For cleansing skin.	19. Toilet soap.	Any mild soap.	1 Doz.
For measuring or stirring solutions.	20. Measuring spoons.	Inexpensive plastic or metal.	3 sets
For splinting broken arms or legs.	21. 3 doz. splints, plastic or wooden, ⅛ to 1¼ in. thick, 3½ in. wide by 12 to 15 in. long.	A 40-page newspaper folded to dimensions, pieces of orange crate sidings, or shingles cut to size.	As indicated.

First Aid

First aid training should be given to occupants of the building or plant. Six persons in every hundred should be formally trained. The American National Red Cross has a Standard First Aid Course in which they will instruct your personnel. Emergency portable first aid kits should be kept, and their responsibility assigned to persons for resupply and delivery to the scene of an emergency or disaster. Six emergency actions to save lives until medical help arrives are:

1. Keep the injured person lying down, with his head level with the rest of his body unless he has a head injury. In that case, raise his head slightly. Cover him and keep him warm.

2. Do not move the injured person except to remove him from fire, flood, smoke, or anything that would further endanger his life.

3. Examine the injured person to determine whether emergency action is necessary. If he is not in danger of bleeding to death, or is not in shock, it is better for the untrained person to leave him alone.

4. Do not give an unconscious or semiconscious person anything to drink.

5. Do not let an injured person see his wounds.

6. Reassure him and keep him comfortable.

For bleeding. Take this emergency action. Apply pressure directly over the wound. Use a first aid dressing, clean cloth, or even the bare hand. When bleeding has been controlled, add extra layers of cloth and bandage firmly. Do not remove the dressing. If the wound is in an arm or leg, elevate it with pillows or substitutes. Do not use a tourniquet except as a last resort.

For burns. Remove clothing covering the burn unless it sticks. Cover the burned area with a clean dry dressing or several layers of cloth folded into a pad. Apply a bandage over the pad, tightly enough to keep out the air. Do not remove the pad. *Do not use grease, oil, or any ointment* except on a doctor's order. On *chemical burns*, such as caused by acid or lye, wash the burn thoroughly with water before covering with a dry dressing.

For broken bones. Unless it is absolutely necessary to move a person with a broken bone, do not do anything except apply an ice bag to the injured area to relieve pain. If you must move him, splint the broken bone first so the broken bone ends cannot move. Use a board, thick bundle of newspapers, even a pillow. Tie the splint firmly in place above and below the break, but not tightly enough to cut off circulation. Use layers of cloth or newspapers to pad a hard splint.

Broken bones in the hand, arm, or shoulder should be supported by a sling after splinting. Use a triangular bandage or a substitute such as a scarf, towel, or torn width of sheet and tie the ends around the casualty's neck. Or place his forearm across his chest and pin his sleeve to his coat. In this way the lower sleeve will take the weight of the injured arm.

If you suspect a broken neck or back do not move the casualty except to remove him from further danger that may take his life. If you must move the casualty, slide him gently onto a litter or a wide, rigid board. Then leave him alone until trained help arrives.

If a bone has punctured the skin, cover the wound with a first aid dressing or clean cloth and control bleeding by hand pressure.

For shock. Shock may result from severe burns, broken bones, or other wounds, or from some acute emotional disturbance. Usually the person going into shock becomes pale. His skin may be cold and moist. His pulse may be rapid. He may become wet with sweat. He may become unconscious.

Keep the casualty lying down. His head should be level or lower than his body unless he has a head injury. In the latter case his head should be raised slightly. Wrap the casualty warmly but do not permit him to become overheated. Try to avoid letting him see his injury. If he is able to swallow, give him plenty of water to drink, with salt and baking soda added. Mix one teaspoonful of salt and one-half teaspoonful of baking soda to one quart of water. This will help to prevent severe shock.

Do not give anything by mouth to a person who is vomiting, is unconscious, or semiconscious, or has an abdominal wound.

For suffocation. Suffocation can result from pressure on the neck or chest, contact with a live electric wire, drowning, or breathing-in foreign substances such as liquids, smoke, or gas. The usual signs of suffocation are coughing and sputtering or other difficulty in breathing. As breathing becomes difficult or stops, the face may turn purple and lips and fingernails become blue. Unconsciousness will follow quickly unless you act at once.

First, remove the person from the cause of suffocation. If he is in contact with a live wire, do not touch him. Shut off the current if you can. If not, stand on a piece of dry wood or on paper, and remove the wire from the person with a long dry stick or other nonmetallic object.

If the person is in a room filled with gas, smoke, or water, get him out quickly. Remove any objects from his mouth or throat that may obstruct breathing. Then apply artificial respiration immediately, as follows:

Artificial respiration. *Mouth-to-mouth or mouth-to-nose method.* Tilt the head back so the chin is pointing upward, and pull or push the jaw into a jutting-out position. (These maneuvers should relieve obstruction of the airway by moving the base of the tongue away from the back of the throat.)

Open your mouth wide and place it tightly over the casualty's mouth. At the same time pinch the casualty's nostrils shut or close the nostrils with your cheek. Or close the casualty's mouth and place your mouth over the nose. Blow into his mouth or nose. (Air may be blown through the casualty's teeth, even though they may be clenched.) The first blowing efforts should determine whether or not obstruction exists.

Remove your mouth, turn your head to the side, and listen for the return rush of air that indicates air-exchange. Repeat the blowing effort. For an adult, blow vigorously at the rate of twelve breaths per minute. For a child, take relatively shallow breaths appropriate for the child's size, at the rate of about twenty per minute.

If you are not getting air-exchange, recheck the head and jaw position. If you still do not get air-exchange, quickly turn the casualty on his side and administer several sharp blows between the shoulder blades in the hope of dislodging foreign matter. Again sweep your fingers through the casualty's mouth to remove any foreign matter.

Those who do not wish to come in contact with the person may hold a cloth over the casualty's mouth or nose and breathe through it. The cloth does not greatly affect the exchange of air.

Mouth-to-mouth technique for infants and small children. If foreign matter is visible in the mouth, wipe it out quickly with your fingers or a cloth wrapped around your fingers.

Place the child on his back and use the fingers of both hands to lift the lower jaw from beneath and behind, so that it juts out.

Place your mouth over the child's mouth and nose, making a relatively leakproof seal and breathe into the child, using shallow puffs of air. The breathing rate should be about twenty per minute.

If you meet resistance in your blowing efforts, recheck the position of the jaw. If the air passages are still blocked, the child should be suspended momentarily by the ankles or inverted over one arm and given two or three sharp pats between the shoulder blades, in the hope of dislodging obstructing matter.

Other manual methods of artificial respiration. Persons who cannot, or will not, use the mouth-to-mouth or mouth-to-nose method of artificial respiration should use another manual method. The nature of the injury in any given case may prevent the use of one method, while favoring another. Other methods suggested for use by the American Red Cross are: "The Chest Pressure-Arm Lift Method" (Holger-Nielsen).

When performing any method of artificial respiration, remember to time your efforts to coincide with the casualty's first attempt to breathe for himself.

Be sure that the air passages are clear of all obstructions, that the casualty is positioned in a manner that will keep the air passages clear, and that air is forced into the lungs as soon as possible.

If vomiting occurs, quickly turn the casualty on his side, wipe out his mouth, and reposition him.

When the casualty is revived, keep him as quiet as possible until he is breathing regularly. Loosen his clothing, cover him to keep him warm, then treat him for shock.

Whatever method of artificial respiration you use, it should be continued until the casualty begins to breathe for himself, or until there is no doubt that the person is dead.

To move injured person. Do not move an injured person except to prevent further injury or possible death. If you must move him, keep him lying down flat. Move him on a wide board, such as an ironing board or door, and tie him to it so he will not roll off.

If you have nothing to carry him on, get two other persons to help carry the casualty. You must kneel together on the same side of the casualty and slide your hands under him gently; then lift him carefully, keeping his body level. Walk in step to prevent jarring, and carry him only far enough to remove him from danger.

Reference Material

Medical publications. Any one of the following publications from a list provided by the Bureau of Health Education of the American Medical Association would be helpful when a physician is not available.

What to Do Until the Doctor Comes
> Wilham Bolton, M.D., 145 pp., Cloth, $2.00 (Reilly & Lee Co., 325 West Huron St., Chicago, Illinois)

Book of Health "A Medical Encyclopedia for Everyone"
> Randolph Lee Clark, M.D., 768 pp., 1,400 illustrations, Cloth, $10.00 (Elsevier Press Inc., 402 Lovett Blvd., Houston 6, Texas)

Ship's Medicine Chest and First Aid at Sea
> U.S. Public Health Service and War Shipping Administration, 498 pp., illustrated, $3.50 (U.S. Government Printing Office, Superintendent of Documents, Washington 25, D.C.)

Office of Civil and Defense Mobilization (OCDM) publications. The following OCDM publications can be requested through your local civil defense director, or purchased from the Superintendent of Documents, U.S. Government Printing Office, Washington 25, D.C. at nominal cost:

Civil Defense Preparedness, G.P.O. 825110

Fire Fighting for Householders, PA-B-4, revised May 1958, reprinted June 1959

First Aid: Emergency Kit, Emergency Action, L-2-12, revised April 1958, reprinted June 1959

Handbook for Emergencies, 1958

What do Do Now About Emergency Sanitation at Home, H-11-1, revised August 1958, reprinted December 1958

What You Should Know About Radioactive Fallout, PA-B-7, revised May 1958

Facts About Fallout Protection, L-18

OCDM films. The following films are available through state civil defense offices or regional headquarters of the Office of Civil and Defense Mobilization:

Bombproof
Crisis
Day Called "X", The
House in the Middle, The
New Family in Town
Operation Ivy
Rehearsal for Disaster
Time of Disaster
To Live Tomorrow

Red Cross Films. The following first aid films can be obtained through your local Red Cross chapter:

Easy Does It
First Aid
First Aid for Burns in Civil Defense

Educational material can be secured and passed out to all employees, especially a small wallet sized card, "Civil Defense Preparedness" G.P.O.* 825110, and training programs should be conducted to test your program, and coordination of employees and building occupants.

* Government Printing Office.

46 / **FIRE PROTECTION**

(*Sources:* "Safety Rules for Flammable Drum Storage Rooms," The Protectoseal Co., Chicago; *Buildings* magazine, *Third Annual Handbook of Building Operation,* pp. 104-105; *FIA Sentinel;* chart, "Use the Proper Extinguisher," reprinted with the permission of the Factory Insurance Association)

The object of fire protection is to safeguard life and property. The building should be of such construction that it will limit the progress and spread of any fire, with provisions made for the installations of alarms, sprinkler systems, and other fire fighting equipment.

Fire protection should be given proper consideration from the beginning of design to insure the best protection of its occupants, and possible substantial savings in insurance costs. Fire is likely to create panic. We cannot eliminate panic, however the conditions from which it is likely to arise, whether we occupy a new or old building or plant, can be avoided. Exits should be adequate, well-placed, marked properly, and built of material that will be fire resistant if fire strikes. Good fire prevention and protection facilities do not just happen. They have to be carefully planned, and this is accomplished most effectively when a new building is being planned or renovations made. Fire insurance companies generally maintain a staff to aid with fire protective problems and construction considerations.

The use of fireproof and fire resistant materials in a building prevents loss of life, property and inventories. It is instrumental in the preservation of employment. Because initial cost is sometimes prohibitive, all buildings are not made of fireproof or fire resistant materials. Insurance payments received as a result of fire losses are rarely adequate to cover the cost of new construction due to increased cost, for the loss of income incurred while a building is being reconstructed, or from loss of business resulting in diverting customers to new sources of supply in time of emergency. Capital is invested in buildings with the thought of securing a permanent and continuing income. For these reasons, fireproof and fire resistant materials must be considered in new construction, renovations, or when new equipment is purchased that requires the use of special building materials. A building may be considered fireproof of fire resistant, but its contents will generally burn.

Fires may occur in a fireproof building as a result of ignition of flammable materials which may be stored in the building. Therefore, it is imperative that these materials be stored properly, and a constant check made on their proper use. If we eliminate the *cause,* we will not be left with the *effects* of a fire.

It is important to know the various classes of fires, the type of extinguishing agent to use, and the capabilities of extinguishers. *Use the proper fire extinguisher.* (See Figure 46-1.)

The prime requisite for the protection of a building from the ravages of combustion, is a modern and efficient fire protection system. This system should incorporate fire detection devices, automatic and manual extinguishing systems, and manual fire alarm boxes.

The greatest bulwark of modern fire protection is the automatic sprinkler system. Properly installed, sprinkler systems will extinguish a fire quickly, or they will control the spread of a fire.

Types of Sprinkler Systems

Wet pipe system. The entire system is filled with water under pressure. Water is maintained to the sprinkler head, where a plug will melt at a low temperature and releases the water immediately. The wet pipe system should only be used in areas protected against freezing temperatures.

Dry pipe system. The pipe contains compressed air extending from the sprinkler head to a dry pipe valve. When the fuseable plug melts, the air pres-

USE THE PROPER EXTINGUISHER

CHART OF TYPICAL FIRE EXTINGUISHERS

TYPE OF EXTINGUISHER		Water pails (with or without cask or drum)	Pump Tank	Water Type	Soda and Acid	Anti-Freeze: Calcium Chloride	Anti-Freeze: Loaded Stream	Foam	Dry Chemical‡	Liquefied Gas: Carbon Dioxide	Liquefied Gas: Freon 1301	Vaporizing Liquid††
SUITABLE FOR — CLASS A	Wood Paper Cloth	YES	YES	YES	YES	YES	YES	YES	Only with ABC powders.	No, except very small fires.	No, except very small fires.	No, except very small fires.
SUITABLE FOR — CLASS B	Flammable Liquids	NO	NO	NO	NO	NO	YES	YES*	YES	YES	YES	YES
SUITABLE FOR — CLASS C	Electrical Equipment	NO†	NO†	NO†	NO†	NO†	NO†	NO†	YES	YES	YES	YES
SUITABLE FOR — CLASS D	Combustible Metals	NO	NO	NO	NO	NO	NO	NO	Special Powders	NO	NO	NO
Composition of extinguishing material		Water with or without calcium chloride.	Water with or without calcium chloride.	Water	Water with products of sodium bicarbonate solution and sulphuric acid reaction.	Water with dissolved calcium chloride and corrosion inhibitor.	Water with dissolved potassium carbonate and special salts.	Foam from reaction of aluminum sulphate and sodium bicarbonate solutions with foam stabilizer.	Usually powdered compounds of sodium or potassium bicarbonate or ammonium phosphate base. Other formulations available for special hazards.	Carbon dioxide as gas and snow.	Monobromotrifluoromethane as gas.	Carbon Tetrachloride specially treated with corrosion inhibitor and freezing point depressant.
Principal extinguishing effect		Quenching	Quenching	Quenching	Quenching	Quenching	Quenching or Smothering	Smothering	Smothering	Smothering	Smothering	Smothering
Method of operating		Throw	Pump	Invert and bump on floor, or trigger type.	Invert	Invert and bump on floor, or trigger type.	Invert and bump on floor, or trigger type.	Invert	Invert and bump on floor, also plunger valve, or trigger type.	Valve, or trigger type.	Trigger type.	Pump, valve, or trigger type.
Means of expelling extinguishing agent		Throw	Hand Pump	Carbon dioxide cartridge, or stored pressure.	Chemical reaction to form carbon dioxide.	Carbon dioxide cartridge, chemical reaction, or stored pressure.	Carbon dioxide cartridge, or stored pressure.	Chemical reaction to form carbon dioxide.	Carbon dioxide cartridge or stored pressure.	Under pressure in extinguisher.	Under pressure plus stored pressure.	Hand pump or stored pressure.
Effective range		5-10 feet	30-40 feet	30-40 feet	30-40 feet	30-40 feet	30-40 feet	30-40 feet	5-20 feet	3-8 feet	4-6 feet	20-30 feet
Approximate duration of discharge at room temperature		Variable	5 gal.-2 minutes; 2½ gal.-1 minute	2½ gal.-1 minute	2½ gal.-1 minute	2½ gal.-1 minute	2½ gal.-1 minute	5 gal.-1 minute; 2½ gal.-1 minute	10-20 seconds	10-20 seconds	10 seconds	¾-1 minute
Approximate Weight fully charged		25-30 lbs.	2½ gal.-35 lbs.; 5 gal.-65 lbs.	2½ gal.-35 lbs.	2½ gal.-35 lbs.	2½ gal.-35 lbs.	2½ gal.-35 lbs.	2½ gal.-35 lbs.; 5 gal.-70 lbs.	12 lb.-40 lbs.; 20 lb.-55 lbs.	7½ lb.-35 lbs.; 15 lb.-50-60 lbs.; 20 lb.-55-75 lbs.	7 lbs.	1 qt.-7 lbs.; 1 gal.-25-35 lbs.; 3 gal.-75 lbs.
Requires protection from freezing		Yes, unless calcium chloride solution is used.	Yes, unless calcium chloride solution is used.	YES	YES	NO	NO	YES	NO	NO	NO	NO
Maintenance req.: Semi Annual / Annual; Pressure Test: *5 years, **10 years, ***12 years		None. Empty and refill	None. Inspect, partly discharge, refill and tag.	Weigh cartridge, recharge water and tag. Inspect pressure gauge. *	None. Discharge, refill and tag.	Weigh cartridge, restore liquid and tag. Inspect pressure gauge. *	Weigh cartridge, restore liquid and tag. Inspect pressure gauge. *	None. Discharge, refill and tag.	Weigh cartridge and tag. Inspect pressure gauge. *	Weigh and tag. ***	Weigh and tag.	None. Inspect, partly discharge, refill and tag. Inspect pressure gauge.

† Fires in electrical equipment can be safely attacked with extinguishers of this type ONLY AFTER electric current has been cut off.

* A special type foam should be used for "Polar Solvents" (alcohol, acetone, ketone, etc.).

‡ Effective for initial attack on fires in combustible fibers but should be followed up with fine water spray.

Should not be used where open low voltage contacts are employed.

CALCIUM CHLORIDE SOLUTIONS (Calcium chloride furnished by extinguisher manufacturers contains a corrosion inhibitor)

Freezing Temperature	Water		Calcium Chloride
10° F.	2 gals.	1 qt.	5 lbs.
Zero F.	2 gals.	1 pt.	6¼ lbs.
10° below zero F.	2 gals.		7 lbs. 6 oz.
20° below zero F.	2 gals.		8 lbs. 6 oz.
30° below zero F.	2 gals.		9 lbs. 2 oz.
40° below zero F.	2 gals.		10 lbs.

Specific Gravity	Degrees Baumé
1.139	17.7
1.175	21.6
1.205	24.7
1.228	26.9
1.246	28.5
1.263	30.2

FACTORY INSURANCE ASSOCIATION
HARTFORD   CHICAGO   SAN FRANCISCO

†† Extinguishers of this type should not be used in the vicinity of equipment which may be affected by the highly corrosive vapors resulting from the toxic effect of gases or vapors generated by the use of this liquid, special precautions MUST BE TAKEN to avoid breathing these vapors particularly in confined or unventilated spaces.

Form No. N-80 Ed-63

Figure 46-1 / Typical chart of available fire extinguishers. (This chart, "Use the Proper Extinguisher," is reprinted with the permission of the Factory Insurance Association.)

sure will drop and water will flow through the sprinkler head. This system can be used in cold areas, however, the dry pipe valve itself must be located in a heated area in order to prevent freezing.

Preaction system. The pipe contains air, which may or may not be under pressure, and the water is held back by an automatic valve operated by a heat actuated device, which is generally more sensitive than the normal automatic sprinkler. These devices open the valve to allow water to flow into the pipes before the fuseable element of the sprinkler head melts. This sounds an alarm, which sometimes permits employees to extinguish the fire with portable units prior to the melting of the heads.

Deluge system. This system is used where unusual fire hazards exist and where large quantities of water are needed quickly over large areas. All heads are open, and water is held from the system by valves which opened either manually or automatically by heat actuated devices.

Combined dry pipe and preaction sprinkler system. This system employs automatic sprinklers attached to a piping system containing air under pressure, with a supplemental heat responsive system of generally more sensitive characteristics than automatic sprinklers installed in the same area.

Carbon dioxide systems. Carbon dioxide, the colorless, odorless, heavier-than-air gas, has proved its value for extinguishing fires in electrical equipment, gasoline, oil, grease, and paints. Since carbon dioxide fire extinguishment leaves no residue, production can usually be resumed immediately. Fixed pipe systems, which vary in size from a few pounds of gas to many tons, provide means of rapid application of the gas to a fire.

Gas for *high pressure systems* is stored in steel cylinders of 50, 75, and 100 pounds, capacity at approximately 850 psi at normal room temperature. Gas for low pressure systems is stored in refrigerated tanks at 0°F. and 300 psi. Tank sizes vary from one ton to one hundred and twenty-five tons.

Local application systems are designed to apply gas directly to a burning surface—the carbon dioxide extinguishing the fire by separating the flame from the surface supplying the combustible vapor, sometimes for only a few seconds. This action is commonly called "smothering the fire," and dilutes or displaces combustion air at the burning surface with the inert carbon dioxide. A *total flooding system* is designed to flood an enclosure with gas to reduce the oxygen percentage of the atmosphere below that needed to sustain combustion. *Extended discharge systems* are designed to continue gas discharge for the maintaining of a proper concentration until extinguishment is accomplished.

Carbon dioxide systems are usually automatic in operation with actuation by fixed-temperature thermostats, rate-of-rise (temperature) releases, or smoke detectors. It is always desirable to have separate reliable means of manual operation for use should the automatic system fail. Some merits of carbon dioxide systems are quick clean extinguishment on special hazard fires.

Automatic sprinklers are used to "back up" carbon dioxide systems because of the supply limitations of such systems, the more complicated release devices required, and the severity of hazards to be protected. As with any mechanical equipment a carbon dioxide system must receive periodic maintenance, preferably semiannually.

Automatic sprinkler alarms. Nearly all automatic sprinkler systems include an *alarm* which is operated by the flow of water, which operates a water alarm or sets off an electric alarm. Both systems can be connected to ring a bell, and the electric can be connected to a local fire alarm system. This type of system insures immediate notification of the local fire department.

Standpipe systems are another form of protection. This is generally a vertical pipe located in the stairtower or in some other central point in a building. Hose is connected on a swinging rack or reel to be used in case of fire. A control valve is located at each hose station and should be checked once a week. The water should be tested through the hose once every six months.

In large office buildings, plants, schools, or stores, this testing may be more convenient during the evening hours. In high buildings, the city water pressure is not always sufficient to supply water to upper stories and auxiliary pumps or tanks are often required to make the standpipe system operative for these stories. Pumps should be checked once every six months, and also placed on a periodic maintenance schedule.

Manual fire alarm boxes should be installed in prominent locations. They should have distinct instructions on them. An adequate number of fire extinguishers for given areas should be visible to the eye.

Sprinkler heads will accumulate dust. Generally, cleaning once each year will be sufficient. Extreme care must be taken not to trip one of the heads. A competent employee should be selected to accomplish this job. A small portable vacuum, or a small paint pail and a new paint brush may be used to remove the dust.

Auxiliary battery systems should be installed to set off fire alarms in the event of an electric power failure. These batteries should be tested once a month, and water added if required.

To insure that a fire protection system is completely operative, a weekly inspection of pressures, alarms, position of all valves, condition of equipment, and the accessibility of all valves and equipment should be made weekly.

All *hydrants* should be pressure tested once per year, along with the hoses. The drip valve is an important part of any hydrant. In most hydrants, the drip valve is designed to drain the entire barrel down to the level of the valve seat. This valve is generally a solid brass casting, leather faced, and works as a slide valve. This drip arrangement closes tight generally on the second turn in opening. It is not necessary to open the hydrant wide open to close the drip. In areas where a hydrant cannot drain automatically, the drip valve opening can be plugged in factory assembly at request. It is then necessary to pump the water from the hydrant barrel in freezing temperatures. Be sure to drain the hydrants every fall to prevent freezing and breaking. Antifreeze is sometimes added to the hydrant barrel during the fall, after draining or pumping, to insure protection.

Fire Prevention Procedure

Fire prevention is a year-round activity which is the responsibility of the building superintendent or plant engineer. A fire committee should be formed and must have the support of top management. The committee should be headed by one or two fire marshals. Zone marshals should be appointed for each zone into which the building should be divided. A sufficient number of wardens should be appointed in each fire zone to assist the zone marshals.

A weekly fire inspection report should be made by the building superintendent or plant engineer when the inspection is made. Conditions should be noted and corrective action taken if required.

WEEKLY INSPECTION OF FIRE PROTECTION EQUIPMENT

Date ....

No.		Remarks
1	Two outside sprinkler valves separating direction of flow around building.	Open Shut
2	Sprinkler valve outside security area. Pump pressure inside. Alarm setting.	Open Shut Satisfactory Checked
3	Sprinkler valve outside warehouse. Pump pressure inside. Alarm setting.	Open Shut Satisfactory Checked
4	Sprinkler valve outside treasurer's dept. Pump pressure inside. Alarm setting.	Open Shut Satisfactory Checked
5	Sprinkler valve outside IBM room. Pump pressure inside. Alarm setting.	Open Shut Satisfactory Checked
6	Sprinkler valve outside of boiler room. Pump pressure inside. Alarm setting.	Open Shut Satisfactory Checked
7	Inspection of hose house and hydrant next to boiler room.	Checked
8	Inspection of hose house outside of warehouse.	Checked
9	Inspection of hose cart.	Checked
10	Report on water pressures.	Good Fair Poor
11	Condition of fire extinguishers.	Good Fair Poor

General Remarks:

Signed ....(Inspector)

The training of fire teams should be the responsibility of the building superintendent or plant engineer if the members are from his department. If personnel from other departments are appointed, they should be instructed by a trained fire expert, with several periods of practical instruction. The fire committee with the building superintendent or plant engineer, should make an inspection once per month. Recommendations should be made by the committee, evaluated, and required action taken by the building superintendent or plant engineer. The basic purposes of the fire committee should be outlined and building and plant fire rules established. Rules for each building and plant will vary. Suggested basic building or plant rules are:

1. Safety dispose of trash, scraps, and debris.
2. Keep all equipment repaired.
3. Check all fire doors. Eliminate any obstructions.
4. Check all fire extinguishers. Recharge if necessary. Replace defective parts.
5. Replace all missing or defective hoses.
6. Check valves for easy operation and tight closure.
7. Clean and dispose of yard trash.
8. Test fire pumps.
9. Keep orderly hose houses.
10. Keep a check on all outside valves.
11. Check to see that welding and cutting tags are used.
12. Inspect to see that flammables are stored properly.
13. The circuit to a machine or motor should be shut off while repairs are being made.
14. Watch the fire teams in action and grade their performance.
15. Keep important records in fireproof cabinets. Inspect after normal working hours to see that records are not left on file cabinets, desks, tables, and other places.
16. Number file cabinets in office areas according to the value of their contents, to be removed in case of fire. The most important being numbered "1", the next "2", and so on.
17. Salvage covers should be purchased to place over material or equipment to minimize water damage.
18. The committee is responsible for Fire Prevention Week Activities. (See "Fire Prevention Week Activities.")

While the inspection is being made by the fire committee, all good practices in housekeeping should be kept in mind, and all discrepancies brought to the attention of the building superintendent, plant manager, or person responsible. If building or plant rules are adhered to, the chance of a fire will be minimized greatly. Effective *fire protection* in *any* building or plant should be kept on a day to day basis. Good housekeeping and accepted mechanical maintenance practices are the foundation of any fire protective system.

Fire security is dependent on capable leadership and good organization. The action taken immediately after a fire is discovered and before the arrival of the fire department greatly influences the net result of a fire. Good planning and organization is of the utmost importance for the protection of personnel as well as the building itself. Floor plans showing the flow of personnel to fire exits should be distributed. (See Figure 46-2.) A floor plan should also be made available showing the location and types of all fire extinguishers and alarms. (See Figure 46-3.) The building should be divided into zones with a zone marshal being responsible for these specific duties:

1. Evacuation of personnel (including the physically handicapped).
2. Preservation of company property; limiting the spread of fire.
3. Training of appointed wardens and their alternates in handling of fire procedures, such as fire fighting equipment, exits, and other responsibilities.
4. Fire prevention through reduction or elimination of hazardous materials or conditions.
5. Maintain order outside the building, moving employees from roadways and away from the buildings.
6. Persons should be designated to direct fire trucks to the fire.

A minimum of two fire drills each year should be held.

If a building or a plant is shut down during vacation, the following reminders should be kept in mind:

1. Plan by analyzing watchman service for adequate coverage.
2. Clean plant thoroughly, especially hazardous areas.
3. Repair firedoors and extinguishers. Be sure all fire doors are closed.
4. Protect outside, as thoroughly as interior. Clean all debris and control grass and weeds.
5. If design permits, shut off electrical power in each plant area. Maintain only circuits necessary for activities.
6. Check all fire pumps and automatic controls.
7. Shut off fuel supplies as close to source as possible.

Safety Factors

Welding and cutting. All welding and cutting should be restricted to safe areas. This equipment should not be used in the presence of flammable vapors, liquids, or tanks which have previously contained such materials. All combustibles should be at least thirty feet away. Men should be assigned to watch for sparks, and ample fire protection equipment should be on hand, with the area patrolled for at least one-half hour after completion.

Smoking. Enforce the NO SMOKING rule in restricted areas.

Training the watchman. The watchman should know:

1. How to quickly call the municipal fire department.
2. Location of alarm boxes.
3. Others to be called in times of emergencies, names and numbers.
4. How to start fire pump, and the location of all valves controlling sprinkler systems.
5. Location of valves controlling water, steam gases, fuel oil, or other flammables.
6. Location of switches that control power and lighting systems.

Figure 46-2

Figure 46-3

7. Proper fire fighting methods, and equipment and know how to use it.

Refresher courses should be held at least once per year with written exams conducted once every six months. This will instill the knowledge required in the watchman's mind and keep it refreshed.

Electrical equipment and wiring. The practice of employing competent and well-trained electricians cannot be overemphasized. The National Electric Code, which is revised and printed yearly, should be recognized as the guide for installation of electrical equipment. A copy should be secured each year with changes noted and referred to the electricians. A check should be made to insure their complete understanding of the changes. After electrical equipment and wiring have been installed, they must be kept in good condition by periodic inspections and by providing required maintenance.

Defective wiring causes many electrical fires. Wiring is affected by overloading, vibration, moisture, corrosion, heat, and cold. These conditions weaken the insulation and can cause a short circuit, arcing, and a fire. Common causes of fires at circuit breakers are pitted contacts, loose parts, and loose connections. In an air circuit breaker, arcing can produce molten pieces of metal which can escape if the box is not tight enough, or if the cover is not well secured. In an oil circuit breaker, dirty or low oil can cause arcing, ignition, or an expulsion of the oil. Burned out motors are caused by overloading, using types not suited to operating conditions, or by too frequent starting or jogging. Heavy dust and dirt clogging the ventilator space of a motor, or improper ventilation, can cause a motor to run hot. Fires can also start from electric lamps in contact with combustibles, or by ballasts on fluorescent fixtures, which can overheat and ignite combustible materials, liquids, or vapors in contact with them.

Static electricity. Where there is moving machinery and equipment, a volume of static electricity is built up which may discharge a spark, causing an explosion or fire. Static electricity is created by friction when two substances made of different materials are brought together then separated. Paper passing over rollers on a printing machine, and a belt moving on a pulley are two examples of how static electricity can be built up. In each instance, one substance comes in contact with the other, then moves away from it. Static buildups are greater in the winter months when the air is dry. The generation of static cannot be prevented. Spark discharging accumulations can be prevented by:

1. *Grounding Machines.* These are the simplest, most practical, and effective means. This is done by connecting a piece of wire from a metal part on the machine to a water pipe, or plate buried in the ground. This supplies a path for the static to flow away from the machine.

2. *Humidification.* This can be secured by introducing a fine spray of steam into the air, or by installing humidifiers in large air handling units used for air conditioning. Small unit humidifiers for small installations may also be utilized.

3. *Ionization of Air.* This permits the static to flow out in all directions and can be accomplished by the use of gas flames.

Grounding of machinery is considered the best method. Periodic checks should be made to insure that all connections are intact, tight, and that a gap in the ground has not been made. Static discharges are extremely dangerous whenever flammable vapors or gases are present in the atmosphere.

Spontaneous combustion is one of the leading causes of plant and building fires. This is the result of improper storage of oily, solvent, or other chemically laden rags, clothes, or other materials. Ignition is produced by a chemical reaction, and starts with a slow oxidation which generates heat. This heat hastens the chemical action until it smolders and bursts into flame. The best preventative measure to stop fires by spontaneous combustion from rags or clothes containing oil, chemicals or solvents is to provide approved metal containers (Underwriters' Laboratory Approved). These cans must be emptied periodically and their contents disposed of so that they will not be a fire hazard.

Storage and handling of flammable liquids. Static electricity discharges are extremely dangerous wherever flammable vapors, gases, or combustible dust is present in the atmosphere. Conditions that cause static discharges have been discussed in the preceding paragraphs (Static Electricity). The most practical method of avoiding a fire or explosion, is by controlling the vapors and preventing them from accumulating to the amount that they become a fire hazard.

If flammable liquids, oil, or gases, are to be stored in a plant, special storage rooms should be constructed completely isolated from the main area. If an established plant has not the means of taking storage of flammables into consideration, it should be done *immediately*.

Walls, ceiling, and floors for flammable storage rooms should be of thick construction, to meet the requirements of the insurance company. They are generally made from concrete, brick, concrete block, or a combination of these materials. If iron and steel are used as supporting columns or beams, they should be covered with one or a combination of the following materials, concrete, or clay products.

The floor should be pitched toward the center of the room, where a drain should be located to carry away any spilled liquids or leaks from drums to an outside sump area. Windows should be of standard steel sash which open outward and contain wire glass. A good approved ventilating system should be installed to prevent any buildup of explosives or harmful vapors or gases. Light fixtures should be explosion-proof. The light switch and all fuse boxes or circuit breakers must be located outside the room. All entrances must be equipped with fireproof doors, and have a slightly raised sill to insure that any spills would not leave the room. Storage racks should be grounded, and provided with approved grounding accessories to accommodate all types of flammables stored. All drums with flammables should be grounded to the rack. If flammables are transferred from the drum to a safety can, the can should also be grounded. (See Figure 46-4.)

When drums are stored on racks, they should be placed on their sides with the side holes toward the top. The original cap should be replaced with a pressure or vacuum relief fitting. The pressure relief valve is used to automatically relieve excessive vapor pressures, and to close automatically to stop evaporation when the internal pressure drops below the hazard point. This fitting is generally equipped with a metal plate flame arrestor, which prevents exterior sources of ignition from igniting the vapor content within the drum. Excessive pressure can be built within the drum from the sun, or a fire, that can cause volatile liquids to expand and explode. A vacuum relief valve permits the rapid withdrawal of

GROUND DRUMS—Prevent Static Electric Spark

Figure 46-4 / Method of grounding a drum.

liquid from the drum, and maintains a balanced atmospheric pressure within the drum to permit a free flow of liquid from the drum. The greatest fire hazards occur when transferring flammable liquids from storage drums to various containers. When transferring liquids from a storage drum, a fully protected transfer pump or a self-closing faucet should be used. The pump should have fire baffles at the spout and inlet strainer inside the drum. The faucet should have a fire baffle and strainer in the spout. Both the pump and faucet should be made of nonferrous metals. The faucet should be a spring type that will dispense the liquid when depressed. Flexible hose can be attached to the faucet for containers that have small openings.

This room should be included on all watchman's rounds, to aid in detecting small leaks which may prevent a major disaster. Only trained electricians should be allowed to work on the equipment in this room, and periodic electrical inspections should be scheduled.

Storage of paints and oils. Paints and oils should be kept away from open flames and stored in metal lined, ventilated, locked closets. Carbon tetrachloride is not recommended for use in connection with electrical maintenance and should not be stocked. Trichloroethylene is a noninflammable solvent recommended for cleaning electrical parts.

Fire Prevention Week

Fire Prevention Week is observed each year during that week in which the anniversary date of the Great Chicago Fire (October 9, 1871) occurred, which destroyed an estimated $168,000,000 in property, and killed two hundred and fifty people. Despite the fact that fire prevention is a year round responsibility, this one week's observance does permit an exceptional opportunity to emphasize the extreme need for reducing the excessive destruction of property and loss of life by fire, and to re-emphasize those measures which can and should be taken.

Every building superintendent or plant engineer has a definite stake in this important project. Fire Prevention Week activities provide an opportunity for employee education through:

1. Demonstrating the fundamental causes of fire and proper method of extinguishment.
2. Revealing the cost of needless fire waste.
3. Showing what each employee can do to reduce the danger of fire in his work area.
4. Promoting a fire safe attitude.

The objectives are accomplished by:

a. Preparation of plant or building exhibits, which stress the importance of fire prevention, reporting and correcting fire hazards, turning in alarms promptly, and knowing the location and use of fire extinguishers.
b. Conducting a supervisors' training session during the week prior to Fire Prevention Week devoted to fire prevention as it applies to each supervisor's department.
c. Distribution of Fire Prevention Week folders and pamphlets to all employees.
d. Conduct demonstrations showing brigade drill, proper extinguishment methods and use of latest fire fighting equipment.
e. Presentation of fire films in the cafeteria during lunch periods.
f. Have a fire drill during the week.

The plant fire brigade should be instructed in the preparation of equipment for the winter months. Drills should be held in cooperation with the local municipal fire department. These concentrated activities make a lasting impression on employees so that the importance of fire prevention and protection during the remainder of the year is not soon forgotten.

47 / GAS MASKS

(*Source:* "The Place of the Gas Mask in Industry" by S. J. Pearce, Branch of Health Research, Bureau of Mines, U. S. Department of the Interior)

A person choosing respiratory protective equipment for a specific job or problem first should ask himself several questions:

Is there sufficient oxygen to support life?

What is the nature and concentration of the contaminent?

For how long will respiratory protection be needed?

What is the location of the contaminated area with respect to the fresh air?

How active is the wearer expected to be?

When one answers these questions, he can choose a suitable respiratory protective device—assuming he is familiar with the limitations and operating characteristics of the various types.

Gas masks are not designed to be used, nor can they be used safely, under all conditions. However, once the limitations of the gas mask are recognized, one finds that there is a range of conditions within which the gas mask can be used safely and relatively comfortably. In fact, it is the device of choice for use under such circumstances.

Limitations are not unique with gas masks; every respiratory protective device has some limitations.

1. Since a gas mask adds no oxygen to the air being breathed, it cannot be used in atmospheres containing less than sixteen per cent oxygen.

2. A gas mask is also limited to atmospheres that contain no more than two per cent, by volume, of a single harmful gas or a combination of gases (three per cent of ammonia).

3. Not all canisters will protect against all gases.

On the other hand, the gas mask has certain favorable features. The wearer is not hampered by trailing air lines; hence he can enter and leave a contaminated area through different openings. The gas mask is relatively light; its total weight, as worn, ranges from three and one-half pounds to seven pounds. It is mechanically simple and requires a minimum of maintenance. Training a person to wear a gas mask is much simpler than training him to wear the more complex type of respiratory protective devices.

There are many types of gas masks available. Some gas masks have canisters designed to protect against a single gas, such as ammonia; others protect against two classes of gases, such as acid gases and organic vapors; and the universal gas masks give protection against all industrial gases, vapors, and smokes.

Gas masks approved by the Bureau of Mines have passed rigid tests and are known to be reliable and capable of performing their intended function.

Gas masks are widely used by men in fumigating buildings and grain bins, in operating and maintaining chemical plants, in tank-gaging operations of the petroleum industry, in fire-fighting work, in plants where ammonia or other refrigerants are used, and in missile-fueling activities, to name only a few. Gas masks are generally kept in boiler rooms for general emergencies.

Gas masks should not be used as a substitute for good engineering practices, such as controlling toxic gases and vapors at the source or removing or dilution of them through proper ventilation. Hence, in industry, gas masks usually are not worn throughout the working day, but are used for short periods during repair or adjustment operations, or are kept ready for emergencies, such as fires or ruptured pipe lines.

If, after considering all the foregoing factors, you decide to use gas masks, the proper type and quantity should be purchased and the location for each mask should be chosen so the mask will be readily available when needed. It is advisable to store gas masks intended primarily for emergency use just outside the area where a gas emergency might occur. We know of instances where sudden outbursts of gas have occurred and all the available gas masks were in the gassed area and thus were inaccessible. What might have been a minor mishap became a serious matter, because the situation worsened while other gas masks were being obtained.

Training

Each person who might be called upon to use a gas mask should be properly trained in its use. The training should cover the following:

1. A discussion of the reasons for using the gas mask.
2. A description of its construction, operating principles, and limitations.
3. Instruction in the proper fitting of the gas mask to the wearer and in testing it for gas tightness.
4. Actual wearing of the gas mask in normal air while engaging in activities that would be expected in an emergency situation.
5. Wearing of the gas mask in an atmosphere containing an odorous material, such material being removable by the canister being used.
6. Instruction in the proper use and maintenance of the gas mask.

The instructor should be familiar with, and guided by, the material on the instruction card inside the lid of each gas mask case. He also should know the information given on the canister and gas mask labels.

Several important points should be observed in using gas masks:

The wearer of a gas mask should be certain that the atmosphere he is about to enter is not deficient in oxygen.

He should enter the contaminated area cautiously, and if the odor of the contaminent is noted, he should return to fresh air and correct the cause of the leakage in his gas mask.

He should always return to fresh air before replacing an exhausted gas mask canister with a fresh one.

He should be sure that he is in fresh air before removing the facepiece.

If a highly toxic atmosphere is to be entered, and there is any doubt as to the length of remaining life of a partially-used canister, a fresh canister should be used. It is dangerous to try to squeeze the last few minutes of life out of a gas mask canister.

Wherever practicable, the "buddy" system should be used. One of the far-fetched ideas is that wearing of a gas mask will offset the harmful effects of gas inhaled prior to donning the mask. The *truth* is that a gas mask would prevent inhalation of additional gas, but it would have no curative properties to overcome the effects of the gas already inhaled. Further *false* notions follow:

False Notions

1. *If a person's face is covered he is protected against gas.* This is false. The idea may sound fantastic, yet we know or cases where men have put on gas mask facepieces *only* and have entered noxious atmospheres. They found out their mistake the hard way. A gas mask facepiece alone gives no protection against harmful gases.

2. *Any gas mask is better than none.* This false notion has prompted veterans of the armed forces to use surplus or souvenir service gas masks incorrectly for protection against ammonia or carbon monoxide or in oxygen deficient atmospheres.

3. *The efficiency of the canister is the only thing to consider in a gas mask.* This is false. An efficient and effective canister is essential, but it is equally essential that the proper facepiece be used, that it be in good repair, and that it be fitted to the wearer's face in a gas-tight manner as proven by the proper tests.

4. *Conventional-type prescription spectacles, with side pieces or bows, can be worn with gas mask facepieces without interfering with the gas-tightness of the face-fit, particularly if the bows are thin.* This is also false. Many tests made by men with varying facial shapes and sizes in a gas-filled chamber have proved this to be erroneous. Two gas mask facepieces now manufactured have provisions for supporting prescription eye glasses within the facepiece, but in neither facepiece is there anything between the facepiece and the wearer's face.

5. *If a gas mask will protect against the inhalation of a two per cent gas-air mixture for thirty minutes, it will protect against a four per cent, gas-air mixture for fifteen minutes or against a six per cent gas-air mixture for ten minutes under the same wearing conditions.* This is false. It is not correct to extrapolate to concentrations higher than two per cent (three per cent for ammonia), since canisters are designed to handle this concentration of gas, but might allow some of the gas to leak through the granular fill at higher concentrations, depending on the type and thickness of absorbent. Extrapolation to concentrations lower than two per cent is correct; for instance, if a gas mask will protect against the inhalation of a two per cent gas-air mixture for thirty minutes, it would be expected to protect against a one per cent gas-air mixture for sixty minutes or a 0.5 per cent gas-air mixture for one hundred and twenty minutes under the same wearing conditions.

6. *If the canister heats up, it is no good.* Here is another false idea. In general, the opposite is true, particularly if carbon monoxide is known to be present. When the catalyst in the universal gas mask canister performs its intended function of converting carbon monoxide to carbon dioxide, heat is liberated in proportion to the concentration of carbon monoxide. With concentrations of carbon monoxide above two per cent, the heat liberated can raise the temperature of the canister high enough to melt the solder on the canister. If excessive heating of the canister is noted, it is an indication that the wearer is in a high concentration of gas and that he should proceed with greater caution. The chemical or physical absorption of other gases and vapors, including water vapor, is accompanied by the liberation of heat. The amount of heat depends on the type and concentration of gas, and the type of absorbent. If a gas mask canister does not heat up in the presence of carbon monoxide, the wearer should return to fresh air immediately and replace the canister with a fresh one.

7. *A universal gas mask canister can be used safely for protection against the inhalation of carbon monoxide until its resistance increases significantly.* This is also false. The testing of nine universal gas mask canisters that had been used or had been unsealed for some time, showed that they gave no protection whatever against carbon monoxide. Yet the inhalation resistance of six of these canisters was

essentially the same as for new unsealed canisters, and that of two others was only slightly higher. However, if the inhalation resistance of a universal gas mask canister is found to be high, the canister probably is no good and should be discarded.

8. *Universal gas mask canisters will protect against the inhalation of all types of gases for two hours or until the window indicator changes color.* False again. The two-hour limitation, and the indication of the timer or window indicator apply only to protection against the inhalation of carbon monoxide. The only way to be sure if a gas mask canister is exhausted against other gases is by detecting the odor or irritating effect of those gases in the air entering the facepiece from the canister.

9. *The head harness of the gas mask facepiece should be adjusted only tight enough to be "comfortable."* Generally false. This may be true for persons with full, fleshy faces, but it is definitely false for persons with thin faces. The head harness should be tightened until the wearer obtains a gas-tight fit, preferably by the "positive pressure" test. This test for facepiece fit is made by closing off the exhalation valve of the facepiece and exhaling gently into it to build up a slight positive pressure within it. A gas-tight fit is indicated by the absence of any outward leakage of air around the periphery of the facepiece. If leakage of gas is detected by odor or irritating effect when a person enters a contaminated area while wearing a gas mask, he should return to fresh air to readjust the head harness. Such adjustment should not be made in the contaminated area because the facepiece could be pulled away from the face in so doing and thus allow a high concentration of the gas to enter the facepiece and possibly incapacitate the wearer.

The foregoing coverage of the gas mask may seem heavy on "do's" and "don'ts". We do not want to discourage those who are using or who may choose to use gas masks. Rather, we want to reveal the facts so that, being informed, such persons can use this most useful respiratory protective device more intelligently—and consequently more safely.

48 / INSURANCE

The operation of a building can depend upon the amount of settlement received from an insurance peril. For this reason, it is important that building owners and building superintendents review annually, the type and amount of protection they carry. The amount of coverage should be adequate to present day economic standards, as values change, replacement costs fluctuate, and various times there are changes in the types of coverage available. Where values frequently change, a six-month review is recommended. A similar review of liability insurance should be made annually and statistics secured from the carrier covering claims, accident rates, severity rate, cost per accident, and statistics from similar industries for comparison. Building owners and operators should be well schooled in the types of insurance available, their use, and application.

Review coverage to determine:
1. If the description of the building in the policy is up to date, and accurate.
2. If the character of the tenancy has changed.
3. If the neighborhood environment has changed.
4. If the economy has affected the value of the building.

Periodic inspections should be made to determine if fire hazards, or other areas that may result in a major breakdown, accident or injury are inspected thoroughly.

Fire Policy Provisions

The amount of collectible loss an owner will receive, in the event of damage to his building, is related to the adequacy of the amount of insurance carried. It is therefore important that the owner and the building superintendent understand the policy provisions.

Coinsurance clause. The coinsurance clause applies the principle that if the owner insures for less than a certain percentage of the actual value of the building, he assumes part of building coverage as a self or coinsurer with the company, the owner must assume the same proportionate share of the loss. With this principle, the company requires that the insured must carry insurance up to at least 80 per cent of the actual value of the property or he will not receive the full amount of the loss. The usual coinsurance requirement is 80 per cent at the time of loss. In some instances such as a sprinklered building, the amount required is 90 per cent.

LOSS ADJUSTMENT UNDER COINSURANCE

(80 per cent clause)

A. *Insurance exceeding 80 per cent of value is carried:*

Value of property	$10,000
Insurance required	8,000
Insurance carried	9,000
Losses up to $9,000—Will be paid in full.	

B. *Insurance to 80 per cent of value is carried:*

Value of property	$10,000
Insurance required	8,000
Insurance carried	8,000
Losses exceeding $8,000—Face of policy paid ($8,000).	
Losses under $8,000—Paid in full.	

C. *Insurance to less than 80 per cent of value is carried:*

Value of property	$10,000
Insurance required	8,000
Insurance carried	5,000
Losses exceeding $8,000—Face of policy paid ($5,000).	
Losses under $8,000—Paid in proportion of five-eighths of loss.	

The following *insurable perils* should be thoroughly understood:

Fire	Windstorm and hail
Smoke	Earthquake and volcanic eruption
Explosion	Vandalism and malicious mischief
Boiler explosion	Sprinkler leakage
Robbery	Riot, riot attending, strike, civil commotion
Water damage	Aircraft and vehicles
Civil authority	Contractual liability
Public liability	Employer's responsibility to employees
Burglary	
Fidelity	

49 / MOVING

Plans for moving should take into consideration what is to be moved, the placement of·the furniture and equipment in the new location, the selection of the mover, and the date for moving. The placement of furniture and equipment should be drawn into a colored, scaled floor plan. Floors or areas can be designated by special colors—1st floor blue, 2nd floor green, and so on. A piece of colored three inch paper tape, the same color as the one designated to a certain area, should then be applied to each piece of equipment in a specified place, such as lower left hand corner. If this is impossible on some pieces of equipment, use an obvious spot. The equipment should then be numbered in the order in which it will be moved into the new location. If a truck can handle twenty-eight items (to be computed by the square footage of each item), the twenty-eighth item should be loaded first, so that the number one item will come off the truck first. If further identification is required, the floor number could be added like 2, the bay A, item number 8, or 2-A-8. The floors of the new location should be marked with the same color tape, and corresponding numbers. *Example:* Desk 2-A-8 will be placed on the second floor, bay A, and the lower left hand corner of the desk will be placed over the number 8 in this area.

If several entrances are to be used, an entrance number can be added, or a color system adapted for one story operations, having certain colors delivered to corresponding colored doors. The tape could be applied over or attached to the door. The paper tape will adhere to the desk, and is less likely to be removed or torn off. Many colors are available which aid in quick identification.

It is important to include the scheduling of delivery of new equipment in the moving plans. In some instances, it is wise to have medium sized items delivered prior to the move, to the old location, so that employees may have an opportunity to acquaint themselves with the equipment. It will also present the opportunity of ironing out any problems with the equipment and to trade in or dispose of any excess equipment.

When selecting the moving contractor, it is good practice to obtain several bids. This will ascertain having a realistic appraisal of the job and the bidding.

A direct move without transfer should be specified, and a penalty clause inserted, if the date for completing the move is not kept. The contract should also cover the contractor's liability, and responsibility for correcting damage or loss that may occur in the course of the move. Insurance certificates should be submitted for amounts of damages specified.

Employee Participation

While planning the move, the employees should not be forgotten. They have an interest in the move and should be kept informed. Good communications will help them accept the change. This can be accomplished at management meetings, or employee magazines or memorandums.

To execute a successful move, you must have departmental participation, move sequence, and coordination. One person from each department should be assigned as a contact man. This man's responsibilities should be to attend the orientation meeting, and to tag all the equipment to be moved from his department, according to the approved layout which has been prenumbered, and to assist at the receiving of new equipment, and removal of excess equipment. In orientation meetings, the contact man can become familiar with the plans, so he can answer employee questions. He can record any missing equipment after the move and report it. He will be the clearing agent for all problems and questions, so that the number of persons who would have to contact the planners, would be kept to a minimum.

Although the contractor will do the actual work, a few employees should be on hand at the old location to help him identify the items to be loaded in proper sequence, which can be figured out in a special loading layout. Other employees should be located at the new location to spot the equipment in its proper location. The spotters should be provided with the approved new location layout.

If items show up that are not on the layout, they should be placed where they fit temporarily, placed to one side, or sent to a storage area. During such a move, it is generally impossible to make layout changes.

Other items to be considered are:

1. Installation of telephones prior to the move.
2. Notification of persons supplying services such as, office machines, deliveries, and other suppliers.
3. Is a change in insurance coverage required?
4. Change of address on stationery.
5. Was there a change in the telephone number?
6. Installation of electric outlets.
7. A system of requests for study of any problems which may arise should be typed and sent forward to the planners' group for study and recommendations.

All problems should receive quick follow-up. Moving problems should be solved promptly because of the lasting impression made on the personnel. Good service will help the employees to get settled more promptly. Some problems cannot be solved immediately. A new office means a change in working habits, and some employees require time to adjust to the changes.

A good moving job requires careful attention to the objective, careful planning of all the aspects of moving, communications with the employer prior to the move, providing the services required to operate at the new location, and the follow-up after the move has been completed.

50 / RECORDS

(*Sources:* Remington Rand Systems, New York; *Plant* magazine)

Machinery and equipment records are the basic requisites for establishing a sound maintenance program, as it is necessary to have a thorough knowledge of the type of equipment you have, and which portion of this equipment will require maintenance services. Properly designed record forms will supply historical data for justification of equipment replacement, repair costs, and initial cost. Other data supplied by the record card is as follows:

1. Lists equipment lubrication requirements.
2. Records a list of spare parts that should be carried in stock.
3. Supplies engineering specifications.
4. Gives the original purchase date, installation cost, purchase order number, and other upkeep costs.
5. Provides a basic record for identifying plant assets.

In order to start any maintenance program, a physical inventory of all machinery and equipment must be made.

A simple form should be used in taking an inventory of all plant or building equipment. A number system should be initiated and a number assigned to each piece of equipment. The number should be stamped on a metal tag and attached to the unit. A "Maintenance Descriptive Sheet" should be made on every piece of equipment, then on all new equipment as it is received.

See Figure 50-1, Figure 50-2, and Figure 50-3 for examples of Maintenance Record Cards which aid in keeping machines in better working conditions to produce better work, cost controls, and less machine downtime.

Work Orders provide:

The *production department* with a record of trouble spots, frequency of breakdowns, and production time lost.

The *maintenance department* with a record of trouble areas, that additional training may be required by the operator or maintenance personnel.

The *accounting department* with information of exactly what material and time were expended to maintain or repair a machine, and aid in inventory control.

Work orders also pinpoint responsibility, improve operations, and aid in assigning work in an orderly manner.

Accurate scheduling, adherence, and adjustment through experience, operating hours, and conditions, is the key to a successful maintenance program. When schedules are adhered to, defects are generally found in the early stages, when corrective measures normally can be made in a matter of minutes. If operation is

Figure 50-1

MAINTENANCE DESCRIPTIVE SHEET

Department ....
Inv. No. ....
Purchase Data ....

Item .... Manufacturer ....
Purchase Order No. .... From ....
Model .... Serial No. .... Type ....
H.P. .... R.P.M. .... Amps .... Volts ....
Phase .... Frame .... Cycles .... Cap. ....
Other: ....

....

Spare Parts On Hand: ....

....

....

....

....

Frequency of Periodic Inspections: ....

Remarks: ....

....

....

....

permitted until the failure stage, minor defects such as slight misalignment, vibration, over-lubrication, casting flaws, overheating, and many others, may result in many hours of downtime. It can be said that preventive maintenance is the balance between theoretical requirements and practical experience. This is where records can be used in measuring the results of a program. After a piece of equipment has been in operation for a period of time, the record may indicate that inspections should be made more frequently, or may be spaced further apart, as over-inspection can prove very costly and directly defects the purpose of your program. Frequency tables should be adjusted by experience to gain maximum dollar benefit from record keeping.

Figure 50-2

REQUISITION FOR MAINTENANCE SERVICES

Department:

Description of Work:

....

....

....

(For Maintenance Dept. Use) Job. No. ....
Labor: ....
Materials: ....
Other: ....
Total: ....

....

APPROVALS

....
Department Head   Maintenance Department

Data Processing

The use of data processing equipment in handling some of the scheduling, costing out jobs, inventory control, maintenance programs, and other duties of maintenance departments, keeps administrative cost to a minimum. The maintenance employee should be instructed in filling out a data processing card, using a code number for the type of labor, and the hours worked. Similar cards are filled out when materials are drawn from the stores department. These cards are sent daily to the data processing department. The progress of the job and a comparison of estimated time against actual time can be developed from this information. After recording the exact amount of material used, inventories can be adjusted. If various departments are charged for services, this can also be determined and charged immediately. Daily progress of jobs which require several days, is easily followed. If a job appears to be running excessively high, it will be spotted immediately. The system of charging other departments for services will make operating departments more maintenance conscious, as the cost of repairs can be quickly shown.

The use of these records will aid in training others who must estimate jobs,

Figure 50-3

as estimated figures against actual figures will be readily accessible. Scheduling and preventive maintenance programs can be put on data processing equipment, and exact daily, weekly, and monthly records and reports will be easily available.

Considerations for Retaining Records

Statutory Limitations. Certain federal statutes, such as the Social Security Act, Wage and Hour Law and state statutes, require that certain records be retained for specified periods.

Business Reference Value. What is their direct value in conducting the business?

Record Copy (the original or a duplicate copy).
Temporary Value.
Legal Value.
Supporting Record.
Research Value.
Is the Record Vital?
Determination of What a Record Should Do.
Historical Value. Facts and events relating to the growth and progress of a company should be retained.

Protection of Vital Records

Vulnerability to Disaster. Flood, fire, explosion, attack, or nuclear explosion.
After the Disaster. The possibilities with which you may be confronted are:
1. Resisting unjust claims.
2. Determining accounts payable.
3. Collection of accounts payable.
4. A plan to resume vital operations as soon as possible.
5. Being able to prove the entity of the business.
6. Collection of insurance indemnity.

Recommendations. Select a minimum number of records with which to accomplish the six situations outlined above. Store these records in a separate location, keep them up to date and establish a retention schedule.

Record Storage Considerations

Location. Should be as close to the office as possible.
Size. Suitable to handle all inactive records with 25 per cent expansion allowance.
Layout. Large enough to handle storage racks and laid out to aid in removing records through retention schedule.
Ventilation. A humidity range of 55 per cent to 75 per cent is desirable, and circulation adequate to prevent a heat buildup which may cause the records to dry out.
Aisles. Should be a 30 to 36-inch width. One service aisle of five feet should be included.
Fire Protection. Maintain a rigid fire prevention rule. Sprinkler systems are a matter of choice due to the possibility of accidental discharge of a head. Fire extinguishers should be installed and clearly marked. The "No Smoking" rule should be strictly enforced, with signs posted to that effect.
Equipment. Standard steel shelving purchased to handle the particular weight of the items to be stored need not be a deluxe type. A simple style will suffice. Sturdy cardboard boxes are sufficient to hold the records. These are generally sized 10 by 12 by 15 inches.
Lighting. The installation of lighting fixtures should conform to the aisle arrangement. 20-25 footcandles are sufficient.

Figure 50-4

DAILY WORK REPORT

AREA	Broom Swept	Dry Mopped	Damp Mopped	Machine Scrubbed	Waxed	Machine Buffed	Dusted	Vacuumed	Walls	Windows	Woodwork

Indicate jobs done by "x"

Employees Assigned: ....

Date: ....

Hours: ....

Total ....

....
Foreman

Floor Load. Should be calculated according to the weight of the items to be stored, plus the weight of the storage racks, generally on a per foot basis.

Security. The area should offer safe storage from dirt, dust, fire, flooding, and unauthorized entry. If a watchman's tour is made, consideration should be given to placing a station in the area designated for security. Depending upon the nature of the records, other facilities may be installed, such as burglar alarms and outside protection service.

Reference. A reference room or area should be provided with a table, chairs, and other necessary items for personnel who come to the area to examine or search for records.

Structure. Should be fireproof or be divided from the other part of the building by means of a fire wall.

Materials. In most cases should be fireproof in the doors, roof, and floors.

Special Considerations. In planning a security area, considerations should be given to the storage of microfilm, magnetic tapes, and punch cards. These items generally require special temperature and humidity requirements. With the constant increase of these types of systems in all types of office buildings and plants, their inclusion is most desirable.

Figure 50-5

CLEANING SCHEDULE

Month ....

AREA

....

Job	*Frequency*
Broom sweep	
Dry mop	
Damp mop	
Scrub (machine)	
Wax	
Buff (machine)	

Figure 50-5 (Continued)

Dust	
Vacuum	
Walls	
Windows	
Woodwork	

Foreman

51 / **SAFETY**

Accidents do not happen, they are caused. More accidents are caused by people than by machines. The most effective means by which the accident rate may be reduced, is by preventing human error and carelessness. Accidents can be reduced by incorporating safety into every detail of a building or plant operation. Success in safety depends on knowing what an accident is, how, and why it occurred, prevention methods, and how they can be achieved. A safety program must have the approval and support of "top management". The responsibility for a safety program rests with supervisory personnel. Safety work may be carried on by line organizations, a safety director, or a committee system. Regardless of the system employed, an organization must be formed, and the following points established:

1. Scope of activity and extent of authority.
2. Time, place, and frequency of meetings.
3. Planned order of program, and mandatory attendance.

Organization Goals

To create and maintain a continuing interest in safety by *all* employees, both management and hourly.

To conduct regular inspections in order to prevent accidents, and to ascertain that all safe practices are being followed. This applies to the actual building, machinery, equipment, and occupants.

To investigate and find all facts concerning all accidents.

To make a complete analysis of the causes, and to list them.

To select the best method of correction, and to see that it is applied and continued in the interest of safe practices.

To plan for the purchase of safe equipment, covering proper guards, and to see that safety is included in the design of equipment and building layout.

To establish disciplinary procedures, and to study accident reports.

Employee Participation

The *greater* the *employee participation* in the safety program, the more effective it will be. Suggested activities for the employee are:

1. Safety suggestion system.
2. Safety campaigns and contests.
3. First aid training.
4. Safety meetings.
5. Plant fire bridges.
6. Participation on safety committees, and in organizations.

Inspection

Most accidents are the responsibility of the building superintendent or plant manager. Accidents may be prevented by discovering and eliminating the cause. He should not be the "cause" by his failure to accept the responsibility of safety and accident prevention in his building or plant. Well planned inspections, systematically applied, are an effective means of discovering hazardous conditions.

Inspection of the following items may be considered the beginning of an effective safety program:

1. Ladders and scaffolds.
2. Dust, fumes, gases, and vapors.
3. Housekeeping.
4. Stair towers.
5. Need for machine safety guards.
6. Eye protection equipment.
7. Protective clothing and gloves.

8. Methods of handling material.
9. Hand tools.
10. Cranes and hoists.
11. Elevators.
12. Grounding of electric equipment.
13. Short circuits and overloads.
14. Acids in open containers.
15. Proper storage of paints, gasoline, and other liquids.
16. Oil on floors.
17. Pressure vessels.
18. Oiling methods.
19. Slippery floors.

Many other items can be added to this list. A list of the hazards in the building should be made and checked through regularly scheduled inspections. This listing will vary for each type of building or plant, according to function each is performing.

Types of Accidents

The following list shows the various types of accidents for which a building superintendent, plant manager, or other supervisory personnel are responsible.

Type	Cause
OBJECT	Machines, electrical equipment, chemicals, and motor vehicles.
ACCIDENT	Falls, slips, drowning, to be wedged or pinned.
UNSAFE ACTS	Operation without authority. Operating or working at unsafe speeds. Making safety devices inoperative. Failure to use safety equipment. Unsafe loading practices.
PERSONAL CAUSES	Disregard of instructions. Improper attitude. Lack of knowledge. Mental deficiencies. Fooling or horseplay.
ENVIRONMENTAL	Improper guarding. Improper illumination. Defective parts. Improper ventilation. Improper dress. Poor housekeeping.

All the accidents listed and many others can be prevented through *inspection, training, proper maintenance, suitable layout, proper ventilation* and *illumina-*

tion, supervision, and *discipline.* All of *these* corrections are the responsibility of management, with the building superintendent or plant manager as their representative, being responsible for the majority of the accident causes listed.

Handling of Materials

The handling of materials is the principal single source of accidents and injuries in American industry. Twenty-five per cent of all injuries are caused from some form of materials handling. Accident analysis shows that the substitution of mechanical facilities for handling materials over manual methods, reduces accidents greatly.

Mechanical Methods:

1. Hoisting apparatus.
2. Overhead travelling cranes.
3. Conveyors.
4. Mechanical shovels.
5. Elevators.
6. Chutes.
7. Electric trucks, tractors, and hand trucks.
8. Sliding materials on skids or rollers.
9. Wheelbarrows.

Some form of hand labor is generally the cause for the largest number of permanent injuries. These injuries are generally caused by the handling of objects such as sheet metal, machinery, lumber, freight, sheet iron, and steel. Special safety *practices, training* and regular *inspections* should be devoted to these types of materials.

With mechanized handling, strain from lifting excessive loads is almost obsolete. When lifting, it should be remembered that the back is to be kept as *erect* as possible, so that the body is *over* the load. This will utilize the heavy leg muscles and places minimum tension on body parts subject to injury from lifting.

Costs of Accidents

Accidents are costly not only to employees, but to employers, the injured man, his family, and to society as a whole.

Indirect Costs:

1. Cost of time lost by injured employee.
2. Cost of time lost by other employees who stop work out of curiosity, sympathy, or to offer assistance.
3. Cost of time lost by foreman's investigations, reports, hearings, and training new employee.
4. Cost of damage to product, machinery, and building.
5. Cost of inplant medical aid not covered by insurance.

Direct Cost of Accidents:

1. Hospitalization.
2. Doctor bills.
3. Compensation.

Safety Performance

Appraisal of safety performance can be attained only by the knowledge of at least three basic items.

1. The accident frequency rate of the firm:

$$\text{Accident Frequency Rate} = \frac{\text{Number of Disabling Injuries} \times 1{,}000{,}000}{\text{Total Number of Man-Hours Worked}}$$

2. The accident severity of the firm:

$$\text{Accident Severity Rate} = \frac{\text{Number of Days Lost} \times 1{,}000}{\text{Total Number of Man-Hours Worked}}$$

3. The comparison of these rates, with other rates of the same or similar industries employing good practice.

Example: What are the accident frequency and severity rates of a firm with 90 workers averaging 40 hours a week each, if in six months, four workers were injured, and if jointly they lost 100 days from work?

$$\text{Accident Frequency Rate} = \frac{4 \text{ Injuries} \times 1{,}000{,}000 \text{ Man-Hours}}{90 \text{ Workers} \times 40 \text{ Hours per Week} \times 26 \text{ Weeks}} = 4.2+$$

$$\text{Accident Severity Rate} = \frac{100 \text{ Days Lost} \times 1{,}000}{90 \text{ Workers} \times 40 \text{ Hours per Week} \times 26 \text{ Weeks}} = 1.19+$$

A disabling injury is usually defined in practice, as one causing loss of working time beyond the normal shift, during which the injury was incurred.

Uses of Accident Rates:

1. To measure the accident experiences of departments, divisions, or firms.
2. To determine from month to month, or for any specific period, if accidents are increasing or decreasing.
3. For comparative purposes, and for accident prevention contests.

Safety Training

Unless employees know how to use it, and where it is located, safety equipment is of no use. Employees should be trained in the proper use of equipment, through instruction periods giving complete explanation and demonstration of the equipment. Each employee should be given the opportunity to use it, as the purposes of practice are proficiency and retention. The employee will learn by doing. This equipment should be identified by special signs, using specific colors, or markings placed near the equipment. The color will identify the specific type of equipment. If equipment, such as fire extinguishers, are mounted on a pole, the color code should encircle the pole, in order to make it visible to everyone in the immediate area.

When an employee is hired, it should be made certain that he understands that *all* accidents should be reported. Accident reports and records are a necessity. These records should be permanent, and based on accurate information. This form must be designed carefully, so that the safety engineer or person responsible for the safety program can interpret the record, to determine the cause of the accident. It should contain the required information for insurance companies carrying compensation risk, government organizations, industrial commissions, or the insurance carrier. The responsibility for the reporting of accidents should rest on the foreman or department head, as he is responsible for the actions of his employees. The cooperation of the individual making the report can be secured by explaining to him, that reporting absolute facts of the accident will be beneficial to his operation, and may prevent someone else from being injured.

Safety is the responsibility of every employee and employer for twenty-four hours a day, and for every day in the week. Its importance cannot be over-emphasized. An everlasting interest must be maintained by all employees. A safety organization is a *must*. It pays many dividends to the employer.

Have you checked your *accident rates lately, indirect* and *direct* costs of accidents, and *compensation payments?*

Ten Commandments of Safety for Supervisors

(*Source:* "Ten Commandments of Safety for Supervisors," reproduced by special permission of the American Management Association. Further reproduction prohibited.)

1. You are a supervisor and thus, in a sense, have two families. Care for your people at work as you would care for your people at home. Be sure each of your men understands and accepts his personal responsibility for safety.

2. Know the rules of safety that apply to the work you supervise. Never let it be said that one of your men was injured because you were not aware of the precautions required on his job.

3. Anticipate the risks that may arise from changes in equipment or methods. Make use of the expert safety advice that is available to help you guard against such new hazards.

4. Encourage your men to discuss with you the hazards of their work. No job should proceed where a question of safety remains unanswered. When you are receptive to the ideas of your workers, you tap a source of firsthand knowledge that will help you prevent needless loss and suffering.

5. Instruct your men to work safely, as you would guide and counsel your family at home—with persistence and patience.

6. Follow up your instructions consistently. See to it that workers make use of the safeguards provided them. If necessary, enforce safety rules by disciplinary action.

Do not fail the company, which has sanctioned these rules—or your workers, who need them.

7. Set a good example. Demonstrate safety in your own work habits and personal conduct. Do not appear as a hypocrite in the eyes of your men.

8. Investigate and analyze every accident—however slight—that befalls any of your men. Where minor injuries go unheeded, crippling accidents may strike later.

9. Cooperate fully with those in the organization who are actively concerned with employee safety. Their dedicated purpose is to keep your men fully able and on the job and to cut down the heavy personal toll of accidents.

10. *Remember:* Not only does accident prevention reduce human suffering and loss; from the practical viewpoint, it is no more than good business. Safety, therefore, is one of your prime obligations—to your company, your fellow managers, and your fellow men.

By leading your men into "thinking safety" as well as working safely day by day, you will win their loyal support and cooperation. More than that, you will gain in personal stature. Good men do good work for a good leader.

—CHARLES P. BOYLE

52 / SCHEDULING

One of the greatest cost reductions that can be made in a plant or building is achieved by detail planning which leads to proper scheduling. In order to prevent interruptions in production schedules due to breakdown in machines or building facilities, maintenance work of a preventive nature to eliminate failure of machines or equipment through lack of repair or attention must be performed. There is sometimes a conflict of ideas between production and maintenance departments that creates special problems in the scheduling of preventive maintenance. Production management desires to obtain maximum machine and facility utilization at all times, therefore they are reluctant to give up machine and facility production time to permit maintenance work. Maintenance management wishes to gain maximum utilization of maintenance personnel on a planned and scheduled basis, avoiding unscheduled emergency work. The decisions have to be made:

1. To run machines and use facilities at maximum utilization levels with no scheduled maintenance, other than emergency repairs?

or

2. Have a preventive maintenance program to reduce emergency repairs, which will cut down output on a scheduled basis, rather than risk long delays with breakdowns?

The answer to these questions can be supplied by an analysis of historical data, or starting a system to provide such data, to be gathered over a six month to a one year period, then evaluated to determine your break even point.

Objectives of a Planning
and Scheduling Program

1. To set up a maintenance program on a scheduled basis which will integrate production schedules with the best utilization of maintenance and production personnel.

2. To obtain optimum maintenance at least cost. This would mean the lowest maintenance cost per finished product.

3. To reduce downtime and breakdown time. When a plant or a department is completely shut down for a certain period, consideration should be given to the expected life of machine and facility components in critical machines or equipment.

4. To maintain accurate records of equipment and facilities covering man hours, parts replacements, and costs. Good records will reveal if nonessential jobs are being done, or if your scheduling is not correct.

5. To provide required inspections for essential equipment that may cause a shutdown of production or endanger life or safety practices.

6. To eliminate conflicts or craft restrictions, and to allow for *proper* inventories of parts, tools, and other articles, being careful not to over stock.

Most manufacturers furnish recommended maintenance schedules with their equipment, along with maintenance manuals and parts catalogs. Their recommendation should be followed for the first few cycles, then *judgment should be made* if *more* or *less* maintenance is required for your particular operation. The average hours of running time will have to be known for the cycle to estimate the correct maintenance scheduling. Delivery dates on replacement parts should be determined to aid in proper scheduling. Maintenance manuals are of utmost importance and provide a good basis for training of personnel and in recommending proper techniques.

Schedules should be reviewed once each year to determine their accuracy. Changes may be required through purchases of new and better equipment, new tools, relocations, and better methods.

Recommended Maintenance Schedules
for Certain Building and Plant Facilities

Weekly

Air Compressor. Drain water.
Boilers: Clean panel box.
       Turn filters.
       Clean cones.
       Clean scanner tube.

Blow down.
Clean outside (front and back).
Clean motor belts.
Check boiler water treatment (also cooling tower).
Check all drains.
Check sprinkler valves and pump pressures.

Biweekly

Check heater relays in boiler.
Check boiler stacks.
Check grease and water in electric trucks.
Check water in fire alarm batteries.
Check lawn mower (change oil, clean, and adjust).
Check packing on engine room pumps.
Check tractor (oil and grease).

Monthly

Boilers: Check fire bricks.
        Check electrodes.
        Clean programmer.
        Test safety valves.
Climate changers, oil and grease.
Check conveyor.
Clean motors, drain and clean cooling tower.
Clean, oil, adjust, pumps in engine room.
Run purge compressor (October through April).

Bimonthly

Check filters.
Check strainers in all faucets.
Grease, oil, check hydraulic level in lift dock.
Rotate transfer pumps.

Every Three Months

Change oil in air compressor.
Check battery charger.
Oil overhead outside doors.
Grease and oil inside fans in lavatories.
Oil filters.
Clean and inspect floor machines and vacuum cleaners.
Check roof fans.
Purge compressor (oil in crankcase).
Check warehouse hand trucks.
Oil, grease, and clean transfer pumps.
Clean drains in all water fountains.
Clean and spray drains in lavatory floors.

Every Four Months

Grease and oil fans in lavatories (outside).
Oil and grease warehouse roof fans.
Check unit heaters.

Every Six Months

Rotate air compressors.
Clean out boiler heaters.
Tighten all electric and telephone boxes.
Clean outside of electric trucks and paint if necessary.
Weight carbon dioxide fire extinguishers.
Check calking on flag poles.
Check guard fence.
Check oil manhole.
Clean oil strainers on boilers and transfer pumps.
Clean sprinkler heads.
Check unit heaters and thermostats in penthouse.
Clean soap dispensers.
Clean inside water fountains.
Blow down water heaters.
Check inside pump couplings.

Yearly

Change to auxiliary engine room pump.
Wash ceilings and window sills in all lavatories.
Check boiler valves.
Vacuum all ceiling panes.
Wash all desks.
Clean condenser tubes.
Remove condenser head.
Dismantle and clean motors on electric trucks.
Wash all file cabinets.
Check all fire extinguishers.
Shut water off and drain hose bibs.
Check all light tubes.
Dismantle and clean roof fan motors.
Check toilet seats and fasten loose rubbers.
Wash wastepaper baskets.
Wash glass partitioning.
Inspect roof.

Every Two Years

Replace all light tubes.
Vacuum drapes.
Vacuum panels around anemostats.
Clean purge compressor float valve.

(*Source:* "The Watchmen's Handbook"—This material used by permission of American District Telegraph Co., copyright owner.)

The Watchman

Promptness. It is important to always report for duty on time. A watchman who is ill or unable to report for any other reason, should be sure to communicate with his employer in time to enable him to get a substitute.

Reporting for duty. Upon reporting for duty a watchman should make his presence known to his superior and ask if there are any special orders. If so, written notes should be made so that they will not be forgotten.

Smoking. There should be no smoking during tour of duty.

Alcohol. Never drink anything intoxicating before or during your period of duty.

Check your equipment. Before starting on the first round, all equipment should be checked. See that you have your watchman's clock, or tour key, flashlight, extra batteries and bulbs are available, and other allied equipment. Check your watch to make sure it is correct. If a revolver is provided, it should be inspected carefully.

Never leave the building. During your period of duty (unless your tour or patrol requires it) never leave the building.

Visitors. Never allow unauthorized persons to enter the premises. Never allow personal acquaintances to visit you during your period of duty.

Report broken rules. If you see anyone breaking the *no smoking* rules or any other safety rule; or if you see any evidence that such rules have been broken, such as cigarette butts on the floor, report such violations of safety rules to your superior.

Packages. Never allow anyone to leave the premises after closing hours with a bundle or package unless you have been notified by someone in authority to do so, in which case, for your own protection, you should ask for a written order permitting the removal of the package from the premises.

Telephone. Before starting your first round, check the telephone (or telephones, if there are several connections) to make sure which are connected and whether they are in working order.

Know your premises. Your first duty is to know your premises thoroughly. Check carefully through the following list and if there is anything on it that you do not know, ask your superior to tell you. You should know the following:

1. Where all stairways and doors lead to.
2. Locations of all fire and other emergency exits.
3. What stocks or materials are stored on the different floors, and in the various rooms and closets, throughout the premises.
4. Locations of fire alarm boxes.

5. Location of telephones.

6. Location of all emergency fire fighting equipment.

7. Locations of light switches, so that if emergency demands you can turn on the lights in any part of the premises without delay.

8. Locations of fire standpipe lines, fire hydrants and hose reels, so that in case of a fire you can show the fireman to this equipment without delay.

9. Location of control switches of elevator motors.

10. If the premises are sprinklered, you should know the locations of all valves controlling the supply of water to the sprinkler system and where extra sprinkler heads are kept.

11. Locations of fuse boxes, power control switches, steam valves, hydrants and any other control devices relating to the machinery and operations within the premises. In case of fire or other emergency, it often is important for the fire-man or other emergency forces to operate or close such devices and you should be able to give them any needed information without delay.

12. You should know how to operate all of the above equipment and devices that you might need to use in case of emergency. If you do not know this, ask your superior to arrange for the engineer or other competent person to give you any instructions you need.

13. You should know the locations of control room and shut off switches for air-conditioning or ventilating systems.

14. If your duties include attending to the heating system, make sure that you thoroughly understand its operation, so that if anything goes wrong, you will be able to detect it and take proper action. If unable to cope with the situation yourself, notify your superior.

15. To insure that you know your plant thoroughly, you should make a complete tour of the premises during the daytime, asking your superior or other employees for information about equipment, machinery and operations that you may need to assist you in your work.

16. The following information, names, addresses and telephone numbers should be kept posted at your headquarters:

a. Location of nearest street fire alarm box if your plant is not directly connected to your local fire bureau.

b. Telephone numbers of the police department and fire department.

c. The name, address, and telephone numbers of your superior or other employees that special conditions in your plant might require you to call in emergencies, such as the plant superintendent, engineer, foreman, and others. Consult with your superior to get any of this information that you need.

Making your rounds. You should always make your rounds on time, and that you should follow the exact route, that has been laid out for you. Of all your patrols, the first round is that most important. If anything is wrong it is important to discover it as soon as possible. The following is a checklist of some main points to watch for on your first round.

1. Has any motor or machine been left running that should have been turned off at the end of the normal shift? If so, attend to the condition yourself if you can. If you are in doubt what to do, notify your superior immediately.

2. Have any water faucets or other water outlets been left running? If so, shut them off.

3. Have any unnecessary lights been left burning? If so, turn them out.

4. Test the telephone to make sure that it is in working order.

5. Check all doors, windows, and skylights, and see that they are closed, to prevent possible damage from rain or snow, as well as to protect the premises against intruders.

6. If any windows are broken, fix them temporarily, and notify your immediate superior.

7. Check to see that all passageways leading to exits, fire doors, and equipment, are unobstructed. If they are try to move the item, if not possible report it to your superior.

8. Check to see that all fire doors that should be closed are closed.

9. Investigate any unusual odors, especially odors of smoke or gas.

10. Check to see that boxes, rubbish or other dangerous materials that might spread a fire have not been left near boilers or other heating units. Oily rags that might cause spontaneous combustion should be placed in a metal container or removed from the building.

Taking care of yourself. Always direct the beam of your flashlight ahead of you. Even if you know your plant well enough to go through a dark room without a light, someone may have rearranged the furniture.

Be on guard against open elevator doors, shafts and other floor openings. You should know where the first aid equipment is located and have access to it, so you can help yourself in case of slight injury. If you suffer a more serious injury or become ill, summon aid immediately.

Watchmen's Patrol Systems

Most employers equip their premises with some type of system which enables the watchman to record his patrols of the premises. These systems are of two main types: (1) Time recording systems, usually known as "Watchclock" systems and, (2) Central Station Watchman's Reporting Service.

Watchclock systems. This type of system usually consists of a portable clock which the watchman carries with him on his tour and a series of stations or keys distributed about the premises. Inserting the key into the clock records upon a paper roll, chart or dial inside the clock, the time when each station is visited. The following day the watchman's superior examines the tape in the clock to see if the rounds were made on time and in the order prescribed, during the preceding night.

If you are supplied with such a watchclock system, be sure that you visit your stations on time, and in the order prescribed. Do not take "shortcuts", omit visiting any station or change the order in which you are scheduled to visit them. If an emergency arises that compels you to delay or otherwise depart from the routine that has been set for you, be sure to inform your superior of this fact and the reason, when you turn in the clock upon completing your period of duty.

Central Station Watchman's Reporting System. With this type of system, the watchman is in contact with outside personnel, which are ready to come to his aid in time of emergency. This system consists of one or more preliminary and transmitting stations distributed throughout the premises, and a register key which the watchman carries and inserts and turns in the stations during his rounds. With this type of system the stations must be visited in regular order, the key is so constructed that it will fit in the station only if the preceding ones have been visited in their correct order. Signals from the transmitting stations must be on time or the *Central Station* (outside contact) will investigate.

What to Do
Upon Discovering a Fire

Always remember "the first five minutes at a fire are worth the next five hours." If 'the firemen are summoned *right away* and start fighting the fire in its earliest stages, they can nearly always put it out before it causes much damage.

If you discover a fire that is so small that you are *sure* you can put out with sand, water or a fire extinguisher, you should extinguish the fire. Having done so, examine carefully the area of the fire, to make sure that it is completely out, with no danger of breaking out again. If there is the slightest doubt, call the fire department. It is far better to be safe than sorry.

How to summon the fire department. The best way to summon the fire department in your case will depend on what type of protection has been provided your building.

1. If the premises are protected by a *manual fire alarm system* connected to the local fire department, all you have to do is pull the box.

2. Some buildings are equipped with *Local Interior Fire Alarm Systems.* Operating a box of this type system does not summon the fire department, but merely sounds an alarm on the premises, to warn the occupants. *Make sure* that you know what type fire alarm system your premises are equipped with and that you know what it will do, how to operate it and the locations of all the alarm boxes.

3. Telephone or pull a street fire alarm box. If you phone make certain that in the excitement of reporting the fire you give the name of your premises and address distinctly. The telephone number of the fire department should be memorized by all the watchmen. The location of the nearest fire alarm box should also be memorized by all watchmen.

Security Survey

Outdoor. A survey of your outdoor areas should be made to determine if security can be improved. Windows that could be used to gain entrance should be screened or barred. In some cases it may be desirable to wire the windows to set off an alarm, should they be broken or forced, doors may also be wired. By designating certain doors for entrance and exit pilferage can be controlled.

Parking lots may be fenced in for authorized cars only, with entrance and exit made through a guard gate. An employee identification system can be installed, and authorization required by all visitors. Trucks should have authorized passes, and be routed through a guard gate. The perimeter of the plant should be lit up by floodlight at night.

Internal. A survey of your interior area should be made to determine if security can be improved. Windows that could be used to pass material out should be screened. Employee entrances and exits can be designated to insure that all employees pass through guarded doors only. It is recommended that all personal packages be checked with the guard when entering the plant, and picked up when leaving. Shipping areas should be screened and locked so that drivers would not have access to any merchandise when authorized personnel are not present.

54 / **MAINTENANCE STANDARDS**

(*Source:* "Techniques of Plant Maintenance and Engineering," Clapp & Poliak, Incorporated, New York)

It is generally considered impossible to secure 100 per cent productivity at all times from the maintenance department. However, it is possible to decrease the unproductive times considerably through good supervision, better planning and scheduling, and through work simplification and sampling methods, along with work measurement techniques.

Sound planning and scheduling procedures should be put into operation. This is the direct responsibility of *every* maintenance supervisor. This will insure that the job can be done when scheduled, and that the correct *number* of men have been assigned to the job. Tool requirements should be established, and crafts dispatched to the job in proper sequence along with the knowledge of their next job and its location, in order to avoid wasting time waiting for further assignments.

Methods of Determining Standards

Estimates. The most common way to determine maintenance standards is by estimating. It is fairly easy to estimate the cost of materials, and sometimes rather difficult to estimate the time required to perform the job. The labor estimate can only be defined as the probable time required to perform a job, based on the best judgement of the person making the estimate. Therefore the personal experience, knowledge, and ability of the estimator will determine the quality of the estimate. Employees will not respond to poor estimates. If the estimates are too tight, they lose interest in trying to meet the goal; if they are too loose, they lose confidence in the program.

Historical records. This is a refined method of estimating using the average time values based on past experience. Historical work orders are assembled showing all maintenance work that has been performed with average times arrived at through the grouping of similar jobs and obtaining standard times. The disadvantage of this method is that its accuracy is low and reflects only what has been done in the past. If you induce a new method of performance, secure better tools, or new equipment, the standard would then become loose, and you may have difficulty adjusting the standard. In this way past inadequacies become built into the system.

Measurement by standard time data. This is the most accurate method of determining job times. The standard data should be gathered through the use of actual time studies, or through synthetic time such as measurement time method or work factor. The use of this method makes it possible to compute the job time by dividing the standard time by the actual time.

Work sampling. The primary objective of a work measurement program is to determine the things over which the workman has no control and that are reducing his effectiveness, and therefore his efficiency. The analysis of work sampling survey reports will provide many kinds of information that may be useful to management. You will be able to determine the average number of man-hours required to do specific jobs. This information can be used to set up performance standards, and also to estimate costs on future jobs. Work sampling is a method of obtaining facts about machine or human activities. Two methods of work sampling are the random sampling and the continuous observation. The latter method requires greater man power assignment and cost, but provides more representative data more quickly.

Introducing the Program

Prepare a manual explaining the program. State how and by whom it would be executed. Outline the role each person is to play—engineer, maintenance foreman, supervisor, and other personnel. A representative of each of these groups should receive a copy of the manual before publication and should be asked for comments prior to publication.

Inform all personnel and union representatives of your plan and solicit their cooperation and assistance. Distribute copies of the manual to persons taking part in the execution of the program mentioned above. Several days after the manuals have been distributed, a meeting should be called to go over the survey procedures in detail and to answer any questions they may have.

Select the person or group to be surveyed and arrange for the observers who are generally supervisors or engineers from either the maintenance or operations department. It is recommended that a minimum of 50 per cent of a department or group be surveyed at one time to prevent the work from being loaded on to the observed persons.

Observers are required to be at the plant gate a half hour before the shift starts. When they arrive each is told which workman he will follow and what the man's classification is. The observer introduces himself to the employee at the gate, advises him he will be with him all day, and stays with him for the entire shift. The employees' supervisor does not know that his group is being surveyed until his workmen show up in the shop or on the job accompanied by the observer.

In his report, the observer accounts for every minute of the employee's day from the time he enters the plant until he leaves at the end of the shift, except for the official lunch period, noting the starting time to the nearest minute for every change in operation or activity in the left-hand column of his form. He also writes a brief description of the activity in the right-hand column.

The observer stays out of the way of the workman and asks him as few questions as possible. As the shift progresses, the "general remarks" section of the survey report is filled in. The remarks may consist of the observer's personal opinions, and deal with such things as shoddy work, unsafe practices, lack of instructions, and similar information, particularly the matters that may have affected the workman's effectiveness. The observer may also report unsafe practices, poor workmanship, loafing, and so on, on the part of other workmen in the general area although they may have no connection with the work he is observing.

The next day the observer goes over his survey report, coding each entry and computing the elapsed time for each activity. To assist in the coding he uses the "survey time breakdown code". Then the "time analysis summary" is prepared to summarize total time by each code, from the data shown on the observer's report, the "time study check list" and the table shown in part. The observer also goes over his "general remarks", and clarifies them wherever necessary.

Using the Findings

As soon as possible after completion of a survey, the survey group supervisor goes over every report in detail with the supervisor of the shop or group surveyed and his section supervisor. The purpose of this review is to direct the supervisor's attention to the things that can be done immediately to improve the effectiveness of the workmen. Situations that require top management consideration and decision are reviewed with the supervisors for informational purposes, but nothing is done about them until management directs that action be taken.

When the survey results show that representative information has been obtained, then conclusion may be drawn. The number of surveys that must be run will vary. We consider that we have representative information when our "time analysis summaries" show practically no change in statistics from previous surveys.

When representative information is obtained a written report is prepared, listing situations that need top management's attention and suggesting solutions. This report is reviewed by the supervisor of the survey group and the assistant project director. The latter then discusses the findings with plant supervisors, tells them what corrective action he expects them to take, and sets a date for accomplishment.

In conclusion, the importance of the "time breakdown code" is stressed. It is essential to allow adequate time for drawing up this survey, since it is the yardstick for measuring the work.

Survey Time Breakdown Code

Code   *Productive Time*

A   1. *Actual Time:*

        a. To include only that time actually spent working directly upon the equipment being repaired or job assigned.

b. Any work with tools necessary and incidental to the job. *Note:* Some job assignments do not involve direct work on equipment or making repairs. In such cases use the proper productive code. The craft and job classification plus a brief description of job assignment in the survey notes will assist in coding each survey report entry. *For example:* A tool crib operator's productive duties consist of material procurement. So code as M. A crane operator's main productive activity is transportation of equipment or rigging. So code as T.

C   2. *Communication Time*—to include the following:

a. Supervisor to worker instruction.
b. Reports by workers to supervisors.
c. Discussions between craft worker and other craft workers regarding the equipment.
d. Discussions between craft worker and unit operators in regard to equipment.
e. Telephone calls for material.
f. Writing up time sheets.
g. Filling out work orders.
h. Writing orders for material.
i. Tagging out of equipment to be worked on.
j. Studying drawings and specifications, requisitions, bills of materials, or any written or printed information pertinent to assigned job.
k. Records or check lists required for PM program.

M   3. *Material Procurement Time*—to include the following:

a. Gathering material or tools.
b. Hunting for material or tools.
c. Putting away material or tools.
d. HP survey to determine that material or tool is not contaminated and may be used or returned to storage.

T   4. *Transportation and Handling Time*—to include the following:

a. Walking (includes walking to get HP permit, materials, tools, and instructions).
b. Riding.
c. Loading or unloading tools, material, or equipment.
d. Rigging.
e. Climbing.
f. Use of crane to lift materials or equipment into place.
g. Driving to and from work to haul materials or tools or equipment.

CL   5. *Cleaning Time*—to include the following:

a. Clean-up of equipment before, during, and after repair, including cleaning and decontamination of parts.

b. Clean-up of tools after use, including decontamination.

c. Gathering and disposing of used materials and other refuse in a working area.

d. Time to scrub body or hands to remove chemicals or contamination.

e. Washing hands that have become so soiled that they must be cleaned in order to go on with job. *Note:* Removal of machine gaskets is considered cleaning time.

SHP   6. Safe Work Permit and HP Permit (preparing and obtaining, issuance of dosimeter). Does not include waiting on safety engineer of HP. Code WOC for waiting time.

Non-Productive Time

1. *Delay Due to Others:*

WO   a. Waiting for operator. *For example:* Waiting for operator to get equipment ready for repair. (Actual time to turn equipment over to craftsmen. Does not include waiting time before operator starts turnover procedure. This time is coded WOC.)

WT   b. Waiting for transportation.

WM   c. Waiting for material delivery.

WS   d. Waiting for supervisor. *For example:* Waiting for supervisor to make decision as to method of repair.

WOC   e. Waiting for other crafts. *For example:* (1) Waiting for other crafts to complete their portion of a job so that the observed worker can proceed; (2) Radio-active contamination and clean-up; and (3) Waiting on HP safety engineer, infirmary nurse, late bus at start of shift, and materials or toolroom clerks.

WWA   f. Waiting for work assignment. *For example:* Worker runs out of scheduled work and has notified supervisor but has not been given a new assignment.

WCW   g. Waiting for co-worker. Lost time due to assignment of two people to a one-man job. (Necessary in many cases.)

PC   h. Protective clothing, (dress and undress) personal or anti-C clothing.

U   2. *Unavoidable Delays:*

a. Attempting to use telephone but it was busy, cannot get person called.

b. Waiting to make the several necessary packing adjustments to a pump just put back in service after a repacking job.

c. Repair or malfunctioning equipment or tools.

3. *Other Delays:*

L   a. Lunch—includes preparation, coffee or coke break.

S   b. Smoking—includes travel to and from processing area to clean area.

MIS   c. Miscellaneous—includes the following:

(1) Washing hands for lunch and at end of shift.

(2) Personal needs.

(3) Idle time when not waiting for others to perform work or for work assignments. *Note:* Record and code all miscellaneous time. A description of miscellaneous activity in the survey notes is unnecessary. Any excessive use of miscellaneous time can be noted under General Remarks.

SM d. Safety meetings.

UB e. Union business (workman's committee, gripe sessions, phone calls, posters, talking with shop steward).

Figure 54-1

Survey No. .... Observer: ....

GENERAL REMARKS:

1. Worker used open end wrench to tighten tubing connections. This is correct tool.

2. Worker had to work on floor when bending tubing. A bench would have made it easier.

3. 8:45—Co-worker studied drawings, apparently trying to figure out what to do.

4. 8:55—Made mistake. Scrapped tubing, about nine or ten inches.

5. Metal and burnable waste observed in waste containers. Metal scrap mostly copper tubing.

6. 9:15—Maintenance engineer visited job.

7. Bottom of D/P cabinet dirty. Covers for other instruments laying in bottom of cabinet.

8. Worker disconnected piece of tubing from another instrument from which water drained. He was checking to see how tubing fittings were made up.

9. 10:35—Up to now co-worker has done little helping. Helper or co-worker is actually a 2/c mechanic fitter (fitter).

10. 10:45—Co-worker measured for a tubing run.

11. Foreman found tubing fitting worker went to sponsor's warehouse to get cutter. He found it in sponsor's warehouse.

12. 11:16—Two electricians delivered materials to general work area. Parked material in front of instrument panel.

13. 11:22—Operations operator took lunch box and left for lunch.

14. 12:30—Another workman used desk top as work bench on which to saw piece of instrument.

15. 12:30—Co-worker trying to make up a piece of copper tubing.

16. There were not enough welding shields to protect eyes of surrounding workers from arc flashes.

17. 12:45—Two electricians showed up to work on installing square duct in or on instrument console. Area already congested before they arrived. They were in way of men working on tubing.

18. 1:02—Had to rework a piece of tubing on which he had made a mistake.

Figure 54-2

T IME A NALYSIS S UMMARY

Survey No. .... Observer: ....

Craft .... Classification .... Date ....

SUMMARY (*Analysis of Time Used*)	ACTUAL SURVEY TIME (*Recorded*)		ACTUAL EFFECTIVE TIME (*Estimated*)		POTENTIAL EFFECTIVE TIME (*Estimated*)	
	Time Man-Min.	*Per cent of 8-hr. Shift*	*Time* Man-Min.	*Per cent of 8-hr. Shift*	*Time* Man-Min.	*Per cent of 8-hr. Shift*
Productive Time						
1. Actual time.	250	52.1				
2. Communication time.	82	17.1				
3. Material procurement time.	25	5.2				
4. Transportation time.	46	9.6				
5. Safe work and/or **HP** permit.						
6. Cleaning time.	4	0.8				
7. Estimate available due increase effective (−15 per cent).						
Total Productive Time	407	84.8				
Non-Productive Time						
1. *Delays Due to Other Groups:*						
a. Waiting for operator.						
b. Waiting for transportation.						
c. Waiting for material.						
d. Waiting for supervisor.						
e. Waiting for other craft.	9	1.9				
f. Waiting for work assignment.						
g. Waiting for co-worker.	1	0.2				
2. *Unavoidable Delays:*						
3. *Time For:*						
a. Protective clothing.	21	4.4				
b. Union business.						
c. Procedures.						
d. Defective equipment or tools.						
e. Safety rules or meeting.						

SUMMARY (Analysis of Time Used)	ACTUAL SURVEY TIME (Recorded)		ACTUAL EFFECTIVE TIME (Estimated)		POTENTIAL EFFECTIVE TIME (Estimated)	
	Time Man-Min.	Per cent of 8-hr. Shift	Time Man-Min.	Per cent of 8-hr. Shift	Time Man-Min.	Per cent of 8-hr. Shift
4. Other Delays:						
a. Lunch.	24	5.0				
b. Smoking.						
c. Miscellaneous.	18	3.7				
5. Ineffective Time.						
6. 15 per cent of estimate available increase.						
Total Non-Productive Time	73	15.2				

Figure 54-3

STANDARD JOB TIMES FOR FLOOR CLEANING OPERATIONS
(*Time in Minutes per 1,000 sq. ft.*)

Sweeping

Unobstructed	9
Slightly obstructed	10
Obstructed	12
Heavily obstructed	16

Machine Scrub

Unobstructed	25
Slightly obstructed	35
Obstructed	40
Heavily obstructed	45

Dust Mopping

Unobstructed	7
Slightly obstructed	9
Obstructed	12
Heavily obstructed	16

Machine Polish

Unobstructed	15
Slightly obstructed	25
Obstructed	30
Heavily obstructed	35

Damp Mopping

Unobstructed	16
Slightly obstructed	23
Obstructed	27
Heavily obstructed	32

Vacuum (wet pick-up)

Unobstructed	20
Slightly obstructed	27
Obstructed	31
Heavily obstructed	35

Wet Mop and Rinse

Unobstructed	35
Slightly obstructed	45
Obstructed	50
Heavily obstructed	55

Vacuum (dry pick-up)

Unobstructed	14
Slightly obstructed	17
Obstructed	19
Heavily obstructed	23

Hand Scrub

Unobstructed	240
Slightly obstructed	300
Obstructed	330
Heavily obstructed	360

Strip and Rewax

Unobstructed	100
Slightly obstructed	120
Obstructed	140
Heavily obstructed	180

Hand Scrub (long brush)

Unobstructed	75
Slightly obstructed	105
Obstructed	120
Heavily obstructed	135

TIME STUDY CHECK LIST

Survey No. __MTR-ETR #119__

Craft __Mechanic Fitter__

Date __4-28-60__

Observer __P. C. Leahy__

PRODUCTIVE TIME CODES						NON-PRODUCTIVE TIME CODES																	
						Waiting For								Time For						Other			
Actual Time	Communi-cation	Material Procurement	Transport-ation	Safe Work HP Permit	Cleaning	Operator	Trans-portation	Material	Supv'r.	Other Crafts	Work As-signment	Co-Worker	Unavoid-able Delay	Protective Clothing	Union Business	Procedure	Defective Tools or Equipment	Safety Rules or Meeting	Lunch & Coffee	Smoking	Miscel-laneous
A	C	M	T	SHP	CL	WO	WT	WM	WS	WOC	WWA	WCW	U	PC	UB	P	DET	SM	L	S	MIS

Column Totals:

Code	Total
A	250
C	82
M	25
T	46
CL	4
WCW	1
WOC	9
PC	21
L	24
MIS	18

Grand Total

Figure 54-4

Figure 54-5

STANDARD JOB TIME LIST
(Time in Seconds)

Dusting

Ash Tray	15
Book Cases	
13x35x12 inches	22
36x30x8 inches	33
12x40x12 inches	26
42x24x11 inches	49
Cabinets	
36x77x18 inches	106
30x66x18 inches	42
Calculators	
Small	7
Large	9
Chairs	
Large	63
Medium	35
Stenographer's	22
Cigarette Stand	25
Clock, Desk	8
Clock, Wall	20
Desks	
Large	48
Medium	43
Small	38
Desk Items (miscellaneous	3
Doors	
Without glass	25
With glass	40
Elevator Cabs (inside)	196
Files	
4 drawer	22
5 drawer	27
Fire Extinguishers	16
In and Out Trays	8
Lamps and Lights	
Wall Fluorescent	8
Desk Fluorescent	18
Table lamp, shade	35
Floor lamp, shade	35
Partitions, Glass-50 sq. ft. per unit	60
Rack, Coat, and Hat (6)	90
Radiators and Window Ledge (124x15 inches)	45

Radiator (flush with wall) (40"x30"x6')	21
Sand Urns	60
Spittoons	180
Tables	
Large	60
Medium	35
Small	22
Telephone	9
Typewriter (covered)	7
Vending Machine	60
Venetian Blinds (standard)	210
Wastebaskets	15

Lavatory Items

Cleaning Commode (with partition)	180
Door (spot wash)	50
Door Latch	10
Mirrors	
25x49 inches	20
60x21 inches	20
88x31 inches	40
Napkin Dispenser	13
Napkin Disposal	10
Paper Towel Dispenser	7
Paper Towel Disposal	10
Shelving	
20 inches long	8
126x6 inches	60
Urinals (complete)	120
Wainscoting	
75 to 100 feet long	25
Wash Basin, Soap Dispenser	120

Washing

Glass Partitions	
Clear—8 sq. ft. per unit.	60
Opaque—20 sq. ft. per unit.	60

Miscellaneous

Door (washing)	150
Drinking Fountain	90
Vacuuming	
Large Divan	190

Figure 54-6

	0+	100+	200+	300+	400+
1	.208	21.042	41.875	62.708	83.542
2	.417	21.250	42.083	62.917	83.750
3	.625	21.458	42.292	63.125	83.958
4	.833	21.667	42.500	63.333	84.167
5	1.042	21.875	42.708	63.542	84.375
6	1.250	22.083	42.917	63.750	84.583
7	1.458	22.292	43.125	63.958	84.792
8	1.667	22.500	43.333	64.167	85.000
9	1.875	22.708	43.542	64.375	85.208
10	2.083	22.917	43.750	64.583	85.417
11	2.292	23.125	43.958	64.792	85.625
12	2.500	23.333	44.167	65.000	85.833
13	2.708	23.542	44.375	65.208	85.042
14	2.917	23.750	44.583	65.417	86.250
15	3.125	23.958	44.792	65.625	86.458
16	3.333	24.167	45.000	65.833	86.667
17	3.542	24.375	45.208	66.042	86.875
18	3.750	24.583	45.417	66.250	87.083
19	3.958	24.792	45.625	66.458	87.292
20	4.167	25.000	45.833	66.667	87.500
21	4.375	25.208	46.042	66.875	87.708
22	4.583	25.417	46.250	67.083	87.917
23	4.792	25.625	46.458	67.292	88.125
24	5.000	25.833	46.667	67.500	88.333
25	5.208	26.042	46.875	67.708	88.542
26	5.417	26.250	47.083	67.917	88.750

55 / **TRAINING**

If you were asked to define your position as a sanitarian, building manager, building superintendent, or by whatever title your position is designated, what would your answer be? It may be described as follows:

"You are charged to protect the capital investment of your employer and his building, and to provide a clean and healthful atmosphere."

Part of your responsibility, I am sure, is the training of your personnel. Why is training required? Training is required because of increased labor costs; because of the constant introduction of new products and machines into the market which require special techniques in order to use them, and above all, to insure that your employer is getting maximum utilization of every dollar spent for labor and materials. These points are true, whether applied to a sanitation program or to a building maintenance program covering equipment.

Where does our training program begin? The training program begins with you, your supervisor and foreman, and with your employees. First let us consider "you". Are you satisfied that you are now operating as a modern supervisor? Have you kept up with new products, materials, and techniques? You are responsible for planning the work of your unit. It is upon these plans which the performance of your employees depend. It is also the way in which you organize the work, the way you divide and assign the work load, that makes it possible for your employees to handle the entire program efficiently. You are responsible for motivating your employees towards performing a willing and capable job. I ask, "Is this you?" If not, it may be time for you to reconsider how you *plan, organize, control, motivate* or *coordinate*. Does your subordinate management personnel understand these functions fully, and know exactly how you want them performed? If they do not, training should begin immediately.

Your employer feels that you are responsible to find new methods covering the following:

1. Increase productivity.
2. Control quality of work.
3. Train your employees.
4. Plan the work.
5. Promote safety and improve housekeeping.
6. Control costs and reduce waste.
7. Maintain machines and equipment; set up periodic inspections on floor machines and other mechanical tools used, including physical building equipment and mechanical building equipment.
8. Keep good discipline.
9. Handle grievances.
10. Write reports.

Many other items for which you are responsible, may be added to this list. If you feel that you are not handling any one of the items mentioned, in a proper manner it is probably time for you to consider further training for yourself. This can be accomplished through reading, demonstrations by manufacturers, work seminars, correspondence education, and college training.

The next consideration is the performance of management personnel and supervisors under you. Their training depends upon what you want to accomplish. Training may be given to them through the above mentioned recommendations for your own training, or by direct instruction from you. (Instructional consideration should be given to these people in the field of "work sampling" and "work simplification".)

The training of your employees should begin the moment they walk through the front door and are interviewed by the personnel department. From this very moment, habits, practices, and working rules should be put into effect. Training in building sanitation and maintenance is not effected only through instruction periods or courses. Situations change constantly in the sanitation and maintenance field, which makes perpetual training a requirement. You will be constantly making on the spot decisions, and these should always conform with good practices. If a sanitation employee is required to make decisions for himself, and if in your opinion they are not in line with good practices, on the spot correction must be made immediately, and a precedent and pattern set forth on the particular situation upon which you made judgement.

Let us consider the point of plant safety. Many dollars are spent by firms for the promotion of safety programs. If we continually train our employees in safety on the job, the need for special safety programs will be reduced. This is one example where perpetual training is required. The need for safe practices along with training is always present, and is your direct responsibility. Emergency situations, new practices, and new tools are changed more frequently in your depart-met than in any other department within the same company.

It must be remembered that your employees should be selected properly. Training is easier, and many training problems are eliminated if the right person is in the right job. If your employee is properly trained, he will have developed correct habits and skills. This will result in a good possibility of your getting things accomplished. If your employee is not trained properly, he will develop undesirable habits and will prove to be ineffective, and a hindrance to your operation. It is important to consider mentioning standards in the initial interview with an employee. This will impress upon him that he must carry his work load.

We are now ready for "Training Program Considerations". We should establish, what training is to be given to the new employee, and to what depth we are going to train him.

Training Program Considerations

It is important to have every employee in the building maintenance force trained to do every job, if possible. After this has been accomplished, it can be determined which of the employees can do certain jobs in the most efficient and thorough manner. After every employee has been thoroughly trained in all positions, the jobs should be assigned according to performance. Advantages derived from this method are:

1. Provision for required depth in the department in order to operate effectively and efficiently.
2. Better understanding by each employee, of the job done by his fellow worker.
3. Training of the employee to serve as a replacement during vacation, in time of sickness, death in the family, or other reasons.

Every employee should understand the job of his fellow employee in order to have a better understanding of the work load of the other employees. The work load is determined by management and for psychological purposes of the employee, the positions should be kept equal. Special consideration should be given to physically handicapped employees.

It is recommended that the training be done by the building superintendent, as he is responsible for the employees' performance. (In some organizations this training may be delegated to the service of a training department or a training director.) Training his employees gives the building superintendent a thorough understanding of all jobs and functions which will result in his being able to communicate more intelligently with higher management concerning his needs and department operations. He will also develop a better understanding of his organization for contract negotiations and budget purposes.

Another important factor in the training being conducted by the building superintendent is that in the testing of new products, he will be able to instruct his personnel in the application of these products and can better determine their net result and usefulness. This leads the building superintendent into maintaining a constant evaluation of new products, which in turn if accepted, may require changing or rescheduling jobs if the product proves to be more effective than the one being utilized.

When a new employee is hired, a thorough orientation between the employee and the immediate supervisor should take place. The following reminders are suggested:

A. *Job Factors:*

1. *Job Title (and Grade).* If job is under "Job Evaluation Program," use job evaluation book to show specific job title and grade. Otherwise, give job title and indicate how this job relates to other jobs in the department.

2. *Duties.* Explain briefly the functions of the department, so that employee can see the broad picture; give general idea of individual's work.

3. *Pay Rate and Pay Basis.* See that employee knows hourly rate; when pay days occur; when his *first* pay day occurs; and time and method of pay check distribution.

4. *Hours of Work.* Give starting and stopping time and lunch period times as well as total normal hours per day and per week.

5. *Time Card Use.* See that the employee knows the location and use of time card rack where his time card will be located. Demonstrate use of time clock. Explain rules and regulations concerning use of time card and time clock; and relation of time card to pay check. Explain what to do when errors in time card use occur.

6. *Probationary Period.* Tell employee length of formal probation in the department; explain why such an arrangement exists. Tell employee that the company is also "on probation" as his employer; urge employee to discuss matters frankly with you.

7. *Absence and Tardiness.* Explain company and departmental rules and procedures concerning notification in advance of absencies; explain tardiness policy. Point out that company loses when an employee is not on the job since company overhead and fixed costs must be met even though employee does not get paid.

8. *Supervision.* Be sure employee knows the name of and meets all management persons in the department with whom he will be in contact.

9. *Smoking.* Explain smoking rules and reasons therefor; name or show nearest "smoking" area and any regulations concerning its use.

10. *Rest Period, Location of Rest Areas and Lavatories.* If definite rest periods are established, give times and procedures; if no definite rest periods, explain company policy in this respect. Indicate nearest lavatory location.

11. *Sanitary Regulations.* Explain to the employee we are vitally interested in

sanitary conditions. Acquaint him with the rules and regulations governing sanitary conditions in such places as his work area, rest area and lavatories.

12. *Leaving Department.* The supervisor should know where each employee is at all times—*be sure* that this is understood.

13. *Telephone Use and Personal Letters.* Explain company policy concerning telephone calls, both incoming and outgoing; explain that personal letters are not to be written, sent, or received on company time or through company channels or using company materials.

14. *Visits to First Aid Room.* Acquaint employee with location of first aid room. Explain the importance of reporting an accident or illness to his supervisor in order that he may be referred to the first aid room immediately.

15. *Fire Drills.* Explain to the employee that fire drills are held from time to time for the purpose of protecting the well-being of all employees. Tell him what he should do when a fire drill occurs.

16. *Accident Prevention.* Point out existing types of accident hazards and emphasize the need for care. Explain that all accidents should be reported to the supervisor immediately. Explain importance of this in relation to workmen's compensation and other employee's benefits.

17. *Educational Opportunities.*

18. *Union Status.* Advise employee if he or she will be eligible to join a union; if so, name union, tell whether joining is obligation or not (union or open shop); advise length of waiting or probationary period, or other facts that he or she should know about membership.

19. *Work Policy.* Explain to the employee that each person within a department is expected to carry his own work load. Failure to do this can place unnecessary burdens on others.

B. A complete explanation of the job should be given to the employee, including a schedule with the time allotted for each specific job and the areas to be covered. Explain what tools are to be used, how they are to be cared for and in what condition they are to be stored when the employee is through using them.

C. The employee is then assigned to work with the supervisor or one of the better workers for a period of one week, with an assigned area equal to that of the other employees. This will have the new employee working with another employee and teaches him to carry his own work load. After one week the employee should be able to handle his assigned duties by himself.

D. A demonstration should be arranged showing the tools with which an employee will work. He should be provided with a complete schedule of the frequency of operations, explaining whether the job is to be done daily, weekly, or monthly.

E. After one month on a job, the employee is assigned to a new area or another job. He is trained with another employee as described previously. If there are more than five different jobs per shift, the training on five jobs should be sufficient to give the department enough depth in personnel qualifications.

F. A check on the progress of the employee should be made weekly during the first month, and semimonthly while training on other jobs. The immediate supervisor should be consulted on the employee's progress and of any deficiencies in his work. His strong points should be noted and these should be discussed.

If he is acceptable, he should be offered encouragement. The employee should also be encouraged to discuss any deficiencies that he may see in the cleaning program and any new ideas that he may have relating to his work.

G. Training is recommended by conferences, lectures, demonstrations, training films, film strips and slides. There are many sources of supply for this type training. After each period of instruction, a discussion should be held, followed by a class conducted on practical applications, under close supervision, with on-the-spot corrections.

H. Various manufacturers, if their products are purchased, will demonstrate the correct way in which their products are to be used.

Caution: These demonstrations should be observed by the building superintendent before the manufacturer's representative is permitted to describe his product and method to the working force, in order to determine whether or not the method is acceptable to him.

I. A re-evaluation of jobs and job descriptions should be made at least once each year. The maintenance program may change as the building ages and many physical changes may be made each year. Several jobs may have to be revised and rescheduled. If a complete revision or rescheduling is not necessary, with only small changes made in any of the jobs, it is important that these changes be noted on the employee's schedule. If an employee should suddenly become ill and is unable to report for work, this would facilitate providing the employee who will be temporarily handling the job with a complete up to date schedule.

J. Many times, if a building superintendent has a building under good control, he is lax in sampling his employees' work. It is recommended that employees' work be sampled once per year. Job procedures should also be simplified once per year. In reviewing procedures, method and order of sequence should be included for each job. This will eliminate the wandering of employees to all sections of the building and will result in greater efficiency. The employee should be required to perform his job in proper sequence and his whereabouts known in times of emergency. A check should also be made to determine that the employee has the proper tools available to him. Make certain that he is trained to carry the necessary tools with him to eliminate his retracing his steps. Employees should be checked for unavoidable delays which may be eliminated through rescheduling or with a conference held with the originator of the delay.

The practice of making on-the-spot corrections cannot be over emphasized. Do not wait for someone else to do it or tell you about it. This is *your department, your building, your responsibility*—then you can be sure of *your job.*

K. Introduce the employee to a sufficient number of people employed in his immediate work area in order to eliminate any unnecessary strangeness in his starting to work.

Methods of Instruction

Every building maintenance manager must constantly keep himself informed of new methods, techniques, systems, and products. This information must be transmitted to all operating personnel. It is essential that he be able to present effective instruction, to insure that his personnel understands exactly in what manner he expects his building and its equipment maintained.

A good instructor is a person who plans his work carefully, in order to be effective. Teaching is an art, not a science. In the acquisition of this art, it is possible to establish flexible principles or fundamentals, which may be used as guides toward the goals of proficiency and excellence. It is upon these established fundamentals of learning, that a good instructor must build his instruction, in order to qualify himself as a teacher.

An instructor must know his students. He must understand the persons he will teach and the way in which they learn. He must see the course of instruction from the viewpoint of the student. He must realize that his students are interested in the "Why", "Who", or "What" of what they are asked to do. He should keep in mind that good instruction and instructors remain in the mind of the student. Students are quick to detect the incompetent person. Most persons are capable of mastering the essentials of building maintenance training if they are taught well. *An instructor should have a thorough knowledge of his subject.*

Fundamentals of Instructional Situations

The following facts are presented to the instructor for thoroughly training a student for maintenance work.

The five stages of the teaching process are as follows:

1. Understanding.
   a. Principles of learning.
   b. Stages of instruction.
   c. Preparation.
2. Presentation.
3. Application.
4. Examination.
5. Review and/or critique.

Understanding

Principles of Learning

The only justification for instruction is learning. What causes a man to learn? We know from experience, that to learn, we must have a reason or motive for learning. We must understand what we are learning and be able to practice it.

Three fundamentals of learning on which instructional methods are based are *motivation, understanding,* and *practice.*

Motivation. When training a person, we cannot depend on his inclinations. To expose a person to knowledge is not enough to guarantee that he will open his mind to new ideas. Something must be done to cause the employee to apply himself mentally and physically to the instruction received. In choosing a method of instruction, a type should be used that will instill motivation, create his desire to learn, and make him realize that the instruction fills his personal need. He will be influenced by both his own and the instructor's attitude, when factors favorable to learning predominate.

Clarify the objective. A person's attitude at the beginning of an instruction period is favorable to receive the instruction because he is curious to find out what is going to happen. From this point, what he sees and hears, determines his response.

Understanding. Instruction must be planned so that understanding in your personnel's mind is accomplished with the shortest expenditure of time. The best way to help a person to understand a subject is to progress from the known to the unknown. All learning must start at a point of knowledge already possessed by the instructor. Aiding people in understanding can be effective through speech, however this can be supplemented, and greater achievements realized, when the five senses are used to full capacity when teaching. Understanding can also be accomplished by the functional approach. This is generally accomplished through associating the subject with practical examples and application.

Practice. The purposes of practice are proficiency and retention. The purpose of practice is to learn by doing. Supervision is of prime importance, as you must not permit incorrect habits to be formed. Length and number of practice periods should be sufficient to insure the understanding of what is to be accomplished by every employee.

Stages of Instruction

The presentation accomplishes motivation and understanding by clarifying, observing, and explaining ideas through lectures, discussions, and demonstrations. Application will perfect the understanding of skills and techniques through practice. Examination verifies the understanding and efficiencies, and provides motivation and guides for learning.

Preparation

Every lesson which is taught should have a basic *outline or lesson plan.* In the preparation of the instructor's manuscript, the student represents the framework around which the instructor will base his lesson.

The steps in lesson preparation are based on a logical thought process. Good instruction depends directly on the care and thought the instructor puts into its preparation. The key to an effective lesson preparation is knowing the six following steps:

1. Consider the lesson objective.
2. Gather necessary information and materials.
3. Study and analyze the material.
4. Determine and write the lesson plan.
5. Conduct rehearsals.
6. Check final arrangements.

It should always be remembered that the value an employee derives from his instructor, is care and thought which an instructor puts into his preparation.

Presentation

The presentation stage of instruction is important in the teaching process because it represents the teaching and showing ways of instruction. The actual delivery of the prepared lesson to the class during this stage of instruction puts the instructor's preparation to test.

Methods of conducting the presentation. There are three methods of conveying instruction to a class. They are the *lecture*, the *conference*, and the *demonstration*. Every presentation has an introduction. The introduction should gain the employees' interest, and prepare his mind for receiving the instruction. The introduction is your first chance for motivation. It should arouse interest, clarify the objective, and relate to a previous lesson or experience.

The *lecture* or the talk is an oral discourse by the instructor. Its advantage lies in the fact that many ideas can be presented in a short time, and it is adaptable to instructing large groups, or for a general orientation. One of the disadvantages of the lecture type of instruction is that it has complete lack of student participation. If possible, applicable training aids, such as charts, slides, and other available presentations should be used. A talk should not exceed fifty minutes in length. Short talk periods of fifteen to twenty minutes, combined with demonstrations and practical work periods are preferred to the lecture type method of instruction.

The *conference* is an oral discussion by the instructor, augmented by active class participation. It has the distinct advantage over the lecture method, in that it enables the instructor to determine by class participation, whether or not the instruction is making the correct impression. It allows the student to clear up any point he does not understand by asking questions. This type of instruction stimulates thinking and expression of thought. There are two general types of conferences; the information type and the development or direct discussion type.

Information Type. During this type of conference the instructor states facts which he wishes the employees to learn, then answers questions asked by them, covering points which are not understood. The information conference is generally used when the instructor is sure that the students will understand his presentation.

Development or Direct Discussion Type. The development or direct discussion conference requires the student to develop the ideas which the instructor desires to teach. This is accomplished by the instructor's putting leading questions to the students, which he must answer by using his own reasoning and judgement powers. This type of conference generally requires the student to have sufficient basic knowledge of the subject, so as to have reasonable answers to leading questions.

Demonstration is an accurate portrayal of a procedure, technique, or operation. It is the showing phase of instruction. Demonstrations are used to illustrate, either step by step, or in its entirety. Because it exemplifies the demonstrator's skill, the demonstration must be well prepared in detail, and must be rehearsed to secure proficiency. *Note:* A demonstration may constitute a complete lesson in itself.

Combination of Methods. The three basic methods are not mutually exclusive of each other. Any one of the three may be used to present a complete lesson, however, they are used to best advantage in combination with each other.

Application

The application stage of instruction is that part of the teaching process in which the student learns by doing the practical work. Learning by doing is one of the easiest and most natural ways of learning. It is readily adaptable to teaching almost every maintenance subject. By performance of an action, the student completes his understanding, and by repetition of it, he becomes proficient. The application stage may comprise a part of a lesson or a complete period or periods of instruction. If it is practical in your training, it is recommended that 15 per cent of the time be spent in telling, 25 per cent in showing, and 60 per cent in doing.

In preparing a period of practical work, the instructor first determines what kind of a training problem confronts him. If the problem is to train individuals, he may use one or a combination of three basic methods:

1. *Controlled (Group Performance) Method.* The instructor explains and demonstrates step by step. Class "imitates" works with instructor.
2. *Independent Method.* Instructor explains and demonstrates. Employee then performs at his own rate of speed. Corrections are made by instructor or assistants.
3. *Coach and Pupil Method.* Instructor explains and demonstrates. Employees are paired off as a coach and pupil. The pupil performs and the coach supervises. The coach becomes the pupil, and the pupil, the coach. Instructor and assistants supervise.

The three methods mentioned above can be used in combination with each other. Two or more used in the same period will add variety and inject interest into the instruction.

Examination

Knowing that he will be judged by the result of his examination or test, the employee's pride spurs him on to make more of an effort to learn.

Purposes of testing:

1. To bring instructional process to a logical conclusion.
2. To determine whether the student understands the subject and has developed the ability to apply it.

Types of tests:

1. Oral.
2. Written.
3. Performance.

Good questions will have a specific purpose and will be understood by the entire class. One point should be emphasized in each question, and each question should require a definite answer. This should stimulate thinking and discourage guessing the answers.

The *oral* test is based on the questions and answers generally used at the end of a class. Good questioning technique enables the instructor to impress the essentials on the employee's mind, and develops confidence in his ability to learn.

A good questioning technique is to ask the question in a clear voice, pause, look at the entire class, then call on an individual by name.

The *written* test is one in which the student writes his answers or solutions to the questions. The written test may be one of two types—essay or objective.

The *performance* test is conducted by having the student perform the job. A test of this type will definitely answer the question, "Can he do it?" There are three main parts to this test:

1. Good directions to the individual.
2. Directions to the checker.
3. Check list and score sheet for recording results.

In preparing an oral, written, or performance test, the instructor must first decide what he is trying to measure. He then decides the best method of measuring, and selects the best testing method, or a combination of tests which he will use.

Characteristics of a good test:

1. Valid.
2. Reliable.
3. Comprehensive.
4. Easy to take.
5. Easy to score.
6. Fair.

Review and/or Critique

The final stage of instruction which always follows the application or examination is the review and/or critique. The term "critique" is usually referred to the review given after the examination or applicatory exercise. The instructor reviews the knowledge, skills, and techniques acquired during the instruction period. This stage completes the picture by clarifying any phases of instruction which were not completely understood and any main points which should be re-emphasized.